W9-AFT-660

SPOT TESTS

IN ORGANIC ANALYSIS

SOLE DISTRIBUTORS FOR THE UNITED STATES OF NORTH AMERICA:

D. VAN NOSTRAND COMPANY, INC.

120 Alexander Street, Princeton, N.J. (Principal office)
257 Fourth Avenue, New York 10, N.Y.

SOLE DISTRIBUTORS FOR CANADA:

D. VAN NOSTRAND COMPANY, (CANADA) LTD.

25 Hollinger Road, Toronto 16

SOLE DISTRIBUTORS FOR THE BRITISH COMMONWEALTH EXCLUDING CANADA:

D. VAN NOSTRAND COMPANY, LTD.

358 Kensington High Street, London, W. 14

Library of Congress Catalog Card Number 56-13142

ALL RIGHTS RESERVED. THIS BOOK OR ANY PART THEREOF MAY
NOT BE REPRODUCED IN ANY FORM (INCLUDING PHOTOSTATIC
OR MICROFILM FORM) WITHOUT WRITTEN PERMISSION FROM
THE PUBLISHERS

SPOT TESTS

IN

ORGANIC ANALYSIS

by

FRITZ FEIGL, Eng., D. Sc.

Laboratório da Produção Mineral, Ministério da Agricultura,
Rio de Janeiro; Professor at the University of Brazil;
Member of the Austrian and Brazilian Academies of Sciences

Translated by

RALPH E. OESPER, Ph.D.

Professor Emeritus, University of Cincinnati

Fifth, enlarged and revised English Edition

BRIAR CLIFF COLLEGE
LIBRARY
SIOUX CITY, IOWA

ELSEVIER PUBLISHING COMPANY

AMSTERDAM   LONDON   NEW YORK   PRINCETON

1956

First English Edition, 1937 (translation by J. W. Matthews)

Second English Edition, 1939 (translation by J. W. Matthews)

Third English Edition, 1946 (translation by Ralph E. Oesper,
on the basis of the translation by J. W. Matthews)
[under the title *Qualitative Analysis by Spot Tests,
Inorganic and Organic Applications*]

Fourth English Edition (in two volumes), 1954
(translation by Ralph E. Oesper)
[under the title *Spot Tests, Vol. I, Inorganic Applications*]

Fifth English Edition, 1956 (translated by Ralph E. Oesper)
First Reprint 1958

QD
81
.F453
1956

PRINTED IN THE NETHERLANDS BY
N.V. DRUKKERIJ G. J. THIEME, NIJMEGEN

To the dear memory of Hans E. Feigl, who has shown much understanding for the use and value of analytical problems as applied to organic-synthetic studies and by pointing out pertinent examples has stimulated his father's interest in the fascinating field of organic spot test analysis

31829

31289

FOREWORD TO THE FIFTH EDITION

The monograph published in 1954 as the second volume of "Spot Tests" was devoted entirely to the application of spot and drop tests in qualitative organic analysis. This extended treatment of a fairly new field has met with such cordial reception that a new edition has already become necessary. The present volume has been composed to fill this demand.

In these prefatory paragraphs it seems well to repeat what was said in the Foreword of the preceding edition. Particular stress was laid there on the predicted usefulness of the points of view and the experiences yielded by the chemistry of specific, selective and sensitive reactions when applied to research problems in the field of qualitative organic analysis. These predictions have been extensively realized. So many new tests have now been developed that the present text is not merely a repetition of its predecessor but it constitutes an essential and fundamental enlargement. A comparison of the two will demonstrate this growth and also the many improvements in a great many of the tests and procedures.

In fact, the role of spot tests in organic analysis is now so apparent that the publishers felt fully justified in making the treatise on this branch of analytical chemistry a book in its own right. For this reason, it has been decided that the former Vol. II of *Spot Tests* will appear, in its new edition, under the title *Spot Tests in Organic Analysis*. Likewise, the corresponding volume on inorganic spot tests will undergo a similar change of title. By the "Volume I" referred to in the present text is meant the book that in its 4th Edition appeared as *Spot Tests, Vol. I, Inorganic Applications* and that in its enlarged 5th Edition, shortly to be published, will bear the title *Spot Tests in Inorganic Analysis*.

The textual content has been arranged basically along the lines adopted in the previous edition. The description of the procedures and their chemical foundations have again been presented along with copious references to the literature. The didactic factors have also been given due attention. In order to save space, the description of the reagents and reagent solutions have been incorporated, where feasible, directly in the working directions. Despite these and other economy measures, the number of pages has increased by nearly 200.

The most notable changes necessitated by this unavoidable extension of the text are: The introductory chapter (Development, Present State, and

Prospects of Organic Spot Test Analysis) now includes a more intensive treatment of the basic philosophy of the analytical use of organic reactions, and emphasis has been laid primarily on the truth that there are close relationships between the search for new organic reagents for use in inorganic analysis and the problems of qualitative organic analysis. The new paths taken by the author to discover tests for organic compounds are abundantly illustrated by characteristic examples. He sincerely hopes that others will follow his pioneering efforts and devote some of their research abilities and facilities to this same end. This chapter which before had 19 pages is now increased to 28 pages.

Chapter 3 (Preliminary Tests) now contains 25 sub-sections with 62 tests as compared with the previous 16 sections describing 44 tests. This enlargement gives an opportunity to demonstrate that simple preliminary tests, which hitherto have been used sparingly or not at all, sometimes are capable of giving important or even decisive clues regarding the nature of the sample.

Chapter 4 (Detection of Functional Groups) now contains 49 sub-sections with 116 tests in place of 29 sections and 101 tests. So far as is now possible, interference and impairments of the selectivity of the tests by other organic materials have been brought to the fore. This aspect is admittedly in need of great extension and here again the experiences of others will be of great assistance.

Chapter 5 (Detection of Individual Organic Compounds) now includes not 51 examples but 78. Tests that are of significance for the chemistry of natural products are included and they show how promising and informative the use of spot tests can become in even such a difficult province.

Chapter 6 (Application of Spot Reactions for Special Technical and Scientific Purposes) is made up of 62 examples as compared with 36 in the previous edition. In this chapter, attention is directed to the identification of medicinals by means of spot tests, a new feature of the book due largely to the enthusiasm and confidence of my colleague Professor E. Silva (Pernambuco). The results already achieved in this important field justify the expectation that the various pharmacopeias will not much longer totally neglect and disregard spot tests.

A special chapter has been included to provide a bibliography of studies of spot reactions in organic analysis, i.e. a list of papers etc. which could not be considered at all in the preceding chapters or only to a minor extent.

Many of the procedures developed by the author appear in print for the first time. The same is true of many slight but essential improvements in the procedure, advances which resulted from careful examinations of known tests. The interest and diligence of the author's coworkers have been invaluable in this phase of the work.

The extension and intensification of organic spot test analysis has taken but a short time and this growth has exceeded all expectations. It is primarily the fruit of the flight of the author into the most intensive kind of mental effort, where he hoped to find a refuge from the hopelessness and sorrow engendered by the death of his only child, who embodied the entire bright future of his parents. They were justly proud of this young man, who had been the student and collaborator of P. Karrer and Sir Alexander Todd, and who had passed away at the threshold of a promising career. Hans E. Feigl, who was an associate in some of the publications drawn on for this edition, thus shared to an extent in this project.

In the days of deep despair, it was my friend Ralph E. Oesper who urged me not to abandon my research activities, but rather to go on with them in the manner that my gifted and enthusiastic son would have wished them to be continued.

This effort would do him real honor. Dr. Oesper has not only contributed in this wise to the book but his complete understanding of the aims of the author and his interest in the text itself carried his labors far beyond those of a mere translator. He also aided by soliciting from various sources many compounds not readily available, compounds which were essential to the development and checking of new tests. Without his assistance and encouragement, this book might not have appeared at all. The author lacks words to thank him adequately.

After the publication of the first monograph on organic spot test analysis, the author received many communications from all parts of the civilized world. These letters testified to the interest of organic chemists, biochemists, and analysts in this branch of chemical activity. Their comments and suggestions were most helpful, since they called attention to many pertinent problems as well as to possibilities of bettering the procedures and their explanations. Accordingly, I invite the readers and users of this new edition to support me similarly in my endeavours to encourage the growth and fruitfulness of organic spot test analysis.

Rio de Janeiro, July 1956   FRITZ FEIGL

FOREWORD TO THE FOURTH EDITION

Because of its relatively narrow scope, the author has treated organic spot test analysis in previous editions of this text merely as a supplement to inorganic spot test analysis, even though these two provinces were of interest to different circles of chemists. Despite this handicap, many organic spot tests have been welcomed into qualitative semimicro- and microanalysis, and in fact some of them have become the basis of quantitative methods of determination. However, organic spot test analysis has by no means enjoyed the popularity accorded its inorganic counterpart. Consequently, some fellow chemists and reviewers of previous editions have repeatedly expressed the wish that the two divisions of spot test analysis might receive separate presentations. This commendable desire has led the author, since 1949, to institute studies of known tests and also to seek new tests, which are applicable to organic spot test analysis. These efforts yielded so many useful results that the mass of factual material has now become adequate to justify the publication of a monograph dealing with the employment of spot reactions in qualitative organic analysis.

The author has had a double objective in composing this book as Volume II of his text on spot test analysis. Firstly, the effort has been made to give a complete description of tests that are applicable as spot reactions in qualitative organic semimicro- and microanalysis. This facilitates comparisons with other familiar tests and procedures, especially with those that are important for technical purposes (testing of materials) and for analytical problems in the biological sciences (clinical studies, testing of medicinals, foods, etc.). Inorganic spot test analysis owes its popularity primarily to its suitability to the solution of such problems (particularly the first named) and to the publication of the favorable experiences gained with these methods. Accordingly, there is every reason to anticipate that organic spot test analysis will likewise find a wider circle of use as soon as its methods have been tried out in as many quarters as possible, and perhaps improved, and tested with regard to their usability in various spheres of application of qualitative organic analysis. Preparative organic chemistry will be included here and also the study of natural substances, where it is frequently desirable to find out with the smallest possible amount of test material whether certain syntheses and degradation reactions with organic products have occurred.

The second objective of this book is to stimulate studies that will lead to a wider development of organic spot test analysis, especially with regard to new, unambiguous and sensitive tests. Even now it may be stated that it will be possible to incorporate into the technique of spot analysis many reactions for organic compounds, tests which are scattered through the literature and which in part have received no attention. It is also expected that useful stimuli for the improvement and the working out of new tests will result when due attention is given to the vast material critically assembled in the chemistry of specific, selective and sensitive reactions. In particular, researches on the use of organic reagents in inorganic analysis will point the way to new or hitherto neglected paths in qualitative organic analysis. General comments along these lines are given in the introductory chapter and practical applications will be found in chapters III-VII. The new tests of this kind worked out by the author and his collaborators have mostly not been published as yet and are described for the first time in this book. The search for new tests is a field of endeavor which deserves more interest on the part of investigators, especially organic chemists, who are particularly fitted to bring valuable contributions because of their experiences, and through the planned observation of analytically applicable effects in the reactions of organic compounds. The appeal for the extension of organic spot test analysis should strike an all the more responsive chord today, since it has been found that sensitive spot tests, particularly those based on color reactions, play an important, sometimes decisive role in chromatographic analysis. It is certain that paper chromatography will come to be one of the most important and rewarding fields of application of spot reactions.

The use of spot reactions in qualitative organic analysis and their respective procedural details are given in chapters III–VI. The divisions employed are those used in the previous editions. They are: preliminary tests; detection of functional groups; detection of individual compounds; applications for technical and scientific purposes.

The chapter on preliminary tests has been entirely rewritten, since in the previous edition only about nine pages were devoted to the discussion of the detection of metallic and nonmetallic elements in organic materials, a coverage obviously insufficient for so important a topic. Since rapid preliminary tests often provide valuable diagnoses, their diverse application has now been discussed in such breadth that the sixteen sections cover not less than 69 pages. The inclusion of many new tests for functional groups and individual compounds has expanded the respective chapters from 73 and 31 pages to 114 and 96 pages. The number of examples of the application of spot tests to technical and scientific purposes has been raised from 16 to 36 and the accompanying increase in pages is from 8 to 43. *In toto*, the book contains the complete or orienting description of over 200 tests. When possible, stress was laid on stating exactly the underlying chemical reactions. The pertinent data regarding sensitivity and reliability are included for the great majority of the tests; references to the pertinent literature will likewise be found a useful feature. Consequently, the readers and users of the book are provided with not only the fundamentals for the direct applications of spot reactions in qualitative organic analysis, but also they will find here useful hints for selecting spot reactions for problems posed by chromatography, testing of materials, examination of medicinals, etc.

The author has endeavored to describe as many spot reactions as possible in such detail that it should be possible to translate the reactions to the macro scale and also to institute intelligent refinements in order to enhance the sensitivity of the tests. In order to give this monograph the character of an independent manual of organic spot test analysis, the chapter on spot test technique, which was composed by Professor Ph. W. West (Louisiana State University) for Volume I was included here also. Furthermore, all tests for inorganic materials which are left in the residues after organic samples are decomposed, have been described in sufficient detail, that reference to Volume I in such cases will not be necessary, except for amplification of background information.

The author wishes also to emphasize that his monograph is not intended to replace the well tested and valued texts dealing with qualitative organic analysis. This book merely supplements such works. Organic qualitative procedures frequently require chemical operations which cannot be carried into spot test analysis, or physical methods are necessary that lie beyond the scope of this text. Organic spot testing is still limited to a relatively small field of operation, when we consider the great number and variety of organic compounds which may be object of qualitative analysis. Nonetheless, it may be expected that organic spot test analysis will play eventually the same kind of role in chemical analysis as did its inorganic counterpart; it will become an integral part of qualitative organic analysis and will stimulate the latter's further development. One of the functions of this book is to contribute to this end.

Organic spot test analysis is of practical importance not only for the professional analyst, but also for the organic chemist, the biologist and the pharmaceutical chemist, who often are faced with the problem of quickly identifying or detecting chemical ingredients in small amounts of organic materials. Furthermore, organic spot test analysis can be of great value to chemical students in the later stages of their training. They can be expected to have then acquired the manual dexterity for working with small amounts, and they should also have an understanding and an interest in the chemical basis of spot reactions. Occupation with organic spot testing confers not only

a knowledge of analytical problems and their solution on the semimicro-
and micro-scale, but at the same time it points up the great diversity in the
modes of reactions of many organic compounds. This fact has a high edu-
cational value, which should be put to use. This advantage can be secured if,
in the course of his work in preparative organic chemistry, the student is
shown how to employ spot reactions for the identification of starting materials, intermediates, and final products, a problem which can often be solved
with tiny quantities of sample and in a very short time. More competent
persons will have to decide whether spot testing is a feasable addition to the
laboratory course in organic chemistry. However, the author is convinced
that this would be a correct procedure, because it follows the line which he
himself has always taken in research, publication, and instruction in spot
test analysis, namely, chemical analysis should not be regarded as routine
work or drudgery, but rather as the pursuit of experimental chemistry with
analytical goals.

As stated in the beginning of this Foreword, the author has now spent four
years on studies directed toward the improvement and extension of organic
spot test analysis. This was made possible not only by the comprehensive
and helpful attitude of Dr Alvaro Paiva de Abreu, director of the Laboratorio
da Produção Mineral, but also through the invaluable assistance of the
National Research Council, who provided the author with assistants and
fitted up his laboratory. Consequently, he deems it a privilege to make public
acknowledgement of his gratitude to this body and its president, Admiral
Alvaro Alberto da Motta e Silva.

The author also wishes to express his heartfelt thanks to Professor Ralph
E. Oesper (University of Cincinnati) for his excellent translation of the
German manuscript, for his valued advice on many points, and for his kind
patience with the many last minute changes, which are an inevitable feature
of the composition of a text dealing with a field which is so alive these days.

Rio de Janeiro, October 1953   FRITZ FEIGL

CONTENTS

CHAPTER 6. APPLICATION OF SPOT TESTS FOR TECHNICAL PURPOSES 445

CONTENTS   XIX

Chapter 1

Development, Present State and Prospects of Organic Spot Test Analysis

From the standpoint of a formal priority, the organic province of spot test analysis is older than its inorganic counterpart since the earliest spot tests were used for the detection of an organic compound. In 1859 Hugo Schiff reported that uric acid can be detected by placing a drop of a water solution of this acid on filter paper which had been impregnated with silver carbonate. Silver precipitates and the finely divided metal produces a gray to black fleck which stands out prominently against the white paper. This test demonstrated the fundamental practicality of spot reactions on filter paper and by actual trial Schiff also showed that this method of procedure permits the attainment of a considerable degree of sensitivity. At the then state of chemical analysis, this was truly a remarkable finding. It coincided with the beginnings of the classical studies by Christian Friedrich Schönbein and Friedrich Goppelsroeder, who in their "capillary analysis" demonstrated the great analytical significance of the spreading of liquids and solutions of organic and inorganic compounds with consequent localized fixation in filter paper of small amounts of the dissolved materials. The publications of these three pioneers obviously contain descriptions of effects which have been used to the widest extent in modern spot test analysis. Accordingly, it is logical to inquire why real attention was not given to spot reactions on filter paper until a much later date (around 1920), attention which might have led to the founding first of inorganic and then of organic spot test analysis. The correct answer to this question is readily revealed by a consideration of the history of the spot test detection of inorganic materials. In the beginning, chemical reactions were employed which respond not only to slight, often minimal, amounts of a particular material, but which in many cases also make possible its detection in the presence of other substances. Such reactions were fairly uncommon as long as inorganic reagents predominated in inorganic analysis. This situation was not changed until the advent of organic reagents, especially those which give colored reaction products. Only then was it possible to work out numerous sensitive and un-equivocal methods of detection and determination. The nickel-dimethyl-glyoxime reaction, introduced into qualitative and quantitative inorganic analysis by L. Tschugaeff (1905) and O. Brunck (1914), has become the classic example of this type of progress even though Cazeneuve, Denigès, and Il-linsky had previously described useful color reactions employing organic reagents. Consequently, the earliest efforts of the present author to elaborate spot reactions were directed particularly toward combining the advantages of organic reagents with those of the Schönbein-Goppelsroeder capillary analysis. It was found that when drops of the test- and reagent solutions are brought together on filter paper, colored reaction products are fixed on the surface of the paper and produce flecks or rings within a circle wetted by water, and can thus be distinctly detected. This type of spot tests, in which inorganic and organic reagents can be used, is obviously limited to reactions which require neither strong heating or evaporation, nor a highly alkaline or acidic reaction theater. The procedural aspect of spot test analysis received a very useful extension when it was found feasible to unite drops of the test- and reagent solutions on non-porous surfaces (spot plate, watch glass, micro test tube, etc.) where the limitations no longer apply. A decisive impulse to the development of inorganic spot test analysis came however from the logical but, at the time, novel idea that the restrictive preference for certain kinds of reactions and ways of carrying them out is a handicap. In every case, the sole objective is the discovery and employment of all possibilities through which the highest sensitivity and certainty can be at-tained with drop reactions. A logical result of this goal was the inclusion and trying out of kinds of reactions which had previously received no or only inadequate attention in chemical analysis. Typical examples are: the wide-spread use of organic compounds as precipitation-, color-, and masking agents; the utilization of catalysed and induced reactions; solid body re-actions and reactions in the gas phase; reactions which yield fluorescent prod-ucts or those which quench fluorescence; interfacial effects (adsorption, capil-larity, flotation). Last, but not least, was a proper consideration of the enor-mous influence of the reaction conditions on the course of the reactions and the physical nature of the reaction products. In short, and using a terminology which has now been generally accepted, it may be stated that inorganic spot test analysis is the outstanding field of application of specific, selective and sensitive reactions with the objective of solving problems in qualitative microanalysis.

Spot reactions will reveal as little as 0.001–10 micrograms (gamma $= \gamma$) of material (solid or in drops of a solution). Those low "limits of detection" or "limits of identification" correspond, in so far as solutions are being examined, to great dilutions or low concentrations. If these limits of detection or identification can be attained with spot tests, it is proper to speak of micro tests.* It is evident that only larger amounts of materials will respond to less sensitive spot reactions. In general, only such spot reactions are used as are applicable to microanalytical or at least semi-microanalytical problems. The identification limit and limiting concentration, as determined experimentally, are guides in this appraisal.

Spot test analysis presents a very important problem, namely what determines the specificity, selectivity, and sensitivity of its procedures. In other words, what factors influence these characteristics in the positive and negative direction? The scientific treatment of this problem, which is of fundamental importance to all procedures of qualitative and quantitative analysis constitutes the "chemistry of specific, selective and sensitive reactions." This field of experimental chemistry includes the consideration of the numerous relations of analytical chemistry to other areas of chemistry, and studies suggested by spot test analysis (especially the search for new organic reagents) have brought the importance of this field to the attention of chemists.**

Although inorganic spot test analysis developed relatively fast, its development was nevertheless gradual and some time elapsed before its usefulness in qualitative semimicro- and microanalysis was extensively appreciated. Consequently, it is understandable why not much attention was given to the applicability of spot reactions for the detection of organic compounds and the characteristic groups they contain until (since about 1930) the important foundations of inorganic spot testing had already been laid and the fundamental conditions of its further development recognized. The number of spot reactions, which can successfully be applied in qualitative organic analysis, has now become large enough to justify the use of the term "organic spot test analysis", and all the more so because every indication points to the deepening and widening of this field.

Organic spot testing likewise strives to attain microanalytical goals. Therefore all possibilities must be explored in order that the specificity,

---

* Many spot reactions are the equal of the crystal precipitations of the classical qualitative microanalysis with respect to quantity sensitivity (limit of identification) and in most cases they are superior to the latter with regard to concentration sensitivity (dilution limit). None the less, identifications by means of spot reactions are frequently called semimicro tests in Anglo-Saxon countries. This obviously incorrect designation originated in the fact that for many years microanalysis was identified with micromanipulation. However, the objective of qualitative microanalysis is the identification of extremely small quantities of material, no matter what particular technique is employed. Precisely this point was very impressively demonstrated by spot reactions. Compare Chapter 1 in Volume I regarding this point.

** See F. Feigl, *Chemistry of Specific, Selective and Sensitive Reactions*. New York, 1949; F. Feigl, *Research*, 4 (1950) 550.

selectivity and sensitivity of the particular test may be brought to a maximum. In this connection, it must not be forgotten that when dealing with organic compounds, the objective of the analysis and the analytical utilization of chemical reactions should be considered from standpoints which differ from those adopted with respect to inorganic compounds. In qualitative inorganic analysis the aim is to detect metallic and nonmetallic elements and it is practically always possible to do this by chemical means. In contrast, in qualitative organic analysis the detection of elements has only an orienting value, because the important goal is the detection of particular compounds or the identification of characteristic groups in organic compounds, whose ultimate constituents are usually known. Chemical methods cannot contribute beyond a limited extent to the solution of these two problems, especially the former. The reason resides not only in the enormous number of organic compounds and the variety in their architecture. The decisive factors are that with many organic compounds chemical changes occur under conditions which cannot be realized in analytical work, and furthermore a uniform mode of reaction is encountered incomparably more often than with inorganic ions. Consequently, specificity and selectivity are much rarer in tests for organic compounds than in inorganic identifications, and separation processes, such as those successfully used in the systematic qualitative inorganic scheme in the form of group precipitations, or group solutions, play little or no part in qualitative organic analysis. Most tests for organic materials depend on the participation of certain groups in chemical reactions; but entirely apart from the fact that many important groups are not reactive, it must be kept in mind that the detection of groups gives informmation only about a certain region of the molecule of an organic compound. Therefore, reliable identifications of individual compounds by purely chemical tests are infrequent. As a rule, appeal must be made also to physical methods based on the determination of physical properties related to the structure and size of the organic molecule. Therefore the state of aggregation of the test material is also involved. Despite these limitations, chemical tests have a considerable practical importance in qualitative organic analysis. Problems whose solution is facilitated by analytical procedures seldom involve totally unknown materials or artifical mixtures. The available information regarding origin, method of preparation, intended use, etc., as well as the color, form of aggregation, and so on of the sample almost invariably give clues as to the direction the examination should take. Frequently, the analyst is not asked to detect a particular compound, but is required merely to find out whether members of a particular class of compounds are present. For this latter purpose, it is often sufficient to prove the presence of a given group, or even of given elements. Accordingly, chemical methods can contribute a great deal to the solution of many of the problems encountered in the study of organic materials. Consequently, efforts must be made to discover and apply all reactions of organic compounds, which may be valuable as analytical aids.

The objectives and problems of qualitative inorganic analysis are thus quite different from those of qualitative organic analysis. Frequently these fields also differ with respect to the reaction milieu and the mode of reaction. The analytical employment of reactions of inorganic compounds involves ionic reactions in aqueous solutions almost exclusively, but this is not true of purely organic compounds. Although water-soluble organic acids, bases, and salts and their corresponding reactive ions are known, the majority of organic compounds are non-ionogens of hydrophobic character, and the aqueous medium does not play the dominant role in their reactions as it does in inorganic analysis. Many organic compounds react only when dissolved in organic liquids, or when in the gas phase, in melts, and non-homogeneous systems. As a rule, such reactions proceed much slower than ionic reactions in aqueous solutions, they are incomplete, and frequently are accompanied by side reactions. Despite these handicaps, molecular reactions of organic compounds in the absence of water deserve every attention because, on occasion, such reactions provide an entirely satisfactory substitute for the lack of reactivity in water solutions.

The use of organic reactions in analysis is still inconsiderable in comparison with their widespread employment in preparative chemistry. However, procedures are known for the detection of many organic compounds and for the groups they contain, and these tests can be applied, directly or with proper modifications or additions, in organic spot test analysis. It should be noted that the importance of the special working techniques generally used in spot testing should not be overrated. The working with drops of a solution is admittedly a very essential part of spot test analysis and superficially it appears to be its most characteristic feature. However, spot testing owes its development not solely to its peculiar technique, but primarily to the efforts to find suitable subjects for this technique. This leads to the search for reactions which can be used for analytical purposes. The consideration of the facts and findings of the "chemistry of specific, selective and sensitive reactions" renders excellent service in this connection.

Organic spot test analysis can be discussed under three headings, each with distinct objectives. In accord with their importance, separate chapters are devoted to them in this text. They are:

1) The identification or detection of non-metallic and metallic elements; the behavior on ignition and combustion; the proof of the basic or acidic

character; the possible redox functioning of organic compounds; the study of the behavior toward reactive and non-reactive solvents.

2) The identification or detection of certain groups (the so-called functional groups) included in the molecule of organic compounds.

3) The identification or detection of individual organic compounds.

The solution of the problems cited in 1) involves the use of "preliminary" tests. In many of the procedures there are close relationships to inorganic tests. For example, the test for elements in organic compounds and in salts of organic acids and bases requires first of all a disintegration of the sample by wet or dry methods, followed by identification of the characteristic decomposition products by means of suitable methods borrowed from inorganic spot test analysis. The same is true when organic compounds are to be examined with regard to their possible acidic or basic character, or their possible ability to participate as principals in redox reactions. Experience gained from inorganic spot test analysis is likewise very valuable when attempts are being made to improve existing preliminary tests or to develop new varieties of such tests. However, preliminary testing also presents problems whose solution is sometimes facilitated by the procedures of organic spot test analysis. Instances are nitration tests and testing for aromatics discussed in Chapter 3.

Preliminary tests are extremely valuable adjuncts to the chemical examination of organic materials because, with little expenditure of material and time, they yield important clues for the tests to be undertaken subsequently. Nevertheless the real province of qualitative organic analysis, and hence also of organic spot test analysis, is the detection of certain groups in organic compounds, and the identification or detection of individual compounds. Without exception, chemical procedures for the solution of these problems are based on the fact that organic compounds enter into chemical reactions not as whole individuals but through the action of certain groups. There are two ways of utilizing such reactions: If groups are present, which react in such fashion that addition compounds, salts, condensation-, oxidation-, or reduction products are formed, which because of color, solubility, etc. can serve for the identification of the starting material or the groups contained in it, it is permissible to speak of "direct tests". In contrast, "indirect tests" make use of the reactivity of certain groups to arrive at compounds which in their turn can be identified by salt formation, condensation, etc. Usually, indirect tests involve the use of operations which are commonly employed in preparative organic chemistry for the tearing down, building up, and transformation of compounds.

It need hardly be stressed that any direct or indirect tests used in spot test analysis must be satisfactory with respect to sensitivity and reliability, and also must meet the requirement of being quickly conducted in a satisfactory fashion with amounts of material of the order of micrograms to milligrams. It is particularly essential that the preparative operations required in indirect tests be such as can be accomplished without much apparatus and loss of material. Consequently, in organic spot test analysis it is often necessary to forego the use of reactions which lead to the goal when carried out on a macro scale. Precisely as in inorganic spot test analysis, it by no means follows that analytical macro methods can be used directly as a matter of course. The reverse process, namely the adoption of the methods of spot testing on the macro scale is possible far more often, though not always. This special position of the methods of spot test analysis is based not merely on their special technique, but above all in accepting specificity, selectivity and sensitivity as the prime analytical objective.

With respect to the analytical utility of direct and indirect tests, it seems natural to assume that direct tests, which are more rapid, are also more sensitive, since they are not burdened with the supplementary operations and the consequent inevitable losses of material involved in the indirect tests. On the other hand, precisely because of the supplementary steps, the indirect tests would be expected to have a lower sensitivity, but instead a greater specificity or selectivity. All experience shows however that so far as sensitivity is concerned these assumptions are unreliable generalizations, which need not be taken seriously either in the use of known direct or indirect tests, or in the search for new ones. Both types of tests are of equal value in spot test analysis, provided they meet the requirement of sensitivity and reliability.

What was said concerning the past and present development of inorganic spot test analysis * holds also for its organic counterpart. It is mostly a matter of adapting known macroanalytical tests to spot testing, and of finding new tests. Frequently the two objectives are closely related since the knowledge of the chemistry of a test can lead to such extensive improvements that a practically new test results. Adaptation and improvement of existing tests have not yet received the attention they deserve, and much fruitful work along this line can be confidently expected. Color reactions, whose chemistry is known, should be particularly considered in this connection, because such studies will lead to an understanding of the details of the procedure, and also give a certain measure of guidance relative to specificity and selectivity, points which still need to be investigated. Furthermore, the literature of analytical chemistry contains descriptions of many color reactions between organic compounds (usually in the presence of concentrated

* Compare Chapter 1 of Volume I.

acids and alkalies) which obviously were discovered empirically or accidentally. When they are examined to determine their possible use in spot test analysis, studies should also be undertaken to elucidate their chemical bases. Both endeavors contribute to the removal of the doubt, which still exists in many quarters, regarding the reliability of color reactions in organic analysis.

Very useful suggestions for the working out of new direct tests are obtained by considering studies dealing with the analytical employment of the ability of acid and basic organic compounds to form salts with inorganic ions. On the basis of such investigations, which occupy a broad field of interest in the chemistry of specific, selective and sensitive reactions, it can now be stated with assurance that analytically useful effects of organic reagents can invariably be attributed to the presence and activity of certain groups in the molecule of the compound in question. For example, if dioximes, acyl-oinoximes, derivatives of a,a'-dipyridyl, and 8-hydroxyquinoline react sensitively and in selective fashion with certain metal ions to yield colored insoluble or soluble salts, then this salt-formation, which occurs because of the presence of the respective functional groups:

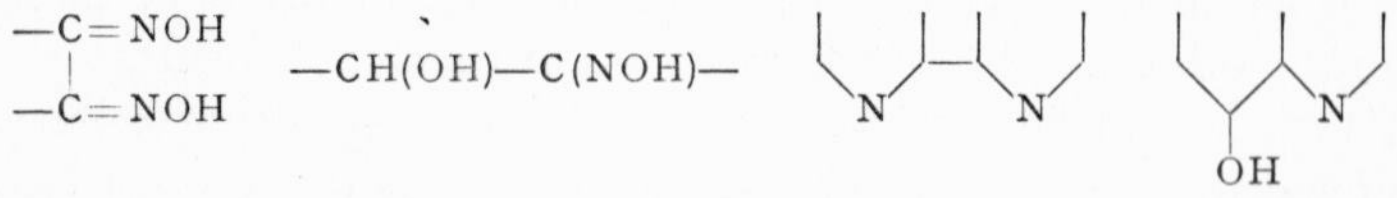

can almost always be applied conversely to the detection of the particular groups of the organic reagent. This is nothing more than an application of the long standing principle that binary reactions can be used analytically for each of the reactants.* Pertinent examples will be found in the practical sections of this text.

It is readily apparent that the employment of binary reactions for the detection of either of the participants is not limited to the formation of salts, but must hold also for other types of reactions. The following example illustrates this point. A sensitive and specific test for hydrazine is based on its practically instantaneous condensation with salicylaldehyde to yield a precipitate of light yellow salicylaldazine:

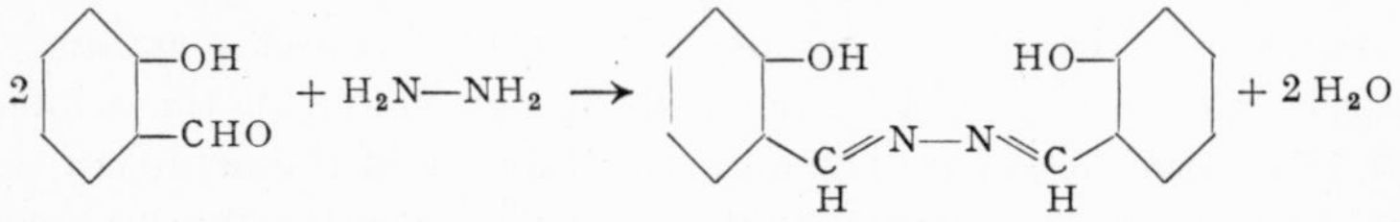

This condensation occurs when an aqueous solution of salicylaldehyde is added to acid solutions of hydrazine salts. The salicylaldazine shows an in-

---

* Compare, in this respect, the suggestions advanced by R. Pallaud, *Chim. Analyt.* **34** (1952) 194.

tense yellow green fluorescence in ultraviolet light, permitting the ready detection of even small quantities of this product. (The condensation products of m- and p-hydroxybenzaldehyde do not fluoresce.) As was to be expected, the formation of fluorescent salicylaldazine can be used conversely for the detection of salicylaldehyde and of compounds which split off hydrazine (e.g., hydrazides of acids). The use of the condensation of hydrazine can be carried a step farther if consideration is given to the findings of the chemistry of specific, selective and sensitive reactions relative to the activity of certain groups in organic reagents. In accord with the concept of group action, it could be expected that since all o-hydroxy aldehydes and ketones contain the same functional group as salicylaldehyde, they too would necessarily condense with hydrazine and yield fluorescent aldazines. This was found to be the case; most of the fluorescence hues are the same and the sensitivities of these spot test reactions are so satisfactory that it was possible to develop a sensitive general test for o-hydroxyaldehydes and o-hydroxyketones, which can be successfully applied to even very complicated members of this class of compounds.

Proceeding from the dual analytical employment of inorganic-organic reactions, a further step can be taken, namely the preparation of organic reagents may be expected to make possible a test for the organic compounds involved in such preparation procedures. In other words, the sample being studied must be subjected to the conditions of the preparation of a particular organic reagent, which in turn can then be identified by means of inorganic ions. Here again there is an obvious close relation to analytical research directed toward the discovery of organic reagents for inorganic ions. Of course, the analytical employment of preparation procedures should not be limited to the production of organic reagents and their detection by an inorganic ion; the goal must be more general. The possibility of an analytical utilization exists whenever the main product of a synthesis or preparation procedure can be detected by means of an appropriate inorganic or organic reagent, or whenever this product is characterized per se by its color, fluorescence, solubility features, etc. Furthermore, it must not be forgotten that the detection of a characteristic side product may serve in some cases as a direct or indirect proof of the presence of a particular organic participant in the preparation process. Obviously, such cases require the recognition of the stoichiometric reaction underlying the preparation procedure. It is clear that the attainable yield of the particular organic product is no longer the most important factor. Instead, the analytical usefulness of the procedure depends solely on whether certain products of the synthesis or preparation procedure are formed at an adequate rate and in amounts sufficient to exceed the identification limits of their direct or indirect detectability. In such instances, low yields lose their deterrent effect and certain interesting aspects come into view.

In the first place, it may be expected that preparation procedures conducted on a small scale can still yield enough of the desired product to make its detection possible either directly or by macro-, semimicro- and micro tests. An excellent example, which demonstrates that it is worth carrying out syntheses with small amounts of material for analytical purposes, is provided in the classic preparation of alizarin (Graebe, Liebermann, Perkin, 1869). In this procedure, anthraquinonesulfonic acid is fused with a caustic alkali in the presence of alkali salts of oxidizing acids:

This reaction succeeds even with the dry residue from a drop of a colorless 0.004 % solution of anthraquinonesulfonic acid and leads to the violet sodium alizarinate. Consequently, it is possible to detect 2γ anthraquinonesulfonic acid through this preparation of alizarin. It must not be expected that such macro $\longrightarrow$ microtransformations will lead to the desired goal in all cases. However, when this is not possible, attempts can be made to depart from rigid adherence to complicated working directions to achieve simplifications that are in line with analytical techniques. Such modifications might include: changes of concentration and amounts of the reactants; shortening of the reaction period; shifting of the reaction into the vapor phase; etc. The emancipation from rigid procedures may even go much further if it is kept in mind that the sole objective is to detect an organic compound through its participation in a selected reaction. Consequently, it frequently is profitable to scan the literature with respect to reports of the formation of certain compounds; in other words, to search for announcements of methods which have no present value from the preparation standpoint because the yields are inadequate. Such methods include: thermal and chemical fission processes; exchange of groups; fusion and sintering reactions; etc. If such methods of forming the desired compounds go fast enough, if they can be translated into the chemical analytical technique, and if small amounts of the resulting product can be reliably detected by a simple test, then a better analytical utilization can be secured in this novel fashion than by a familiar method of preparation which fails to meet adequately the conditions just set forth.

Even though modifications of the customary procedure usually lead to lower yields, this disadvantage can be overcome in large part when only analytical goals are being sought. Ordinary preparation procedures often necessitate the isolation of intermediate products and purification of the final product. Both of these steps entail unavoidable losses. However, such loss of the prime material is not encountered or need not be considered if the test can be conducted on the reaction mixture without isolation of the intermediate products or without removal of the side products. This is often possible.

An excellent example of an indirect test accomplished through the synthesis of a characteristic organic compound displaying a sensitive reaction, is again provided by the formation of the fluorescent aldazines by condensation of hydrazine with o-hydroxyaldehydes. These aldehydes can be prepared from phenols (with a free *ortho*-position) by means of the familiar Reimer-Tiemann reaction, which has been widely used in preparative organic chemistry since its discovery in 1875. In this procedure, phenols and chloroform are refluxed for a considerable time with strong caustic solutions. The following net reaction occurs:

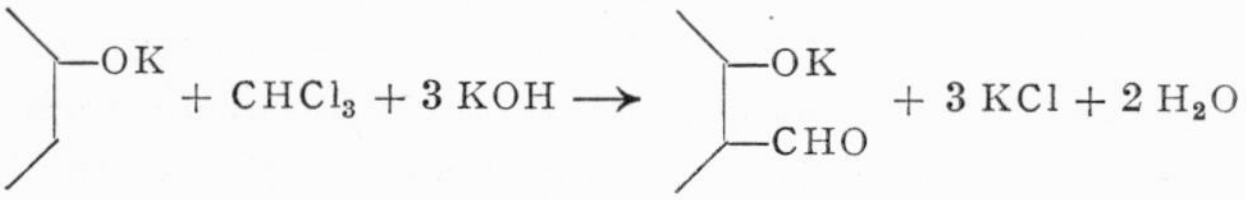

As a rule, the Reimer-Tiemann reaction gives low yields of o-hydroxyaldehydes, and this fact, together with the relative complexity of the procedure, would seemingly present little promise of satisfactorily realizing the synthesis with only small quantities of a phenol. However, if chloroform is added to an alkaline solution of a phenol or to a solid alkali phenolate, and the excess chloroform then evaporated, the quantity of o-hydroxyaldehyde produced is sufficient to be detected by the formation of the fluorescent aldazine. On the basis of this finding, it was possible to arrive at a new test for phenols with a free *ortho*-position, since the reaction can be successfully conducted with as little as one drop of the solution being tested for phenol.

The familiar Skraup synthesis of quinoline (1882) pointed to the possibility of a test for glycerol. This reaction, which fundamentally can be expressed:

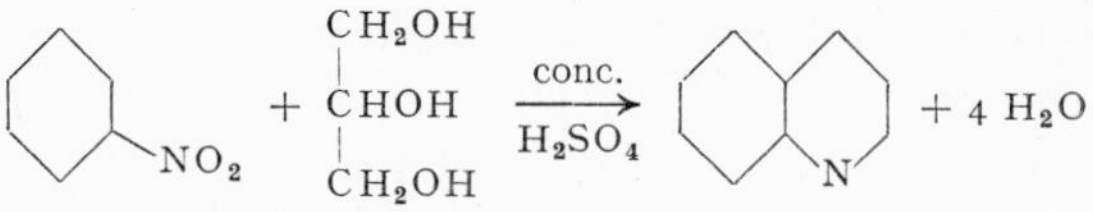

was of no value as a means of detecting glycerol so long as there was no suitable specific test for the resulting quinoline. However, if the nitrobenzene is replaced by o-nitrophenol, 8-hydroxyquinoline results:

$$\text{(o-nitrophenol)} + \begin{array}{c} CH_2OH \\ | \\ CHOH \\ | \\ CH_2OH \end{array} \xrightarrow[H_2SO_4]{\text{conc.}} \text{(8-hydroxyquinoline)} + 4\ H_2O$$

This product (oxine) is a widely used precipitant for numerous metal ions, yielding light yellow inner complex salts which, in most instances, give an intense yellow-green fluorescence in ultraviolet light. As anticapated, the oxine produced by the micro Skraup-synthesis can be detected through the production of fluorescent oxinates. This test is so sensitive that it reveals the formation of oxine when as little as one drop of a dilute solution of glycerol is warmed with o-nitrophenol and concentrated sulfuric acid. After the oxine has been synthesized in this fashion, the fluorescent metal oxinate is obtained by making the reaction mixture basic and adding a magnesium or aluminum salt. It should also be noted that oxine produces fluorescent salts not only by reaction with Mg^{+2}, Zn^{+2}, and Al^{+3} ions, but the same fluorescence effects are obtained as are displayed by the formula-pure oxinates when this reagent is adsorbed by coming into contact with the hydroxides or oxides of these metals. Derivatives of oxine, including its water-soluble sulfonic acids, which do not function as cation precipitants, are likewise chemically adsorbed to yield fluorescing systems. These adsorption effects can be utilized in sensitive drop reactions for 8-hydroxyquinoline and its derivatives. They, like the fluorescent aldazines of o-hydroxyaldehydes, prove that the fluorescence depends on the presence and activity of particular groups in organic compounds, and hence can be called on for the detection of these groups.

A striking example that demonstrates the use of a preparation of an organic reagent for the detection of a participant in the synthesis is found in the sensitive test for phenols which was developed from the detection of cobalt by means of 1-nitroso-2-naphthol (Illinsky-Knorre, 1885). The basis of this sensitive test is the production of a red-brown cobalt (III) chelate compound and the further fact that, in conformity with the functional group activity in organic compounds, other *ortho* nitrosated phenols behave analogously to the nitrosonaphthols. The chelate compounds may be formed directly by warming phenols, which have a free *ortho* position, with an acetic acid solution of sodium cobaltinitrite. The following successive reactions occur in the mixture:

$$[Co(NO_2)_6]^{-3} + 6\ H^+ \rightarrow Co^{+3} + 6\ HNO_2$$

$$\rangle\text{—OH} + HNO_2 \rightarrow \rangle\begin{array}{l}\text{—OH}\\\text{—NO}\end{array} + H_2O$$

$$\rangle\begin{array}{l}\text{—OH}\\\text{—NO}\end{array} + \tfrac{1}{3}Co^{+3} \rightarrow \rangle\begin{array}{l}=O\\=N\end{array}\!\!\searrow Co/_3$$

Accordingly, this procedure which succeeds also with phenols having complicated structures, presents a synthesis which is conducted in the presence of a reagent for the reaction product. This is a matter of fundamental importance.

As a final example, reference is made to the interesting tests which have grown out of the synthesis of diphenylcarbazide (Skinner and Ruhemann, 1881) which is produced by the condensation of phenylhydrazine and urea:

$$OC\!\!\begin{array}{l}\diagup NH_2\\\diagdown NH_2\end{array} + \begin{array}{l}H_2N\text{—}NHC_6H_5\\H_2N\text{—}NHC_6H_5\end{array} \rightarrow OC\!\!\begin{array}{l}\diagup NH\text{—}NHC_6H_5\\\diagdown NH\text{—}NHC_6H_5\end{array} + 2\ NH$$

In qualitative inorganic analysis, diphenylcarbazide serves as a very sensitive reagent for quite a few metal ions, with which it produces colored inner complex salts. Nickel diphenylcarbazide is produced with neutral and ammoniacal nickel solutions, and the violet salt, which is insoluble in water, dissolves readily in ether, chloroform, etc. Hence the occurrence of the condensation can be readily demonstrated through the formation of this highly colored salt. Consequently there is this possibility of detecting either urea or phenylhydrazine by a sensitive test. If unsymmetrical mono alkyl- and arylhydrazines are used in place of phenylhydrazine, the resulting derivatives of diphenylcarbazide react analogously to the parent compound because they too contain the same salt-forming groups. Accordingly, condensation with urea can be used as a general means of detecting mono alkyl-(aryl) hydrazines. The reaction scheme of the diphenylcarbazide synthesis shows plainly which groups of the two reactants are involved in the condensation. It can therefore be anticipated that modified diphenylcarbazides will be produced by employing certain derivatives of urea. For instance, urethans can also be detected by the synthesis of diphenylcarbazide. All of these syntheses, as well as the related tests for diphenylcarbazide through formation of the violet nickel salt, can be conducted within the bounds of spot test analysis.

It was pointed out on page 10 that when preparation procedures are being adapted to analytical purposes the attainable yields are far less decisive than the rapid formation of products which can be detected with high sensitivity. In other words, when new organic tests are being sought, it is permissible to give serious consideration to reports of the formation of organic compounds and their chemical behavior which at present have no standing in preparation chemistry. A characteristic instance follows.

If mixtures of sodium formate and alkali salts of sulfonic acids are sintered or fused, the sulfonic group is replaced by the carboxyl group:

$$R—SO_3Na + HCOONa \rightarrow R—COOH + Na_2SO_3$$

This reaction, which was reported in 1870 by V. Meyer, has no value as a method of preparing carboxylic acids because the unavoidable losses due to thermal decomposition are too great. Nevertheless, it provides the basis of a characteristic indirect test for aliphatic and aromatic sulfonic acids, sulfones, and for sulfonamides through the formation of the heat-resistant alkali sulfite, which can be readily detected. The entire procedure is simple, rapid, and can be accomplished within the technique of spot test analysis. This example emphasizes the important fact that it sometimes is profitable to modify a preparation procedure which is too complicated to have any analytical value and to transform it into a formation procedure which is readily accomplished and feasible from an analytical standpoint. A case in point is a test for aliphatic esters of fatty acids, which is based on a classic synthesis of acyloins (Bouveault-Blanc, 1903). The usual procedure prescribes prolonged warming of an ether or benzene solution of the ester with metallic sodium to form the sodium salt of the endiol, which, after mechanical removal of the excess sodium, is saponified to the acyloin:

$$2\,R—COOR + 4\,Na \rightarrow \begin{matrix} R—C—ONa \\ \| \\ R—C—ONa \end{matrix} + 2\,RONa$$

$$\begin{matrix} R—C—ONa \\ \| \\ R—C—ONa \end{matrix} + 2\,H_2O \rightarrow \begin{matrix} R—CHOH \\ | \\ R—CO \end{matrix} + 2\,NaOH$$

At first glance it would seem improbable that this procedure, which demands considerable time and equipment, could be converted into an operation simple enough for analytical purposes and for spot test analysis in particular. Actually, the reactions can be accomplished with one drop of the ester and within one minute and still yield sufficient acyloin to be detectable by a sensitive color reaction with 1,2-dinitrobenzene.

The foregoing discussion has dealt with the chemical backgrounds of several new types of tests for functional groups and individual organic compounds. The aim has been to demonstrate that in the light of deliberations and experiences regarding the chemistry of specific, selective and sensitive reactions, it is possible to endow syntheses and modes of formation, which attracted little if any attraction over a long period of years, with an actual analytical value. Interesting possibilities in the search for new tests for organic compounds are thus unfolded and they can be of prime importance to the development of organic spot test analysis. Other valuable orienting ideas can be gleaned from the chemistry of specific, selective and sensitive reactions as will be shown in the remainder of this introductory chapter and likewise in the description of many new and improved tests contained in Chapters 4–6.

Primarily because of the hydrophobic character of many organic compounds, but also sometimes for other reasons, great importance attaches in qualitative organic analysis to reactions whose initiation and progress do not require the presence of water as an independent phase. In indirect tests which involve separate synthesis operations, primary reactions in organic solvents, reactions in the gas sphase, fusion reactions, and the like are plausible. However, reactions of these kinds are also of great importance in direct tests for organic compounds. For example, salicylaldehyde and 8-hydroxyquinoline, which volatilize somewhat at room temperature and still more when gently warmed, can be detected within the technique of spot test analysis with high sensitivity through the formation of fluorescent products by the action of the vapors on hydrazine or metal hydroxides, respectively. Derivatives of these parent compounds contain the same functional groups but their vapor pressures are too low to permit their reaction in the gas phase. Consequently the analogous mode of reaction, which likewise leads to fluorescent products, holds only for reactions in solutions. Therefore selective reactions may be the basis of specific tests when it is possible to transfer the reaction locale from the solution into the gas phase. This possibility should be kept in mind quite generally when considering the detection of organic compounds which are sublimable or volatile per se or which can be volatilized with water vapor.

Compounds which yield characteristic gaseous fission products when subjected to dry pyrolysis can sometimes be detected indirectly by an interesting reaction in the vapor phase. Unfortunately, it is impossible to make reliable predictions in such instances because the nature and course of thermal decompositions depend on nature and constitution of the pyrolyzed material and the conditions of the heating. It is very likely that complicated processes are involved in many cases.* Nevertheless, definitive fission processes and

* Thermoanalytical studies of the kind instituted by Cl. Duval (*Inorganic Thermogravimetric Analysis*, Amsterdam, 1952) with inorganic and inorganic-organic compounds will doubtless provide much information of great importance and significance in clearing up pyrolytic decompositions involved in analysis.

fission products seem to be the rule in many classes of organic compounds. Familar instances are: formation of halogen hydrides on combustion of compounds containing halogen, even though they contain little hydrogen; production of hydrogen cyanide in the pyrolysis of many nitrogenous organic compounds. In contrast, relatively few of the latter yield dicyanogen when they are thermally decomposed, and the evolution of ammonia is limited to the pyrolysis of urea derivatives, guanidine salts and some of its derivatives. Similarly, the release of trimethylamine is characteristic of the pyrolysis of choline and betaine. When compounds containing carbon and oxygen are decomposed by heating, they invariably give water off in the form of superheated steam which can bring about hydrolytic splittings that are not realizable by the wet method. For example, when sulfoxylate compounds, oxymethylene compounds, salicin, and cellulose are subjected to dry heating, the resulting steam participates in the formation of hydrogen sulfide, formaldehyde, salicylaldehyde and furfuraldehyde together with acetaldehyde, as the case may be. These respective cleavage products may be detected easily in the vapor phase by sensitive tests and accordingly conclusions may be drawn as to the presence or absence of the initial materials.

Great analytical importance attaches to the formation of characteristic gaseous compounds in stoichiometrically defined fusion and sintering reactions of organic compounds between appropriate reactants. This point is illustrated by interesting reductive and oxidative cleavages, which are realizable in melts of a sodium formate or benzoyl peroxide. When a mixture of sodium formate and hydroxide is heated to 205°, hydrogen is released:

$$HCOONa + NaOH \longrightarrow Na_2CO_3 + 2H^+$$

Similarly, benzoyl peroxide (m.p. 103°) can serve as a source of oxygen:

$$(C_6H_5CO)_2 O_2 \longrightarrow (C_6H_5CO)_2O + O$$

It has been found that compounds with p-phenylenediamine- and p-nitrosamine structure produce p-phenylenediamine when fused with sodium formate-hydroxide. For example, in the case of aniline yellow, the reductive cleavage can be represented:

Since p-phenylenediamine is easily detected in the vapor phase by the blue color produced with aniline persulfate, and since even complicated members of these classes of compounds are susceptible of smooth reductive cleavage, even in micro quantities, the process has considerable practical value in the testing of azo dyestuffs.

Remarkable effects can be obtained with benzoyl peroxide fusions. For instance, O-ethyl and N-ethyl compounds undergo the oxidative cleavages:

$$R-OC_2H_5 + O \longrightarrow ROH + CH_3CHO$$
$$>N-C_2H_5 + O \longrightarrow >NH + CH_3CHO$$

Here again, the resulting acetaldehyde can be detected in the vapor phase by means of the color reaction (blue) with sodium nitroprusside solution containing piperidine. The detection of these groups has hitherto been rather difficult, but the fusion with benzoyl peroxide within a minute or two is quite simple when micro quantities are taken for examination. This represents real progress and is typical of the services which can be rendered by spot test analysis.

From the analytical standpoint, it is interesting that hydrolytic cleavages, such as occur in pyrolyses of organic compounds, can likewise be accomplished in many instances by heating the material with concentrated sulfuric acid. At first glance, this effect is somewhat astonishing since concentrated sulfuric acid is ordinarily viewed as a classic dehydrant. However, it is easy to understand its action as a water donor, especially on warming, if it is remembered that the concentrated acid, which in fact is a hemihydrate, always contains some water which does not volatilize on heating but is brought to a state equivalent to superheated steam. The latter is able to accomplish hydrolysis which cannot be brought about by hot water or with H^+ and OH^- ions at all or but slowly and incompletely. Clear instances of this hydrolytic action of concentrated sulfuric acid are provided in the tests for monochloroacetic acid and phenoxyacetic acid, in which the sample is heated to 150–170° with concentrated sulfuric acid and the resulting formaldehyde then detected in the vapor phase. The following series of reactions occurs:

$$CH_2ClCOOH + H_2O \longrightarrow CH_2OHCOOH + HCl$$
$$C_6H_5OCH_2COOH + H_2O \longrightarrow CH_2OHCOOH + C_6H_5OH$$
$$CH_2OHCOOH \longrightarrow CH_2O + CO + H_2O$$

Similarly, the production of formaldehyde when oxymethylene compounds are heated with concentrated sulfuric acid to 150–170° can be ascribed to the hydrolysis brought about by the concentrated acid or more correctly the water it contains:

2

Concentrated sulfuric acid can function as a water donor under milder conditions also. For instance, the characteristic blue color reaction for diphenylamine with nitrate (nitrite) is yielded at once when *as*-diphenylurea or diphenylguanidine is dissolved in concentrated sulfuric acid, warmed gently, and then treated with alkali nitrate (nitrite). This color reaction is not shown by *sym*.diphenylurea or *sym*.diphenylguanidine. Consequently, there is no doubt that the water present in the concentrated sulfuric acid accomplishes the cleavages:

$$OC\big\langle {}^{N(C_6H_5)_2}_{NH_2} + H_2O \longrightarrow CO_2 + NH_3 + HN(C_6H_5)_2$$

$$HN{=}C\big\langle {}^{N(C_6H_5)_2}_{NH_2} + 2\,H_2O \longrightarrow CO_2 + 2\,NH_3 + HN(C_6H_5)_2$$

The relationships are equally clear with respect to N-nitroso and *p*-nitrosodiphenylamine. In these instances, it is merely necessary to warm the compounds with concentrated sulfuric acid to cause them to split into diphenylamine and nitrous acid which then yield the blue color:

$$\left. \begin{array}{l} ON{-}N\big\langle {}^{C_6H_5}_{C_6H_5} \\[2mm] HN\big\langle {}^{C_6H_5}_{C_6H_4NO} \end{array} \right\} + H_2O \longrightarrow HN(C_6H_5)_2 + HNO_2$$

These examples demonstrate plainly that hydrolytic fissions must be regarded as essential partial reactions when color reactions occur in concentrated sulfuric acid. Insights into the chemistry of many color reactions, that were discovered empirically, have been obtained in this manner as well as by considering the activity of concentrated sulfuric acid as a dehydrant and oxidant. Obviously, such new approaches will yield valuable hints and leads in the search for new color reactions and tests.

A reaction in the gas phase can occur and be employed in analysis when a mixture of two solids, which though stable at room temperature, produces a gas when warmed because of the thermal decomposition of one of the solids, and provided this gas then reacts with the other solid. A pertinent example is a mixture of molybdenum trioxide with organic compounds. On heating, the volatile organic decomposition products react with the solid molybdenum oxide to give molybdenum blue. This interpretation is supported by the fact that readily volatile organic compounds, such as alcohol, ether, etc., on contact with hot molybdenum trioxide reduce it to molybdenum blue. Such production of the blue oxide can be applied within the technique of spot test analysis for the detection of traces of organic materials. This purpose can also be accomplished by means of potassium iodate. Even prolonged heating at 350° has no effect whatever on this salt. However, if a mixture of the iodate with organic materials is heated, there is rapid reduction to potassium iodide. This reduction can be disclosed by treating the sinter residue with a drop of acid, when iodine will be set free because of the familiar iodate-iodide reaction. Although there is no doubt that these two tests involve the action of gaseous decomposition products on a solid co-reactant, this action does not exclude the possibility that the redox reaction really begins as a solid-solid reaction, which perhaps proceeds to a considerable extent. The following example may show that this is actually the case. In inorganic spot test analysis, free (unbound) sulfuric acid is detected by its action on heated methylenedisalicylic acid. Red quinoidal formaurindicarboxylic acid is formed:

$$HO-\langle\ \rangle-CH_2-\langle\ \rangle-OH\ +\ H_2SO_4\ \longrightarrow$$
$$\underset{HOOC}{\quad}\qquad\qquad\underset{COOH}{\quad}$$

$$HO-\langle\ \rangle-CH=\langle\ \rangle=O\ +\ 2\,H_2O\ +\ SO_2$$
$$\underset{HOOC}{\quad}\qquad\qquad\underset{COOH}{\quad}$$

In this reaction, concentrated sulfuric acid functions as dehydrant and oxidant. Unexpectedly, it was found that the red formaurindicarboxylic acid is also formed when a mixture of sulfosalicylic acid (m.p. 120°) and methylenedisalicylic acid (m.p. 238°) is heated to 150°. (In this way, 5 γ sulfosalicylic acid can be detected by means of a drop reaction.) It is natural to suppose that the sulfosalicylic acid reacts by producing sulfur trioxide, and the latter then reacts with methylenedisalicylic acid in the same ways as concentrated sulfuric acid. However, this is not the case. The red formaurindicarboxylic acid can be produced by heating the mixture of sulfosalicylic and methylenedisalicylic to only 100° or to 120°, i.e. to the melting point of sulfosalicylic acid. Consequently, in the sulfosalicylic acid-methylenedisalicylic acid system, the same reaction may occur either as a solid-solid reaction, as a solid-melt reaction, and as a solid-gas reaction.

Similar types of reaction are likewise possible in the system: citric acid (m.p. 152°) – urea (m.p. 132°). The ammonium salt of citrazinic acid, which has a blue fluorescence, is produced by heating this mixture to 150°. The fluorescence reaction, which will reveal as little as 2 γ citric acid, involves two partial reactions. First of all, biuret and ammonia are formed when urea is heated above its melting point:

$$2 \ OC{\Large<}^{NH_2}_{NH_2} \ \longrightarrow \ O{=}\overset{\overset{\displaystyle NH_2}{|}}{C}{-}NH{-}\overset{\overset{\displaystyle NH_2}{|}}{C}{=}O + NH_3$$

The superheated ammonia generated in this decomposition can react directly with citric acid and produce citrazinic acid by the reaction:

$$\underset{\underset{\displaystyle HOOC \ \ OH \ \ COOH}{|\ \ \ \ \ |}}{\overset{\overset{\displaystyle COOH}{|}}{H_2C{-}C{-}CH_2}} \ + \ 2 \ NH_3 \ \longrightarrow \ \text{citrazinic acid} \ + \ 3 \ H_2O$$

According to this representation, this is a solid-gas reaction, or, if it is assumed that the citric acid is melted, a gas-melt reaction. It has now been found that the fluorescent citrazinic acid is likewise formed when the mixture of citric acid and urea is heated to only 110–120°, i.e., below the melting point of either of the reactants. It was found, in addition, that the non-fusing alkali- and alkaline earth citrates likewise react under these same conditions to produce fluorescent alkali salts of citrazinic acid.

These reactions in the sulfosalicylic acid-methylenedisalicylic acid and citric acid (citrate)-urea systems reveal two important facts. Firstly, they demonstrate the analytical usefulness of the participation of organic compounds in sintering and fusion reactions; secondly, they show that the respective chemical reaction can occur even at temperatures below the decomposition temperature of a thermally decomposable compound. This latter fact signifies that a readiness to react can be manifested by a low-melting compound even in temperature regions which heretofore have not been thought worth studying. Accordingly, it may be expected that organic compounds, which melt or decompose at fairly low temperatures, can by fusion or sintering be made to participate in reactions which are not realizable in the wet way. An excellent example of this possibility is found in the behavior of benzoin when it is fused with sulfur. The redox reaction

$$C_6H_5CHOHCOC_6H_5 + S^0 \ \longrightarrow \ C_6H_5COCOC_6H_5 + H_2S$$

occurs immediately in the vicinity of the melting point of benzoin (137°) and the resulting hydrogen sulfide may be detected by means of lead acetate paper. This finding has been made the basis not only of a specific test for elementary sulfur but it was also the starting point for the finding that many fusible compounds containing a secondary alcohol group react analogously to benzoin and even when they are present in small amounts. Consequently a spot test for the secondary alcohol group was worked out.

Equally impressive is the analytical usefulness of the immediate production of intensely colored molecular compounds, in the form of solvates, when quinones or nitro compounds are fused with tetrabase (m.p. 91°) or when amines are melted with p-nitrophenetole (m.p. 60°) or duroquinone (m.p. 110°). Minute quantities of quinones, nitro compounds and amines can be detected in this simple manner. It is obvious that such observations uncover interesting prospects for the development of new direct and indirect tests in organic analysis and especially in organic spot test analysis.

Characteristic examples in even the earliest contributions to spot test analysis indicated the possibilities of extensions of "fluorescence analysis". For a long time, the latter restricted itself primarily to registering chance fluorescences of organic and inorganic compounds, whereby data were obtained which are of importance in the testing of materials, determinations of origins, etc. The extension motivated by spot test analysis consisted essentially of including a stoichiometrically defined production of fluorescent products as a test for one of the compounds participating in the particular reaction. The mode of reaction is irrelevant here; the procedure may involve the formation of soluble or insoluble salts, condensation products, etc. It is essential either that fluorescent products be formed through the reaction of non-fluorescent materials, or that there be a characteristic change of the fluorescence hue in a fluorescing system. Such fluorescence reactions make direct tests possible. One method of employing fluorescence reactions for indirect tests is to produce, by suitable methods, non-fluorescent compounds, which can then in turn be detected by fluorescence reactions. The tests for o-hydroxylaldehydes, glycerol, and citric acid, which were discussed above, demonstrate the usefulness of this procedure in organic spot test analysis. In general, direct and indirect tests based on fluorescence reactions go far toward satisfying the requirements of selectivity and sensitivity. A limitation is imposed however by the fact that many organic compounds are fluorescent in their own right, or sometimes because of traces of impurities of unknown nature. Furthermore, non-fluorescent compounds can quench fluorescence by absorbing ultraviolet light. Such interferences are especially serious near the detection limits of fluorescence reactions. Some relief is afforded by comparison tests, by isolating the fluorescent compounds, and by observing the behavior of fluorescent materials when subjected to pH changes, which frequently are accompanied by characteristic alterations in the fluorescence or by the disappearance of the fluorescence.

Although not much evidence is available as yet, it does appear that the fluorescence of a compound is sometimes dependent on its phase state and degree of dispersion. This point is illustrated by the metal oxinates and also by the condensation products of hydrazine with o-hydroxyaldehydes. The former fluoresce both in the solid state and when dissolved in organic liquids. In contrast, the aldazines of the o-hydroxyaldehydes fluoresce only in the solid state, and not at all, or only to a minimum extent, when dissolved in ether, chloroform, etc. The dependence of fluorescence of compounds on their phase state and degree of dispersion merits consideration here, because an eventual use of this relation contributes to the enhancement of the specificity or selectivity of fluorescence reactions.

Far more significance attaches to the development of fluorescence resulting from the adsorption of nonfluorescent soluble or insoluble compounds. The following example shows that this can happen: hydrazine condenses with p-dimethylaminobenzaldehyde and yields a water-insoluble yellow aldazine which dissolves in acids with production of an orange quinoidal cation:

$$2\ (CH_3)_2N-\!\!\left\langle\ \right\rangle\!\!-CHO$$

$$+\ H_2N-NH_2$$

$$\downarrow$$

$$CH_3)_2N-\!\!\left\langle\ \right\rangle\!\!-CH=N-N=CH-\!\!\left\langle\ \right\rangle\!\!-N(CH_3)_2$$

$$+\ H^+$$

$$\downarrow$$

$$(CH_3)_2N-\!\!\left\langle\ \right\rangle\!\!-CH=N-NH-CH=\!\!\left\langle\ \right\rangle\!\!=\overset{+}{N}(CH_3)_2$$

Neither the insoluble aldazine or its colored solution in acids is fluorescent. However, if a drop of the orange solution is placed on filter paper, a red (not orange) fleck is formed, which fluoresces luminously red in ultraviolet light, and assumes a blue-green fluorescence when spotted with alkali or ammonia (whereby aldazine base is regenerated). Obviously the explanation is that a fluorescence is produced through the adsorption on filter paper of nonfluorescent ions or molecules. The importance to organic spot test analysis of the discovery of fluorescence effects of this kind, in which filter paper functions somewhat as an active participant, hardly needs to be stressed. This phenomenon of "adsorption fluorescence" is not only of theoretical importance but it has analytical values. It served as the basis of a spot test for hydrazine in solutions diluted to 1 : 50,000,000 and also of a spot test for the hydrazides of carboxylic acids.

Not much use has hitherto been made in qualitative organic analysis and spot test analysis of catalysis reactions. The familiar fact that the catalytic acceleration of chemical changes is often due to traces of materials, which enter into intermediate reactions and which limit their activity to definite homogeneous and heterogeneous reaction systems, indicates that the detection of accelerations of reactions can be made the basis of specific and sensitive tests for the particular catalyst. The importance of catalysis reactions has long been overlooked by those seeking new tests but due consideration of this field has led within a comparatively short time to many sensitive and specific tests in qualitative inorganic analysis and spot test analysis.* Thus there is no doubt that catalytic hastening of purely organic reactions by organic catalysts will similarly be of great value. Despite the large number and variety of organic reactions, catalysis will be encountered in such cases relatively less often of course because the tendency of inorganic ions to participate in catalysis by virtue of polyvalence is absent in the organic province. The analytical employment of catalyzed reactions presents the problem of detecting the acceleration of reactions which innately are sluggish or which in some cases proceed at an infinitely slow rate.

Color reactions present the following possibilities: (1) the catalyzed reaction may yield directly either a colored product or (2) a colorless product may be revealed by adding appropriate reagents. For instance, 1,2-dinitrobenzene gives a color reaction that is based on the fact that organic compounds, which serve as hydrogen donors in an alkaline medium, reduce this pale yellow nitro compound to the violet water-soluble alkali salts of the aci form of o-nitro-nitrosobenzene:

$$\text{C}_6\text{H}_4 \begin{matrix} -\text{NO}_2 \\ -\text{NO}_2 \end{matrix} + 4\,\text{H}^0 + 2\,\text{OH}^- \longrightarrow \text{C}_6\text{H}_4 \begin{matrix} =\text{NO}^- \\ =\text{NO}^-_2 \end{matrix} + 3\,\text{H}_2\text{O}$$

Among the hydrogen donors yielding this color reaction are the acyloins and benzoins, whose —CHOH—CO-group can be converted to the —CO—CO-group by the loss of hydrogen. Accordingly, it was anticipated that catalysts which lead to the formation of o-hydroxyketones as end- or intermediate products in suitable reaction systems, should be detectable through the color reaction with 1,2-dinitrobenzene. This has been found to be the case. For example, when benzaldehyde is warmed with an alkali cyanide it undergoes the familiar benzoin condensation, the cyanide acting as catalyst:

$$2\ \text{C}_6\text{H}_5\text{CHO} \longrightarrow \text{C}_6\text{H}_5\text{COCHOHC}_6\text{H}_5$$

When the goal is the actual preparation of benzoin, concentrated alkali

* Compare P. W. West, *Anal. Chem.*, 23 (1951) 176.

cyanide solution is used, but in line with the catalytic nature of the condensation, even traces of cyanide are sufficient to produce within a few minutes enough benzoin to give a positive response to the color reaction with 1,2-dinitrobenzene. An exceptionally sensitive test thus results for soluble, insoluble, and complex cyanides.

A second instance employs the reaction of formaldehyde with 1,2-dinitrobenzene:

$$2\ CH_2O\ +\ \Big\rangle\!\!\begin{array}{l}-NO_2\\-NO_2\end{array}\ +\ 4\ OH^-\ \longrightarrow\ \Big\rangle\!\!\begin{array}{l}=NO^-\\=NO_2{}^-\end{array}\ +\ 3\ H_2O\ +\ 2\ HCOO^-$$

Under certain conditions, this redox reaction proceeds so sluggishly that no violet color becomes visible within three to five minutes. However, the color appears much sooner if o-diketones are present. The latter act as catalysts because they are promptly reduced by formaldehyde to o-hydroxyketones, which react at once with 1,2-dinitrobenzene to regenerate the diketone, which then again enters into the reaction with formaldehyde, and so on. Paraquinones and quinoneimides participate in similar partial reactions and therefore a catalytic test for these compounds results. It is much more reliable and sensitive than any of the earlier tests.

The foregoing are model examples of the fact that catalytic reactions may be the basis of color tests for organic compounds that can be employed in organic spot test analysis. Although no comprehensive instances can be cited as yet, it may be assumed with certainty that a catalytic hastening of precipitation- and fluorescence reactions will be of use in analysis.

When catalysts are detected through their hastening of reactions, the prime reactants are always employed in considerable concentrations, and enough of the product is formed so that even insensitive tests, which need not be selective, are adequate. However, in another type of tests, sluggish reactants are invigorated by a suitable catalyst. Obviously, the sensitivity of such tests is not high. Nevertheless, this type of procedure can be expected to be feasible in qualitative organic spot test analysis, particularly if the reaction product of the catalyzed reaction can be readily detected even in small amounts through its self-color, insolubility, fluorescence, or by means of a supplementary reaction. The same holds for accelerations resulting from irradiation with daylight or ultraviolet rays (photocatalysis). Freytag* was the first to call attention to such tests, which can be conducted on paper as spot reactions and which are appropriately called "photoanalytical procedures." It has been found that redox reactions and hydrolyses are especially susceptible to photoanalytical influences. For example, ultraviolet irradiation of

---

* F. Freytag, *Z. anal. Chem.*, 103 (1935) 334; 129 (1949) 366; 142 (1954) 12.

alkaline solutions of coumarin converts the non-fluorescing compound into an isomeric fluorescing product or enormously hastens this transformation. This recent finding has been made the basis of a specific and extremely sensitive test for coumarin, either in the solid, dissolved, or vapor state.

The examples cited in this chapter show the existence of new or hitherto little considered possibilities of using reactions of organic compounds for analytical purposes*. Of course it is not implied that the previous methods of employing organic reactions should be relegated to the rear. The classic methods of qualitative organic analysis and their improvement will continue to play an important part in the development of organic spot test analysis. For this reason it seems well to give here a general survey of the most important types of reaction which deserve attention in the employment of and search for new direct and indirect tests for organic compounds or the identification of characteristic groups contained in them.

(1) *Direct tests*

a) Precipitation and color reactions (including fluorescence reactions) with inorganic or organic reagents in aqueous or organic media.

b) Reactions in the gas phase with dissolved or solid reagents.

c) Reactions of solids with solutions.

d) Reactions of solids with gases.

e) Reactions of solids with melts, and fusion reactions.

f) Reactions of solids with solids, sintering reactions.

g) Adsorption effects.

h) Catalysis reactions, in which the material to be detected acts as catalyst.

i) Catalysis reactions in which the compound to be detected is brought to rapid reaction.

(2) *Indirect tests*

a) Degradation (thermal, hydrolytic, oxidative, reductive) with formation of cleavage products which are detectable by (1) (*a–i*).

b) Syntheses or modes of formation which lead to compounds readily detectable by (1) (*a, g, h*).

c) Ascertainment of the blocking of the reactivity of particular groups (masking of reactions given in 1 *a*).

The great majority of the direct and indirect tests used in organic spot test analysis are satisfactory with respect to sensitivity (limits of identifica-

---

* Most of the new tests were developed during the past three years in the author's laboratory. Details may be found in the pertinent chapters of this book.

tion and dilution). As an average, the detection limits attained lie between 0.4–10 micrograms (gamma) of the sought material per drop (0.05 ml) and fractions of a milligram can still be detected by even the least sensitive tests. Frequently the sensitivity of spot reactions can be improved (sometimes by powers of ten) through refining the technique (micro drops, working in glass capillaries, magnification, etc.). For many purposes it is sufficient to follow the procedures as described in this text, which does not prescribe micro-manipulations. The directions are adequate for a refinement of the tests as well as for conducting them as test tube reactions on the macro scale. The necessary apparatus and manipulations in spot test analysis are discussed in detail in Chapter 2.

The sensitivity attainable in the chemical detection of organic compounds is governed by the same considerations that hold for the detection of inorganic materials. The limits of identification and the dilution limits are not characteristic constants of the underlying reactions, even though they are often employed as numerical expressions of the sensitivity. They are dependent on the particular reaction conditions, the type of observation, the reaction period, the presence of other materials, etc. Therefore, in order to obtain a maximum of sensitivity, the conditioning of tests has the same importance in qualitative organic analysis as in its inorganic counterpart.

The detection of functional groups in organic compounds is further complicated by still another sensitivity-determining factor, namely the influence, sometimes important, exerted by the remainder of the molecule, in whole or in part, with respect to the occurrence, speed, and extent of the chemical reactions of certain groups and also with respect to the discernibility of the characteristic reaction products through its color, solubility, volatility, fluorescence, etc. Definite reasons and reliable predictions concerning such factors can be stated only in exceptional cases. Steric effects on the mobility and reactivity of functional groups often make themselves apparent. Furthermore, the reaction picture and the characteristics of reaction products may be extensively altered by chromophoric, hydrophobic and hydrophilic groups, which are not direct participants in the reaction in question. Such influences are demonstrated by the fact that the attainable identification limits may vary within wide limits not only with respect to their absolute values but also in comparison with the values given by equimolar quantities of various compounds carrying the same functional groups. In fact, cases are known of compounds which do not respond at all to tests which in other instances are quite reliable for the particular functional groups. The earliest report of a test ordinarily covers only a few materials and so does not give a complete picture of the whole field of possible application. This wider view is obtained only after a comprehensive selection of cases has been tried. What has just been said about sensitivity and concentration limits applies equally to the selectivity of tests for functional groups and individual compounds.

In many cases there is a total or partial lack of information regarding the specificity and selectivity of direct and indirect tests for organic compounds or the groups they contain. There have been practically no studies of the lowering of the sensitivity of tests by seemingly indifferent accompanying materials, an effect often encountered in inorganic analysis. The lack of such information is related to the fact that the enormous number of organic compounds makes it incomparably more difficult to review and actually try the tests in this field than in the inorganic field. However, it may be anticipated that with growing interest in organic spot test analysis and its application to the detection of organic compounds in mixtures, new facts relative to specificity, selectivity and sensitivity will be uncovered. Although there are characteristic exceptions, chemical methods in general do not have the same reliability in organic analysis, and hence not in organic spot test analysis, as in inorganic analysis. Nevertheless, in view of past and present experiences, it may be expected that spot reactions will render excellent service in solving special problems encountered in the chemical testing of organic materials, and that they will doubtless be found equal and sometimes even superior to the corresponding macromethods. The economy in material, time and labor accompanying the use of spot reactions is of course a special advantage. This is all the more likely because there are now in use many tests which are not even realizable in classic micro analysis.

It is self-evident that the organic spot test analysis, which limits itself exclusively to chemical methods, cannot be nearly as serviceable as the classical qualitative organic macro analysis, which does not hesitate to enlist physical methods. For the latter, chemical methods constitute a kind of preliminary examination whose objective is to provide information about preparative measures to be taken for the isolation of compounds and preparation of derivatives, which can be definitely identified by physical methods. Since the extension of organic spot test analysis requires the improvement of existing methods and the discovery of new tests, it seems certain that efforts along these lines will also enrich the chemical methods of classical qualitative organic macro analysis. The experiences gained from organic spot test analysis in the examination of organic materials have already proven very useful supplements to the statements contained in the standard works on qualitative organic analysis. Some of these texts are:

N. Campbell, *Qualitative Organic Chemistry*, New York, 1939
N. D. Cheronis and J. B. Entrikin, *Semimicro Qualitative Organic Analysis*, 2nd ed., New York, 1956

H. T. Clarke, *Handbook of Organic Analysis*, London, 1928, reprinted 1937.

D. Davidson and D. Perlman, *A Guide to Qualitative Organic Analysis*, Brooklyn, 1952

C. H. Huntress and S. P. Mulliken, *Manual of the Identification of Organic Compounds*, New York, 1941

O. Kamm, *Qualitative Organic Analysis*, 2nd ed., New York, 1932

S. M. Mc Elvain, *The Characterisation of Organic Compounds*, 2nd ed., New York, 1953

H. Meyer, *Nachweis und Bestimmung organischer Verbindungen*, Berlin, 1933

H. Middleton, *Systematic Qualitative Organic Analysis*, 2nd ed., London, 1943

H. T. Openshaw, *Laboratory Manual of Qualitative Organic Analysis*, 3rd ed., Cambridge, 1955

M. Pesez and P. Poirier, *Méthodes et Réactions de l'Analyse Organique*, Volume III, Paris, 1954

L. Rosenthaler, *Der Nachweis organischer Verbindungen*, 2nd ed., Berlin, 1923

F. Schneider, *Qualitative Organic Microanalysis*, New York, 1946

R. L. Shriner, R. C. Fuson and D. Y. Curtin, *The Systematic Identification of Organic Compounds*, 4th ed., New York, 1956

S. Siggia and H. T. Stolten, *Introduction to Modern Organic Analysis*, New York, 1956

F. J. Smith and E. Jones, *A Scheme of Qualitative Organic Analysis*, London, 1953

H. Staudinger, *Anleitung zur organischen qualitativen Analyse*, 6th ed., Berlin, 1955

S. Veibel, *The Identification of Organic Compounds*, Copenhagen, 1954.

When dealing with organic spot test analysis, it must always be remembered that it is and must be more than mere technique, description of procedures, and a collection of recipes. The purely manual aspect, which plays duch a particularly important role in spot test analysis, deals with the conducting of specific, selective and sensitive tests. However, an exact knowledge of the chemistry of the reactions involved and the reasons for all the steps taken is indispensable to a real understanding of a procedure, through which the specificity, selectivity and sensitivity can be brought to a maximum. In this way, analytical labors become experimental chemistry conducted on genuine scientific lines and thus come to stand in close relation to many provinces of chemistry. Spot test analysis, both inorganic and organic, owes its development and present rank to adherence to this thesis, and this *leitmotiv*, which is also of high didactic value, will be our constant and unfailing guide in this text.

Chapter 2

Spot Test Techniques

1. Introduction

The term "spot test analysis" is a generic term referring to sensitive and selective tests based on chemical reactions whereby the use of a drop of the test or reagent solution is an essential step. The tests are microanalytical or semi-microanalytical in nature and are applicable for the investigation of both inorganic and organic compounds. An important part in spot test analysis is played by the actual manipulations with drops of unknown substances and reagents, and the method is not dependent on the use of auxiliary optical magnification.

In general, spot test procedures are the ultimate in simplicity. The elegance of the method derives from the nature of the reagents used, together with the advantageous use of reaction conditions, so that the utmost of sensitivity and selectivity can be obtained with a minimum of physical and chemical operations. As much as possible, separations and conditioning reactions are integrated in the test procedure so that the final test becomes a unitized operation that can be applied directly for the identification of the substance in question. The tests are ordinarily run by using one of the following techniques:

1. By bringing together one drop each of the test solution and reagent on porous or non-porous supporting surfaces such as paper, glass, or porcelain.
2. By placing a drop of the test solution on a medium impregnated with appropriate reagents (filter paper, asbestos, gelatin).
3. By placing a drop of reagent solution on a small quantity of the solid specimen (fragments or pulverized particles, evaporation or ignition residues).
4. By subjecting a drop of reagent or a strip of reagent paper to the action of liberated gases from a drop of the test solution or from a minute quantity of the solid specimen.
5. In an extended sense, spot reactions may also include tests accomplished by adding a drop of test solution to a larger volume (0.5 to 2 ml) of reagent solution and then extracting the reaction products with organic solvents.

The choice of procedure to be followed will ordinarily be dictated by the nature of the sample and the reagents available. The equipment and manipulations required are all simple and the techniques utilized can be learned without difficulty. The essential requirements for the successful application of spot test procedures include: (1) a knowledge of the chemical basis of all of the details of the tests used so that every step of the procedures can be understood and executed intelligently; (2) strict observance of trustworthy experimental conditions; (3) scrupulous cleanliness of the laboratory and equipment; (4) the use of the purest reagents available. Whenever possible, tests should be repeated to insure reproducibility. It should always be a rule, also, to run both blanks and controls.

The most essential manipulation in spot test work is the actual "spotting" of reactants. It is frequently necessary, however, to undertake certain preliminary operations to provide the most advantageous reaction conditions. Particularly in cases where complex samples are to be investigated, preliminary separations, either physical or chemical, may be required. Various operations such as drying, evaporation, ignition, oxidation or reduction, and adjustment of pH, are often employed; in cases where organic substances are to be identified, it is often necessary to undertake syntheses on a small scale, and preparative operations are common.

On the basis of the preceding remarks, the following discussion is presented to summarize the laboratory and equipment needs for spot test analysis, together with some of the essential operational techniques.

2. Laboratory and Equipment Requirements

Laboratory needs for the application of spot tests vary greatly, depending on the number and type of analyses anticipated. Under any circumstances, the space devoted to spot test work should be so designed and arranged that it can be kept scrupulously clean and, if possible, free of laboratory fumes. Proper lighting is also of the utmost importance in spot test operations. Diffused daylight is ideal for observation of colors and precipitates encountered in the analyses, but good daylight-type fluorescent lighting is also very satisfactory and has the advantage that it is constant. The arrangement of the work sections of the spot test laboratory should be given careful consideration. The actual performance of the tests themselves can be restricted to a very small area because the amount and type of equipment needed is at a minimum. Most important is to have an ample supply of reagents immediately available to the analyst. Sections devoted to sample preparation, cleaning of glassware, preparation of solutions, and general macrochemical operations should be as remote as possible from the spot test workbench.

The requirements for a spot test laboratory suggested above can be met in a good many ways, depending on the amount of space available and the volume of work anticipated. For industrial laboratories or large research laboratories, a special room designed for spot test investigations is desirable. A separate laboratory is also of advantage in universities where instruction in spot test methods is introduced. In this connection, it is quite logical that the spot test laboratory can also be used in teaching other microchemical techniques. It is practical to include selected spot tests in the general qualitative analysis course, and in such cases a few sets of reagents and a spot test workbench can be incorporated in the general qualitative analysis laboratory.

In many cases where space is at a premium, it is necessary to restrict the area devoted to spot test work and make this section a part of some general laboratory. From the standpoint of the space involved, this is easily done because these procedures demand a minimum of equipment and the working area required is exceedingly small as compared to that needed for most analytical techniques. It should be kept in mind that most spot tests are extremely sensitive; consequently, it is necessary to have the test section so located that the amount of fumes and dusts can be kept at a minimum.

A very satisfactory arrangement for occasional spot test work is to set aside a portion of a hood. This special section of the hood should have access to gas, electricity, and water and should have excellent lighting. Because the number of working tools required is so small, it is entirely practical to keep most of the ordinary equipment on hand in the hood space. Where certain tests are anticipated as being routine, the necessary reagents can be kept also in the hood, while chemicals and special reagents for occasional use can be kept in a near-by section of the laboratory, together with such auxiliary apparatus as balances, ultraviolet lamps, centrifuges, dryers, ovens and furnaces.

The laboratory devoted to spot test analysis must be provided with a wide selection of chemicals. While the amount of chemicals required is quite small, it remains important to have a variety of reagents available. Certainly the various organic and inorganic reagents commonly used must be stocked and a complete supply of general acids, bases, solvents, and oxidizing and reducing agents should be on hand. It is highly desirable to have a set of solutions of various organic substances available so that controls can be run on tests. It is also highly desirable to have respresentatives of diverse classes of organic compounds for use in running controls. A collection of plant products and standard samples of chemicals, minerals, and various technical products is also of great value in the preliminary examination of

unknown materials. In this connection, it is well to have simplified procedures outlined on cards mounted near the required reagents.

Portable laboratories and portable kits can be designed for use in spot
test work, whereby the necessary chemicals and equipment for a variety
of tests can be included in a minimum amount of space. For greatest flexibility,
however, the well-equipped spot test laboratory will include an assortment
of general laboratory apparatus as well as supplementary reagents and
chemicals.* The following list is suggested as a guide for the stocking of a
versatile laboratory.

Glass- and porcelain-ware

Assorted sizes of beakers, volumetric flasks, Erlenmeyer flasks, suction
flasks, round-bottom flasks, distillation heads, Conway cells[1], crystallizing
dishes, evaporating dishes, filter sticks, separatory funnels, extraction
pipets, fritted glass crucibles, graduated cylinders, pipets, burets, weighing
bottles, storage bottles, vials, test tubes (macro-, semimicro- and micro-),
centrifuge tubes in various sizes, microscope slides, cover glasses, and spot
plates should be available.

In addition to these glass items, there should be some counterpart items
made of porcelain and quartz. Especially in the case of porcelain items,
there should be both white and black crucibles, dishes, and the well-known
spot plates in assorted sizes. An important recent innovation is the introduction of polyethylene bottles, which are of great value in the storage of
stock solutions. There is available, also, low actinic glassware, which is
particularly useful in the storage of certain organic reagents that tend to
decompose when exposed to low wavelength light.

It is absolutely necessary to keep a permanent stock of glass rods and
pipettes.

Metal utensils

Platinum ware is standard for many spot test operations; and there should
be available platinum dishes, foils, crucibles, and boats. Nickel crucibles and
stainless steel beakers and dishes are also of value. Aluminum pans and
dishes are very useful since because of their low cost they can be discarded

---

* The various laboratory supply houses stock microchemical apparatus along with standard
laboratory items. In the United States, the Microchemical Specialties Company, Berkeley, Cali-
fornia, and the Arthur H. Thomas Company, Philadelphia, Pennsylvania, have particularly
good assortments of microchemical equipment. The British Drug Houses Ltd. (London) and the
Eastman Kodak Company (Rochester) supply most of the reagents of importance for spot test
analyses.

The publications of H. K. Alber and R. Belcher on standardization of microchemical
apparatus should be noted. The Subcommission on the Standardization of Microchemical
Apparatus, of the Commission of Pure and Applied Chemistry, is making cooperative studies
on the standardization of laboratory equipment.

References pp. 56, 57

after use. Absolutely indispensable are forceps and spatulas of nickel plated steel.

Iron ware

There should be a good assortment of microburners as well as Tirrill and blast burners. Other essential metal ware items are sand baths, water baths, tripods, ring stands, clamps, rings, and buret holders.

Special equipment and apparatus

The following equipment and apparatus can be considered as essential in the spot test laboratory: trip scale, torsion balance, analytical balance, pH meter, ultraviolet lamp, infrared lamp, centrifuge, ovens, dryers (a common hair dryer is very useful in spot test operations), furnaces, hot plates, steam baths (an electric baby bottle warmer makes an excellent steam bath for microchemical use), microdistillation assembly, electrographic apparatus, and cooling blocks.

In addition to the above items, it is desirable to have a spectrophotometer (such as the Beckman model DU or model B), a stereoscopic microscope, chemical microscope (or, preferably, a polarized light microscope), electric timer, and a melting point apparatus.

3. Working Methods

Consideration of the methods used in the laboratory must start with a discussion of the chemicals and solutions used. In general, a very good assortment of reagent quality inorganic chemicals should be available. Quarter-pound bottles are more than adequate in most cases. Organic chemicals are widely used in spot test laboratories and a good selection of organic reagents should be on hand. In most cases a few grams of organic reagents is sufficient; and these materials may be stored in the original bottles, preferably in a darkened cabinet. In some cases the organic reagents should be kept under refrigeration.

The wide use of organic reagents requires an appreciation of the characteristics of such materials. Many such reagents tend to decompose upon standing, particularly when they have been made up in solution. It is often possible in such cases to retard deterioration through the use of low actinic glassware.

Polyethylene containers can be used to store almost any organic or inorganic compound. Such containers are so inert chemically that they offer great advantages in the storage of the more reactive reagents. Although polyethylene bottles cost somewhat more than standard glass bottles, they should soon pay for themselves in saving of chemicals, breakage and time that would normally be required in the replacement of deteriorated solutions.

Chemicals and reagents actively used at the spot test workbench should be kept in containers most convenient for use. For dry chemicals it is usually sufficient to keep them in plastic-stoppered glass vials. Because the actual spot reactions usually require not more than a drop or two of liquid reagents, it is well to keep such materials in small dropping bottles. Bottles of the type shown in Fig. 1 are very satisfactory where there is no danger of the stopper becoming frozen. Bottles equipped with pipets are very convenient for most work, and the type shown in Fig. 2 or the Barnes dropping bottle shown in Fig. 3 are very satisfactory. All such bottles should be of resistant

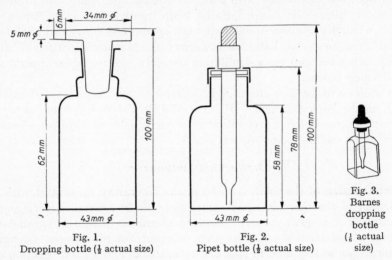

Fig. 1.
Dropping bottle (½ actual size)

Fig. 2.
Pipet bottle (½ actual size)

Fig. 3.
Barnes dropping bottle (⅙ actual size)

glass. Before being filled the bottles should be cleaned thoroughly and rinsed. Alkaline solutions that may attack glass may be stored in bottles coated inside with paraffin, although in most cases it is now preferred to store such solutions in polyethylene bottles. It is possible to obtain such bottles with nozzles so that reagents can be sprayed from the bottle by merely squeezing the sides; or droplets of reagent can be added by tipping the bottle and allowing reagent actually to run into the spray nozzle, after which the number of drops taken can be regulated by the amount of pressure applied to the sides of the bottle.

Sampling

In any analytical work one of the most important of all operations is the taking of samples. It is a total waste of time and effort to make careful analyses of samples that are not representative. For spot test operations it must be kept in mind that such investigations can be utilized in the detection of inhomogeneities in the sample, or the tests can be utilized for ascertaining the average or general composition of a gross sample. Where selected portions of a sample are to be examined, it is often advisable to use low-power magnification and to sort the particles with the aid of a low-power wide-angle microscope. Sorting can be accomplished in such cases through use of fine glass fibers that have been moistened with glycerol or some other viscous and inert agent which can serve to collect the desired particles. Random impurities in many solid samples can best be studied by first dissolving the sample and then isolating the impurities through use of gathering agents, chromatographic techniques, or selective extractions. In some cases no such isolation methods need be applied; instead, highly sensitive spot tests are used directly for the detection or rough estimation of the impurity.

Materials in the gaseous state are sometimes subjected to spot test investigation. Materials of this type present peculiar problems because they are usually invisible substances. In handling gas samples, the desired constituent may be scrubbed from a given volume of the sample and subsequently examined, or a "catch" sample of the gas can be collected and the gross sample subjected to analytical investigation.

Samples of liquid unknowns present few problems for the selecting of representative samples, especially if the total sample can be stirred thoroughly to insure good mixing. In those cases where individual liquid samples must be taken and combined for later study, it is important that representative samples be secured by mixing like portions secured at the different locations.

The problem of proper sampling is so important that when there is a doubt concerning the reliability of samples for investigation, special treatises should be consulted for information on the products and sample methods used.

Grinding and mixing of solids

Solid samples are usually subjected to chemical treatment in the course of the analytical examination. These processes include: dissolution in water, acids, or alkalies; fusion with disintegrating agents such as sodium carbonates sodium peroxide, sodium pyrosulfate; volatilization of certain component-(simple distillation, sublimation, or the fuming of the sample with hydro, fluoric acid, hydrochloric acid, sulfuric acid, etc.), and extraction with organic solvents. Whatever treatment is employed, it is the general rule that the maximum reactive surface of the solid should be provided so that complete and rapid reactions may occur. This requirement is met in the case of slightly soluble compounds only when they are freshly precipitated and gently dried. Ignited materials, especially natural or technical products, must usually be pulverized beforehand because a direct testing on compact surfaces is possible only in exceptional cases.

Agate mortars are preferred in the pulverizing of solid materials. Mortars and pestles of glass or of good quality porcelain are satisfactory for many

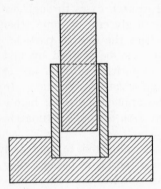

purposes although they lack the resistance of agate. Very hard specimens should be broken up in a steel diamond mortar before final pulverizing in agate. Fig. 4 shows a micro mortar.

To insure a uniform particle size, it is necessary to screen the powdered material through tightly stretched fine silk cloth. Such sifting is accomplished by adding the sample to the micro sieve and gently tapping the cloth so that the finest particles of the powder fall through the meshes and the coarser fragments are retained. The latter are then reground and

Fig. 4. Micro mortar (actual size)   the sifting and grinding continued until the total sample has been reduced to such a fine state of subdivision that it has passed through the cloth. Only when a perfectly homogenous material is being examined may the coarser residue be rejected and the first portion taken for chemical examination.

A very satisfactory arrangement for the sieving of samples is shown in Fig. 5. It consists of an open glass tube or micro beaker over which is stretched a circle of very fine silk. The cloth can be cemented in place or it can be fastened by means of a rubber band or piece of string.

Pulverized samples are mixed with powdered reagents only if the materials are thoroughly dry. The mixing can be done in crucibles, on watch glasses, or on glazed paper. Dry powders that are not hygroscopic can be weighed satisfactorily in tared aluminum dishes or on glazed paper. The mixing of powders can be performed with platinum wires or thin glass rods. Micro spatulas are very

Fig. 5.
Micro sieve (actual size)

useful, and wooden toothpicks are of general value in the handling of powdered materials. Rather uniform specimens of some solid samples can be obtained by use of streak plates of unglazed porcelain. The sample is rubbed against the porcelain plate and the sample is collected in the form of a streak which can be subsequently observed for its color and then taken up in appropriate reagents and analyzed by spot test procedures.

Evaporating, drying, igniting, fusing

The concentrating of solutions, removal of solvent or volatile constituents of solutions, and evaporation of solutions to dryness may be carried out, in most cases, in glass, porcelain, or platinum micro crucibles. The apparatus shown in Fig. 6 is very convenient for all of these operations. It consists of an aluminum block *Al* fitted with thermometer wells *T*; cavities for two or three micro crucibles are also provided in the block, and a small glass bell carrying a stopcock is fitted tightly to the top of the block. With this apparatus it is possible to remove water and volatile compounds under reduced pressure at temperatures below the normal boiling points. If the bell is placed on a well-fitted ground-glass plate the assembly can be used as a micro desiccator. (See also ref. [2].)

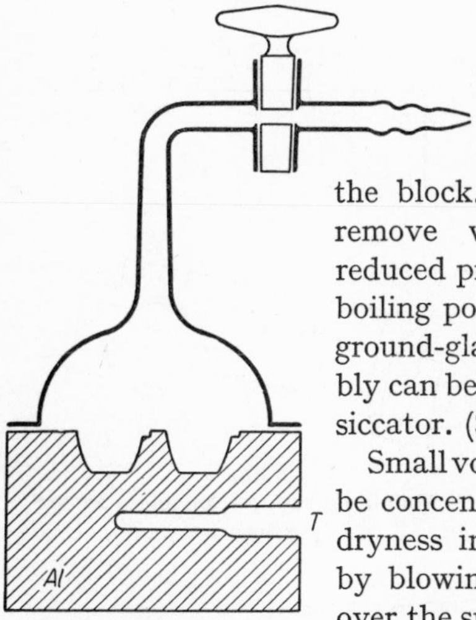

Small volumes of liquid can be concentrated or taken to dryness in centrifuge tubes by blowing dry, filtered air over the surface of the liquid while the centrifuge cone is immersed in a water bath. Fig. 7 shows the details of the apparatus for such an operation.

Fig. 6.
Aluminum block for concentrating solutions, etc. (½ actual size)

If the temperature of a water bath is not sufficient to remove volatile compounds, an infrared lamp can be used advantageously,* and air or sand baths can be employed so as to obtain higher temperatures. A simple air bath is shown in Fig. 10. It consists of a nickel crucible with a copper wire triangle suspended in it through lateral slits. The triangle supports a micro crucible or micro beaker. The crucible can be heated directly by a burner or hot plate and the temperature checked by suspending a thermometer in the crucible. The thermometer is best protected

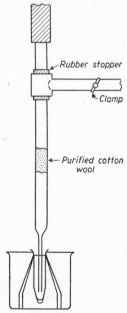

Fig. 7.
Set-up for concentrating a solution in a centrifuge tube (½ actual size)

* A special radiator for analytical work has been described. [3]

by a metal shield. If the bath is filled with fine sand, the vessel containing
the liquid to be evaporated can be placed on or in the sand.

When evaporation or fuming operations result in the evolution of clouds

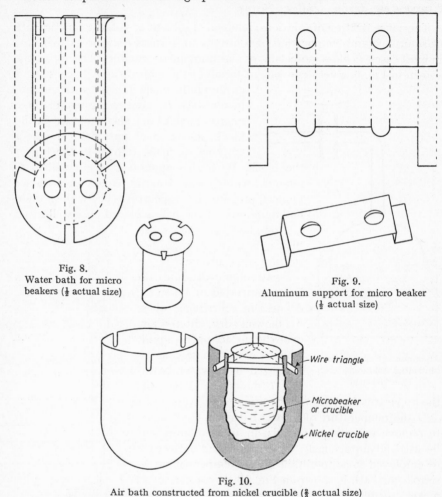

Fig. 8.
Water bath for micro
beakers ($\frac{1}{2}$ actual size)

Fig. 9.
Aluminum support for micro beaker
($\frac{1}{2}$ actual size)

Wire triangle

Microbeaker
or crucible

Nickel crucible

Fig. 10.
Air bath constructed from nickel crucible ($\frac{2}{3}$ actual size)

of acid vapors or noxious gases, the apparatus should be set up in a hood,
or a hood arrangement should be constructed through use of an inverted glass
funnel connected to an aspirator pump as shown in Fig. 11. *

Platinum spoons, or silica casseroles and watch glasses are very useful

* Appropriate apparatus are described by Gorbach. [3a]

when evaporating small volumes of liquid samples. Clear silica utensils are particularly useful in this case because, after the evaporation or ignition, the residue can be inspected directly over black glazed paper or other suitable backgrounds.

Fusing of powdered materials can be accomplished very conveniently, in most cases, through use of platinum spoons (Fig. 12) or platinum loops. Fluxes may be collected on platinum loops and then touched to powdered samples and the melt subjected to oxidizing or reducing flames, as desired. Platinum micro crucibles may also be used for fusions, particularly when muffle furnaces are available.

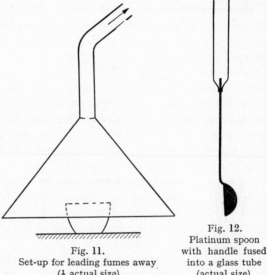

Fig. 11.
Set-up for leading fumes away
(¼ actual size)

Fig. 12.
Platinum spoon
with handle fused
into a glass tube
(actual size)

Addition and control of drops

The adding of a drop of test solution or reagent is basically a very simple operation and can be done in a variety of ways, depending on the circumstances. For the application of drops of reagent, it is generally unnecessary to maintain careful control of drop size. On the other hand, the measurement of the sample drop should, in many cases, be controlled carefully so that the same size drop is taken each time. This is particularly important when semi-quantitative estimates of materials are desired.

The simplest method of taking drops is to use a reagent bottle, such as the Barnes type (Fig. 3), which is stoppered with a dropper pipet. Control of the delivery of liquids can be maintained by means of the rubber cap. When drops of liquid are to be placed on paper or spot plates by means of such pipets, the latter should be held at right angles to the horizontal receiving surface. The pipet tip should be not more than one or two centimeters above the place where the drop is to be delivered. If drops of the test solution and the various reagents are to be placed on filter paper in succession, care must be taken to assure that successive drops all fall as near as possible to the center of the first drop. In a few exceptional cases it is desirable to use adjacent spots so that the reactants diffuse together and the course of the

References pp. 56, 57

reaction observed as the mixing occurs. Under any circumstance, it is important that the pipet tip remain free from any possible contamination. Therefore, all drops should be allowed to fall freely and the tip of the pipet must never be touched against the receiving surface.

Dropping bottles equipped with turn caps are also very convenient for the adding of reagents. It is somewhat more difficult to control the amount of reagent added with this type of bottle but, with a little practice, adequate control can be maintained.

Glass rods are very useful in transferring drops of solution or reagent where careful control of drop size is not required. A glass rod 3 millimeters in diameter delivers drops of about 0.05 ml volume, while smaller drops can be delivered by using rods of smaller diameter. The use of glass rods, however, is permissible only for exploratory work because close regulation of drop size is too difficult. If the rod is not wetted sufficiently there is danger that the drops will flow off too slowly and the operator will be tempted to touch the filter paper or other substance with the rod. This results in liquid being sucked off the rod with resultant loss of control of drop size. If rods are used they should be used only once and then placed in a receiving beaker containing a rinse solution.

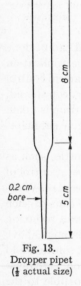

8 cm

0.2 cm
bore →

5 cm

Fig. 13.
Dropper pipet
(½ actual size)

Platinum loops are very convenient for the transfer of drops. A platinum loop can be fashioned permanently in a fine platinum wire; if desired, the size of the loop can be adjusted to deliver any predetermined size drop. Loops can be calibrated and the volume of sample delivered can be indicated by pasting a label on the handle of the loop holder.

Drops are often delivered by means of pipets of various descriptions. Calibrated capillary pipets are very useful where exact measurement of solution volumes is desired. Transfer pipets are also utilized widely and can be prepared readily in the laboratory. Dropper pipets with rubber bulbs are particularly useful and can be prepared in the laboratory or can be obtained from supply houses or drug stores (Fig. 13). Dropper pipets for accurate delivery of drops can be made by using large capillary tubing and blowing out storage bulbs if necessary. By retaining the flat surface of the tube end, more careful control of drop size is maintained. It is also helpful to coat the outside walls of the pipets in this case with silicone grease so that only the end of the pipet can be wetted.

An extremely useful device for accurately delivering known amounts of

References pp. 56, 57

solution is the micro pipet-buret * described by Gilmont.[4] These pipets can be made to deliver from 0.0001 ml to 1 ml of solution. They have a glass reservoir and delivery tip and the volume of solution delivered is controlled by means of a synthetic ruby plunger, which is passed through a teflon gasket. The control of the volume of solution delivered is maintained by means of a micrometer screw activating the synthetic ruby plunger. A micrometer gauge reads directly in terms of volume delivered. The pipet can be mounted on a ring stand and a solution of the sample to be analyzed can be stored in the pipet and accurate volumes of sample delivered as desired. This device is also of importance in research work where new spot tests are being studied and if it is desired to maintain accurate control of volume of all reagents used in the procedure.

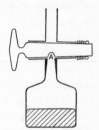

Fig. 14.
Apparatus for delivering uniform drops of mercury ($\frac{1}{3}$ actual size)

Figure 14 shows a small apparatus for delivering uniform drops of mercury; it consists of a storage vessel and is closed by a glass cock whose plug has a depression in place of the usual bore. The size of the drop is determined by the size of the depression and, consequently, different sized drops can be delivered by varying the depression. One advantage of this "mercury dropper", which can also be used to deliver drops of other liquids, is the tight closing of the storage vessel and the unvarying size of the drops discharged. The vessel is filled by taking out the cock and inserting a shortstem funnel in the delivery tube.

Separation methods (operations)

While it is true in spot test work that the tests are unitized as much as possible in order to eliminate the tedium of separation procedures, it still remains necessary in many cases to isolate desired materials or to eliminate possible interfering substances through application of separation techniques. The most elegant method of separation is that of masking. In such operations, interfering materials are usually sequestered as soluble complexes or pseudo salts. Such methods have the obvious advantage that no subsequent separation of phases is required and so the separation can become an inherent step in a simplified spot test procedure. No special discussion of technique is required here because the only operation involved is the addition of the necessary conditioning agent.

Precipitation methods remain standard for analytical separations. The more complex the unknown, the greater the likelihood that separations of some sort are desirable or necessary. Particularly in the case of unknown

* These pipet-burets are available from the Emil Greiner Company, New York City.

inorganic mixtures and in the investigation of commercial products is it necessary to use some classification system of separation which will serve to isolate certain groups of substances for subsequent spot test investigation.

When spot reactions are made on paper, either by bringing together two drops or by spotting a reagent paper with a drop of the test solution, any insoluble compounds formed are precipitated directly in the paper, and the unchanged constituents of the solutions undergo capillary diffusion. The latter will then be present throughout the whole spotted area, particularly in the circular zone surrounding the precipitate. Precipitation and filtration are thus accomplished in the surface of the paper. Additional spot tests can be made then on the spotted area, either on the product that has precipitated there, or on the circular zone surrounding the precipitate. Spot reactions on paper not only accomplish a direct precipitation and filtration but also make it possible to purify precipitates by washing. This can be done by placing drops of water, or of a suitable wash liquid, on the center of the spot; the concentric ring around the precipitate is thus extended by capillary diffusion. If the filtrate is of no importance for additional tests, it is better to bathe the spotted paper in an appropriate wash liquid, which can be renewed if necessary. When it is desired to wash a precipitate by repeated treatment with drops of water, each drop should be completely absorbed before the next drop is added.

It is generally better to dry the spots before washing them. This fixes the precipitate more firmly in the capillaries of the paper and there is less likelihood of its being washed away. Spots are dried best and most quickly by a blast of warm air. This localizes the material that has remained in solution and undergone capillary diffusion; the accumulation will be greatest on the side of the paper toward the blast. This is an advantage if further tests by later spot reactions are to be made on the filtrate that has been separated by capillary action.

The testing for dissolved materials that have diffused out of a patch of precipitate should be made by spotting laterally. It is best to place a drop of the appropriate reagent on the dry paper beyond the primary spot. The reagent will spread uniformly from the point of application, and characteristic reaction pictures will be produced at the junction of the two spots. If colored reagents are used in this manner, even slight changes in color are quite apparent.

Solids can often be tested directly to determine their solubility in dilute acids, alkalis, and the like, by spot reactions on paper. A small quantity of the pulverized sample is heaped on a strip of filter paper and spotted with 1 or 2 drops of the solvent. The action is hastened by warming in a current of heated air. Complete solution is obviously established if the sample disappears. Partial solution can be detected by applying suitable reagents near the site of the original reaction. Direct spotting of solids on paper is not limited to the determination of solubility, but can be used also if soluble colored reaction products are formed by the action of reagents and have then diffused away through the capillaries of the paper. Frequently, characteristic spot reactions can be made directly on white paper through this type of filtration.

The precipitation and filtration following spot reactions on paper may not be applied to all cases, because strongly acidic or alkaline solutions cannot be used, nor is it feasible to subject reaction mixtures to prolonged and intensive heating. Neither is it possible, as a rule, to detect and isolate small quantities of colorless reaction products on paper. Consequently, other means must be employed to separate solid and liquid phases. The choice of the method is determined by the particular needs of the moment.

When considerable quantities of liquid are involved, and if the solid or precipitate is of no further interest, a portion of the liquid can be withdrawn by a pipet for examination. The fine constricted end of the pipet is closed with a wad of cotton drawn out to a point. If the suspension is sucked into the pipet, the liquid which arrives in the tube will be free of precipitate. The pipet will deliver a perfectly clear liquid if the tip is carefully washed after removing the cotton.

A useful filter pipet [5] is shown in Fig. 15. It is constructed of glass tubing (6 mm diameter). A rubber bulb is attached to the short arm A; arm B is ground flat; arm C is drawn out to a fine capillary. A short piece of rubber tubing D is fitted over the top of B. A disk of filter paper of the same diameter as the outside diameter of the tube is cut from a sheet of filter paper by a sharp cork borer or hand punch and is placed on the flat ground surface of B. Tube F is placed on the paper, which is held in

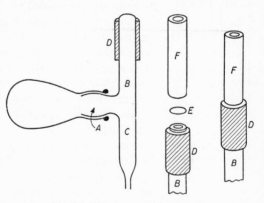

Fig. 15. Filtering pipet (actual size)

position by sliding the rubber tubing over it just far enough to hold it when F is removed. The filter pipet can be used either by placing a drop of the solution on the filter disk or by immersing B into the crucible, test tube, or other container holding the liquid to be filtered. The bulb is squeezed between the thumb and middle finger and the dropper point is closed with the index finger; the solution is thus allowed to pass through the paper when the bulb is released. The pipet is inverted over the spot plate, etc., in an inclined position with the bulb uppermost when it is desired to discharge drops of the filtered liquid. The liquid in the tip is forced onto the spot plate, etc., by manipulating the bulb. The precipitate on the paper can be removed for any further treatment by simply sliding the rubber tubing D over the arm B.

Another method of filtration employs an Emich filter stick, fitted into a heavy wall suction tube by means of a rubber stopper. The suction tube contains a micro test tube to receive the filtrate (Fig. 16). The filter stick contains a small asbestos pad.

Often filtration is not the best method of separating solid and liquid phases. Sedimentation of insoluble materials by centrifuging is sometimes preferable. In addition to greater speed, this procedure has the following advantages: no retention of the mother liquor by the filtering medium; the precipitate, freed from most of its moisture, is compressed into a small volume; the structure of the solid phase (crystalline or amorphous) has no effect on the sharp separation of the phases. The receptacles for centrifuging (centrifuge tubes) can be so chosen for size that the isolation of minute quantities of precipitate or of small volumes of filtrate can be effectively accomplished.

A micro centrifuge tube is shown in Fig. 17, together with a glass support. This arrangement is useful for heating or evaporating on the water bath. A variety of centrifuge tubes with capacities of 0.5 to 3 milliliters should be available.

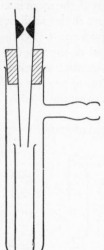

Fig. 16.
Set-up for microfiltration, using filter stick and suction (actual size)

Centrifuge tubes are conveniently supported on a rack consisting of a wooden block provided with 9 to 12 holes, evenly spaced and 5/8 of an inch in diameter, 1/2 inch deep. Wide selections of micro centrifuges are now on the market. Those which are driven electrically (1500 to 3000 r.p.m.) are preferable to hand-operated centrifuges. The centrifuge should be provided with a metal shield and cover to protect the operator. Dangerous vibration of the instrument is avoided by always loading the carrier equally. This is done by counterbalancing the tube containing the sample by an opposing tube

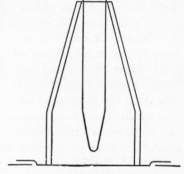

Fig. 17.
Micro centrifuge tube and support
($\frac{2}{3}$ actual size)

containing an equal weight of water or an approximately equal volume of the liquid being centrifuged. The cover of the centrifuge must not be lifted until the rotor has come to rest.

Precipitations are usually made in conical micro centrifuge tubes. The precipitate collects at the bottom of the tube when the suspension is centrifuged. A dropper pipet is usually used to remove the supernatant liquid because the liquid cannot conveniently be poured off directly. A dropper pipet suitable for this operation can be made easily from glass tubing; suggested dimensions are given in Fig. 13. A transfer capillary is convenient for removing the mother liquid or centrifugate, particularly from smaller tubes (0.5 to 2 ml capacity). The pipet is made of glass tubing (internal diameter about 2 mm) which can be drawn from wider

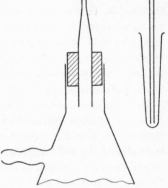

Fig. 18.	Fig. 19.	Fig. 20.
Removing supernatant liquid from a centrifuge tube by suction ($\frac{1}{2}$ actual size)	Stirrer (glass) ($\frac{1}{2}$ actual size)	Device for withdrawing liquid from a centrifuge tube by suction ($\frac{1}{2}$ actual size)

tubing. The length is 20 to 25 centimeters. One end is drawn to a tip with a fine opening by heating in a micro flame. The correct method of transferring the liquid to the capillary pipet is made evident by Fig. 18. The centrifuge tube is held in the left hand, and the pipet slowly pushed toward the precipitate so that the point of the capillary always remains just below the surface of the liquid. This is continued until almost the entire solution is in the pipet and the tip is about 1 millimeter above the precipitate.

The liquid is drained from the pipet into a clean, dry centrifuge tube.

Precipitates are washed by adding the wash solution directly to the precipitate in the centrifuge tube and stirring thoroughly either with a platinum wire or by means of a stirrer (Fig. 19). This is readily constructed from a glass rod. The suspension is then centrifuged and the clarified liquid removed with the aid of a pipet as just described. This operation may have to be repeated two or three times to insure complete washing.

Centrifuge tubes are cleaned with a feather or a small test tube brush. The tubes are filled then with distilled water and emptied by suction using the device shown in Fig. 20. After the suction has been started and the liquid drawn out, the tube is filled several times with distilled water without removing the suction device between emptyings. Dropper pipets are cleaned by repeated fillings with water; the bulb and tube are finally separated and both rinsed with distilled water from a wash bottle. Transfer capillary pipets are cleaned by blowing a stream of water from a wash bottle through them.

Small quantities of a precipitate can be collected by centrifuging in a micro centrifuge tube, and thus made more visible and accessible to further treatment. This method of separating solid and liquid phases can, therefore, be substituted for filtration in many instances. If the problem is merely the detection of formation of minimal quantities of precipitate that can produce not more than a slight opalescence if the precipitate is colorless, it is frequently necessary to centrifuge for considerable periods to accomplish the separation of the finely dispersed solid phase.

In some instances, a separation can be made quickly by means of flotation. This can be accomplished by shaking the suspension with an organic liquid that is not miscible with water. The surface tension is altered and the fine particles of the solid aggregate and collect as a thin film in the water-organic interface. This method is recommended particularly when it is necessary to detect the formation of a precipitate in a considerable volume of solution after a reagent has been added. The aggregation and localization by flotation or shaking-out succeeds best in neutral and acidic solutions. This treatment with an organic solvent is conveniently done in macro or micro test tubes provided with glass stoppers.

The flotation technique described above finds a number of applications in spot test work. More important is the use of liquid-liquid extractions (and liquid-solid extractions), which promise to become a very important means of analytical separation. Extraction procedures are of particular interest because they offer a means of separation comparable in efficiency to precipitation but still require much less time to perform. In the past the greatest number of applications of extraction techniques was found in the separation of organic compounds. While organic compounds are still very well adaptable to separation in this way, it is important to note that many inorganic substances are now being separated by liquid-liquid extractions. In some cases chelate salts are formed and are then isolated by extraction; while, in many other instances, inorganic salts themselves are selectively extracted by suitable organic liquids. A number of devices are available for making extractions. Liquid-solid extractions can be accomplished in micro Soxhlet extractors, and liquid-liquid extractions can be carried out in small extraction funnels or in extraction pipets. A very convenient extraction pipet * has been described by Carlton.[6] The pipet consists of a capillary tip 6 cm long, 7 mm outside diameter, and 1.8 mm inside diameter; a bulb blown just above the capillary tip 4 cm long, 1.15 cm outside diameter, and about 2 to 3 ml capacity. An upper stem, 5 cm long, 7 mm outside diameter, and 5 mm inside diameter, is attached to the upper part of the bulb and a rubber bulb of 10 ml capacity is attached to the upper stem. None of the dimensions is critical. When low boiling liquids such as ether, chloroform, carbon tetrachloride, or carbon disulfide are used as extractants, a capillary of about 0.7 or 0.8 mm bore is recommended. Mixing is accomplished by drawing the liquids into the pipet and then expelling them, repeating the procedure several times. By using a rubber bulb of considerably greater capacity than the pipet, a large quantity of air is drawn into the pipet after the liquids have been drawn up; and the bubbling of this air through the two liquid layers provides a very efficient means of mixing. When thorough mixing has been accomplished, the two layers are permitted to separate and then the rubber bulb is squeezed until the lower phase has been removed from the pipet. By means of this device, efficient separations of many substances can be carried out in a matter of 10 to 20 seconds.

Three kinds of manipulation with gases or vapors are used in spot test analysis. Gases (vapors) are employed as auxiliary reagents for precipitation, alkalization, or oxidation of solutions. On the other hand, the liberation of small quantities of gases (vapors) as characteristic products which can be identified by subsequent reactions is the basis of certain tests. Finally, distillation of organic liquids may be an essential step in preparing organic samples for testing. The apparatus required for handling gases (vapors) is determined by the purpose at hand.

Spot reactions on paper involving the action of gases or vapors (H_2S, NH_3, halogens, steam) can be conducted by leading the gas directly from the generator, or by placing a strip of filter paper over the neck of an open flask filled with hydrogen sulfide water, ammonium hydroxide, etc. The steamer (Fig. 21) can be used as a gas generator, if the flask is filled with

---

* These extraction pipets are commercially available from the E. H. Sargent Company, Chicago, Illinois.

hydrogen sulfide water, bromine water, or ammonia water and the material to be gassed placed on the side arm. Heat is then applied to the flask.

The separation of certain groups of metals by treating the acidic or ammoniacal solution with gaseous hydrogen sulfide is a common step in chemical analyses. In spot test analysis, this precipitation can be accomplished by saturating a small volume of the solution with hydrogen sulfide in a micro centrifuge tube. The hydrogen sulfide is admitted through a fine capillary to prevent loss by spattering. The delivery tube is made by drawing out 6 mm glass tubing to form a capillary of 1 to 2 mm bore and 10 to 20 cm long. A plug of bleached cotton wool is inserted in the wide part of the tubing; then the capillary end is heated in a micro burner and drawn down to a finer tube of 0.3 to 0.5 mm bore and about 10 cm long. Fig. 22 shows the complete arrangement. The fine capillary delivers a stream of tiny bubbles; consequently, the solution does not spatter out of the micro centrifuge tube. The gas must be started through the tube before plunging the end of the capillary into the solution. Otherwise, the solution will rise in the capillary; and when the hydrogen sulfide is admitted, a precipitate will form in the capillary and clog it. The end of the sulfide precipitation can be easily detected through an increase in the size of the rising bubbles. At room temperature, this point is usually reached in about 3 minutes.

Fig. 21.
Apparatus for treating paper with gases or vapors (actual size)

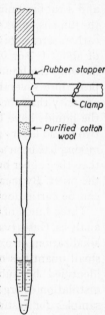

Fig. 22.
Set-up for precipitating sulfides by leading in hydrogen sulfide ($\frac{1}{2}$ actual size)

— *Rubber stopper*

`—Clamp`

←— *Purified cotton wool*

An adequate supply of various types of special apparatus of small capacity must be kept on hand. These are required for the liberation of volatile compounds after decomposing small quantities of solid materials or solutions with acids or alkalis. An apparatus[7] designed for the detection of carbonate, sulfide, etc., is shown in Fig. 23. It consists of a micro test tube of about 1 milliliter capacity and can be closed with a small ground-glass stopper fused to a glass knob. The gas is evolved in the tube, aided if necessary by gentle warming, and is absorbed by the reagent. Since the apparatus is closed, no gas escapes; and if enough time is allowed, it is absorbed quantitatively. A drop of water may replace the reagent on the knob.

In this case the gas is dissolved, and the drop may then be washed onto a spot plate or into a micro crucible and treated there with the reagent. The apparatus shown in Fig. 24 is sometimes preferable, particularly when minute quantities of gas are involved. The tube is closed by a rubber stopper and the glass tube, blown into a small bulb at the lower end, may be raised or lowered at will. A change of color, or the presence of reaction products, may be made more distinct by filling the bulb with powdered gypsum or magnesia.* In some cases, it may be desirable to suspend a small strip of reagent paper from a glass hook fused to the stopper (Fig. 25). The apparatus shown in Fig. 26

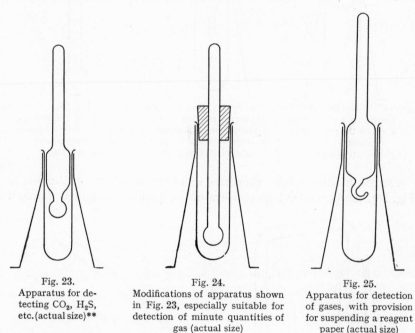

Fig. 23.
Apparatus for de-
tecting CO_2, H_2S,
etc. (actual size)**

Fig. 24.
Modifications of apparatus shown
in Fig. 23, especially suitable for
detection of minute quantities of
gas (actual size)

Fig. 25.
Apparatus for detection
of gases, with provision
for suspending a reagent
paper (actual size)

is used when a particular gas is to be identified in the presence of other gases. In this arrangement, the stopper of the micro test tube is a small glass funnel, and the impregnated filter paper is laid across it to absorb the gas. The impregnated paper permits the passage of the indifferent gases and retains only the gas to be detected. The latter forms a nonvolatile compound which can be identified by a subsequent spot test. Another use-ful apparatus (Fig. 27) consists of a micro test tube containing a loosely fitting glass tube narrowed at both ends. The lower end is filled to a height

* According to a suggestion by H. Kappelmacher (Vienna).
** An original improvement was recently described by Reckendorfer.[8]

of about 1 millimeter with an appropriate reagent solution. If the gas evolved forms a colored product with the reagent, it can be seen easily in the capillary.

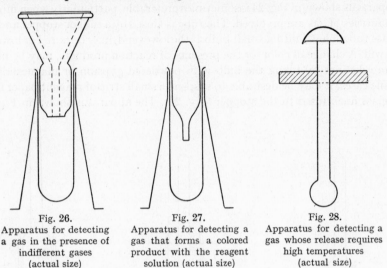

Fig. 26.
Apparatus for detecting a gas in the presence of indifferent gases (actual size)

Fig. 27.
Apparatus for detecting a gas that forms a colored product with the reagent solution (actual size)

Fig. 28.
Apparatus for detecting a gas whose release requires high temperatures (actual size)

A simple hard glass tube, supported in a circular hole in an asbestos plate (Fig. 28), can be used if high temperature or ignition is required to free the

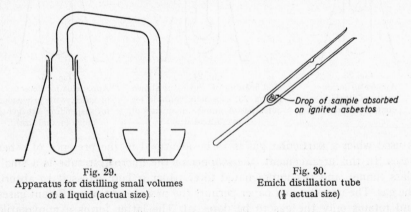

Fig. 29.
Apparatus for distilling small volumes of a liquid (actual size)

Drop of sample absorbed on ignited asbestos

Fig. 30.
Emich distillation tube (½ actual size)

gas. The open end of the tube is covered with a small piece of reagent paper kept in place by a glass cap.

Micro distillation is sometimes required; the chromyl chloride test for chloride is an example. Very small quantities of material can be distilled in the apparatus shown in Fig. 29. A micro crucible or micro centrifuge tube can be used as the receiver. The apparatus shown in Fig. 30 is satisfactory for most applications calling for distillation. Fractionation can be accomplished by heating the liquid and noting the rise of the vapors in the reflux tube. As the vapors rise they condense as rings of droplets in the tube. Various fractions can be collected as separate samples by adjusting the rate of rise of the condensate rings, using a thumb to close off the upper outlet.

One of the most useful methods of analytical separation is that of chromatography. This technique is applied when a solution contains several substances which can be adsorbed on a given adsorbent. The separation is accomplished by passing the solution through a column of the adsorbent so that the adsorbates will be found in the zones or bands on the adsorption column. The substance which is most strongly adsorbed forms a band at the top of the column. Succeeding bands are situated further down the column their position being determined by the respective strength of their adsorption. If the various constituents separated are colored substances, the respective bands will be colored. It is possible, however, to detect colorless materials by streaking the column after the chromatogram has been developed and the column extruded from the chromatographic tube. Of particular importance is the fact that chromatographic techniques can be applied to the separation of both organic and inorganic substances. Also, small amounts of material can be separated in this manner; and in many cases, separations can be effected that could not be accomplished with other techniques.

Procedures for chromatographic separations cannot be given here. It is generally necessary to evolve specific procedures for given separations; hence the choice of adsorbents, solvents, eluants, etc. will have to be made on the basis of the substances being separated. The general techniques and principles of chromatography have been discussed in a number of authoritative books.[9] In addition to the books on the subject, there are some excellent reviews that should be consulted. D. L. Clegg has reviewed the field of paper chromatography.[10] The annual reviews of analytical chemistry which are published in *Analytical Chemistry* each year, also contain excellent reviews of current developments in chromatography.

Electrochemical methods of separation are often used in spot test analysis. Differential diffusion is sometimes used, particularly in paper chromatography, in which an electric field is utilized to bring about desired separations. More important in spot test work itself is the use of electrographic methods which are utilized in the examination of metals, alloys, and ores. The principle of this separation is based on the application of anodic dissolution of metals. In practice the test substance is used as the anode with aluminum foil serving as the cathode. Filter paper, moistened with the proper reagent, is placed between these two electrodes and the migration of metals when the proper voltage is impressed across the poles brings about the development of a print locating the exact position of the metals transferred from the surface of the test sample. A general discussion of these methods has been presented by Hermance and Wadlow.[11]

Various types of apparatus are commercially available for electrographic tests. A simple apparatus for electrographic work is shown in Fig. 31. It consists of an aluminum plate as the negative pole on which is laid first a layer of filter paper moistened with potassium chloride solution and then the reagent paper moistened with water or acid. A copper plate with a copper rod soldered to it serves as the positive pole. The current is furnished by a 1.5 volt dry cell and the potential drop across the electrodes can be controlled by a simple rheostat.

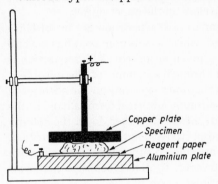

Fig. 31. Electrographic apparatus

4. Special Techniques

The majority of spot test reactions result in the formation of distinctive colors. Quite logically, many of these reactions lend themselves to colorimetric analyses; and it is possible to adapt such color reactions to special techniques having the high sensitivity and simplicity common to spot test procedures in general. Such methods are finding wide usage in industry where an estimate of quantities is desirable and some sacrifices in accuracies can be made in favor of speed, simplicity, and portability. The term "spot colorimetry" has been suggested for this type of technique by Tananaeff.

Spot colorimetry can be performed on spot plates, or the tests can be run on filter paper. The use of confined spots as introduced by H. Yagoda [12] has proved particularly attractive. Yagoda described the process for impregnating suitable spot test paper with paraffin rings so that the area of the spots can be confined to definite limits. Such papers are now commercially available. Spot colorimetry on confined spot test paper has the advantage that very often standard spots can be preserved for use as permanent standards. Confined spot testing can be run with reactions producing colored solutions and, in many cases, it is also applicable for use with colored precipitates.

In addition to the use of spot colorimetry, the tests which produce insoluble reaction products that are colorless or only slightly colored can be utilized in "spot nephelometry." The nephelometric procedures are performed on black spot plates.

Spot reactions on paper do not always involve the union of a drop of the test solution and one of the reagent. Sometimes filter paper is impregnated with the proper reagent and the dry reagent paper is spotted with a drop of the test solution. This procedure, which assumes, of course, the availability of stable reagents, has the advantage that there is no mutual dilution of the reagent and test solution. A better localization and visibility of the reaction products at the place where the spot has formed is achieved, as compared with the result of bringing two drops together. A still better effect is obtained by impregnating filter paper with reagents which are so slightly soluble in water that no bleeding occurs when a drop of the test solution strikes the paper. Organic reagents which are only slightly soluble in water, but which dissolve readily in alcohol or other organic solvents, have this advantageous characteristic. Slightly soluble compounds, that can be precipitated on paper and in its capillaries by certain chemical reactions, can also be used in this way.

Spotting on reagent paper impregnated with an insoluble compound involves a reaction of dissolved materials with an insoluble reagent. This procedure cannot be used in macro analysis because compact materials, in general, react too slowly. If, however, these same solids are finely divided by precipitation in the capillaries of paper and are thus endowed with an extensive reactive surface, they will undergo chemical changes almost as rapidly as soluble reagents.[13] The localization of characteristic reaction products, with consequent better visibility and increase in the sensitivity of the test, is not the sole advantage of using reagent papers impregnated with insoluble compounds. In many cases, a highly desirable homogenizing and stabilizing can be accomplished by impregnating filter paper with insoluble compounds which then behave like soluble materials. For instance, it is not possible to prepare a good stable alkali sulfide paper; it oxidizes to sulfate too rapidly and furthermore the highly soluble alkali sulfide is washed away when the paper is spotted with an aqueous solution. On the other hand, it is easy to impregnate filter papers with slightly soluble sulfides (ZnS, CdS, Sb_2S_3, etc.). Such papers are stable; each has its maximum sulfide ion concentration (controlled by its solubility product) and hence it precipitates only those metallic sulfides whose solubility products are sufficiently low. Antimony sulfide paper precipitates only silver, copper, or mercury in the presence of lead, cadmium, tin, iron, nickel, cobalt, and zinc. Another striking example is the detection of iron by spotting on paper impregnated with the difficultly soluble white zinc ferrocyanide. In this form the test is far more sensitive than when it is made by uniting drops of a ferric solution and an alkali ferrocyanide, or by spotting on potassium ferrocyanide paper. The latter also is less stable than zinc ferrocyanide paper. Consequently, if possible, it is always better to impregnate filter paper with "insoluble" reagents than with soluble ones.

It is easy to impregnate filter paper with reagents that are soluble in water or in organic solvents. The proper solutions are prepared in beakers or dishes and the strips of filter paper are bathed in them. Care must be taken that the strips do not cling to the sides of the container, that they do not touch each other or stick together, because this may prevent a uniform impregnation. The immersion should last for twenty to thirty minutes; the solution should be stirred quite frequently, or the vessel swirled, to produce uniformity. The strips are taken from the bath, allowed to drain, pinned to a cord (stretched horizontally) and allowed to dry in the air.

Instead of soaking the strips in the solution, reagents can be sprayed onto

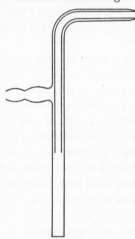

Fig. 32.
Atomizer head for spraying
reagents ($\frac{1}{2}$ actual size)

filter paper. The atomizing tip shown in Fig. 32 is excellent for this purpose. The impregnating solution is placed in a wide test tube which is then closed with the atomizing head. The paper is held horizontally and the spray expelled by blowing into the apparatus. The paper is sprayed first on one side and then on the other.

Filter paper is impregnated by soaking it in the appropriate solutions or by spraying when it is desired to prepare a stock of reagent papers. The following procedure[14] is recommended for single experiments or when, for special reasons, the spot produced by a drop of a solution must be dried before adding a drop of the other reactant. V-shaped strips of filter paper are spotted on each side, taking care that the spots stay in the center of the strips as nearly as possible. The strips then remain so stiff that they can be stood on the table and allowed to dry. The impregnated strips are cut at the crease before they are used.

Homogeneous impregnation can only be accomplished through gradual, uniform drying on all sides. If paper is soaked with a salt solution and then dried by exposing it to a stream of heated air from the drying apparatus, the rapid evaporation and the subsequent capillary diffusion always leads to an accumulation on the side of the paper turned toward the blast. This effect can be detected immediately in the case of colored reagents, because the color is far less intense on the side of the paper turned away from the blast. The localization of a reagent on one side of the paper is an advantage, particularly for water-soluble reagents, because it is desirable to have the largest possible quantity of reagent available at the place where the spot is made in order that there will be a rapid and complete reaction with the materials in the test drop.

If strips of filter paper are dried in a blast of hot air, they should either be held on both ends with forceps or laid on a ribbed porcelain plate at such distance from the hot air apparatus that the current of warm air presses the paper against the porcelain plate. The completion of the drying is determined easily because the paper, which while moist adhered to the plate, now rises and flutters in the current of air.

There are no general procedures for impregnating filter paper with compounds produced by precipitation on and in the paper. As a rule, the strips are soaked with the solution of one of the reactants, dried, and then immersed in the solution of the appropriate precipitant. The excess reagents are then removed by washing and the paper dried. If this method is used, the order in which the solutions are applied, as well as their concentrations, makes a difference. The best conditions must always be determined by trial. It is a general rule that filter paper should be plunged quickly and uniformly into the particular reagent solution to avoid the production of zones (layers) of different concentrations. When highly impregnated reagent papers are being prepared, the precipitation of a difficultly soluble reaction product must never be attempted by a single treatment with concentrated solutions. The moistening and precipitation must be carried out separately with dilute solutions, and the reagent paper should be dried between the successive individual precipitations. If this procedure is not followed, a film rather than a homogeneous impregnation will result, and the reagent will come loose from the paper after it is either washed or dried. The excess liquid is removed after each phase of the impregnation by passing the paper through a small wringer at a uniform rate. The paper is best washed by spreading it on an inclined glass or porcelain plate. The spray of distilled water used for washing is distributed by means of a glass tube provided with a number of openings. In case the product precipitated in the paper is not particularly insoluble, it is best to wash slightly with water and then with dilute alcohol. Overheating must be avoided when drying the paper; as a rule, 60° to 80° C suffices. Sometimes it is preferable to use a reagent, if possible, in the gaseous form (hydrogen sulfide for precipitating sulfides or ammonia for precipitating oxides) rather than in solution; there is then no danger of washing away the precipitate. For the same reason, it is often advantageous first to form an adherent compound which cannot be washed off the paper and then carry out the reaction producing the desired reagent. For instance, a good lead sulfide paper is produced—not by soaking the paper in a lead salt solution followed by treatment with hydrogen sulfide water or gas—but rather by forming zinc sulfide on the paper and converting this into lead sulfide by bathing in a solution of a lead salt. Steigmann[15] has developed an excellent method for impregnating filter paper with water-soluble acid organic reagents.

RECOMMENDED FILTER PAPERS FOR SPOT TEST USE *

Manufacturer	Designation	Remarks
Schleicher and Schüll.	595	Fast absorption rate
Schleicher and Schüll.	601 (German)	Special spot test paper
		Medium absorption rate
Munktell	OK	Medium absorption rate
Whatman.	50	Slow absorption rate
Whatman.	120	Special spot test paper
		Fast absorption rate

* See Ph. W. West and W. C. Hamilton, *Mikrochem. ver. Mikrochim. Acta*, 38 (1951) 100.

Dannenberg[16] has recommended that inert, powdered, water-soluble or insoluble carriers (silica, starch, sugar, salts, etc.) be moistened with solutions of reagents and then dried. In this way, stable powder mixtures are obtained, which can be used in spot test analysis as dry reagents in place of reagent solutions. They often are better than the latter with respect to stability and economy.

The equipment described in this chapter and designed originally for inorganic spot test analysis can also be used for all spot tests hitherto recommended for organic materials. Semi-micro and micromethods of preparative organic chemistry are needed only for preliminary separations in special cases, or for the previous isolation of products to be tested. In this connection see the excellent presentation in the text by Cheronis and Entrekin[17] and also the instructive papers by Albers[18] and Hallett[19].

REFERENCES

1. Comp. E. J. Conway, *Microdiffusion Analysis and Volumetric Error*, 2nd ed., London, 1947, Part I.
2. T. S. Ma and R. T. E. Schenck, *Mikrochem. ver. Mikrochim. Acta*, 49 (1953) 245.
3. E. Abrahamczik, *Z. anal. Chem.*, 133 (1951) 144.
3a. G. Gorbach, *Microchemisches Praktikum*, Heidelberg, 1956.
4. R. Gilmont, *Anal. Chem.*, 20 (1948) 1109.
5. E. R. Caley, *Ind. Eng. Chem., Anal. Ed.*, 2 (1930) 77.
6. J. K. Carlton, *Anal. Chem.*, 22 (1950) 1072.
7. F. Feigl and P. Krumholz, *Mikrochemie*, 7 (1929) 83.
8. P. Reckendorfer, *Mikrochim. Acta*, (1955) 1008.

9. L. Zechmeister and K. Cholnoky, *Principles and Practice of Chromatography*, New York, 1943; H. H. Strain, *Chromatographic Adsorption Analysis*, New York, 1942; E. Lederer and M. Lederer, *Chromatography, A Review of Principles and Applications*, 2nd ed., Amsterdam, 1956; R. C. Brimley and F. C. Barrett, *Practical Chromatography*, New York, 1953; F. H. Pollard and J. F. W. McOmie, *Chromatographic Methods of Inorganic Analysis*, New York, 1953.

10. D. L. Clegg, *Anal. Chem.*, 22 (1950) 48. Consult also R. J. Block, R. Le Strange and G. Zweig, *Paper Chromatography*, New York, 1952; J. N. Balston and B. E. Talbot, *A Guide to Filter Paper and Cellulose Powder Chromatography*, London, 1952; F. Cramer, *Papierchromatographie*, 2nd ed., Berlin, 1953.

11. H. W. Hermance and H. V. Wadlow, *Electrography and Electro Spot Testing, Physical Methods in Chemical Analysis*, Vol. 2, New York, 1951, pp. 156-228.

12. H. Yagoda, *Ind. Eng. Chem., Anal. Ed.*, 9 (1937) 79.

13. F. Feigl, *Manual of Spot Tests*, Chapter 3, New York, 1943.

14. F. L. Hahn, *Mikrochemie*, 9 (1931) 34.

15. A. Steigmann, *J. Soc. Chem. Ind.*, 64 (1945) 88.

16. E. Dannenberg, *Anal. Chim. Acta*, 8 (1953) 310.

17. N. D. Cheronis and J. B. Entrekin, *Semimicro Qualitavive Organic Analysis*, New York 1947.

18. H. K. Albers *et al.*, *Ind. Eng. Chem., Anal. Ed.*, 12 (1940) 305, 764; 13 (1941) 127, 656; *Mikrochim. ver. Mikrochim. Acta*, 29 (1941) 294; *Anal. Chem.*, 21 (1949) 1283, 1555; *Mikrochim. ver. Mikrochim. Acta*, 36/37 (1951) 175.

19. L. T. Hallett, *Ind. Eng. Chem., Anal. Ed.*, 15 (1942) 956.

Chapter 3

Preliminary (Exploratory) Tests

General Remarks

The objective of the so-called preliminary or exploratory tests is to provide reference points and guiding principes which have value with respect to the detection of individual compounds by characteristic reactions or to the chemical analysis of mixtures. This kind of examination is particularly useful in the analytical study of organic materials because of the great number and variety of compounds for whose detection there are no systematic schemes of analysis such as are available in inorganic analysis. The best that can be attained in the case of mixtures of organic compounds is a separation of certain individuals or members of certain types of compounds. Means to this end include the appraisal of solubility characteristics in acids, bases and organic liquids, distillation in air or steam, sublimation, adsorptive separations (chromatography). Such procedures, as preliminary analytical steps, are often demanding with respect to material and time; they are not always applicable, frequently they are not wholly reliable, and they inevitably involve loss of material. In addition, the number of chemical reactions of organic compounds that have analytical value is still quite limited and consequently relatively few specific and selective tests for such compounds are available. Every orientation or hint which can be drawn from preliminary studies conducted within the technique of spot test analysis and with little expenditure of time and material consequently is very valuable when an analytical study of organic samples is being conducted.

Both negative and positive findings are informative in exploratory tests, whose most important objectives in qualitative organic analysis are to learn the presence of certain elements, or to discover whether acidic or basic compounds are at hand, or to uncover redox effects or other special characteristics. Orientation of this kind as well as conclusions derived from physical properties (color, odor, fusibility, etc.) can indicate the presence of certain compounds and members of certain types of compounds. The results of such exploratory tests can often relieve the analyst of the need of making special tests, which sometimes are tedious and troublesome. For instance, if a simple preliminary test has established the absence of nitrogen there is obviously no necessity of testing for nitro-, nitroso-, amino-, or oximino compounds. Similarly, if sulfur is absent, compounds containing SH-, SO_3H-, or SC-groups cannot be present, and tests for such compounds is a sheer waste of time. The same holds true with regard to groups which contain nonmetals or metals, whose absence can be demonstrated with certainty by simple preliminary tests. Consideration of the results of different preliminary tests on the same sample can likewise yield important clues. If one preliminary test has proved the presence of nitrogen and another exploratory procedure has shown the sample to be a neutral compound, the variety of nitrogenous compounds that need to be considered and tested for is reduced considerably. On the other hand, it is apparent that additional tests may be required if, for instance, preliminary tests have established the presence of nitrogen (sulfur, etc.) as well as redox or aromatic qualities. So many and varied preliminary tests are available, that full consideration should always be given to their revelations in rationalizing subsequent analytical studies of the sample.

The analyst is not always expected to furnish exhaustive information about the kind and amount of all the constituents present in a given sample. Often it is sufficient to know whether certain elements, compounds, or members of certain classes of compounds are present or absent. Preliminary tests may then be decisive or they may provide reliable guidance in the choice of confirmatory tests, particularly if the intensity of the results of the preliminary tests is taken into account. It should not be forgotten that at times the analytical examination may be confined to the use of sensitive tests to establish the absence of a particular item. Appropriate preliminary procedures can render excellent service in such instances, in fact they sometimes are all that is necessary. Therefore, the widely accepted view that the results of preliminary tests are merely diagnostic is wholly false. Rather, the preliminary tests can at times lead to results which are of such clarity in the appraisal of materials that they render further and different tests superfluous.

The following sections contain descriptions of preliminary tests which can be carried out rapidly and with small amounts of materials by means of the spot test technique. It is earnestly advised that they be tried on the sample before proceeding to the tests for functional groups discussed in Chapter 4. The results of the latter tests must always be brought into accord with the corresponding findings yielded by the preliminary tests. In chemical analysis, it is a cardinal rule that tests should be repeated and if possible confirmed by other tests having different sensitivities. This rule applies also to preliminary tests, which can be conducted within the spot test technique, not only with the respective orginal samples but also with sublimates, and evaporation

BRIAR CLIFF COLLEGE
LIBRARY
SIOUX CITY, IOWA

residues of aqueous and alcoholic, etc. extracts. The relatively small additional consumption of time and material required by additional different preliminary tests will be more than compensated by the resulting greater certainty in the insights into the composition of the sample and through the wider fund of information that will serve in the choice of other analytical examinations.

It should be pointed out that there is no sharp boundary between chemical preliminary tests and tests for functional groups. Reactions of certain functional groups are invariably involved whenever organic compounds or their particular cleavage products take part in chemical reactions. Preliminary tests—with the exception of non-chemical proofs and solubility tests—occupy no special position in this respect. However the differentiation employed in this text between preliminary tests and tests for functional groups is sufficiently justified by the fact that the latter tests are invariably more selective.

1. Non-chemical Proofs; Combustion Tests and Examination of Ignition Residues

Every chemical examination of organic substances should be preceded by several gross observations as to the homogeneity of the material, its color and odor. If the sample is a solid, homogeneity may be determined to a certain extent by examining a fraction of a milligram with a magnifying glass or under a microscope. The heterogeneity of mixtures of colored and colorless constituents, which appear homogeneous to the naked eye, can often be revealed under magnification. Similarly, amorphous ingredients can be distinguished from crystalline constituents, or different varieties of crystals can be differentiated by this means. If the optical examination makes it probable that only a single substance is at hand, it is advantageous to attempt to determine the melting point of the sample, provided it melts without too much decomposition. Should the first portions melt at a temperature considerably lower than the rest of the sample, there is great probability that a mixture is at hand. If, however, the sample melts uniformly, i.e., within a very narrow temperature range, a portion should be recrystallized from a suitable solvent and the determination repeated with the "purified" material.* If the rise in melting point is not greater than 1°, the material may be regarded as being pure. Melting point tables [1] should then be consulted to discover what compounds have the observed melting point. There is no

---

* The number of recrystallizations needed to obtain pure products varies with the materials and samples, but in general two recrystallizations are required. Consult in this respect S. M. McElvain, *The Characterization of Organic Compounds*, New York, 1945, p. 6 ff.

such simple method of so considerably limiting the number of possibilities when, because of extensive decomposition, it is not possible to determine a satisfactory melting point. With respect to materials that cannot be melted, but which nevertheless can be dissolved in water or organic liquids, there is a possibility of testing for homogeneity by constructing chromatograms. In these, the constituents of the solution are separated adsorptively.*

A test to discover whether the sample or one of its ingredients sublimes may be of great value in establishing the purity of the material or in obtaining pure products. This information can also be utilized in the subsequent chemical examination of the sample. Sublimation tests can be successfully made with milligram amounts of the sample between two watch glasses. One serves as the heating vessel; the other (smaller) watch glass placed on it, is cooled with moist filter paper and serves as condenser. With compounds which can be sublimed at water bath temperature, it is advisable to use a micro dish covered with a watch glass, whose convex side is cooled with a drop of water.[2] The sublimate is caught on the concave side of the watch glass. As a rule, products obtained by sublimation are of highest purity. Decisive melting point determinations can be conducted with sublimates, and chemical tests, including spot tests, can be conducted with confidence on such products. In case one component of a mixture can be completely removed by sublimation, the residue can be subjected to chemical tests. The same holds for solutions which contain volatile and nonvolatile materials.

Color examinations provide various hints as to the nature of a sample since the majority of organic compounds are colorless in daylight. A yellow color, which persists when the solid is dissolved, indicates nitro-, nitroso-, azo compounds, quinones, o-diketones, aromatic polyhydroxyketones, certain dyes, etc. A red, blue, yellow or green color indicates that the solid may contain dyestuffs or certain organometallic compounds, especially normal or complex salts. If the sample is a solid, it should always be tested with respect to its behavior on contact with water, organic liquids, acids and bases. The observation of a resistance of the color, the formation of colored solutions, changes in color or discharge of color, can sometimes be of great value, especially in conjunction with the findings yielded by other preliminary test

---

* A detailed discussion of chromatographic separation and analysis, which have acquired high importance in modern microanalysis, is beyond the scope of this text. See, for example, L. Zechmeister and L. v. Cholnoky, *Principles and Practice of Chromatography*, New York, 1943; L. Zechmeister, *Progress in Chromatography 1938–1947*, New York, 1950; H. H. Strain, *Chromatographic Adsorption Analysis*, New York, 1942; R. J. Block, *Paper Chromatography*, New York, 1952; E. Lederer and M. Lederer, *Chromatography, A Review of Principles and Applications*, 2nd Ed., Amsterdam, 1956; R. C. Brimley and F. C. Barrett, *Practical Chromatography*, New York, 1953. It should be noted that spot tests can be frequently and successfully used for the identification of materials which have been adsorptively separated.

and tests for functional groups. It is well to examine the sample in ultraviolet light to determine possible fluorescence properties. Some organic compounds fluoresce strongly in daylight and/or in ultraviolet light.[3] While daylight fluorescence is relatively rare and gives valuable indications, no decisive significance can be attached, in general, to a fluorescence in ultraviolet light, because even slight admixtures or contaminants may be responsible for such fluorescence. In some cases, they partially quench an existing fluorescence. In contrast, great analytical value is attached to revelation of fluorescence by products obtained by sublimation.

If a sample fluoresces in daylight or ultraviolet light, a test should always be made to determine if the fluorescence persists on the addition of acid or base, or if it is quenched, or changed in color. Such trials may have diagnostic value. When making fluorescence tests it should be remembered that the state of aggregation of the sample can play a part. Not all compounds fluoresce in both the solid and dissolved state; sometimes the fluorescence is confined to the solid state. (Compare page 221.)

In connection with the test for color and fluorescence it should be noted that some compounds when dissolved in concentrated sulfuric, phosphoric, or perchloric acid, have a characteristic color or fluorescence which disappears when the solution is diluted with water. This phenomenon is called halochromism or halofluorism.[4] This term is also applied to color and fluorescence effects, whose production involves other materials present in the same solvent, in so far as the color or fluorescence disappears on dilution with water. The chemistry of these changes is not quite known. Solutions of halochromic and halofluoric materials may contain colored solvates of the particular materials, and these loose addition compounds dissociate into their components on dilution. Tests for the formation of such colored addition compounds, which are of particular significance in the study of steroids,[5] can be made with dust particles of the solid plus a drop or two of concentrated sulfuric acid, etc. on a spot plate, or in a micro test tube if warming is necessary.

Since the vast majority of organic compounds are odorless, the detection of an odor can be of aid. Included among the compounds, which exhibit characteristic odors even at room temperature because of a considerable vapor pressure, are members of various classes of compounds. Pertinent examples are: alcohols and phenols; mercaptans; lower fatty acids and alicyclic monocarboxylic acids; naphthenic acids and their amides and esters; aldehydes; naphthol esters; amines; indole and indole derivatives; nitriles and isonitriles; coumarin; allyl compounds. The odor varies in intensity from case to case and also in character (attractive, repellant), which in itself is a guide of sorts.

The following classification of odors * of some organic compounds gives a certain picture of the range of this quality.

TABLE 1

Character of odor	Typical examples
1. Ethereal	ethyl acetate, ethyl alcohol, acetone, amyl acetate
2. Aromatic	
a) almond	nitrobenzene, benzaldehyde, benzonitrile
b) camphor	camphor, thymol, safrol, eugenol, carvacrol
c) lemon	citral, linalool acetate
3. Balsam	
a) floral	methyl anthranilate, terpineol, citronellol
b) lily	heliotropine, styrene
c) vanilla	vanillin, anisaldehyde
4. Musk	trinitro-*iso*butyl toluene, ambrette musk, muscone
5. Garlic	ethyl sulfide
6. Cacodylic	cacodyl, trimethylamine
7. Empyreumatic	*iso*butyl alcohol, aniline, cumidine, benzene, cresol, guaiacol
8. Rancid	valeric acid, caproic acid, methylheptylketone, methylnonylketone
9. Narcotic	pyridine, pulegone
10. Nauseating	skatole, indole

It should be noted that sometimes the type of the odor depends on the quantity or concentration of the particular substance. A comparison of the odor with that of small amounts of the corresponding pure compound can sometimes serve for orientation purposes. Odor tests are best carried out after rubbing several milligrams of the solid material or a drop of a liquid on the palm of the hand to obtain a greater surface from which the evaporation is faster. When dealing with solutions it is often useful to place a drop or two on filter paper and allow them to evaporate from there.[6] When testing the odor of materials, it should be observed whether the initial odor persists, disappears, or is replaced by another type of odor. It is advisable also to conduct odor tests with tiny amounts in a micro crucible and heat to 100–150°.

Extremely small quantities of certain compounds can be discerned by their odors. This is shown by Table 2.**

* Taken in part from P. Karrer, *Organic Chemistry*, 4th English edition, New York, 1950, p. 933.
** See the preceding acknowledgement.

References pp. 148–150

TABLE 2

Substance	Still detectable in 1 ml		Dilution
	number of mols	micrograms	
Ionone	$16 \cdot 10^5$	$5 \cdot 10^{-10}$	$1 : 2 \cdot 10^{15}$
Ethyl disulphide	$15 \cdot 10^6$	$2 \cdot 10^{-9}$	$1 : 4.5 \cdot 10^{14}$
Skatole	$16 \cdot 10^6$	$3 \cdot 10^{-9}$	$1 : 3.3 \cdot 10^{14}$
Vanillin	$20 \cdot 10^6$	$5 \cdot 10^{-9}$	$1 : 2 \cdot 10^{14}$
Coumarin	$33 \cdot 10^6$	$9 \cdot 10^{-9}$	$1 : 1.1 \cdot 10^{14}$
Citral	$40 \cdot 10^6$	10^{-8}	$1 : 10^{14}$
Butyric acid	$69 \cdot 10^6$	10^{-8}	$1 : 10^{14}$
Vanillin	$72 \cdot 10^6$	$2 \cdot 10^{-8}$	$1 : 5 \cdot 10^{13}$
Guaiacol	$20 \cdot 10^7$	$4 \cdot 10^{-8}$	$1 : 2.5 \cdot 10^{13}$
Nitrobenzene	$32 \cdot 10^7$	$6 \cdot 10^{-8}$	$1 : 2 \cdot 10^{13}$
Heliotropine	$40 \cdot 10^7$	10^{-7}	$1 : 10^{13}$
Thymol	$15 \cdot 10^8$	$4 \cdot 10^{-7}$	$1 : 2.5 \cdot 10^{12}$
Pyridine	$31 \cdot 10^8$	$4 \cdot 10^{-7}$	$1 : 2.5 \cdot 10^{12}$
Safrol	$48 \cdot 10^8$	10^{-6}	$1 : 10^{12}$
Bornyl acetate	$14 \cdot 10^9$	$5 \cdot 106^6$	$1 : 2 \cdot 10^{11}$
Methyl acetate	$16 \cdot 10^9$	$2 \cdot 10^{-4}$	$1 : 5 \cdot 10^{11}$
Carvone	$22 \cdot 10^9$	$5.5 \cdot 10^{-6}$	$1 : 1.8 \cdot 10^{11}$
Trimethylamine	$22 \cdot 10^{10}$	$2 \cdot 10^{-5}$	$1 : 5 \cdot 10^{10}$
Phenol	$26 \cdot 10^{10}$	$4 \cdot 10^{-5}$	$1 : 2.5 \cdot 10^{10}$
Menthol	$26 \cdot 10^{10}$	$7 \cdot 10^{-5}$	$1 : 1.4 \cdot 10^9$

Since the discernment of odor is not an objective test, but is a matter of the operator's olfactory capabilities, the figures in the preceding table have only a limited quantitative meaning and furnish no more than an approximate orientation. But even assuming that for the average individual the limits of detecting odor are at one thousand times the stated molecular values, there might always be dilutions at which the most sensitive chemical tests fail. It follows therefore that only in the case of materials which give off a very intensive smell is there a possibility of identifying by chemical tests those compounds whose presence has been indicated by odor tests. On the other hand, odor tests can sometimes furnish indications of the presence of slight contamination or admixtures in odorless materials. It should also be noted that some materials, which are odorless when pure, ordinarily are assumed to possess a characteristic odor because they are usually contaminated with an odoriferous impurity. Familiar examples are acetamide and acetylene.

2. Burning and Pyrolysis Tests

When organic and metallo-organic compounds burn in the air, the external picture is not the same in all cases, even though approximately like conditions are maintained with respect to the form of the powder, temperature reached, and rate of heating. The reason is that combustion involves numerous partial processes such as dehydration, thermal cleavages, reaction of water that is split off at high temperatures and is therefore superheated, oxidation processes that proceed slowly or rapidly, etc. Consequently, various items of information can be gleaned by carefully noting the manner in which the sample burns.

The burning test is conveniently conducted by first placing fractions of a milligram of the sample on an inverted porcelain crucible lid or in a small evaporating dish and applying a small flame beneath. It should be noted whether explosion or detonation occurs, due to nitro, nitroso, azo compounds or azides. If this is not the case, the trial is repeated with 5–20 mg of the sample and note is taken of fusion, liberation of gases, etc. From time to time, the flame is applied directly to the material from above so that it will ignite before it volatilizes. Should the substance carbonize, the flame is increased and finally the sample is heated strongly.

The most important aspects given by the burning test are: [7]

Aromatic compounds	burn with a smoky flame
Lower aliphatic compounds	burn with an almost non-smoky flame
Compounds containing oxygen	burn with a bluish flame
Halogen compounds	burn with a smoky flame
Polyhalogen compounds	in general, do not ignite until the flame is applied directly to the substance which then momentarily renders the flame of the burner smoky
Sugars and proteins	burn with characteristic odor

If non-volatile organic substances or salts of organic acids or bases are heated rapidly with limited access of air, a kind of dry distillation occurs. This may involve, as important partial phase, removal of water, hydrolysis, pyrolytic cleavage, oxidation and reduction. From the analytical standpoint it is important to note that products may result which are easily detected in the vapor phase through contact with suitable reagent papers. Such products include: acidic or alkaline vapors; hydrogen cyanide; dicyanogen; acetaldehyde; reducing gases; hydrogen sulfide. Up to the present, there has been no systematic study of the behavior of organic compounds when subjected to dry heating. However, such preliminary studies * have revealed that in

* From experiments by M. Heynemann and C. Stark.

TABLE 3

Compound	H+	OH-	HCN	(CN₂)	Reducing vapors	H₂S	CH₃CHO
Thiourea	—	+	+	—	+	+	—
Uric acid	+	—	+	+	—	—	—
Nitroso-R salt	+	+	—	—	+	+	—
Saccharin	—	+	—	—	+	+	—
Rhodamine B	+	—	—	—	+	—	+
Barbituric acid	+	+	+	—	—	—	—
Cinchonine	—	—	—	—	+	—	—
Glucose	+	—	—	—	+	—	+
Aminophylline	—	+	+	+	—	—	—
D, L-Isoleucine	—	+	+	—	+	—	—
Alloxantin	+	+	+	+	—	—	—
Benzidine	—	+	+	—	+	—	—
Hydrazobenzene	—	+	+	—	+	—	—
Dimethylglyoxime	—	—	+	+	—	—	—
Biuret	—	+	+	+	—	—	—
Cystine	—	+	—	—	+	+	—
Guanidine carbonate	—	+	+	+	—	—	—
6-Nitroquinoline	+	—	+	—	—	—	—
Polyvinyl alcohol	+	—	—	—	—	—	+
Xanthopterin	—	+	+	+	+	—	—
p,p'-Diamino-diphenyl sulfone	+	—	+	—	+	—	—
1-Naphthylamine hydrochloride	+	—	—	—	—	—	—

many cases valuable hints concerning the nature of the sample can be secured from the positive or negative responses to tests for volatile compounds.

The test is made in a glass tube (length 4 cm, diameter 0.5 cm) which is held in an asbestos support. About 1 or 2 mg of the sample is placed in the tube whose mouth is then covered with a disk of the moist reagent paper. The bottom of the tube is heated with a microflame until distinct charring sets in. This procedure will serve to detect the following decomposition products by means of freshly prepared moist reagent papers:

1. Volatile acids   Congo red paper (blued)
2. Volatile bases   Phenolphthalein paper (reddened)
3. Hydrogen cyanide   Cu acetate-benzidine acetate paper (blued, see p. 93)
4. Dicyanogen   KCN-oxine paper (reddened, see p. 329)
5. Reducing vapors   Phosphomolybdic acid paper (blued, see p. 128)

References pp. 148–150

6. Hydrogen sulfide   Lead acetate paper (blackened)
7. Acetaldehyde   Morpholine-sodium nitroprusside paper (blued, see p. 334)

Table 3 gives the results of tests 1–7 when applied to the pyrolysis products of various classes of compounds.

This compilation shows that a pyrolytic splitting out of hydrogen cyanide occurs surprisingly from so many nitrogenous organic compounds that the negative response of the test for cyanide ions becomes of diagnostic value. The same holds for the relatively seldom detection of dicyanogen and acetaldehyde in the pyrolytic products of organic compounds.

When appraising the detection of gaseous chemical cleavage products it should be noted that mixtures of compounds may behave differently than the separate components because of the occurrence of reactions between them on heating their mixtures. An example is found in the formation of acetaldehyde when a mixture of alkali or alkaline earth salts of acetic acid and formic acid is heated. This is the basis of a test for the purity of formic acid and alkali formates (see page 462). Another pertinent example is the rapid formation of nitrous acid, when a mixture of nitrosamines with carbohydrates, citric acid, tartaric acid, etc. is pyrolized.

3. Examination of Ignition Residues

Important conclusions can be drawn from the behavior of organic compounds when the burning and pyrolytic processes are continued to the ignition stage with access of air. Purely organic materials are completely consumed and leave no residue. The rapid disappearance of carbon and tarry products is an indication of the presence of materials rich in oxygen and hydrogen. In contrast, stubborn persistence of carbon is an indication of the presence or formation of heat-resistant mineral substances, which in fused or sintered form envelop particles of carbon and shield them against complete combustion in contact with air. If such an effect is encountered and it is desired to remove the unburned carbon completely, the cooled residue should be moistened with a few drops of hydrogen peroxide, taken to dryness, and the residue ignited once more. Repeated evaporation with several drops of concentrated nitric acid is still more effective but the possible formation of alkali and alkaline earth nitrates may complicate or obscure the picture of the ignition residue.

By taking account of the quantity of the sample used for the ignition, it is easy to decide whether traces or considerable amounts of an ignition residue remain. The particular demands of the analysis determine whether the residue should be studied in detail.

References pp. 148–150

31829

It is often said that ignition of organic materials containing metals invariably produces a residue which consists entirely of the carbonate of the metal(s) in question. Tables 4 and 5 show that this is not a correct generalization. The tables exhibit the behavior of ignition residues toward water and dilute acetic acid, points that should be a part of every careful investigation.

TABLE 4

Salts of carboxylic acids, phenols, nitro compounds and oximes with:	Ignition Residue		
	Composition	Solubility	
		Water	Dilute Acetic Acid
Alkali metals including thallium .	Carbonate	+	+
Alkaline earth metals	Carbonate and (oxide)	— (+)	+ +
Other bivalent metals	Carbonate and oxide	—	+
Aluminum and other ter- and quadri-valent metals	Oxide	—	—
Noble metals	Metal	—	—
Mercury	No residue		

Alkali and alkaline earth salts of acidic nitro compounds leave no heat-stable nitrate when ignited; this is due to the quantitative conversion into carbonate when alkali or alkaline earth nitrates are heated with carbon or organic compounds.

TABLE 5

Salts of sulfonic acids and mercaptans	Ignition Residue		
	Composition	Solubility	
		Water	Dilute Acetic Acid
Alkali metals including thallium .	Sulfate	+	+
Alkaline earth metals	Sulfate	— or ±	— or ±
Other bivalent metals	Sulfate	+	+
Ter- and quadri-valent metals . .	Basic sulfate	—	±
Mercury	No residue		

Besides the compounds included in Tables 4 and 5, the following organometallic compounds yield carbonate-free residues, or residues which contain carbonate plus heat-resistant other metal salts:

Salts of organic bases with metal acids (molybdic, tungstic, phosphomolybdic acid, etc.)	metal acid anhydride
Salts of organic derivatives of arsenic and phosphoric acid	metal arsenates or phosphates
Stannous and stannic salts of acid organic compounds	stannic oxide
Salts of organic derivatives of antimonic acid	metal antimonates
Salts of organic derivatives of phosphoric acid	metal phosphates
Salts of halogen-bearing carboxylic acids, phenols, oximes, etc.	metal halides (plus carbonate)
Addition compounds of ignition-resistant metal halides or sulfates with organic bases	metal halides or sulfates

Only in exceptional cases should complicated mixtures be looked for when investigating the ignition residues left by organic or organometallic compounds. As a rule, the range of inorganic compounds that come into consideration is quite limited. The examination is facilitated still more by the fact that, in addition to oxides and carbonates, only sulfates, phosphates, arsenates and perhaps halogenates of metals can be present. Sometimes it is sufficient to establish the presence of certain basic compounds, using the term in its broadest sense, i.e. water-soluble and water-insoluble materials susceptible to attack by acids. The following procedures are suitable for this purpose; they can be carried out rapidly with minimal quantities of material. The absence of admixed inorganic compounds is assumed.*

I. Test for alkali carbonate (including thallous carbonate) and alkaline earth oxides.	The ignition residue is taken up in a few drops of water and centrifuged, if necessary. Alkaline reaction toward phenolphthalein indicates alkali carbonate (alkaline earth oxide).
II. Test for carbonates and oxides of alkaline earth metals. (This test[9] utilizes the conversion of the oxides and carbonates into the respective nitrates, which melt	The ignition residue is taken up in water, centrifuged, and the insoluble sediment washed with water until there is no basic response to phenolphthalein. After pipetting off the

---

* When organic compounds are ashed, inorganic neutral compounds may undergo changes because of reduction, loss of water, etc. For instance, sodium carbonate is invariably formed when filter paper containing sodium chloride is ashed.[8]

without decomposition at about 400°.)

III. Test for alumina and phosphates (arsenates) of bivalent metals. (The test employs "nickel dimethyl-glyoxime equilibrium solution", which reacts with insoluble basic compounds [10].)

IV. Test for magnesium oxide and alkaline earth carbonate. (The test utilizes the formation of fluorescing oxinates [11].)

water, the residue is dissolved in several drops of dilute nitric acid, a drop of the solution is transferred to a porcelain microcrucible and taken to dryness. After heating to 350–400° for 5–10 minutes, the cooled residue is treated with a drop of 1 % solution of diphenylamine in concentrated sulfuric acid. A positive response to this nitrate test (blue color) indicates the presence of carbonates or oxides of bivalent metals. The procedure can also serve to show the presence of barium carbonate in ignition residues. The sulfate test is applied.

If I and II have proved the absence of alkali carbonate and also of carbonates and oxides of bivalent metals, a colorless water-insoluble ignition residue may contain, in addition to $BaSO_4$, $PbSO_4$, SiO_2, also alumina as well as phosphates or arsenates of aluminum and the bivalent metals. These latter compounds can be tested for by spotting the residue with a drop of "nickel dimethylglyoxime equilibrium solution". The precipitation of red nickel dimethylglyoxime indicates alumina, phosphate, etc. (The reagent is prepared by adding 1 % alcoholic dimethylglyoxime solution to a neutral nickel salt solution and filtering.) Alumina can be separated from phosphates, etc. by digestion with very dilute hydrochloric acid and filtering. After washing the insoluble residue, it is ignited gently and then tested with the equilibrium solution. The evaporation residue of the filtrate is tested in the same way.

The ignition residue is suspended in a few drops of water and a drop placed on a small disk of quantitative filter paper. The spotted paper is laid on a porcelain crucible containing a little solid 8-hydroxyquinoline ("oxine"). The volatilizing oxine produces metal oxinates which fluoresce intensely yellow-green in ultraviolet light (quartz lamp). The fluorescent fleck is held over acetic acid vapors. If the fluorescence disappears, the presence of magnesium and/or calcium oxinate is indicated. If the fluorescence does not disappear, the presence of aluminum oxinate, which is resistant to acetic acid vapors, is indicated.

When ignition residues are to be systematically tested with respect to the metals present, the residue must be brought into solution by treatment with acid or by fusion with alkali bisulfate. In many instances, it is also possible to test ignition residues directly for certain metals by applying selective and sensitive tests. The following compilation shows typical instances:

Antimony^V oxide	Diphenylbenzidine (sulfuric acid solution)	Blue color
Barium (strontium) carbonate	Sodium rhodizonate (acetic acid solution)	Brown-red color
Lead sulfate	Sodium rhodizonate (acetic acid solution)	Red color
Chromium^{III} oxide	Fusion with sodium peroxide	Yellow color
Noble metals	Phosphomolybdic acid	Blue color
Iron^{III} oxide	Fusion with 8-hydroxyquinoline	Black-green color
Manganese^{III} oxide	Benzidine	Blue color
Metal phosphates	Acid ammonium molybdate solution plus benzidine plus ammonia	Blue color
Molybdenum^{VI} oxide	Hydrochloric acid plus potassium xanthate	Violet color
Nickel^{II} oxide	Dimethylglyoxime	Red color
Titanium^{IV} oxide	Chromotropic acid	Violet color
Zirconium oxide	Fusion with bisulfate and treatment with morin	Fluorescence

Discussions of the chemistry of the foregoing and other tests for metals and the details of the procedures (including the identification limits) can be found in Volume I of this text.

4. Identification of Nonmetallic and Metallic Elements Bound Directly or Indirectly to Carbon

In addition to hydrogen, direct binding to carbon atoms is limited almost exclusively to nonmetals. The latter may also be bound indirectly to carbon, i.e. through the agency (interposition) of other nonmetallic atoms. Direct stable unions between metal atoms and carbon atoms are comparatively rare. They are limited to metal salts of acetylene and its homologs (metal acetylides and carbides), and to mercury, which may be directly bound to carbon atoms in numerous aliphatic and aromatic compounds. The great majority of the so-called metallo-organic compounds, that are presented for analytical investigation, will be: normal and inner complex metal salts of organic acids and acidic compounds; chelate compounds of organic acids where the metal atom is part of an anion; salts of organic nitrogen bases of metal acids; addition products of metal salts of inorganic and organic acids with organic compounds; adsorption compounds of acid and basic metal oxyhydrates with basic and acid organic compounds.

The fundamental basis of all tests for nonmetallic and metallic elements (oxygen being the only exception) is the destruction of the organic skeleton of the sample by some convenient means and the consequent arrival at a purely inorganic compound, which can then be detected or identified by the methods of qualitative inorganic spot test analysis. The disintegration of the non-volatile organic material is preferentially accomplished in the dry way by heating with calcium oxide or magnesium oxide in the presence of air, or with an alkaline oxidizing mixture. In both cases the carbon is converted to carbon dioxide. Reductive decompositions with alkali metal fusions are also available; they leave the carbon in the elementary condition, or partly as the alkali carbide. In special cases, organic materials can be successfully disintegrated by heating with molybdic oxide, silver arsenate, and alkali sulfite. An oxidative decomposition in the wet way can be accomplished by digestion and heating with concentrated nitric acid (Carius method) or concentrated sulfuric acid (Kjeldahl method). These latter two methods, which are often referred to (though not entirely correctly) as "wet combustions", are especially suitable when organometallic compounds are to be tested. Sometimes these procedures can be replaced by treating the test material with dilute sulfuric acid containing potassium persulfate plus some silver nitrate as catalyst (see page 103). Direct ignition of an organic material is permissible when the sample is to be tested for ash and accordingly when searching for non-volatile inorganic constituents. Pertinent examples of all sorts of decomposition and disintegration procedures can be found in the following sections.

References pp. 148–150

5. Carbon

A special test for carbon may be necessary to distinguish between in-organic and organic material and to recognize rapidly the presence of organo-metallic or organic compounds as contaminants or components of mixtures with inorganic compounds. The procedure commonly used for this purpose, namely to set fire to the sample in the air and then to note whether glowing occurs or whether tar is formed, is reliable only when dealing with larger amounts of organic substances, which are not volatile or which are not sublimable at lower temperatures. It should also be noted that organic com-pounds can burn without glowing or producing tar if considerable proportions of materials are present which give off oxygen (particularly higher oxides), and that salts of oxalic, acetic and formic acids, when heated slowly in con-tact with air decompose without deposition of carbon. The detection of or-ganic compounds, based on the detection of carbon dioxide formed when they are burned with oxygen, is exceedingly sensitive when the test is conducted on the micro scale[12], but it must be remembered that this procedure requires complete exclusion of air containing carbon dioxide, and also that inorganic carbonates yield carbon dioxide when they are heated strongly. The following tests avoid these limitations, but in the form given here the procedures are admittedly less sensitive than the micro CO_2-test.

(1) Test by ashing with molybdenum trioxide [13]

If organic compounds, of any nature whatsoever, are mixed with bright yellow molybdenum trioxide and gradually heated (the highest temperature should be around 500°) they or their thermal decomposition products (including any free carbon that may have been formed) are oxidized with concurrent production of lower molybdenum oxides (so-called molybdenum blue). Accordingly, this reaction is a kind of total combustion, in which the heated molybdenum trioxide acts as the oxidant. The volatile com-bustion products are carbon dioxide and water, along with nitrous oxide and small amounts of NO_2 when nitrogenous organic compounds are involved. Organic materials containing halogens and sulfur appear to yield halogen hydracid and sulfur trioxide on oxidation with molybdic anhydride.

The oxidation of elementary carbon can be represented:

$$C + 4 MoO_3 \rightarrow 2 Mo_2O_5 + CO_2$$

When this test is used, complete absence must be insured of other compounds which are oxidizable by molybdenum trioxide. For example, anhydrous alkali sulfite or arsenite, under the conditions of the test, likewise reduce molybdic anhydride to molybdenum blue, which indicates that the redox action can also occur as a solid-solid reaction. The impairment of the test by oxidizable inorganic compounds can be averted by evaporating the test material to dryness several times with hydrogen peroxide. Ammonium salts may not be present, since the ammonia gas, which they evolve when they are thermally decomposed, reacts with hot molybdenum trioxide, producing nitrogen, water, and molybdenum blue: *

$$2\ NH_3 + 6\ MoO_3 \rightarrow 3\ H_2O + N_2 + 3\ Mo_2O_5$$

The behavior of ammonia gas proves that molybdic anhydride can react with solid and liquid organic materials which are volatilized at rather low temperatures. In fact, even ether, acetone, benzene, etc. can bring about the production of molybdenum blue in the procedure given here.

Procedure. A hard glass tube (about 75 × 7 mm) closed at one end is used as the reaction vessel. A small quantity of the solid test substance is introduced, or a drop of the test solution is evaporated in the tube at 110°. The tube is then half filled with finely powdered molybdenum trioxide and connected with a pump by means of suction tubing. After the air has been removed, the tube, clamped at an angle, is heated for 1–2 minutes by means of a small burner in such manner that the upper portion of the molybdenum oxide is heated first and then the lower part. If carboniferous material is present, a blue zone appears at the point of contact with the light yellow molybdic anhydride. The size and color intensity of the blue zone varies according to the carbon content of the sample. A blank test should be run when traces of organic material are being sought.

This ashing procedure with molybdenum trioxide revealed:

5 γ carbon in mannite and saccharose
1 γ carbon in urea
3 γ carbon in salicylic acid
8 γ carbon in citric acid

(2) *Test through reduction of silver arsenate to elementary silver* [14]

Brown-red silver arsenate remains unchanged when heated to temperatures up to 900°. In mixtures with organic materials, the heating produces silver arsenite initially. This reduction is due to a topochemical reaction of the silver salt with thermal decomposition products of the particular organic substances. Likewise, any free carbon that may have been produced reacts:

$$2\ Ag_3AsO_4 + C \rightarrow 2\ Ag_3AsO_3 + CO_2 \qquad (1)$$

---

* This effect is in accord with the long known fact, that powdered ammonium molybdate turns blue when heated in a covered crucible. Prolonged heating in air leads of course to yellow MoO_3.

Silver arsenite is not ignition-stable; on heating it undergoes an inner molecular redox reaction to produce free silver and silver metarsenate:

$$Ag_3AsO_3 \rightarrow 2\,Ag° + AgAsO_3 \tag{2}$$

Accordingly, the total process of reduction of silver arsenate by carbon (oxidizable thermal decomposition products of organic compounds behave analogously) can be schematically represented by combining (1) with (2):

$$2\,Ag_3AsO_4 + C \rightarrow 2\,AgAsO_3 + CO_2 + 4\,Ag^0 \tag{3}$$

The occurrence of redox reaction (3) and hence the presence of organic materials, which because of their thermal decomposition reduce silver arsenate to free silver, can be recognized directly by a dark color due to finely divided metallic silver, if considerable quantities of the latter have been formed. Because of much greater sensitivity, it is better to detect metallic silver through its reaction with a hydrochloric acid solution of phosphomolybdic acid. Silver chloride and the highly tinctorial hydrosol of molybdenum blue result. Small amounts of molybdenum blue hydrosol can be extracted from the aquous phase by shaking out with amyl alcohol and thus made more discernible.

Procedure. Several milligrams of silver arsenate are mixed in a micro test tube (1–2 ml) with the solid test substance or with the aqueous solution to be tested. In the latter case, the contents of the test tube should be taken to dryness at 110°. The mixture is covered with about an equal quantity of silver arsenate and then heated for several minutes over a microburner. After cooling, a drop or two of a hydrochloric acid solution of phosphomolybdic acid is added to the test tube. If an organic substance was present, a blue color appears at once or after 1–2 minutes. The intensity of the color obtained depends on the quantity of oxidizable carbon, hydrogen, etc. in the sample. A blank is required when traces of organic matter are being sought.

Reagents: 1) Silver arsenate. Preparation by action of sodium arsenate with silver nitrate. The precipitate should be collected on a sintered glass crucible or it may be isolated by centrifuging. The product is washed thoroughly and then dried at 110°.

            2) 3 % solution of phosphomolybdic acid in hydrochloric acid (1 : 1).

The procedure revealed 5 γ carbon in mannite, saccharin, and urea.

(3) *Test by heating with potassium iodate* [13]

When heated to its melting point (560°), potassium iodate evolves oxygen and leaves potassium iodide: $KIO_3 \rightarrow KI + 3O$. When a mixture of the powdered salt and non-volatile organic substances is heated, the decomposition or, more correctly, the reduction to potassium iodide, occurs even after brief heating to 300–400°. The extent of the reduction depends on the quantity of organic material present and the length of the reaction period. Complete reduction is possible with an excess of organic material; with excess potassium iodate a mixture of iodate and iodide always results. Obviously, hot potassium iodate in contact with organic materials is capable of oxidizing their carbon and hydrogen to carbon dioxide and water with concurrent production of potassium iodide.* It should also be kept in mind that the material fused at the temperature of the test, or its gaseous or molten fission products, can react with the solid potassium iodate. An essential feature of the analytical employment of this solid body reaction is the production of potassium iodide, since the latter reacts with unchanged potassium iodate to produce free iodine as soon as mineral acid is added to the mixture:

$$5 I^- + IO_3^- + 6 H^+ \rightarrow 3 H_2O + 3 I_2$$

Therefore, if a solid sample is intimately mixed with excess of powdered potassium iodate and heated, and the cooled mixture then acidified with dilute sulfuric acid, a liberation of iodine indicates the presence of non-volatile organic materials. If the starch-iodine reaction is applied, the procedure is sufficiently delicate to succeed with even very small quantities of the sample. Inorganic oxidizable materials, such as ammonium salts, alkali sulfite, arsenite, etc. as well as considerable quantities of alkali cyanide must be absent. Ammonium salts and cyanides can be removed by evaporating the test material with dilute caustic hydroxide or hydrochloric acid before heating with potassium iodate. Other oxidizable inorganic compounds (sulfides, sulfites, arsenites, iron(II) oxide, etc.) can be rendered harmless by evaporating the finely powdered sample several times with acidified (HCl) or alkaline hydrogen peroxide solution. The presence of alkali hydroxide or carbonate does not interfere with the reduction of potassium iodate by organic materials.

Procedure. A drop of the test solution is evaporated to dryness in a small Pyrex test tube (7 × 70 mm) or a tiny portion of the solid sample is taken. After mixing intimately with several milligrams of finely powdered potassium iodate, the mixture is covered with potassium iodate, and kept for about five minutes in an oven heated to 300–400°. After cooling, the residue is taken up in sulfuric acid (1 : 2) and tested for iodide or iodine by adding starch solution or by shaking with

---

* When organic compounds containing sulfur or arsenic are heated with potassium iodate plus alkali carbonate, alkali sulfate or arsenate result. It should be noted that alkali bromate, periodate, chlorate and perchlorate behave analogously, i.e., they are reduced to the corresponding alkali halides below their decomposition points when heated in contact with organic compounds. The latter may react directly in form of their melts or through liquid or gaseous pyrolytic decomposition products. In all cases topochemical reactions occur on the surface of the solid alkali salts.

References pp. 148–150

chloroform. It is imperative to carry out a blank test on a like quantity of potassium iodate, since the latter frequently carries small amounts of iodide. The test tubes employed should be ignited briefly before making the test. If the starch reaction is used to reveal the iodine, the starch solution should be added before making the solution acid, since the presence of traces of iodide is essential to the formation of the blue starch-iodine complex. The addition of some mg of thyodene indicator is recommended instead of starch solution.

The procedure gave positive results with:

1 γ carbon in mannite	1.5 γ carbon in saccharose
3 γ carbon in salicylic acid	2 γ carbon in sulfosalicylic acid
0.5 γ carbon in sebacic acid	3 γ carbon in nitroalizarin
2 γ carbon in citric acid	3 γ carbon in benzoinoxime
3 γ carbon in theobromine	6 γ carbon in thionalide

The following were successfully tested, but the limits of identification were not ascertained:

sodium acetate	aluminum (Ca, Mg) oxinate
nickel dimethylglyoxime	zirconium mandelate
cobalt α-nitroso-β-naphthol	barium rhodizonate
mercury succinate	calcium oxalate

6. Hydrogen

(1) Test by heating with sodium sulfite [15]

When numerous non-volatile organic compounds containing hydrogen are heated gently with powdered sodium sulfite (likewise with sodium thiosulfate) they generate hydrogen sulfide. The latter can be detected by reaction with lead acetate or alkaline sodium nitroprusside.[16] The former yields black lead sulfide, the latter soluble violet $Na_4[Fe(CN)_5NOS]$. At present, only conjectures can be advanced regarding the mechanism of the formation of the hydrogen sulfide. As the following list of compounds tested shows, *no* hydrogen sulfide is produced when sodium sulfite is heated with solid hydrocarbons (naphthalene, anthracene) or with hydrocarbon mixtures (paraffin), whereas, with few exceptions, organic compounds, which contain hydrogen and oxygen do produce hydrogen sulfide. Therefore, H_2S-production seems to be characteristic of organic compounds which contain both hydrogen *and* oxygen, and it may well be that the activity of certain thermal decomposition products, including water, may play a role.

Since elementary carbon invariably is left when organic compounds containing oxygen and hydrogen are heated, particularly in the presence of alkali sulfite, and also since water produced during thermal decomposition can function as superheated steam, the following partial reactions, which lead to the production of hydrogen sulfide, appear probable:

$$Na_2SO_3 + 3\,C \rightarrow 3\,CO + Na_2S$$
$$Na_2S + H_2O \rightarrow Na_2O + H_2S$$

It should be noted also that at temperatures above 600°, sodium sulfite disproportionates:[17]

$$4\,Na_2SO_3 \rightarrow Na_2S + 3\,Na_2SO_4$$

This disproportionation may occur to a slight extent even at temperatures below 600° and furnish reaction products on which carbon and superheated steam could act to produce Na_2S or H_2S.

Procedure. The material to be tested is mixed with five times its bulk of dry anhydrous sodium sulfite and heated in a small ignition tube. A disk of filter paper impregnated with 1 % lead acetate or 2 % freshly prepared sodium nitroprusside is placed across the mouth of the tube. The heating is gradual. A light brown to black, or a pink to deep violet color develops, the intensity depending on the quantity of hydrogen sulfide evolved.

The following compounds were tested:[18]

Positive reaction: paraformaldehyde; chloraldehyde; dimethylaminobenzal-dehyde; glycerol; diacetyl; resorcinol; α-naphthol; m-cresol; tannin; glucose; malic acid; tartaric acid; citric acid; stearic acid; benzoic acid; chlorobenzoic acid; salicylic acid; sulfanilic acid; barbituric acid; calcium acetate; acetanilide; sulfonal; alanine; acridine; caffeine; theobromine; quinine hydrochloride.
Negative reaction: naphthalene; anthracene; paraffin; ethyl alcohol; methyl alcohol; phthalic anhydride; urea.

(2) *Test by reaction with fused potassium thiocyanate* [19]

When a fusion of potassium thiocyanate (m.p. 173–179°) is heated to about 430°, it turns blue; after cooling the color disappears [20]. This is probably due to the splitting-off of sulfur, which remains in highly dispersed colloidal form [21] in the molten potassium thiocyanate and which again forms potassium thiocyanate on cooling:

$$KCNS \rightleftharpoons KCN + S^0 \tag{1}$$

There is also the possibility of an equilibrium between potassium thiocyanate and the isomeric potassium isothiocyanate in the melt:

$$N{\equiv}C{-}S{-}K \rightleftharpoons S{=}C{=}N{-}K \tag{2}$$

Whichever explanation of the color change holds, the interesting fact remains that the sulfur dispersed in molten potassium (or sodium) thiocyanate is highly reactive and able to enter reactions which are not realisable in aqueous solutions of these salts. Among such reactions is the formation of Ag_2S with metallic silver; the formation of $Na_2S_2O_3$ with Na_2SO_3; the conversion of metal oxides and sulfates (even $PbSO_4$) into the corresponding metallic sulfides; the partial reduction of Nb_2O_5, WO_3, MoO_3 to the respective metals or lower oxides, etc. The enhanced reactivity of sulfur in molten potassium thiocyanate can be observed also towards non-volatile organic compounds. When such compounds are added to melted potassium thiocyanate or if they are heated together, there is rapid production of hydrogen sulfide. Frequently this effect occurs even at temperatures below 400°, i.e. in still colorless melts of potassium (or sodium) thiocyanate, an observation which proves that the sulfur is activated in the fused salt even before reactions (1) and (2) can be observed with the naked eye. In the case of compounds containing hydrogen and oxygen, it seems plausible that water is split off and acts, at the temperature of its formation, i.e., as superheated steam, on the activated potassium thiocyanate:

$$KCNS + H_2O \rightarrow KCNO + H_2S$$

This mechanism seems to be valid for carbohydrates, tannins, gallic acid, pyrogallol, etc.

It is interesting to note that in the case of oxalic acid (either hydrated or anhydrous) the splitting-off according to $H_2C_2O_4 \rightarrow CO + CO_2 + H_2O$ in molten potassium thiocyanate goes so far that mg quantities of oxalic acid are able to yield hydrogen sulfide. The fact that succinic acid and mandelic acid in mixture with potassium thiocyanate liberate H_2S at 200°, shows that water resulting from the anhydrisation of organic compounds without further disintegration of the molecules may also be considered in connection with the formation of hydrogen sulfide in the melt of an alkali thiocyanate.

Another reaction scheme whereby hydrogen sulfide is formed may be the following: in certain organic compounds oxygen atoms can be replaced by sulfur atoms to produce compounds which, in their turn, decompose and split off hydrogen sulfide when heated with potassium thiocyanate. Furthermore, salts of organic nitrogen bases and free amino acids liberate hydrogen sulfide on contact with fused alkali thiocyanate (see pp. 269, 285). This would explain the behaviour of urea and its derivatives, which react with potassium thiocyanate, but are inactive when Test (1) is applied.

It is noteworthy that activated sulfur in potassium thiocyanate has a dehydrogenating effect on organic compounds, when the fusion temperature is raised over 400°. Under this condition, even paraffin forms hydrogen sulfide.

The enhanced reactivity of sulfur in molten potassium thiocyanate can be used for the detection of hydrogen in organic compounds. The following test is reliable, when the formation of hydrogen sulfide occurs rapidly at temperatures below 400°. At high temperatures, molten potassium thiocyanate itself yields a little hydrogen sulfide, probably by contact with the water vapor in the air.

Procedure. One drop of the test solution is evaporated to dryness in a micro test tube and held at 110° for a short time. Alternatively, a little of the solid may be tested. An excess of well dried potassium thiocyanate is then added and the mixture heated to about 200–300° in an oil bath. Filter paper moistened with 10 % lead acetate solution is kept over the open end of the test tube. A black fleck appears if the organic material contained hydrogen.

Reagent: Potassium thiocyanate (pulverized and dried at 110°).

This procedure is not highly sensitive. Nevertheless, amounts of about 500 γ of sugars, oxalic acid and succinic acid, as well as 50 γ of urea, give a positive response.

It is noteworthy that $Na_2SO_4 \cdot 10H_2O$, as well as $Na_2CO_3 \cdot H_2O$ develop hydrogen sulfide when added to fused potassium thiocyanate, whereas the anhydrous sodium salts do not react [23]. It seems therefore that water of crystallization may be detected in this way. Whether this method is also valid for detection of water of crystallization in organic compounds, has not been thoroughly tested as yet.

7. Halogens

(1) Test by conversion into copper halide (Beilstein test) [24]

Organic compounds which contain hydrogen and halogens (chlorine, bromine, iodine, or also cyanogen and thiocyanate groups) are decomposed on ignition with production of the corresponding hydrogen halide.* If the sample is mixed with copper oxide and then heated, copper halide is formed along with carbon dioxide and water. The copper halide gives a characteristic green or blue-green color to a non-luminous gas or alcohol flame. This reaction is given by all classes of organic compounds containing halogen, but it must be noted that certain halogen-free substances containing nitrogen also give a positive response in the Beilstein test; hydroxyquinoline, thiourea, and substituted pyridines as well as certain reaction products of hydrazine with benzoin, are pertinent instances.[25] This is due to the formation of HCN, HCNO or HCNS, whose copper salts likewise color the flame. Organic com-

* L. Rosenthaler, *Z. anal. Chem.*, 108 (1937) 22 states that phosgene ($COCl_2$) and $COBr_2$ are also produced.

pounds containing fluorine do not respond to the Beilstein test because copper fluoride is not volatile.

Procedure. A piece of copper wire, about 1 mm thick, is fused into a glass rod, and the end of the copper wire beaten out to form a spatula 2 to 3 mm wide. The spatula is heated in the oxidizing flame and is thus coated with copper oxide. Such spatulas may be kept on hand. In order to test for halogen, a little of the powdered sample is placed on the spatula, or a drop of a solution (which should contain no inorganic halogen compound) is gently evaporated to dryness. The charged copper wire is then heated fairly strongly in the nonluminous flame of a Bunsen burner (first in the blue inner zone and then in the lower part of the outer zone). A blue or green color appears in the flame, and lasts for a time varying with the halogen content. Sometimes only a momentary flash of color is seen. The yellow flame due to traces of sodium salts is seen almost always, particularly at the start. It may hide the green. This interference can be eliminated by viewing the flame through a cobalt glass.

It is better still to use a platinum spatula. A little copper oxide is mixed with the solid, liquid or dissolved sample and then heated on the tip of the spatula, which has been ignited beforehand.

Halogen was detected in the following amounts:

$0.5\ \gamma$ chloronitrobenzene . . . . . . $C_6H_4ClNO_2$

$0.25\ \gamma$ eosin . . . . $C_{20}H_8O_5Br_4$

$0.25\ \gamma$ iodoeosin . . . . $C_{20}H_8O_5I_4$

Even smaller amounts of halogens may be detected in organic gases, liquids and solids by using a clever device which includes, as an essential part, a micro-flame issuing from a copper capillary tube.[26]

(2) Test by conversion of chlorine, bromine and iodine into silver halide [27]

In the test for carbon described on page 74, the solid sample is heated with silver arsenate. This procedure converts organically bound chlorine, bromine or iodine into acid-resistant silver chloride, bromide or iodide. Cyanide and thiocyanate groups do not follow this pattern because silver cyanide and silver thiocyanate, produced transiently perhaps, are not ignition-proof. On strong heating, silver cyanide yields free silver, and silver thiocyanate is converted into a mixture of silver and silver sulfate. The test given here, which is applicable only to non-volatile organic compounds, accordingly has the advantage that only chlorine, bromine and iodine give a positive response. Though less sensitive than the Beilstein test just described, there is no interference by certain halogen-free nitrogenous compounds.

Procedure. A little of the powdered sample is placed in a small hard glass tube whose end is blown out to a bulb. If the sample is in solution, a drop is evaporated to dryness in the tube. This is best done under slightly reduced pressure by connecting the tube to a suction pump. An excess of powdered silver arsenate is then introduced and the tube is heated. After cooling, 1–3 drops of nitric acid (1:1) is added and the tube is heated in a water bath. Metallic silver and silver arsenate go into solution, and silver halide (AgCl, AgBr, AgI) remain, producing a turbidity or a precipitate according to the quantity of halogen in the sample.

The silver halide precipitate gently warmed with metallic zinc and acetic acid yields the respective halide ions. Concerning the distinction between these ions, compare Vol. I, Chap. 4.

(3) *Differentiation of aliphatic and aromatic bound halogens*

As pointed out under (*1*), the Beilstein test will reveal halogens (with the exception of fluorine) and the halogen-like radicals CN and CNS in all types of organic (and inorganic) binding. The same holds true of the test given under (*2*) for organically bound chlorine, bromine and iodine. Aliphatic and aromatic bound halogen, i.e., alkyl and aryl halogen, can be differentiated in many cases by applying the fact that only the former is split off by alkali hydroxide with production of alkali halide. A better method is to heat the sample for about two minutes with monoethanolamine, $CH_2OHCH_2NH_2$.[28] The latter is not only a strong base but, as an amino alcohol, it has considerable miscibility with, or solvent power for many organic compounds. After any turbidity is removed by adding alcohol, the ethanolamine halide formed in the reaction

$$RHal + CH_2OHCH_2NH_3OH \rightarrow ROH + CH_2OHCH_2NH_3Hal$$

can be detected by precipitation with silver nitrate.

The following odor test likewise is based on the ready mobility of aliphatic bound halogen. The alcoholic test solution is treated with several drops of alkali hydrosulfide solution prepared by bubbling hydrogen sulfide into a 1 % solution of sodium or potassium hydroxide until the pH reaches a value of about 8. The reaction with the test solution: $RHal + NaHS \rightarrow RSH + NaHal$ occurs on standing at room temperature or on slight warming. Even small quantities of the resulting thioalcohols (mercaptans) in the lower members of the series (up to 8 carbon atoms) have a disagreeable penetrating odor, which makes their detection easy. The higher mercaptans smell more like the respective alcohols. Aryl halides react with alkali hydrosulfide in an analogous manner, but only after prolonged boiling. The odors of the thiophenols are similar to those of the mercaptans.

Finally, it should be pointed out that alcoholic solutions of alkyl bromides and iodides react with a saturated alcoholic solution of silver nitrate to produce alkyl nitrate and a precipitate of silver bromide or iodide:

$$RHal + AgNO_3 \rightarrow AgHal + RONO_2 \cdot$$

All of the preceding tests can be carried out in micro test tubes with slight quantities of the solid test substance or several drops of its solution.

8. Iodine

Detection by conversion into iodic acid [29]

When methyl or ethyl iodide is treated with bromine dissolved in glacial acetic acid, iodic acid is formed quickly. This reaction is the basis of an iodo-metric determination of methoxy and ethoxy groups. [30] The behavior of these iodides is merely a special case illustrating the fact that iodic acid is formed by organic compounds, which contain iodine bound to carbon, when treated with bromine (or bromine water). The net reaction is

$$RI + 3\,Br_2 + 3\,H_2O \rightarrow RBr + 5\,HBr + HIO_3$$

Since this reaction proceeds rapidly and with small amounts of compounds containing iodine, the proof of the production of iodic acid may serve as the basis of an indirect test for organically bound iodine.

The following partial reactions probably are valid in the explanation of the chemical foundation of the tests. First of all, bromine acts on organic compounds containing iodine to produce the equilibrium:

$$2\,RI + Br_2 \rightleftharpoons 2\,RBr + I_2 \tag{1}$$

This reaction then continues to a marked extent because of the removal of the iodine from the equilibrium through conversion into iodic acid:

$$I_2 + 5\,Br_2 + 6\,H_2O \rightarrow 2\,HIO_3 + 10\,HBr \tag{2}$$

If the iodic acid produced in (2) is to be detected by the redox reaction

$$HIO_3 + 5\,I^- + 6\,H^+ \rightarrow 3\,H_2O + 3\,I_2 \tag{3}$$

the excess bromine must be completely removed beforehand. This can be accomplished by adding sulfosalicylic acid, which immediately forms bromo-salicylic acid:

$$C_6H_3(OH)(COOH)(SO_3H) + Br_2 \rightarrow HBr + C_6H_2Br(OH)COOH)(SO_3H) \tag{4}$$

Even though the four successive reactions must occur, the conduct of this test for iodine in organic compounds is quite feasible within the technique of spot test analysis. The limits of identification are microanalytical.

Procedure. A micro test tube is used. A drop of the test solution (or a little of the solid) is treated with a drop of a saturated solution of bromine in 5 % potassium bromide and the mixture warmed gently. After cooling, solid sulfo-salicylic acid is added until the color is discharged. A drop of water is added and the liquid shaken. (No bromine vapor may persist above the liquid.) A drop of 5 % potassium iodide solution, which contains 5 % thyodene indicator is then introduced. A more or less intense blue color appears, the depth depending on the quantity of iodine present. Comparison with a blank is advisable if very small amounts are suspected.

This procedure gave positive results with the following in one drop:

0.05 γ methyl iodide	1 γ 4-iodo mandelic acid
0.1 γ iodoform	0.05 γ 7-iodo-8-hydroxy-5-sulfonic acid

Erythrosine and diiodotyrosine responded positively.

The detection of iodine by converting it into iodic acid is not interfered with by other halogens. When using the test it is merely necessary to take account of the presence of oxidizing compounds which can liberate iodine from potassium iodide in acidified solutions. Examples are chloranil, organic per compounds, chloramine, organic derivatives of arsenic acid. Their presence or absence can be determined by stirring a drop of the test solution or solid unknown with acidified potassium iodide solution. If iodine is set free, a new test portion should be taken to dryness along with sulfurous acid and the evaporation residue then subjected to the above procedure. Only organic derivatives of arsenic acid cannot be rendered harmless in this way.

9. Fluorine

(1) Test for fluorine by conversion into alkali fluoride

The Beilstein test for halogens (page 80) in organic compounds is not suitable for the detection of fluorine, since copper fluoride, in contrast to the other copper halides, is not volatile.

On heating non-volatile organic compounds with metallic sodium or potassium, any fluorine present is converted into alkali fluoride.

Fluorides can be detected with high sensitivity through their reaction with "zirconium alizarinate". This test [31] (see Vol. I, Chap. 4) is based on the fact that in mineral acid solution, soluble zirconium salts yield a red-violet color on treatment with alizarin ([inner complex Zr (Aliz)$_4$]) and that this color changes to yellow (color of acid alizarin solution) on the addition of excess fluoride because of the production of complex zirconium hexafluoride ions. The reactions can be represented:

$$Zr^{+4} + 4\ Aliz^- \rightarrow Zr(Aliz)_4$$

$$Zr(Aliz)_4 + 6\ F^- \rightarrow [ZrF_6]^{-2} + 4\ Aliz^-$$

red-violet   yellow

The zirconium alizarinate does not correspond precisely to an inner complex zirconium salt of alizarin; rather it is the hydrosol of a violet zirconium-alizarin lake, i.e., a colored adsorption compound of hydrolysis products of aqueous zirconium salt solutions with alizarin.[32]

Procedure [33]. A few mg of the sample are taken, or a drop of the solution is evaporated to dryness in a small ignition tube. The evaporation is accomplished best by heating while the tube is attached to a suction pump. A piece of potassium (m.p. 62°) the size of a pin head is added. The tube is heated, gently at first, and then strongly for 1 minute. The molten metal thus comes into intimate contact with the sample. After cooling, 0.5 ml water is placed in the tube and a few drops of a strongly acid (hydrochloric) zirconium-alizarin solution. It is not necessary to filter off particles of carbon. In the presence of fluorine, the red color of the zirconium solution fades, and the yellow color of the free alizarin appears.

Instead of melting with potassium, the sample can be ignited with calcium oxide or magnesium oxide. The calcium (magnesium) fluoride in the residue can be tested with zirconium alizarinate (as just described). The ignition with calcium (magnesium) oxide is, however, more cumbersome than the conversion into potassium fluoride.

Reagent: Zirconium–alizarin solution. Commercial zirconium oxide (ZrO_2) is warmed with dilute hydrochloric acid and filtered from any insoluble matter. The solution should contain about 0.5 mg zirconium in 1 ml. Several ml of the zirconium solution is treated with a slight excess of an alcoholic solution of alizarin. The excess alizarin may be recognized by extracting a portion of the solution with ether, which becomes yellow.

Fluorine was detected in:

$$200\ \gamma \quad \text{acetofluoroglucose}\ C_{14}H_{19}O_9F$$
$$200\ \gamma \quad \text{lactosyl fluoride}\ C_{12}H_{21}O_{10}F$$
$$100\ \gamma \quad \beta\text{-fluoronaphthalene}\ C_{10}H_7F$$
$$100\ \gamma \quad o\text{-fluorobenzoic acid}\ C_7H_5O_2F$$

(2) *Test by conversion into hydrofluoric acid*

Vapors of hydrogen fluoride released from metal fluorides by heating with concentrated sulfuric acid roughen glass surfaces as indicated by a more or less intense frosting. Small quantities of hydrofluoric acid which do not produce a visible etching may nevertheless change the glass surface sufficiently so that it is no longer wetted by concentrated sulfuric acid. The acid then does not run off smoothly but collects in drops like water on an oily hydrophobic surface.[34] This effect is due to a surface reaction between the silica of the glass and hydrofluoric acid, the concentrated sulfuric acid functioning as a dehydrating agent (see Volume I, Chap. 4):

$$[SiO_2]_x + 2\ HF \underset{+\ H_2O}{\overset{+\ H_2SO_4}{\rightleftarrows}} [SiO_2)_{x-1} \cdot OSiF_2] + H_2O$$

This schematic equation [35] is intended to show that the surface reaction leads to a silicon-fluorine binding, in which the silicon atoms do not leave their original phase association. Surface reactions without formation of reaction products as independent phases are the essential feature of a chemical adsorption.

The non-wetting effect based on the chemical adsorption of hydrofluoric acid on glass can be utilized for the detection of fluorine in non-volatile organic compounds. It is necessary to convert the fluorine bound to carbon into hydrogen fluoride. For some non-volatile fluoriferous organic compounds it is merely necessary to warm the sample with concentrated sulfuric acid since its dehydrating and oxidative action ruptures the carbon skeleton and hydrogen fluoride is formed. A more reliable procedure is to ignite the test material with calcium oxide; calcium fluoride results. The hydrogen fluoride is then released from the ignition residue by concentrated sulfuric acid. To improve the visibility of the adsorption effect of the hydrofluoric acid, it is better to use sulfuric acid which contains some chromic acid.[36]

Procedure [37]. The solid test substance is mixed with several milligrams of calcium oxide in a small pyrex test tube (capacity about 5 ml). Alternatively, a drop of the test solution is added to the calcium oxide and taken to dryness. The mixture is then ignited, starting the heating at the top and gradually advancing to the bottom of the tube. The cooled residue is treated with 0.5 ml of chromic-sulfuric acid and heated, either over a free flame or for 10 minutes in a water bath. The presence of fluorine is revealed by the uneven wetting of the walls when the tube is shaken; the picture is reminiscent of an oily surface. When small amounts of fluorine are to be detected, a blank test is recommended.

Reagent: Chromic-sulfuric acid. 1 g potassium chromate in 100 ml concentrated sulfuric acid.

This test revealed fluorine in:

50 γ N-Trifluoroacetyl-p-toluidine H_3C—⟨ ⟩—$NHCOCF_3$

12.5 γ α-Hydroxy-α-trifluoromethyl propionic acid

$$\begin{array}{c} H_3C \diagdown \diagup OH \\ C \\ F_3C \diagup \diagdown COOH \end{array}$$

25 γ m-Acetamidobenzotrifluoride   ⟨CF_3 ⟩—$NHCOCH_3$

50 γ 4 : 4'-Difluorobenzophenone   F—⟨ ⟩—CO—⟨ ⟩—F

40 γ Tosyl-m-hydroxybenzotrifluoride ⟨CF_3 ⟩—O—SO_2—⟨ ⟩—CH_3

20 γ Trifluoromethylbenzoic acid   ⟨CF_3 ⟩—$COOH$

50 γ Perfluoro(dicyclohexylethane) $C_6F_{11}CF_2CF_2C_6F_{11}$

10. Sulfur

(1) Test by fusion with alkali metals (Lassaigne's test)[38]

When non-volatile organic sulfur compounds are heated with metallic sodium or potassium, alkali sulfide is formed along with carbon and other reduction products. This treatment involves redox reactions of a molten alkali metal with the solid organic compound and its solid, liquid or gaseous thermal decomposition products.[39]

A sensitive test for the sulfide produced by the alkali metal fusion is provided by its catalytic effect on the reaction

$$2\,NaN_3 + I_2 \rightarrow 2\,NaI + 3\,N_2$$

This reaction is normally so sluggish that a yellow or brown solution of alkali azide and alkali polyiodide remains practically unchanged even after months of standing. The addition of traces of a soluble sulfide, or contact with insoluble metal sulfides (even acid-resistant HgS, As_2S_3, PbS, etc.), initiates the reaction immediately and brings it to a swift conclusion as can be seen by a fading or complete discharge of the color of the solution, or still better by the production of free nitrogen which is evolved as small bubbles. Consequently, sulfides can be detected through their catalytic acceleration of the iodine-azide reaction [40] (compare Volume I, Chap. 4).

The detection of sulfides produced by the fusion of organic compounds with an alkali metal requires the preparation of an acetic acid solution of the fusion residue. Any evolution of hydrogen sulfide from the acid solution can be prevented by the addition of cadmium acetate.

Procedure [41]. A very little of the powdered sample is placed in a small hard glass tube with the end blown out to a bulb. If a solution is used, a microdrop is evaporated to dryness in the tube. (This is best done under slightly reduced pressure by connecting the tube to a suction pump.) A small piece of potassium (size of a pin head) is introduced on a small glass rod, and any sample on the walls of the tube can be stroked down with the potassium. The tube is then carefully heated, starting from the open end, until the potassium is melted and has mixed with the sample. Finally, the tube is heated for a short time to redness, and plunged at once into a micro test tube containing 5 drops of water. Without troubling to filter off the particles of glass and carbon, 1 drop of 20% cadmium acetate is added, followed by 1 or 2 drops of 20% acetic acid and, when cold, 1 or 2 drops of iodine-azide solution. If a sulfur compound is present, bubbles of nitrogen canbe seen.

Reagent: Sodium azide-iodine solution. 3 g sodium azide is dissolved in 100 ml 0.1 N iodine solution. The reagent is stable.

Using this procedure sulfur was detected in:

0.3 γ thiourea, $CS(NH_2)_2$
1.2 γ sulfanilic acid, $C_6H_4(NH_2)SO_3H$
1.2 γ isatin potassium sulfonate, $KO_3S \cdot C_6H_3 \diagup^{CO}_{NH} \diagdown CO$
1.2 γ H-acid, $C_{10}H_4(OH)(NH_2)(SO_3H)_2$
1   γ sulfosalicylic acid, $C_6H_3(OH)(COOH)SO_3H$

(2) *Test by reduction to sulfide in an alcohol flame* [42]

Sulfur in difficultly volatile organic compounds can easily be converted into alkali sulfide by fusing with potassium hydroxide in the reducing portion of an alcohol flame. The resulting potassium sulfide is conveniently detected by the iodine–azide reaction. The following procedure is about ten times as sensitive as the Lassaigne test.

Procedure. The end of a piece of thin copper wire (0.1–0.2 mm) is cleaned by rubbing with emery paper to remove sulfide and washed with distilled water. The clean end of the wire is dipped into a saturated solution of potassium hydroxide in water and cautiously passed into the flame of an alcohol lamp to evaporate the water and to obtain a small bead of molten potassium hydroxide at or near the end of the wire. If the bead does not form at the tip, the wire beyond the bead may be cut off. After breathing on the bead, it is touched to the substance to be tested, so that a little of the latter adheres to the alkali. Then the bead is introduced into the flame, moved slowly into the reducing zone and after a few seconds it is allowed to cool near the wick. The end of the wire is cut off, placed on a slide, treated with a drop of iodine–azide solution and observed under the microscope. If not less than 0.03 γ sulfur is present, the evolution of gas is general and quite vigorous, so that the positive result can be plainly distinguished from that given by the blank. The latter sometimes gives small gas bubbles at single scattered places on the wire. These obviously are due to sulfide inclusions in the copper. A general uniform evolution of gas is never observed when the KOH bead in the blank dissolves.

Reagent: Solution of 1 g sodium azide in 50 ml 0.5 N iodine.

(3) *Test by formation of silver sulfide from volatile compounds* [42]

The tests described under *1* and *2*, which are based on the production of alkali sulfide, cannot be applied successfully to volatile organic compounds. If, however, sulfur-bearing materials are pyrolysed in small capillary tubes, whose inner walls have been silvered, the action of the hot decomposition products yields silver sulfide. Since the latter catalyzes the iodine–azide reaction just as soluble sulfides do, an extremely sensitive test for sulfur in easily volatile organic compounds becomes possible.

Procedure. The sample is reduced with metallic silver in a capillary tube. Ordinary glass tubing is drawn down into 0.5–1 mm capillaries. These are filled with a 0.1 N silver nitrate solution containing alkali tartrate, ammonia and sodium hydroxide and allowed to stand overnight. After rinsing with water, the tubes are dried by warming and drawing air through them. The tubes are then drawn out to 6 to 8 cm so that the ends are as thin as paper. The closed tubes can be kept on hand indefinitely. A tube is prepared for use by breaking off the very fine point and allowing a droplet of the sample to enter. Solid samples are fused, or dissolved in the smallest possible volume of a solvent that has been tested to insure the absence of sulfur. The capillary is closed by touching the tip momentarily to the flame. A zone about 2 cm from the end is heated. When it becomes hot, the capillary bends so that the sample approaches the flame, volatilizes, and is reduced in the superheated zone. At this instant, a light snap is heard. After cooling, the tip is broken off and a drop of iodine-azide solution is allowed to enter. The reaction is observed under the microscope. As little as 0.05 γ sulfur gives a vigorous reaction.

References pp. 148–150

(4) Test by conversion into hydrogen sulfide

When sodium formate is heated above its melting point (250°) it decomposes: $2 \ HCOONa \rightarrow 2H^+ + Na_2C_2O_4$. Consequently, sodium formate melt acts as hydrogen donor and therefore as a strong reducing agent.[43] If non-volatile sulfur-bearing organic compounds are heated with sodium formate, hydrogen sulfide results and the latter can be readily detected, even in traces, by the blackening of lead acetate paper. The procedure given here, though less sensitive than the iodine-azide test, is reliable and fast.

Procedure.[44] A Micro test tube is used. A little of the solid or a drop of its solution is evaporated with a drop of 20% sodium formate solution. The mouth of the tube is then covered with a disk of lead acetate paper and the bottom of the tube heated over a microflame. If sulfur-bearing material is present, the paper develops a grey or black stain of lead sulfide. The color depends on the amount of sulfur.

This procedure revealed:

20	γ	sulfanilic acid
10	γ	thiourea
2.5	γ	sulfosalicylic acid
0.5	γ	phenylthiohydantoin acid
2.5	γ	3-acetamino-4-methoxy-benzenesulfinic acid
8	γ	diphenylthiocarbazone
4	γ	4,4-diaminodiphenylsulfonic acid (sodium)
5	γ	anthraquinone-3-sulfonic acid (sodium)
5	γ	2,6 naphthylaminesulfonic acid
5	γ	Victoria violet
5	γ	taurine
5	γ	methylene blue
6	γ	saccharin
10	γ	sulfanilamide

11. Nitrogen

(1) Test by ignition with calcium oxide (lime test)

When organic compounds containing nitrogen and hydrogen are strongly heated with lime, ammonia results. The various kinds of nitrogen compounds all give this result but the yield of ammonia may vary. The paths by which ammonia is formed from organic nitrogen compounds when heated with lime are not known. It is possible that calcium cyanamide and calcium cyanide are the initial products, and these then hydrolyze on heating with water to produce ammonia. The necessary water is provided in the lime tests by the combustion of the hydrogen, almost always contained in the sample, and reacts at the site of its production in the form of superheated steam, in other words in a particularly reactive state.

The ammonia produced in the lime test can be detected by indicator papers. Especially effective is filter paper moistened with silver nitrate-manganese nitrate solution.[45] On contact with ammonia, a grey or black fleck appears on the white paper. The stain is due to a mixture of free silver and manganese dioxide, resulting from the reaction:

$$4 NH_3 + 4 H_2O \rightleftarrows 4 NH_4OH \rightarrow 4 NH_4^+ + 4 OH^-$$

$$2 Ag^+ + Mn^{+2} + 4 OH^- \rightarrow 2 Ag^0 + MnO_2 + 2 H_2O$$

The test can be intensified still more by utilizing the fact, employed in the detection of manganese (see Volume I, Chap. 3) that when benzidine is oxidized by MnO_2, the highly colored meriquinoidal derivative of this base, namely benzidine blue, results. If the sample is heated with lime in a hard glass tube and a piece of filter paper impregnated with the reagent solution is laid over the open end, it often happens that substances which contain no nitrogen also cause a darkening of the paper. This is due to the formation of pyro-compounds during the incomplete combustion of the organic compound. This interference with the test can be avoided if a little manganese dioxide is mixed with the lime; the evolution of oxygen on heating to redness ensures complete combustion. A little of the ammonia may be oxidized in this case, but since the test for ammonia is very sensitive this loss is of no importance.

The test succeeds likewise with volatile nitrogenous organic bases and their salts. In such cases, the respective bases are liberated rather than ammonia, but they react with silver-manganese paper as does ammonia.

Procedure [46]. A trace of the sample is mixed in a small hard glass tube with a mixture of lime and manganese dioxide. Alternatively, a drop of the test solution is evaporated to dryness in the tube (this is best done under reduced pressure using the suction pump). The residue is then mixed with the lime and manganese dioxide. The open end of the tube is covered with a piece of filter paper moistened in the reagent solution, the glass stopper is put in place, and the tube is slowly heated to redness. A black or gray stain appears on the reagent paper, according to the amount of nitrogen present. The stain immediately turns blue on spotting with benzidine.

Reagents: *1)* A mixture of ignited lime and manganese dioxide (10 : 1).

2) Manganese nitrate–silver nitrate solution. 2.87 g $Mn(NO_3)_2$ is dissolved in 40 ml water and filtered. To this is added a solution of 3.35 g $AgNO_3$ in 40 ml water, and the mixture diluted to 100 ml. In order to neutralize the acid formed by hydrolysis, dilute alkali is added, drop by drop, until a black precipitate is formed;

this is filtered off. The reagent solution thus prepared will keep
if stored in a dark bottle.
3) Benzidine solution: 0.05 g benzidine base or hydrochloride
dissolved in 10 ml acetic acid, diluted to 100 ml with water and
filtered.

Nitrogen was revealed in:

2 γ   sulfanilic acid, $C_6H_4(NH_2)SO_3H$
1 γ   p-nitrosophenol, $C_6H_4(OH)NO$
2 γ   1-nitroso-2-naphthol, $C_{10}H_6(OH)NO$
3 γ   1-amino-8-naphthol-3,6-disulfonic acid (H-acid) $C_{10}H_4(OH)(NH_2)(SO_3H)_2$
3 γ   codeine hydrochloride, $C_{18}H_{21}O_3N \cdot HCl$

(2) Test by fusion with alkali metals (Lassaigne's test)[47]

Nonvolatile organic nitrogenous compounds form alkali cyanide when
heated with metallic potassium or sodium. (Potassium reacts more quickly.)*
This test has been known and used for more than a century for the detection of organically bound nitrogen. It is based on the formation of heat-
stable alkali cyanide, which results from interesting partial reactions, which
have been disclosed only recently by systematic investigations.[51] The most
important role is played by the powerful reducing action of fused alkali
metals. On contact with organic compounds or their pyrolysis products, including free carbon, very reactive hydrogen and alkali carbide are formed
and they lead to a cleavage of organic nitrogenous materials to yield cyanogen compounds. Furthermore, alkali metals can serve as acceptors of the
dicyanogen and hydrogen cyanide, which are produced from the very resistant C–N bond during the thermal decomposition of many organic compounds. As a consequence of the numerous reduction possibilities and from
the fact that some organic nitrogenous compounds split off ammonia or free
nitrogen ** when heated, the conversion of nitrogen to cyanide in the Lassaigne test is not always quantitative. It is remarkable that the addition of
glucose raises the yield of cyanide, probably because of an increased production of active hydrogen and alkali carbide. For instance, under the normal
conditions, the hydrazone of benzophenone yielded 28 % of cyanide, as
opposed to 66 % when mixed with glucose. Accordingly, when dealing with
samples that are poor in carbon, it is better to conduct the Lassaigne test
on a mixture containing glucose.[52]

---

* It has been reported that organically bound nitrogen is converted to alkali cyanide also by
heating with a mixture of potassium carbonate and magnesium powder.[48], [49] Dextrose plus
sodium carbonate has also been recommended as reducing mixture.[50]
** The loss of nitrogen is especially marked in the case of aliphatic azo compounds and aromatic diazo compounds; hydrazo and amino compounds are prone to yield ammonia.

In the original procedure, the cyanide is converted to ferrocyanide and the latter then detected by means of the Prussian blue reaction. The direct test, in which the hydrogen cyanide is set free by adding acid to the reaction mass, and allowing the gas to come in contact with copper acetate-benzidine acetate, is better and more sensitive (Procedure I). Another test is based on the decomposition of yellow cupro-mercaptothio-thiodiazolone by an alkaline alkali cyanide solution (Procedure II). This is less sensitive, however, than Procedure I.

(a) The color reaction, employed in Procedure I (see Volume I, Chap. 4), between hydrogen cyanide and cupric acetate-benzidine acetate is based on the ability of hydrocyanic acid to disturb the equilibrium of the redox reaction:

Cupric ion + Bzd $\rightleftharpoons$ Cuprous ion + Bzd-blue

$$Bzd = H_2N-\langle\bigcirc\rangle-\langle\bigcirc\rangle-NH_2$$

$$Bzd\text{-blue}\ ^{52a} = \left[HN=\langle\bigcirc\rangle=\langle\bigcirc\rangle=NH \cdot Bzd \right] \cdot HX$$

X = univalent acid radical

Normally this equilibrium is so situated that the amount of meriquinoidal benzidine is not visible. However, the great tendency of cuprous ions to form $Cu_2(CN)_2^{-2}$ ions is so great that in the presence of cyanide ions, the cuprous ions are removed from the equilibrium and significant quantities of benzidine blue result. In other words, the oxidation potential of the cupric ions is raised through the cyanide ions or hydrogen cyanide.

Procedure.[53, 54] A small amount of the solid, or a drop of the test solution is placed in a glass capillary with one end enlarged to a bulb. Liquid samples are taken to dryness in the tube. A clean, dry piece of metallic potassium is added with the aid of a glass rod. The tube is heated, starting at the open end, until finally the potassium in the bulb melts and mixes intimately with the sample. The bulb is then briefly heated to redness, and placed while still hot in the bulb of the apparatus described on page 50 (Fig. 26) which contains 5 drops of distilled water. The tube breaks on touching the water. Two drops of 30% acetic acid are added without filtering off the particles of glass and carbon. The funnel stopper is replaced and covered with a piece of filter paper impregnated with copper acetate–benzidine acetate. When large amounts of nitrogen are present, and consequently a large amount of hydrocyanic acid, a blue color forms at once with small amounts, the color may not appear until the contents of the apparatus are heated to boiling with a microburner. The reagent paper must be kept moist all the time, by adding a drop of water when necessary.

References pp. 148–150

Reagent: Copper acetate-benzidine acetate solution. The solutions of copper acetate and benzidine acetate are best stored separately in well-stoppered, dark bottles, and the reagent mixture prepared freshly each time it is needed. (The mixture of acetates will not keep longer than 2 weeks.) Solution (I) 2.86 g copper acetate in a liter of water. Solution (II) 675 ml of a solution of benzidine acetate, saturated at room temperature, plus 525 ml water. Solutions (I) and (II) are mixed in equal volumes to form the reagent mixture.

Nitrogen was detected in:

$\quad$ 6 γ $\quad$ p-nitrophenol, $C_6H_4(OH)NO_2$
$\quad$ 6 γ $\quad$ p-nitrosophenol, $C_6H_4(OH)NO$
$\quad$ 6 γ $\quad$ o-nitrobenzaldehyde, $C_6H_4(CHO)NO_2$
$\quad$ 12 γ $\quad$ α-nitroso-β-naphthol, $C_{10}H_6(OH)NO$
$\quad$ 4 γ $\quad$ azobenzene, $C_6H_5N{=}NC_6H_5$
$\quad$ 12 γ $\quad$ codeine hydrochloride, $C_{18}H_{21}O_3N{\cdot}HCl$

See page 95 regarding modification of the test for compounds containing sulfur as well as nitrogen.

(*b*) The alkali cyanide produced from non-volatile nitrogenous organic compounds when the latter are fused with alkali metals can also be detected by the action of cyanide ion on the yellow cuprous salt of mercaptophenylthio-thiodiazolone.[55] Colorless water-insoluble cuprous cyanide and colorless mercaptan result:

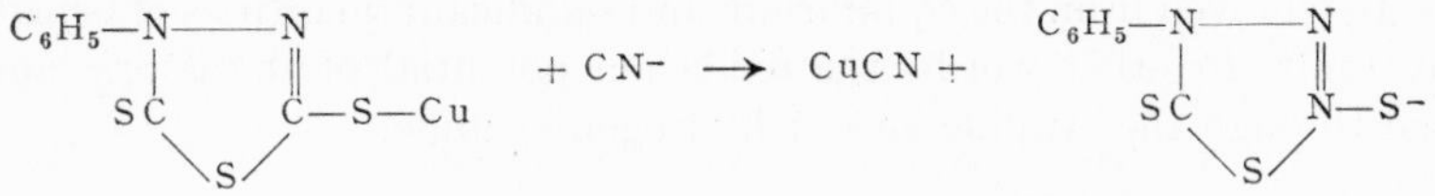

$$C_6H_5{-}N{-}\!\!-\!\!-\!\!N \qquad\qquad C_6H_5{-}N{-}\!\!-\!\!-\!\!N$$
$$S\,C\quad\quad C{-}S{-}Cu \quad + CN^- \ \rightarrow\ CuCN + \qquad S\,C\qquad N{-}S^-$$
$$\diagdown S\diagup \qquad\qquad\qquad\qquad\qquad \diagdown S\diagup$$

This reaction is not interfered with by any alkali-hydroxide, chloride, bromide, iodide, thiocyanate or cyanate which may be present. Only the alkali sulfide produced by the alkali metal fusion of sulfur-bearing organic compounds reacts with the cupromercaptan; it forms black cuprous sulfide. Consequently, the test must be modified somewhat when dealing with samples containing sulfur compounds (see page 95).

Procedure II. The alkali metal fusion is conducted as described on page 92. The cooled residue is taken up in as little water as possible and the carbon particles are removed by centrifuging or filtering. A drop of the colorless alkaline solution is placed in a depression of a spot plate and a drop of the cupromercaptan suspension is added. Discharge of the yellow color indicates cyanide and therefore nitrogen in the organic compound being tested.

Reagent: Cupromercaptan suspension: 5 ml of 0.1 % solution of cupric chloride is treated with 2.5 ml concentrated ammonia and 10 ml of 0.1 % solution of hydroxylamine hydrochloride. The colorless solution is treated with 50 ml of 0.1 % solution of potassium mercaptophenyl-thio-thiodiazolone. The bright yellow suspension of the cupro-mercaptan will remain about 5 days without settling.

The detection of nitrogen in organic compounds by alkali metal fusion followed by identification of the resulting cyanide in alkaline solution is about one-third as sensitive as the test based on the liberation of hydrogen cyanide and its action on copper-benzidine acetate.

If sulfur-bearing organic materials are fused with alkali metal, the resulting alkali sulfide impairs the cupromercaptan test, since even minimal quantities of copper sulfide decolorize the yellow suspension. The sulfide can be removed by lead carbonate; lead sulfide is formed while the alkali cyanide remains unchanged.

Procedure. The alkali metal fusion is conducted in a hard glass test tube. After the mass has cooled, it is treated with 2 or 3 drops of water. The solution is treated with small portions of lead carbonate until some unreacted white carbonate persists. The suspension is centrifuged; the lead sulfide and carbonate deposit nicely. There is no need to pour off the supernatant liquid. It is treated directly in the tube with a drop of the yellow cupromercaptan suspension. If cyanide is present, the color is discharged.

Another test for cyanide in alkaline solution is described on page 459

Test for nitrogen and sulfur in the same sample [53]

Organic compounds containing both nitrogen and sulfur produce cyanide and sulfide when fused with metallic potassium. These products are easily identified by the sensitive spot reaction described on page 87 and page 92, when the stated conditions are maintained. It is then possible to test for sulfur and nitrogen in much less then 0.5 mg of the sample. It is essential to use an excess of potassium, since if sulfur and nitrogen are both present, potassium thiocyanate may be produced instead of potassium cyanide and potassium sulfide.

Procedure. A little of the solid sample, or a drop of the solution which is then evaporated to dryness, is placed in a small hard glass tube with a bulb at one end. A piece of potassium the size of a pinhead is added on a small glass rod, and the tube is carefully heated, beginning at the open end, until the potassium is completely melted and mixed with the sample. The bulb is then heated briefly to redness, and while still hot, placed in the bulb of the apparatus described on page 50 (Fig. 26), which contains 5 drops of distilled water. The hot tube breaks, and a drop of cadmium acetate and 2 drops acetic acid are added, and the apparatus closed with the funnel stopper, on top of which is placed a piece of paper impregnated with copper acetate–benzidine acetate (for preparation, see page 94). On heating gently, the liberated hydrocyanic acid causes a blue fleck on the filter paper, thus indicating that the original sample contained nitrogen.

After liberating the prussic acid, the funnel is removed and the contents of the tube are allowed to cool. Then 1 or 2 drops of iodine–azide solution (for preparation, see page 88) added. Evolution of bubbles of nitrogen indicates that sulfur was present in the sample.

The sensitivity of this test is shown by the weight of material that sufficed to give definite reactions for both nitrogen and sulfur:

16.2 γ thiourea, $CS(NH_2)_2$

6 γ sulfanilic acid, $C_6H_4(NH_2)SO_3H$

9 γ potassium isatin sulfonate, $KO_3S-C_6H_3\underset{NH}{\overset{CO}{<}}>CO$

12 γ 1-amino-8-naphthol-3,6-disulfonic acid (H-acid) $C_{10}H_4(NH_2)(OH)(SO_3H)_2$

If larger quantities of the test material are available, less sensitive tests for alkali sulfide and cyanide will suffice after the sample has been fused with an alkali metal. The nitroprusside test for sulfide (Volume I, Chap. 4) and the cupromercaptan test for cyanide (page 94) are recommended. Both tests can be accomplished as spot reactions on a spot plate with one drop of the solution of the alkali metal fusion residue.

12. Phosphorus

Test by ignition with lime (conversion to phosphate)

Nonvolatile organic compounds containing phosphorus leave heat-resistant tertiary calcium phosphate when ignited with calcium oxide.

The phosphate ions obtained by dissolving the ignited residue in acid are precipitated as crystalline yellow ammonium phosphomolybdate by the action of a nitric acid solution of ammonium molybdate:

$$PO_4^{-3} + 12\ MoO_4^{-2} + 3\ NH_4^+ + 24\ H^+ \rightarrow (NH_4)_3PO_4 \cdot 12\ MoO_3 + 12\ H_2O$$

Traces of ammonium phosphomolybdate can be detected by spotting with benzidine and alkali acetate (see Vol. I, Chap. 4).[56] An intense blue appears; it is due to a blue quinoidal oxidation product of benzidine ("benzidine blue") and a blue reduction product of molybdic anhydride. This "molybdenum blue" is a mixture of MoO_3 and lower oxides of molybdenum. The redox reaction between molybdenum[VI] and benzidine is brought about as follows: NH_3 molecules of the $(NH_4)_3PO_4 \cdot 12MoO_3$ are exchanged for benzidine molecules. However, benzidinium phosphomolybdate is stable only in mineral acid solution. In contact with alkali acetate or ammonia, the complexly bound molybdenum, which has higher reducing power than MoO_4^{-2} ions, is reduced by benzidine with production of the two blue reaction products.

Procedure. One drop of the test solution is placed on a few mg of calcium oxide in a platinum spoon and evaporated. Alternatively, a few grains of the powdered substance are mixed with calcium oxide. The spoon is heated, at first gently, and finally kept for some time at red heat. After cooling to room temperature, two drops of $2 N$ nitric acid are added to dissolve the residue. A drop of ammonium molybdate solution is placed on quantitative filter paper (preferably S & S 589 or equivalent) followed by the contents of the spoon. After 1–2 minutes, a drop of benzidine is added. Then the paper is held over ammonia. When most of the free mineral acid is neutralized, a blue stain is formed on the paper, the intensity depending on the phosphate content. It is advisable to carry out a blank as a check on the purity of the reagents.

Reagents: 1) Ammonium molybdate solution: 5 g ammonium molybdate is dissolved in 100 ml cold water and poured in 35 ml nitric acid (sp. gr. 1.2).
2) Benzidine solution: 0.5 g benzidine or benzidine hydrochloride is dissolved in 10 ml concentrated acetic acid and diluted to 100 ml with water.

Phosphorus was detected by this procedure in the following quantities of organic compounds. Most of them are derivatives of phosphoric or thiophosphoric acid, and have acquired importance as insecticides. Consequently, this test has become of practical importance in this field.[57]

1 γ 1-phenyl-1-chloroethylene-2-phosphinic acid

$$C_6H_5\diagdown \atop Cl\diagup C{=}CH{-}\overset{\displaystyle O}{\overset{\displaystyle \|}{P}}{\diagup}^{OH}_{\diagdown OH}$$

2·5 γ O,O-diethyl-O-p-nitrophenyl thiophosphate (Parathion)

$$O_2N{-}C_6H_4{-}O{-}\overset{\displaystyle S}{\overset{\displaystyle \|}{P}}{\diagup}^{OC_2H_5}_{\diagdown OC_2H_5}$$

5 γ octamethyl pyrophosphoramide

$$(CH_3)_2N\diagdown \atop (CH_3)_2N\diagup \overset{\displaystyle O}{\overset{\displaystyle \|}{P}}{-}O{-}\overset{\displaystyle O}{\overset{\displaystyle \|}{P}}{\diagup}^{N(CH_3)_2}_{\diagdown N(CH_3)_2}$$

8 γ diethyl p-nitrophenyl phosphate (Para-oxon)

$$O_2N{-}C_6H_4{-}O{-}\overset{\displaystyle O}{\overset{\displaystyle \|}{P}}{\diagup}^{OC_2H_5}_{\diagdown OC_2H_5}$$

3 γ tetraethyl dithiopyrophosphate (Sulfotepp)

$$\begin{array}{c} \text{C}_2\text{H}_5\text{—O} \diagdown \overset{\text{S}}{\underset{\|}{\text{P}}}\text{—O—}\overset{\text{S}}{\underset{\|}{\text{P}}} \diagup \text{O—C}_2\text{H}_5 \\ \text{C}_2\text{H}_5\text{—O} \diagup \qquad\qquad \diagdown \text{O—C}_2\text{H}_5 \end{array}$$

13. Arsenic

Test by ignition with lime (conversion to arsenate)

All non-volatile organic compounds containing arsenic leave heat-resistant tertiary calcium arsenate when ignited with calcium oxide.

The arsenic^V in calcium arsenate can be detected by procedures I–III, whose chemical bases are discussed in a–c.

(a) After solution in concentrated hydrochloric acid, free arsenic is precipitated by adding stannous chloride:

$$\text{Ca}_3(\text{AsO}_4)_2 + 16\ \text{HCl} \rightarrow 2\ \text{AsCl}_5 + 3\ \text{CaCl}_2 + 8\ \text{H}_2\text{O}$$
$$2\ \text{As}^{+5} + 5\ \text{Sn}^{+2} \rightarrow 2\ \text{As}^0 + 5\ \text{Sn}^{+4}$$

(b) Red-brown silver arsenate is produced by spotting with acetic acid silver nitrate solution:

$$\text{AsO}_4^{-3} + 3\ \text{Ag}^+ \rightarrow \text{Ag}_3\text{AsO}_4$$

The conversion into silver arsenate is far less sensitive than the reduction to elementary arsenic. It should also be noted that halogen-bearing organic compounds when ignited with lime leave calcium halides which react with silver nitrate, and furthermore silver chloride and silver bromide change color on exposure to daylight (photo halide formation) and this darkening increases the difficulty of detecting the slow precipitation of small amounts of silver arsenate.

(c) Dilute sulfuric acid and cadmium iodide react with calcium arsenate:

$$\text{AsO}_4^{-3} + 2\ \text{I}^- + 2\ \text{H}^+ \rightarrow \text{AsO}_3^{-3} + \text{H}_2\text{O} + \text{I}_2$$

The free iodine can be detected by the sensitive starch test. When applying the redox reaction with iodide, it should be remembered that antimony-bearing organic compounds leave antimony pentoxide or calcium antimonate after ignition with lime, and these products likewise set iodine free. The same is true when the ignition residue contains ferric oxide.

Procedure[58] **I** . A few grains of the powdered substance are placed in a micro test tube of hard glass, or alternatively a drop of the test solution is evaporated to dryness there (preferably by warming and using the suction pump). A few mg of ignited lime is mixed in, and the tube is heated gently at first, and finally to redness for a few minutes. After being allowed to cool completely, the contents of the tube are dissolved in a few drops of concentrated hydrochloric acid (no particles of carbon should remain if combustion has been complete). Two drops of freshly prepared solution of stannous chloride in 35 % hydrochloric acid are added and the mixture warmed. In the presence of arsenic, a black precipitate or brown turbidity appears.[59] The turbidity can be made more visible by shaking the suspension with ether. The dark particles can then be seen at the interface between the ether and water.

Arsenic was revealed in

    12 γ chloroarsanilic acid, $C_6H_3Cl(NH_2)(AsO_3H_2)$

    12 γ dinitroarsanilic acid, $C_6H_2(NO_2)_2(NH_2)(AsO_3H_2)$

    10 γ sodium acetylarsenilate, $C_6H_4(NHCOCH_3)(AsO_3HNa)$

    8 γ sodium p-hydroxyphenylarsenilate, $C_6H_4(OH)(AsO_3HNa)$

    5 γ salvarsan $(OH)(NH_2)H_3C_6$—As$=$As—$C_6H_3(NH_2)(OH)$. 2HCl

Procedure II. One drop of the test solution is added to a milligram of calcium oxide in a microcrucible and evaporated to dryness at 110°. Alternatively, a few grains of the powdered sample are mixed with the calcium oxide. The crucible is then heated strongly, and a drop of silver nitrate is added to the cold ignition residue. Depending on the arsenic content, red-brown silver arsenate separates at once or after several minutes.

Reagent: 7% solution of silver nitrate in 6 N acetic acid

This test revealed arsenic in 60 γ nitrophenylarsonic acid, $C_6H_4NO_2AsO(OH)_2$ and 20 γ salvarsan.

Procedure III.[58] A mixture of the test substance and calcium oxide is prepared and ignited as described in Procedure II. The cooled ignition residue is treated with a drop of 1 : 1 sulfuric acid and the contents of the crucible cooled by setting it in cold water. A drop of cadmium iodide-starch solution * is then introduced. A blue color that appears within 30 seconds indicates arsenic. A blank is recommended when small amounts of arsenic are involved.

Reagent: 5% solution of cadmium iodide in 1% solution of cadmium sulfate. Starch solution or some solid thyodene indicator is added just before the test.

Arsenic was revealed in: 1.4 γ phenylarsonic acid
                               1.7 γ nitrophenylarsonic acid

In the case of aliphatic and aromatic arsonic acids, which in accord with

---

* The use of cadmium iodide solution in place of the usual potassium iodide solution has the advantage that, because of the lower dissociation of CdI_2, the release of small quantities of iodine through dissolved oxygen and traces of nitric oxide is much slower.[60]

the general formula $R-AsO(OH)_2$ contain quinquevalent arsenic, no calcination is needed to effect conversion into calcium arsenate. These acids, analogously to arsenic acid, react directly with acidified alkali iodide solutions:

$$R-AsO(OH)_2 + 2\ HI \rightarrow R-As(OH)_2 + I_2 + H_2O$$

with probable intermediate formation of $R-AsI_2$.[61] The attainable limits of detection are the same as those when the corresponding arsenic compounds are calcined.

Organic compounds of trivalent arsenic can be converted into arsenic acids by evaporation with hydrogen peroxide but the detection of quinquevalent arsenic compounds, formed in this manner, by the addition of acidified potassium iodide solution is not reliable. It has been found[62] that many organic compounds of the most varied kinds leave products containing hydrogen peroxide when they are evaporated with this oxidant, often even after heating to 200°, and they then liberate free iodine from acidified potassium iodide solutions.

14. Antimony

When organic compounds containing antimony are ignited they leave Sb_2O_5 and Sb_2O_4, which may readily be detected by (1) or (2).

(1) Detection with rhodamine B

Antimony pentoxide and tetroxide are dissolved by strong hydrochloric acid in the presence of excess potassium iodide. Iodine is set free and SbI_3 or $H[SbI_4]$ is formed. This complex acid gives a red-violet salt with the basic dyestuff rhodamine B. The chemistry of this sensitive test and the procedure, which has an identification limit of 0.5 γ antimony when conducted as a spot reaction, is discussed on page 472.

Organic arsenic compounds do not interfere with this test. If organic bismuth or gold compounds are present, the test for antimony should be conducted according to (2), because under the conditions of the test there is production of $H[BiI_4]$ and $H[AuI_4]$, which likewise form violet water-soluble salts with rhodamine B.

(2) Detection with diphenylamine or diphenylbenzidine

Diphenylamine or N,N-diphenylbenzidine, dissolved in concentrated sulfuric acid, is oxidized by antimony pentoxide to blue quinimine dyestuffs. The chemistry of the color reaction is the same as that of the oxidation of these amines by nitric acid (see Volume I, Chapter 4).

When testing for antimony in organic compounds, a small sample is ashed in a micro crucible and the residue is treated with a freshly prepared 1 % solution of diphenylamine or diphenylbenzidine in concentrated sulfuric acid. A blue color appears at once or within several minutes if antimony is present. The *limit of identification* of this procedure is 5 γ antimony.

The test may not be applied directly if the ignition residue contains alkali or alkaline earth nitrates. The latter can be completely destroyed by evaporation with concentrated formic acid and subsequent ignition. This treatment converts nitrates and nitrites quantitatively into carbonates, whereas Sb_2O_5 remains unaltered.[63]

15. Oxygen

Test through solvate formation with ferric thiocyanate [64]

Red ferric thiocyanate, like green-blue cobalt thiocyanate (Volume I, Chap. 3), can be extracted from its water solution by shaking with ether, amyl alcohol, and other oxygen-containing organic solvents. In contrast, solvents that are free of oxygen, such as benzene, toluene, carbon tetrachloride, etc., are inactive. Since solid ferric thiocyanate shows this same solubility distinction toward these two classes of liquids, a test for oxygen in organic compounds can be based on this differential behavior. Obviously, this action is due to the fact that the molecules of the oxygen-containing liquid or dissolved organic compounds are capable of forming stable solvates with ferric thiocyanate molecules through the auxiliary valences of their oxygen atoms. The molecules of liquid hydrocarbons and their halogenated derivatives lack these coordination-active atoms, and accordingly form no solvates with this ferric salt. This assumption is supported by the fact that liquid hydrocarbons and their halogenated derivatives acquire the ability to dissolve ferric thiocyanate when either solid or liquid oxygen-containing materials are dissolved in or mixed with them. In principle, this effect is analogous to the solvate formation that occurs when iodine dissolves in organic solvents, producing a brown color. The violet iodine solutions, which probably contain no solvate, change toward brown when coordination-active organic compounds are introduced, and thereby cause the formation of iodine addition compounds which dissolve with a brown color.[65]

It should be noted that sulfur- and nitrogen-containing compounds act like the oxygenated materials relative to the solubility of ferric thiocyanate. Consequently, the test is characteristic for oxygen only if the absence of sulfur and nitrogen has been proved. Furthermore, acids and oxidizing compounds interfere with the test.

Procedure. Filter paper is impregnated by plunging it once into a methyl alcohol solution of ferric thiocyanate and then drying it in the air. The reagent paper must be freshly prepared each time. Several drops of the solution to be tested are placed on the paper. A positive reaction is indicated if a wine-red color appears. Solids should be dissolved beforehand in hydrocarbons or their halogenated derivatives.

> *Reagent:* Separate solutions containing 1 g ferric chloride and 1 g potassium thiocyanate dissolved in 10 ml methyl alcohol are prepared. The solutions are united and allowed to stand for several hours before filtering off the precipitate of potassium chloride.

In the absence of nitrogen and sulfur, the development of a red color in the above procedure (when 20–50 mg of sample is used) indicates the presence of oxygen. On the other hand, a negative response is somewhat uncertain in its implications because no reaction is given by some oxygen-bearing compounds, e.g., high molecular ethers, nitro compounds, etc.

Another procedure, which makes better use of the solvate formation of iron (III) thiocyanate and which also is successful when organic compounds are fused, consists in stirring a drop of the test solution or melt with solid iron (III) thiocyanate.

Procedure. [66] A drop of the test solution is placed on a slide or in a micro test tube and stirred with a thin glass rod, whose tip carries a little solid iron (III) thiocyanate. If oxygen-bearing compounds are present, the drop becomes light to dark red. Solid samples can be melted beforehand on the slide or in the test tube. Since the iron (III) thiocyanate may decompose during the melting, it is better to test a highly concentrated solution in an oxygen-free organic liquid. Chloroform is particularly suited to this purpose.

The stirring rod is charged with iron (III) thiocyanate by dipping the rod to a depth of several millimeters into an ether solution of the reagent, and allowing the solvent to evaporate into the air.

> *Reagent:* Ether solution of iron (III) thiocyanate: 5 grams of potassium thiocyanate and 4 grams of iron (III) chloride (hexahydrate) are dissolved in 20 ml water each. The solutions are united and the mixture is extracted with 30 ml ether. The ether solution can be used at once. It will keep for several weeks if it is stored in the dark.

The *limit of identification* is 5–10 mg and accordingly this procedure is considerably more sensitive than the test on iron (III) thiocyanate paper. For example, diethyl malonate and ethyl mandelate react promptly as do solutions of benzil and stearic acid in chloroform, whereas no solvate formation is seen with these materials and solutions on iron (III) thiocyanate paper.

16. Metals

A direct detection of metallic elements in organic compounds is possible provided the test material is soluble in water to at least a slight extent, or if it can be appreciably decomposed by dilute acids or alkali hydroxides. When this is not the case, the test for metals must be preceded by a destruction of the organic skeleton by ignition (dry method) or by means of oxidizing acids (wet method). Sometimes, losses of material are inevitable when organometallic compounds are ignited. Certain materials (especially diazo-, nitro- and nitroso compounds) explode when heated. Others (particularly inner complex compounds) sublime to a considerable extent previous to their thermal oxidative fission. In some cases, complete ashing is difficult because carbon particles become coated with sintered metal carbonate or oxide which is formed during the thermal destruction of the test material. Ignition residues must be dissolved before undertaking the tests for metals. This dissolution can be accomplished for the ignited oxides of ter- and quadrivalent metals by fuming with concentrated sulfuric acid or by fusion with alkali bisulfate. The difficulties that were pointed out above do not arise if the organometallic compounds are oxidatively disintegrated by digestion with hot concentrated nitric acid (Carius) or concentrated sulfuric acid (Kjeldahl). If the action of the acids is prolonged sufficiently, water-clear solutions of the metal nitrates and sulfates, respectively, will be obtained. These procedures have the disadvantage that they introduce rather large amounts of concentrated acids, which must be removed by evaporation before proceeding with the tests for metal ions.

A rather convenient and rapid process for the wet decomposition of non-volatile organometallic (and purely organic) materials is to heat them with dilute sulfuric acid and potassium persulfate in the presence of soluble silver salts.[67] The decomposition reaction: $H_2S_2O_8 + H_2O \rightarrow 2H_2SO_4 + O$, which is catalyzed by silver ions,[68] yields atomic oxygen. This can bring about the oxidative decomposition of soluble and insoluble organic and organometallic compounds.[69] It has not been determined whether the rupture of the organic skeleton proceeds so far in all cases that the entire carbon content is oxidized to carbon dioxide.* However, it appears certain that, with few exceptions, the disintegration is so extensive that the metals contained in organic compounds are converted to sulfate.

Procedure. 0.01–0.03 g of the material to be tested is placed in a small flask and treated with one or two drops of concentrated sulfuric acid, 2 ml of 0.2 N silver nitrate and 0.5 g persulfate. The mixture is gently heated with constant swirling. As soon as a vigorous evolution of gas occurs, the heating is interrupted. Finally, the liquid is kept boiling for 2–3 minutes to decompose excess persulfate.

---

* Since the oxidative decomposition undoubtedly proceeds via intermediate products, it is possible that compounds are formed which are resistant to activated persulfuric acid to a greater or lesser extent. An instance of this kind is found in the formation of maleic acid by warming hydroquinones and quinones with a sulfuric acid solution of silver sulfate and alkali persulfate.[70]

Table 6 shows the behavior of organic and organometallic compounds of various types when subjected to the procedure just outlined. Of course smaller quantities of the test substance can be taken for semimicro scale operations.

TABLE 6

Compound	Before Oxidation	After Oxidation
Cupferron	yellow suspension	clear colorless solution
Fe(III)-cupferronate	brown suspension	clear light yellow sol.
Cu-cupferronate	brown suspension	clear light blue solution
Dimethylglyoxime	white suspension	clear colorless solution
Pd-dimethylglyoxime	yellow suspension	clear light yellow sol.
Pd-furildioximate	yellow suspension	clear light yellow sol.
1-Nitroso-2 naphthol	brown suspension	clear colorless solution
Pd-1-nitroso-2 naphthol	yellow suspension	clear light yellow sol.
Co(III)-1-nitroso-2 naphthol	brown-red suspension	resistant
Rhodamine B	red solution	clear colorless solution
SbCl$_5$-Rhodamine B	violet suspension	colorless sol.; AgCl ppt.
8-Hydroxyquinoline (Oxine)	light yellow solution	clear colorless solution
Pd-oxinate	yellow suspension	clear light yellow sol.
Mo-oxinate	yellow suspension	clear colorless solution
Bi-pyrogallate	white suspension	clear colorless solution
Sb(III) pyrogallate	white suspension	resistant
K-ethylxanthate	light yellow solution	sulfur deposit
Cu(I)xanthate	yellow suspension	sulfur deposit
Cu(Co, Ni) rubeanate	colored suspension	sulfur deposit
Alizarin blue	blue solution	clear red solution
Cu-alizarin blue	blue suspension	resistant
Benzidine sulfate	white suspension	clear colorless solution
WO$_3$-benzidine or benzoin oxime precipitate	white suspension	colorless sol.; WO$_3$ ppt.
Congo red	blue solution	clear colorless solution
Methylene blue	blue solution	clear colorless solution
Alizarin S.	yellow solution	colorless solution

The table contains organic and organometallic compounds whose oxidative decomposition, with few exceptions, is directly discernible by noting the disappearance of precipitates or discharge of the color of the solutions. Of course, decomposition takes place likewise in colorless aqueous solutions of organic compounds. This was demonstrated in the 5 % sulfuric acid solutions of pyragallol, tannin, sulfosalicylic acid, salicylic acid, and oxine, and

References pp. 148–150

also with a 0.5 % alcohol solution of phenolphthalein. The ordinary reactions for tannin, pyrogallol, etc. no longer met with a positive response after the respective solutions had been warmed with persulfate and silver nitrate. Moreover, metal ions present in solutions where their characteristic reactions had been masked by organic compounds were liberated (demasked) by this treatment.

The attack by persulfuric acid in the presence of Ag^+ ions is not uniform for all organometallic and organic compounds. Certain materials are oxidized but slowly, whereas others, in small quantities, are decomposed rapidly, sometimes almost instantaneously, as can be easily seen by the discharge of a color or in the case of suspensions by the production of a clear colorless solution. At times the oxidation to the colorless state is preceded by the transient production of compounds with other colors. It seems that those compounds which are acid-soluble and those which are readily wet by water are the ones which are most easily decomposed. Since the hydrolysis of the persulfuric acid and the oxidative action proceed side by side, carbon dioxide and oxygen are generated and consequently there is strong foaming. Solid particles of insoluble materials may be trapped in the foam, where they remain unchanged because they encounter there less atomic than molecular (i.e. almost inactive) oxygen. In such cases, careful shaking is necessary and a supplementary addition of persulfate should be made after the foaming has stopped.

As shown in Table 6, very few organometallic compounds are entirely or only partially resistant to oxidation by the procedure described here. Such recalcitrant materials must be decomposed by ignition. In all cases where there is complete decomposition, the sulfuric acid solution can be used for carrying out spot tests for metals, taking proper account of the presence of the silver ions which were deliberately introduced as catalyst.

When organic compounds are oxidatively decomposed by the persulfate-silver mixture, phosphorus, antimonic, boric and arsenic, emerge as phosphoric, antimony, boron or arsenic acid. Halogens are precipitated as silver halides. When halogen-bearing organic compounds are involved, more silver nitrate than usual should be added, since only silver ions and not silver halides are effective as catalyst.

Another wet method for ashing organic and organometallic compounds consists in heating with perchloric acid,[71] whose azeotropic mixture with water (72.5 % perchloric acid) boils at 203° and hence permits reaction at elevated temperatures. Under these conditions, perchloric acid is so strong an oxidant that thiol compounds yield no free sulfur (in contrast to persulfate) but form instead sulfate (sulfuric acid).

17. Mercury

(1) Detection by demasking of potassium ferrocyanide[72]

The tendency of mercuric ions to form water-soluble undissociated mercuric cyanide is so great that they are able to liberate ferrous ions from ferrocyanide ions. If this demasking occurs in the presence of a,a'-dipyridyl, a red color appears because of the formation of $[Fe(a,a'\text{-Dip})_3]^{+2}$ ions. (Compare the detection of iron and ferrocyanide, Volume I, Chap. 3 and 4.) The underlying reactions are:

$$Fe(CN)_6^{-4} + 3\ Hg^{+2} \rightarrow 3\ Hg(CN)_2 + Fe^{+2} \tag{1}$$

$$Fe(CN)_6^{-4} + 3\ Hg(CN)_2 \rightarrow 3\ Hg(CN)_4^{-2} + Fe^{+2} \tag{2}$$

$$Fe^{+2} + 3\ a,a'\text{-Dip} \rightarrow [Fe(a,a'\text{-Dip})_3]^{+2} \tag{3}$$

Mercury salts of organic acids and likewise compounds in which mercury is bound to carbon are capable of demasking ferrocyanide ions. It is not certain whether mercuric ions are active in the second case; it is possible that there is a coordination of alkali cyanide on the organically bound mercury, which likewise could lead to a liberation of ferrous ions.

A demasking analogous to that in (1) and (2) can be effected also by Ag^+ and Pd^{+2} ions (see Volume I, Chapter 3). The test described here is consequently reliable only in the absence of organic silver and palladium compounds. Since palladium compounds will be met but seldom in organic analysis, the interference with the test for mercury will arise only from silver, and even argentiferous organic compounds are relatively uncommon.

Procedure. A micro test tube is used. A drop of the test solution or a slight amount of the solid is treated with one drop each of a 1% solution of potassium ferrocyanide, 2 N ammonium hydroxide, and 1% alcohol solution of a,a'-dipyridyl. The mixture is warmed in the water bath. Depending on the quantity of mercury present, a red or pink color will appear at once or within a few minutes.
Limit of identification: 2 γ mercury.

(2) Test by volatilization of mercury

Mercury compounds of all varieties when heated to dull red heat leave no residue at all or the residue contains no mercury. This behavior, which is unique among metal compounds, is due to the sublimation of mercury salts and also to thermal decomposition with production of mercury vapor. The latter can be detected by the very sensitive test with palladium chloride,[73] in which the reaction

$$PdCl_2 + Hg^o \rightarrow Pd^o + HgCl_2$$

References pp. 148–150

yields free palladium which, in a state of high division, is black. If filter paper, moistened with palladium chloride, is brought into contact with mercury vapor, the brown-yellow reagent paper turns black (Procedure I).

Another test (Procedure II) is based on the production of red cuprous tetraiodomercuriate by the action of mercury vapor on insoluble white cuprous iodide: [74]

$$2 Cu_2I_2 + Hg^o \rightarrow Cu_2[HgI_4] + 2 Cu^o$$

When solid organic mercury compounds are heated, mercury vapor is produced through thermal dissociation and probably also through the action of reducing decomposition products, such as carbon monoxide, acetylene, etc. To detect the mercury vapor by means of palladium chloride or cuprous iodide, steps must be taken to prevent carbon monoxide and volatile tarry products from being formed when the organic material burns. Carbon monoxide likewise reduces palladium chloride to the metal, and tarry products can collect on the reagent paper to form brown or black stains. Both of these interferences can be reliably obviated if the organic material being tested for mercury is ignited in mixture with cupric oxide.[75]

Certain organic mercury compounds produce some ethylene on ignition, and this cannot be prevented even by mixing the sample with copper oxide.[76] Ethylene likewise reduces palladium chloride to free palladium.[77] Obviously, the production of ethylene in the combustion of organic mercurials would be no handicap in the detection of mercury vapor; rather it would be an advantage since more palladium chloride would be reduced under such circumstances. However, it is possible (though not yet proved) that some ethylene is produced when mercury-free compounds burn. In such cases, the reduction of palladium chloride by ethylene would simulate the presence of mercury vapor. Consequently, when in doubt, it is better to trap the mercury vapor initially on a gold surface (wire, foil). Heating this amalgam, will then drive the mercury out and the test with palladium chloride paper can be applied to the vapor.

Procedure I. [75] A small quantity of the test material, mixed with a few centigrams of copper oxide, is placed in a pyrex ignition tube (3/4 inch long, 3/8 inch diameter) and covered completely with copper oxide. The tube is inserted in a hole, small enough to grip it firmly, which has been drilled through an asbestos board. The latter rests on a tripod. The bottom of the tube should protrude below the board. The mouth of the tube is covered with a disk of filter paper, whose diameter is slightly greater than the external diameter of the tube. A drop of 1 % aqueous palladium chloride is placed on the paper. The tube is heated cautiously by gradually raising a low flame, which finally is increased until the bottom of the tube is red hot. A dark stain, sharply outlining the aperture of the tube, indicates the presence of mercury. In case of doubt, the paper should be held over ammonia water. The yellowish brown color of the paper is discharged because of the formation of $[Pd(NH_3)_2]^{+2}$ ions and the stain becomes more obvious. Great care must be taken to prevent the top of the tube from becoming hot, since otherwise the palladous chloride may be reduced by the paper itself.

When only traces of mercury are expected or if there is a chance that ethylene may be evolved, crushed gold leaf should be inserted in the upper part of the ignition tube, which may be provided with a constriction about 1/3 from the bottom to support the thin foil. The substance is decomposed as just described, but without warming the gold leaf, which therefore should be sufficiently far above the asbestos board. The decomposition requires about two minutes. The tube is then pushed down so that the gold leaf can now be heated with the full flame for a short time. The palladous chloride paper should be applied to the mouth of the tube only during the second heating period.

A positive reaction was given by:

    1.75 γ acetoxymercuryethylacetate
    2.25 γ aceto-(2-chloromercuryethyl)mesidide
    2.0 γ bromomercuryethylpyridine-bromomercuriate
    5.0 γ iodomercuryethylpyridine-iodomercuriate
    2.5 γ bis(camphor-10) mercury
    2.5 γ camphor-10-mercury iodide
    2.75 γ bis-3-chlorocamphor-10-mercury

These identification limits for the detection of mercury in organic compounds correspond (with one exception) to about 1 γ of mercury. The lower quantity sensitivity in the case of iodomercuryethylpyridine-iodomercuriate may be attributed to the volatilization of a part of the mercury as mercuric iodide which, under the conditions of the experiment, does not react with palladium chloride. Because of the formation of mercury halides, the test may be less sensitive, or even fail completely for small quantities of mercury, when larger quantities of organic and inorganic halogen compounds are present. In such cases it is better to use Procedure II, employing solid cuprous iodide. This colorless insoluble compound reacts not only with dissolved mercury salts [78], but also with mercury vapor and with vapors of sublimable mercury halides. Red cuprous tetraiodomercuriate results:

$$2\,Cu_2I_2 + Hg(Hal)_2 \rightarrow Cu_2[HgI_4] + Cu_2(Hal)_2$$

When organic compounds containing mercury are ground with dry cuprous iodide or with this salt moistened with water or alcohol, they react. It has not yet been determined whether a general test for organic mercurials can be developed from this observation.

Procedure II. * The method described in Procedure I is used for the destruction of the mercury-bearing test substance. Paper carrying a drop of cuprous iodide paste is used in place of palladium chloride paper. A salmon or red color develops on the paper when exposed to mercury vapor or volatilized mercury halides.

> *Reagent:* Cuprous iodide paste: A solution of 5 g copper sulfate crystals in 75 ml water is mixed with a solution of 5 g sodium sulfite and 11 g potassium iodide in 75 ml water. The colorless precipitate is centrifuged or filtered, washed well with water, and stored moist. Just before the test, some cuprous iodide is stirred with enough water to form a thin slurry.

A positive response was given by amounts of the various test materials containing 4–8 γ mercury.

18. Tests for Basic or Acidic Behavior

The basic or acidic character of organic compounds is due to the presence and activity of certain elements in particular bonding forms which are responsible for the acceptance or delivery (consumption and production) of hydrogen ions (protons) or for the closely related process of the formation of salts. Salt-forming groups are situated, as a rule, at definite locales in the molecule of organic compounds. In some cases, compounds which are neutral in their normal structure can assume an acidic salt-forming character through tautomeric rearrangement or through the action of OH⁻ ions (keto-enol equilibrium, nitro-nitroxyl acid equilibrium).

Practically all stable basic organic compounds are derivatives of ammonia, hydroxylamine or hydrazine.** The salts with strong mineral acids correspond to the ammonium-, hydroxylaminium-, and hydrazinium salts. With few exceptions, these salts are water-soluble. It is of practical importance that the hydrochlorides of all organic nitrogen bases are quite soluble in water if an excess of hydrochloric acid is present. The strength of organic nitrogen bases, with respect to the binding of H⁺-ions or the delivery of OH⁻-ions, depends on the molecular remainder bound to the nitrogen atom. For example, NH₂- and NH-groups bound to alkyl radicals are strongly basic, whereas they are weakly basic when bound to aryl radicals. When these groups are directly linked to a CO-group, the products are neutral, acid-insoluble com-

---

* After studies by F. Feigl with partial modification of the procedure described by J. Stone (*loc. cit.*, ref. 74).

** Besides nitrogen bases there are a few compounds, such as pyrones, and the anthocyanidin pigments of some flowers, which possess oxygen atoms with sufficient basicity to cause them to dissolve in dilute hydrochloric acid.

References pp. 148–150

pounds (acid amides and anilides). Cyclic and noncyclic compounds containing NH-groups adjacent to a CO- or CS-group function as acids. This is likewise true of sulfonamides which contain the -SO_2NH_2 or -SO_2NHR-group.

Hydrogen atoms which can be split off as hydrogen ions, or which can be replaced by an equal number of metal equivalents to form salts, are essential to the acidic character of organic compounds. When hydrogen atoms are linked directly to carbon, they exhibit this faculty only in acetylene and its derivatives, which contain the —C≡C—H-group.* As a rule, acidic H-atoms are contained in OH-, SH-, and NH-groups, which are linked directly to carbon either directly or through an intermediate nonmetallic atom. It is customary to regard the entire salt-forming group bound to a carbon atom as the acidic group. This convention appears also in the nomenclature, as shown in the following exhibit:

$$-C\underset{\diagdown OH}{\overset{\diagup O}{}} \qquad -S\underset{\diagdown OH}{\overset{\diagup O}{=}} \qquad -S\overset{\diagup O}{-}OH \rightleftharpoons -S\underset{\diagdown O}{\overset{\diagup O}{-}}H \qquad -As\overset{\diagup O}{-}OH \qquad =N\overset{\diagup O}{-}OH$$

| Carboxyl | Sulfonic | Sulfinic | Arsonic | Nitroxyl |

$$=N-OH \rightleftharpoons =N\overset{\diagup O}{-}H \qquad\qquad -CH_2-NO_2 \rightleftharpoons -CH=N\overset{\diagup OH}{=}O$$

| Oximic | Nitro (primary) |

$$R-\underset{|}{C}H-NO_2 \rightleftharpoons R-C\overset{\diagup OH}{=}N{=}O \qquad \overset{\diagdown}{\underset{\diagup}{}}C-CH_2-C\overset{\diagup O}{\diagdown} \rightleftharpoons \overset{\diagdown}{\underset{\diagup}{}}C-CH=C\overset{\diagup OH}{\diagdown}$$

| Nitro (secondary) | Enolic |

$$\overset{\diagdown}{\underset{\diagup}{}}C-OH \qquad\qquad \overset{\diagdown}{\underset{\diagup}{}}C-SH \qquad\qquad \overset{\diagdown}{\underset{\diagup}{}}C=\underset{|}{C}-SH \quad or \quad -N=\underset{|}{C}-SH$$

| Phenolic (alcoholic) | Thiophenolic | Thioenolic |

$$-S\underset{\diagdown O}{\overset{\diagup O}{-}}NH_2 \rightleftharpoons -S\underset{\diagdown OH}{\overset{\diagup O}{=}}NH \qquad\qquad -CO-NH-CH_2-$$

| Sulfonamidic | Acid-imide |

Obviously then the establishment of the acidic character of a material, with due regard to the outcome of the tests for metallic and nonmetallic elements described in Section 2 of this chapter, can yield valuable guides as to the direction along which further tests should be made.

When dealing with compounds which are at least noticeably soluble in

---

* Mercury occupies a special position; it has a great tendency to form a stable binding with carbon atoms and so it can take the place of hydrogen in many aliphatic and aromatic compounds (so-called mercuration). See in this connection F. C. Whitmore, *Organic Compounds of Mercury*, New York, 1921. Concerning compounds of metals with alkyl and aryl groups without salt character see E. Krause and A. v. Grosse, *Die Chemie der metall-organischen Verbindungen*, Berlin, 1937.

References pp. 148–150

water, the behavior of dyestuff indicators will decide whether bases, acids or neutral compounds are at hand. Such tests can be conducted with drops of aqueous solutions, or with small amounts of the solid sample placed directly on moistened indicator papers, or on spot plates with microdrops of suitable indicator solutions. Congo red is recommended for acidic compounds; bromthymol blue or phenolphthalein for basic compounds. The use of four kinds of mixed indicators has been proposed [79] for classifying organic compounds, according to the pH, into the following classes: strong acids, intermediate acids, ampholytes, neutral compounds, weak bases, intermediate bases. The orientation in this respect is excellent, provided the details given for the preparation of the indicator solutions have been followed exactly.

Usually a more reliable indication of salt-forming groups in water-insoluble organic compounds is given by their behavior with dilute hydrochloric acid or dilute caustic alkali. Basic compounds are thus taken into solution as the hydrochlorides, and acidic compounds as the corresponding alkali salts.* These dissolution tests can be accomplished with tiny amounts of the sample on a watch glass by adding a drop of acid or alkali, warming gently if necessary. When mixtures are to be tested for a possible content of basic or acidic compounds, it is well to carry out the treatment with acid or base in a microcentrifuge tube, and to segregate any undissolved material by centrifuging. Ammonia or dilute hydrochloric acid should then be added drop by drop to the clear liquid until a distinct alkaline or acid reaction is attained. If a precipitate or turbidity appears, it indicates the presence in the sample of water-insoluble compounds carrying salt-forming basic or acidic groups. When a water-insoluble material dissolves in hydrochloric acid as well as in alkali, an ampholyte is at hand, i.e., a compound whose molecule contains both basic and acidic salt-forming groups.

The foregoing tests for basic and acidic compounds, based on their behavior toward dyestuff indicators, and toward dilute hydrochloric acid and alkali hydroxide, are usually adequate for orientation purposes. Even microgram quantities of water-soluble materials can produce plainly visible color changes of indicators; at least 0.2–2 mg of solid samples are required for securing distinct effects in the solubility tests in hydrochloric acid or alkali. Other procedures for testing the basic or acidic character of slightly water-soluble or insoluble compounds, and also for testing volatile acids and bases,

---

* There are notable exceptions to this rule. R. Adams, *J. Amer. Chem· Soc.*, **41** (1919) 247, showed that many substituted phenols are not soluble even in boiling 10 % caustic alkali and he attributed this to the great water-insolubity of the particular phenols. The same is true of some sulfonamides [80]. Obviously the ability of bases and acids to dissolve in aqueous acid or alkali depends not alone on their acid or base strength but also on their ability to dissolve in water as an unionized molecule. Compare D. Davidson, *loc. cit.*, ref. 79.

are given in the following sections. These tests require no more than fractions of a milligram of the test material.

(1) Tests for basic compounds with nickel dimethylglyoxime- or zinc 8-hydroxyquinoline–equilibrium solutions [81]

When dimethylglyoxime (DH_2) is added to aqueous solutions of a nickel salt, the resulting nickel dimethylglyoxime, being readily soluble in dilute mineral acids, is only partly precipitated because of the immediate establishment of the reversible equilibrium:

$$Ni^{+2} + 2\,DH_2 \rightleftarrows Ni(DH)_2 + 2\,H^+$$

If the precipitate is removed by filtration, the filtrate is a saturated solution of nickel dimethylglyoxime and contains Ni^{+2} and H^+ ions at concentrations corresponding to the equilibrium. If this solution is placed in contact with H^+-ion-consuming (i.e. basic) materials, the equilibrium is disturbed by the removal of H^+-ions, and red nickel dimethylglyoxime precipitates to reestablish the equilibrium. Therefore, this test will reveal the presence of basic materials which are soluble or insoluble in water (Procedure I).

Another equilibrium solution responding to organic bases can be prepared by treating a solution of a zinc salt with excess 8-hydroxyquinoline (HOx) and filtering. Because of the establishment of the reversible equilibrium

$$Zn^{+2} + 2\,HOx \rightleftarrows Zn(Ox)_2 + 2\,H^+$$

the light yellow zinc oxinate, which is soluble in dilute mineral acids, is only partially precipitated. If the clear filtrate is brought into contact with organic bases, H^+ ions are withdrawn and zinc oxinate precipitates. Traces of this salt, which are too slight to be discernible as a turbidity, are clearly revealed by the strong yellow-green fluorescence in ultraviolet light (Procedure II).

Employment of these procedures, which are based on disturbing of defined equilibria, assumes the absence of inorganic basic compounds and also of alkali and alkaline earth salts of weak acids which react alkaline because of hydrolysis. Organic nitrogen bases can be liberated from aqueous solutions of their salts by alkalization with ammonia and then extracted with ether, chloroform, etc. Ammonia should be used* because it is completely removed when the organic solvent is volatilized and the residue heated to 110°. When dealing with organic materials, which burn without residue, or whose ignition

---

* When aqueous solutions of alkali hydroxide are shaken out with ether, the evaporation residue of the ethereal extract always shows an alkaline reaction toward acid-base indicators. This effect is due to the distinct solubility of water in ether with consequent entrance of the alkali into the ether.

References pp. 148–150

residues contain no oxides or carbonates (compare Section 2 of this chapter), a positive response to the test with equilibrium solutions is a strong indication of the presence of organic nitrogen bases.

Procedure I. A drop of the aqueous test solution or the residue from the evaporation of a drop of a solution of non-volatile bases in alcohol, ether or the like, is mixed with a drop of equilibrium solution on a spot plate. If basic materials are present, red crystalline nickel dimethylglyoxime appears, either immediately or after a transient yellow color, depending on the quantity of basic material involved.

Reagent: Nickel dimethylglyoxime–equilibrium solution. 2.3 g nickel (II) sulfate, dissolved in 300 ml water, is united with 2.8 g dimethylglyoxime dissolved in 300 ml alcohol. The precipitate is filtered off.

This procedure revealed the basic behavior of:

5 γ ethylenediamine	15 γ p-phenylenediamine
20 γ diethanolamine	10 γ benzidine
20 γ α-naphthylamine	15 γ tetrabase

Procedure II. A drop of the test solution is taken to dryness in an Emich tube. The cooled residue is treated with a drop of the equilibrium solution and viewed under the quartz lamp. In the presence of non-volatile organic bases, the evaporation residue assumes a yellow-green fluorescence. If desired, following the action of the equilibrium solution, the system may be diluted with water. In this way, even traces of the resulting fluorescent zinc oxinate can be seen.

Reagent: Zinc oxinate-equilibrium solution. Equal volumes of 1 % zinc chloride solution and 1 % water-alcohol solution of 8-hydroxyquinoline are mixed. The precipitate is removed by filtration.

This procedure revealed the basic behavior of:

15 γ diethanolamine
15 γ α-naphthylamine
15 γ p-phenylenediamine
5 γ benzidine
10 γ tetrabase

Sometimes, it is desired merely to establish the presence of basic compounds, without distinguishing between organic or inorganic bases or basic salts. It is sufficient, then, to stir a drop of the equilibrium solution with a little of the test material on a spot plate, and to note the appearance of a yellow-green fluorescence in ultraviolet light.

(2) Test for basic compounds through fixing of hydrogen chloride [82]

If organic nitrogen bases (B) are taken to dryness with dilute hydrochloric acid, the hydrochloride results:

$$B + HCl \rightarrow B \cdot HCl = [BH]Cl$$

Many hydrochlorides of organic bases show the same behavior as ammonium chloride, i.e., they can be heated to the evaporation temperature (120°) of aqueous hydrochloric acid without undergoing significant decomposition, provided the heating period is brief. The water-soluble chloride in the evaporation residue can then be detected through the precipitate of silver chloride produced on the addition of silver nitrate.

Very weak bases do not seem to be able to form a heat-stable union with hydrochloric acid; theobromine and a,a'-dipyridyl are typical examples. However, factors other than the strength of the bases are also responsible for the heat-stability of solid hydrochlorides of organic bases, particularly the duration of the heating. This is shown by the relatively high identification limit of pyridine. Amphoteric compounds in which the basic character is dominant, glycocoll for instance, behave like the organic bases. Water-soluble amphoteric compounds which produce zwitter ions (sulfanilic acid naphthionic acid, etc.) and hence have the character of ammonium salts, do not bind hydrochloric acid, or the hydrochorides decompose, with evolution of hydrogen chloride, when kept at 120° for a short time.

The detection of organic bases through binding of hydrochloric acid cannot be applied in the presence of alkali- and ammonium salts of organic carboxylic- and sulfonic acids, phenols, amides and imides of acids, since these compounds form alkali- or ammonium chloride when evaporated with hydrochloric acid. In such cases it is necessary to separate the nitrogen bases beforehand. This can be accomplished by treating the sample with a solution of alkali hydroxide and then shaking out with ether. Acidic compounds remain in the water layer as alkali salts, while the organic nitrogen bases pass into the ether.

The acetic acid solutions of organic bases can also be used for their detection. When such solutions are evaporated with hydrochloric acid, acetic acid is volatilized and the hydrochlorides of the bases remain behind.

Procedure. One drop of the test solution or a tiny quantity of the solid material (e.g., the residue after evaporating a drop of an ether solution) is placed in a depression of a black spot plate. One drop of dilute hydrochloric acid is added, the mixture is taken to dryness, and the plate is kept for 2–5 minutes in an oven heated to 120°. After cooling, one drop of 5 % silver nitrate solution is added and stirred with a glass rod. If silver chloride precipitates, the appearance of a turbidity (sometimes only after several minutes) indicates the presence of basic compounds.

This procedure revealed:

2	γ ethylenediamine	5	γ glycine
2.5	γ benzidine	2.5	γ cysteine
5	γ a-naphthylamine	25	γ sulfanilamide

25   γ o-phenanthroline   5 γ sulfathiazole
50   γ caffein   5 γ 8-hydroxyquinoline

No reaction was shown below 500 γ by: theobromine, pyridine, a,a'-dipyridyl.

A general test for salts of organic nitrogen bases is discussed on page 121.

(3) Detection of volatile bases

The general tests for basic compounds with nickel dimethylglyoxime – or zinc oxinate – equilibrium solutions (see page 112) permit selective tests for those organic bases which volatilize on warming or which are evolved to a considerable measure with steam. Such bases, which usually are of medium strength, react in the vapor phase with the equilibrium solutions and precipitate red nickel dimethylglyoxime, or zinc oxinate which exhibits a yellow-green fluorescence. The bases in the present category include primary, secondary, and tertiary aliphatic amines with low carbon content which are volatile at room temperature, aniline and also some heterocyclic bases, such as pyridine, quinoline, piperidine.

When testing for volatile bases, it is best to start with water solutions of their salts, which are readily prepared by digesting the test material with dilute mineral acids. The organic bases are liberated from these solutions (which need not be free of any acid-insoluble material) by warming with an excess of alkali- or alkaline earth hydroxide. Amides of carboxylic and sulfonic acids with primary or secondary organic bases are saponified by alkali and the volatile bases driven off by warming.

The test for volatile organic bases by means of their reaction, in the vapor phase, with equilibrium solutions is not directly applicable when ammonium salts are present, since the latter yield ammonia. A separate test for ammonium salts should be made with Nessler solution.

If ammonium salts are present, an alkaline solution of bromine can be used for making the solution basic. The ammonia is oxidized as soon as it is set free:

$$2 \; NH_3 + 3 \; NaOBr \rightarrow N_2 + 3 \; H_2O + 3 \; NaBr$$

However, it must be remembered that hypobromite solution oxidizes many aromatic amines, e.g. aniline, to quinoidal products.

Procedure. [83] A drop of the weakly acid test solution and a drop of 2N sodium hydroxide are mixed in the bulb of the apparatus shown in Fig. 23 (page 49). One drop of one of the equilibrium solutions is placed on the knob of the stopper. The apparatus is closed and placed in boiling water for 1 or 2 minutes. If volatile bases are present, red nickel dimethylglyoxime precipitates in the hanging drop, or white-yellow zinc oxinate is formed which fluoresces yellow-green in ultra-violet light.

Reagent: Equilibrium solutions, see page 113.

This procedure gave positive results
(a) with nickel dimethylglyoxime equilibrium solution:
   15 γ pyridine, 100 γ ethylenediamine, 1 γ methylamine, 10 γ ethanolamine, 20 γ aniline;
(b) with zinc hydroxyquinoline equilibrium solution:
   5γ pyridine, 2.5 γ ethylenediamine, 0.1 γ methylamine, 10γ ethanolamine, 20 γ aniline.

See page 121 regarding the detection of water-soluble salts of organic nitrogen bases and alkali salts of carboxylic acids and organic sulfonic acids.

(4) Test for acidic compounds with iodide-iodate mixture [84]

Water-soluble acidic compounds, of either inorganic or organic nature, liberate iodine from a colorless solution containing both iodide and iodate:

$$5\,I^- + IO_3^- + 6\,H^+ \rightarrow 3\,H_2O + 3\,I_2 \tag{1}$$

The occurrence of the reaction is revealed by a yellowing of the solution, or by the blue color which appears on the addition of starch solution, or by extracting the iodine with chloroform (violet solution).

If the reaction with iodide-iodate solution is carried out in a closed vessel, and with warming (Procedure I), it is possible to detect organic acids which are so weak that they do not yield a sufficient hydrogen ion concentration to affect dyestuff indicators at all, or indecisively at most. Such acids are usually not very soluble, and their reaction with iodide-iodate is due in only small measure to the fact that the equilibrium

$$HAc \rightleftarrows H^+ + Ac^- \tag{2}$$

is shifted toward the right by warming. The essential feature is that the H^+ ions consumed by reaction (1) are delivered by the dissociation equilibrium (2), which quickly re-establishes itself at the expense of the weak acid, which thus constantly replenishes the supply of H^+ ion. Accordingly, just as in the tests described in 1 for basic materials, the present procedure takes advantage of an equilibrium disturbance. The heating in a closed vessel prevents or lessens the loss, by volatilization, of the iodine which is to be detected by means of starch, after cooling.

Water-insoluble higher mono- or dibasic fatty acids, which melt at low temperatures, produce iodine in accord with (1) if a dry mixture of the particular acid and potassium iodide plus iodate is brought to the temperature of a boiling water bath, or if the mixture is vigorously ground at room temperature (Procedure II). Under these conditions, topochemical reactions of non-hydrated hydrogen ions, or non-dissociated or slightly dissociated acids, that are brought to or close to their melting points, obviously occur on the surface of the solid potassium iodide and iodate.

Procedure I. The test is conducted in a micro test tube provided with a glass or rubber stopper. A drop of the alcohol solution of the acid and one drop each of 2 % iodide and 4 % iodate solutions are introduced. The test tube is stoppered and held in boiling water for 1 minute, and then cooled. A drop of starch solution is added and the mixture shaken. If acids are present, a blue to violet color appears. Instead of a starch solution, some mg of solid thyodene indicator may be used.

This procedure established acid character in:

2 γ capric acid	$CH_3(CH_2)_8COOH$
5 γ lauric acid	$CH_3(CH_2)_{10}COOH$
4 γ myristic acid	$CH_3(CH_2)_{12}COOH$
5 γ palmitic acid	$CH_3(CH_2)_{14}COOH$
5 γ stearic acid	$CH_3(CH_2)_{16}COOH$
2 γ sebacic acid	$(CH_2)_8(COOH)_2$

If the highest sensitivity is not required, fractions of a milligram of the solid non-dissolved acids can be warmed directly with the freshly prepared iodide-iodate mixture. In this case, 3 or 4 drops of the starch solution should be added to the cooled solution to produce the blue iodine-starch complex. Again here solid thyodene indicator may be used.

Procedure II. A drop of the alcohol solution of the acid is evaporated to dryness in a micro test tube, several milligrams of potassium iodate containing potassium iodide added, and mixed intimately by means of a thin glass rod. When larger amounts of acid are involved, the production of free iodine is revealed directly by the mixture assuming a yellow-brown color. Small quantities of liberated iodine are detected, as in Procedure I, by adding starch solution.

Reagent: Potassium iodate containing iodide. Finely powdered potassium iodate is heated to incipient fusion in a quartz crucible whereby the iodate is partially converted to iodide. The cooled mass is pulverized. Sometimes the product is light yellow, but it gives neither an alkaline reaction nor does it respond to the starch or thyodene test.

The following revealed acid character when carried through this procedure:

		m.p.
5 γ	capric acid	31°
10 γ	lauric acid	44–48°
5 γ	myristic acid	58°
10 γ	palmitic acid	64°
10 γ	stearic acid	69.4°
5 γ	sebacic acid	133°

Procedures I and II can, of course, be applied also for detecting acids of medium strength and which are only slightly soluble in water (adipic acid, benzoic acid, etc.).

If carboxylic or sulfonic acids do not volatilize or sublime at 110–120°, they will remain when solutions of their ammonium salts are taken to dryness and the evaporation residue heated to 120°. The ammonia is released and evolves. Accordingly, if an organic mixture is to be tested for carboxylic or sulfonic acids, the sample can be digested with ammonia water, filtered if necessary, and a drop of the clear filtrate evaporated in a micro test tube. The residue is kept at 120° for 10–20 minutes, cooled, and then tested with iodide-iodate solution by Procedure I or II. An indication of the attainable identification limits is given by the fact that 5 γ sulfosalicylic and 5 γ benzoic acid could be detected in this manner.

(5) Detection of volatile acids [84]

Those carboxylic acids, which volatilize to a marked degree when heated to 100°, or which are volatile with steam, can be detected through the production of iodine when the acid vapors are brought into contact with iodide-iodate solution. The test can be accomplished with the respective alkali- or alkaline earth salts by warming the solid sample or a drop of a neutral solution with concentrated phosphoric acid. The procedure described on page 247 for the detection of the acetyl group is followed. Those acids whose vapors evolved at water bath temperature react immediately upon iodide-iodate solution include: formic, acetic, propionic, lactic, salicylic. Hydrocyanic acid, in considerable amounts, interferes because of the formation of cyanogen iodide. Likewise, considerable quantities of carbonates must not be present, since carbonic acid reacts to a noticeable extent on iodide-iodate solution. Cyanides and carbonates can be decomposed by warming the sample with the least possible excess of dilute phosphoric acid. (The dyestuff indicator should just show its acidic color.) After the decomposition is complete, a drop of the acid solution or suspension should be taken for the detection of volatile carboxylic acids.

When the ammonium or sodium salts were used, the reaction was positive with

2 γ formic acid	100 γ lactic acid
5 γ acetic acid	10 γ benzoic acid
2.5 γ propionic acid	10 γ salicylic acid

The procedure just given cannot be applied directly in the presence of alkali- or alkaline earth chlorides, bromides, or iodides, since the respective halogen hydracids are evolved when these salts are warmed with concentrated phosphoric acid. A test for halides can be made by means of silver nitrate in a separate portion acidified with nitric acid. If the result is positive, all the halide can be removed from the test solution by precipitation with silver sulfate. The test for volatile carboxylic acids is then carried out with a drop of the filtrate, or a drop of the unfiltered silver halide suspension can be used. Since silver sulfate is not very soluble, it is perhaps best added in the solid state. Nitrates must not be present since the readily volatile nitric acid is liberated when they are warmed with phosphoric acid.

(6) Detection of organic acids through fixing of ammonia [84]

When the ammonium salts of weak organic acids are heated to 120°, they rapidly decompose and lose all of their ammonia. In contrast, the ammonium salts of strong and moderately strong carboxylic and sulfonic acids decompose at this temperature, depending on the heating period, to a greater or less extent but not completely. An exception is found in ammonium formate, which is entirely decomposed even though formic acid is a strong acid. The reason for this divergent behavior is the volatility of formic acid. The formation of heat-stable ammonium salts can be readily detected by evaporating the test material to dryness with ammonia and then heating the residue briefly to 120°. If the residue gives a positive response on treatment with Nessler solution (red-brown precipitate of $HgI_2 \cdot HgNH_2I$) the presence of a strong or medium strong organic acid is indicated.

The direct application of the test obviously requires the absence of free mineral acids and of ammonium salts of inorganic and organic acids. Ammonium salts can be converted into alkali salts by warming with alkali hydroxide solution and the ammonia is completely volatilized. If alkali salts of organic acids or basic solutions of alkali salts are presented for examination, the sample can be fumed with hydrochloric acid and then heated to 120° to remove the unused hydrochloric acid. This treatment leaves behind the non-volatile organic acids, which are then converted to their ammonium salts by evaporation with ammonia. Salts of organic nitrogen bases must not be present, because they are decomposed on evaporation with ammonia with liberation of the organic base and production of the corresponding ammonium salt, which is left on heating to 120°.

Procedure. One drop of the test solution or a pinch of the solid is placed in a microcrucible and taken to dryness with a drop of concentrated ammonia. The residue is kept at 120° for a minute or two in an oven. After cooling, a drop of Nessler solution is added. A red-brown precipitate or a yellow color indicates the presence of strong or medium strong organic acids. The hydrochloric acid and ammonia used must be free from ammonium salts.

> Nessler solution: * 50 g potassium iodide, dissolved in 35 ml water, is treated with saturated mercuric chloride solution until a slight precipitate persists. Then 400 ml of 9 N sodium or potassium hydroxide, clarified by sedimentation, is added. The solution is diluted to 1000 ml, allowed to settle, and decanted.

This procedure revealed:

5 γ oxalic acid	10 γ mandelic acid
10 γ citric acid	10 γ phthalic acid
5 γ tartaric acid	10 γ sulfanilic acid
5 γ malonic acid	5 γ sulfosalicylic acid
10 γ succinic acid	4 γ pyrocatechindisulfonic acid

No reaction was given by acetic, formic, aminoacetic, propionic acid.

Another general test for carboxylic acids and organic sulfonic acids is given on page 448. This test is based on a demasking effect in the dimethyl-glyoxime-alkali-nickel biuret system.

(7) Detection of benzene-soluble acidic compounds [85]

If benzene-soluble acidic compounds, such as higher monobasic fatty acids, aromatic monocarboxylic acids, phenols, imide compounds, etc. are treated, in mg quantities, with a colorless benzene solution of rhodamine B, an intense red color appears. This color is intensified, and is produced with smaller amounts of the cited compounds, if the system is shaken with an aqueous solution of uranyl salts. The red benzene gives an orange-red fluorescence in ultraviolet light. The color (fluorescence) reaction is based on the formation of benzene-soluble red salts of the basic dyestuff rhodamine B with the acidic compounds (H.Ac) or with the complex acids of uranium formed from uranyl salts: rhodamine B.HAc or rhodamine B.H [UO$_2$(Ac)$_3$]. The complex acids are formed:

$$UO_2^{+2} + 3 \text{ HAc} \rightleftharpoons H [UO_2(Ac)_3] + 2H^+$$

* Preparation according to *Standard Methods for the Examination of Water and Sewage*, 7th edition, New York, 1933. The formulations given in the later editions are somewhat different, but the sensitivity of the older reagent is sufficient for the present purpose.

The chemistry of the color (fluorescence) reaction based on disturbances of the equilibrium is discussed in more detail on page 461 in connection with the detection of higher fatty acids in paraffins, waxes, etc.

Procedure. A micro test tube is used. A little of the solid or a drop of its benzene solution is treated with five drops of a saturated benzene solution of rhodamine B and one drop of 1% uranyl acetate solution. The mixture is shaken. If acidic compounds are present, a red or pink color appears, the shade depending on the amount present. The red system fluoresces orange in ultraviolet light.

This procedure revealed:

0.5 γ	benzoic acid	25	γ	benzotriazole
2.5 γ	palmitic acid	20	γ	benzoinoxime
2.5 γ	myristic acid	20	γ	phenylglyoxal
2.5 γ	stearic acid	0.1	γ	picrolonic acid
5 γ	p-nitrophenol	200	γ	nitromethane
5 γ	m-nitrophenol	25	γ	acetylacetic ester
0.5 γ	pentachlorophenol	1	γ	salicylamide
1 γ	salicylic acid	5	γ	salicylanilide

A strong positive response to the color reaction was observed with 100 γ quantities of the following acids: mono-, di-, and tri-chloroacetic acids, phenoxy- and p-chlorophenoxyacetic acids, mercaptoacetic acid, anthranilic acid, N-methyl and N-phenylanthranilic acids, p-aminobenzoic acid, cinnamic acid, mandelic acid, lauric acid. There is no doubt that much smaller quantities of the cited acids may be detected.

The procedure given here makes it possible to detect benzene-soluble acids rapidly in the presence of benzene-insoluble acids, for instance, benzoic acid in the presence of phthalic acid, and salicylic acid in the presence of sulfosalicylic acid. The test is started with the solid mixture (or evaporation residue) which is digested with benzene and the resulting solution subjected to the test.

If halogenoacetic acid is to be detected in the presence of benzene-insoluble acetic acid and halogen acids, the procedure is as follows. A drop or two of the test solution is taken to dryness in a micro test tube. The residue is heated to 130° for several minutes. The cold residue is shaken with a drop of uranyl acetate solution and three or four drops of the benzene solution of rhodamine B. Halogenoacetic acid is present if the benzene layer turns red and the color persists even after the addition of water.

19. Detection of Water-Soluble Salts of Organic Nitrogen Bases and Alkali Salts of Organic Acids [86]

It is easily possible to obtain soluble calcium salts from many water-soluble salts of organic nitrogen bases (also from difficultly soluble sulfates) and from alkali salts of non-volatile organic acids. The first case requires nothing beyond warming with calcium carbonate:

$$2 \,[BH]\, X + CaCO_3 \rightarrow Ca^{+2} + 2\,X^- + 2\,B + H_2O + CO_2 \tag{1}$$

If alkali salts of carboxylic and sulfonic acids (also polynitrophenols) are involved, the material should be taken to dryness with hydrochloric acid and the residue heated for a short time at 110° to drive off the unused hydrochloric acid. There remain, in addition to alkali chloride, the respective non-volatile organic acids (HAc), which promptly react with calcium carbonate:

$$Alk.Ac + HCl \rightarrow Alk.Cl + HAc \tag{2}$$

$$2 \,HAc + CaCO_3 \rightarrow Ca^{+2} + 2\,Ac^- + H_2O + CO_2 \tag{3}$$

The detection of the soluble calcium salts, formed according to (1)–(3), and hence indirectly of the salts cited in the heading, can be accomplished by means of an alkaline solution of sodium rhodizonate (I). A violet basic calcium salt is produced; its probable formula is (II) (see Volume I, Chap. 3).

(I)   (II)

Since only soluble calcium salts, but not calcium carbonate, react with alkaline sodium rhodizonate, the realization of reactions (1)–(3) need not be followed by a removal of the excess carbonate.

The test for salts of organic bases assumes of course the absence of free acids, ammonium salts, and of metal salts which give colored precipitates with alkaline sodium rhodizonate. A preliminary test with this reagent is essential. Moreover, oxalates, phosphates, or arsenates of organic nitrogen bases may not be present, since the underlying acids yield insoluble calcium salts on treatment with calcium carbonate and these products do not react with sodium rhodizonate. However, even considerable quantities of neutral potassium and sodium salts do not interfere.

It should be pointed out with respect to the test described in Procedure II for water-soluble alkali salts of organic acids, that the organic acids left after fuming off with hydrochloric acid can obviously also be revealed by the sensitive iodide-iodate reaction (see page 116). However, the latter is not reliable in the presence of iodine-consuming substances when only small quantities of acid are present. Furthermore, it is always an advantage to utilize reactions of different sensitivities since useful conclusions can often be drawn from the occurrence and intensity of a spot reaction. Procedure II should be preceded by a test for the presence of metal ions which give colored precipitates with sodium rhodizonate. If such are present, the sample should be warmed with sodium carbonate solution (test for ammonia with Nessler reagent) and the filtrate then tested after this precipitation of the carbonates.

Procedure I. (Salts of nitrogen bases.) A spot plate or micro crucible is used. A drop of the test solution is stirred into a thin slurry with the least possible amount of calcium carbonate. When the evolution of carbon dioxide has stopped, a drop of 0.5 N sodium hydroxide and a drop of freshly prepared 0.2% sodium rhodizonate solution are added in succession. If salts of organic bases are present, a more of less intense violet color appears. The shade depends on the quantity of base present.

This procedure revealed:

5 γ	aniline sulfate	10 γ	α-naphthylamine hydrochloride
5 γ	benzidine hydrochloride	50 γ	guanidine sulfate
5 γ	ethylenediamine dihydrochloride	5 γ	diethanolamine hydrochloride

Procedure II. (Alkali salts of organic acids.) A drop of the test solution is taken to dryness, on a spot plate or in a micro crucible, along with a drop of 0.5 N sodium hydroxide. The residue is kept at 110° for several minutes. A drop of water is then added to the cooled residue and stirred with very little calcium carbonate. The remainder of the procedure is as in I.

Positive response was given to this procedure by:

5	γ	tartaric acid	4 γ	adipic acid
2.5	γ	citric acid	5 γ	sulfanilic acid
5	γ	malic acid	10 γ	aminoethanesulfonic acid

20. Orientation Tests Based on Redox Reactions

The combustion tests given in this chapter and the detection of metallic and nonmetallic elements, bound directly or indirectly to carbon, admittedly are redox reactions in their end effect. However, they do not involve reactions of the intact test material, but rather redox reactions of the cleavage products obtained by heating or dehydration.* All organic compounds can be subjected to a decomposition of this kind, even though the volatility of the sample may or may not require the taking of certain precautions. In

---

* Of course there is no reversibility here in the sense of regenerating the initial substance by altering the variables of state.

References pp. 148–150

contrast, there are relatively few organic, metallo-organic, and mixed inorganic-organic compounds that enter directly into stoichiometrically defined redox reactions. Such cases always involve the activity of certain groups in the molecule, on which the reaction begins, and the carbon skeleton may either be preserved or it may split in characteristic fashion at certain places. The test for oxidation or reduction effects exerted by organic materials consequently furnishes leads regarding the presence or absence of particular types of compounds. As a guiding principle, it may be taken that in such tests, which are always conducted in the wet way, the overwhelming majority of all organic compounds prove to be indifferent, and that reducing actions are encountered much oftener than oxidation effects. The latter are restricted to a few classes, or rather groups contained in organic compounds.

(1) Oxidation effects of organic compounds

In inorganic analysis, the best criterion for oxidizing compounds is their ability to release iodine from an acidified solution of alkali iodide. This effect, can of course be expected only from oxidizing agents which, as such, or in the form of reaction products, have a perceptible solubility in dilute acids. It can be established in the case of certain colored quinones and quinoneimide compounds, and organic derivatives of hydrogen peroxide (colorless) and also salts of organic nitrogen bases with inorganic acids, which of themselves oxidize hydriodic acid (chlorates, chromates, molybdates, phosphomolybdates, etc.). This category of organic compounds, which promptly oxidize acidified solutions of alkali iodide, likewise includes the C- and N-nitroso compounds and also the N-chlorosulfonamides (chloramines), which

by virtue of their $R.SO_2{-}\overset{|}{N}{-}Cl$ group, can be regarded as derivatives of hypochlorous acid.*

Alkyl and arylarsonic acids also are in this category of organic oxidants.

The redox reaction between hydrogen peroxide and iodide ions goes too slowly in acid solution to serve as the basis of a general test for organic percompounds, which undergo hydrolysis on contact with water. The oxidation of black lead sulfide to white lead sulfate, which can be conducted as a very sensitive spot test for hydrogen peroxide is very well suited to this purpose, however. Since organic percompounds are very seldom present, no precise description of the lead sulfide test will be given here (see Volume I, Chap. 4). Benzoyl peroxide (dibenzoyl peroxide), an organic derivative of hydrogen

---

* Chloramine B = sodium benzenesulfonchloramide; Chloramine T = sodium p-toluenesulfonchloramid; Dichloramine T = p-toluenesulfondichloroamide; Halozone = p-carboxybenzenesulfondichloroamide. Of these, only Dichloramine T is insoluble in water.

peroxide, does not respond either to acidified iodide or to lead sulfide. The detection of this compound is discussed on page 438.

Characteristic effects can be observed when water- or alcohol-soluble oxidants react with green suspensions of iron(II) hydroxide. The same holds for nitro and nitroso compounds [87], which participate in the following redox reactions, as manifested by a change from green to brown, due to the formation of iron(III) hydroxide:

$$RNO_2 + 6 \ Fe(OH)_2 + 4 \ H_2O \rightarrow RNH_2 + 6 \ Fe(OH)_3$$

$$RNO + 4 \ Fe(OH)_2 + 3 \ H_2O \rightarrow RNH_2 + 4 \ Fe(OH)_3$$

Iron(II) hydroxide is likewise oxidized by those organic derivatives of hydroxylamine and hydrazine which can be split by caustic alkali. The basis of this behavior lies in the fact that hydroxylamine and hydrazine (and also nitrites) which normally are reductants in the presence of alkali hydroxides, are reduced to ammonia by iron(II) hydroxide. Consequently, they function as oxidants with respect to this hydroxide.

Under proper conditions, nitro- and nitroso compounds can be reduced by nascent hydrogen to compounds, which in their turn can be detected by their reducing action on Tollens and Fehling reagents (see page 129).

With respect to the iron(II) hydroxide test, it should be noted that the color change from the green of iron(II) hydroxide to the brown of iron(III) hydroxide is clearly visible only in the absence of colored compounds. The following procedure is recommended for small quantities of nitro- and nitroso compounds, etc.

Procedure.[88] A drop of a freshly prepared 0.1 % ferrous ammonium sulfate solution in 10 % sulfuric acid is treated in a small test tube with a drop of the test solution, mixed with water, alcohol, or dioxan, and then some solid sodium bicarbonate is added. Sufficient alkalinity is thus provided and also a carbon dioxide atmosphere, which combats the autoxidation of the iron (II) hydroxide.

Positive results were given by:

         30 γ nitrobenzene
         25 γ *p*-nitrochlorobenzene
         25 γ *o*-nitrobenzoic acid
         30 γ 5-nitrosalicylic acid

2) *Reduction effects of organic compounds*

Qualitative inorganic analysis utilizes a general test for reducing compounds which is based on their ability to discharge immediately the color of acid solutions of iodine (in alkali iodide), with addition of starch, as indicator, if needed. Since the action of acidic iodine solutions on organic compounds ordinarily proceeds sluggishly and to not more than slight extent, no general preliminary test for reducing organic compounds can be based on this action. Suitable reactions are provided by (a) periodic acid in acid solution, (b) a buffered solution of phosphomolybdic acid, and (c) alkaline masked solutions of copper(II) or silver salts, as well as Nessler reagent. In addition to these inorganic reagents for reduction effects, there is also available a rather sensitive organic reagent, namely an alkaline solution of 1,2-dinitrobenzene. This test is described in item (d), p. 131.

(a) Reduction of periodic acid [89]

Periodic acid has a selective oxidizing action upon compounds with two hydroxyl groups attached to adjacent carbon atoms. Such compounds, dissolved in water or dioxan, give the reaction:

$$RCH(OH)CH(OH)R_2 + HIO_4 \rightarrow 2\ RCHO + HIO_3 + H_2O \qquad (1)$$

Compounds which contain a $>$C(OH)-group adjacent to a $>$CO- or $>$C—NH$_2$-group, and also compounds which contain a —CO—CO-group, likewise react with periodic acid with production of iodic acid:

$$R_1CH(OH)CH(NH_2)R_2 + HIO_4 \rightarrow R_1CHO + R_2CHO + HIO_3 + NH_3 \qquad (2)$$

$$R_1CH(OH)COR_2 + HIO_4 \rightarrow R_1CHO + R_2COOH + HIO_3 \qquad (3)$$

$$R_1COCOR_2 + HIO_4 + H_2O \rightarrow R_1COOH + R_2COOH + HIO_3 \qquad (4)$$

It is likely that redox reactions (2)–(4) do not proceed directly, but are preceded by more or less extensive reactions of water with the CNH$_2$- and CO-groups contained in the starting compounds:

$$>C—NH_2 + H_2O \rightleftarrows\ >C(OH) + NH_3$$

$$>CO + H_2O \rightleftarrows\ >C{<}^{OH}_{OH}$$

These reactions accordingly produce 1,2-glycols, which then react with periodic acid as per (1).* The relative velocity of the oxidation by periodic

---

* According to experimental rate studies there is evidence that an intermediate compound is formed between the 1,2-glycol and periodic acid before the carbon-carbon bond is broken. This intermediate is believed to be a cyclic ester of periodic acid: [90]

$$\begin{matrix} HC—O \\ | \qquad\quad I{-}OH \\ HC—O \end{matrix}$$

acid is: 1,2-glycols $>$ α-hydroxyaldehydes $>$ α-hydroxyketones $>$ 1,2-diketones $>$ α-hydroxy acids.

The iodic acid (or IO_3^- ions) resulting from reactions (1)–(4) can be detected by adding silver nitrate; silver iodate, which is not soluble in dilute nitric acid, precipitates. Since IO_4^- ions are not precipitable by Ag^+ ions, a solution of potassium periodate containing silver nitrate and nitric acid can be used as reagent.

Compounds, which under the conditions of the test hydrolyze to 1,2-glycols, α-hydroxyaldehydes, etc., can also be detected by the behavior toward periodic acid. The detection of anhydrides of 1,2-glycols, the so-called epoxides,[91] whose cleavage proceeds:

$$\begin{array}{c} -\text{HC} \underline{\quad\quad} \text{CH}- \\ \underline{}_{O}\underline{} \end{array} + \text{H}_2\text{O} \rightarrow \begin{array}{c} -\text{HC} \underline{\quad\quad} \text{CH}- \\ | \quad\quad | \\ \text{OH} \quad \text{OH} \end{array}$$

has practical importance. It may be assumed that all hydrolytic splittings are rapid and extensive when hydrolysis products react with periodic acid and are thus removed from the hydrolysis equilibrium.

When testing the behavior of organic materials toward periodic acid, it must be remembered that in addition to the hydroxy- and oxo-compounds noted above, thiols (mercaptans and thiophenols) as well as sulfinic acids and disulfides, likewise reduce periodic acid. The same is true of hydrazones, acid hydrazides, aldoximes and ketoximes, which are cleaved under the conditions of the test and yield alkyl hydrazine, hydrazine, or hydroxylamine, which in turn reduce periodic to iodic acid.

Procedure. [92] One drop of the (aqueous or dioxan) test solution is mixed with one drop of the reagent solution in a depression of a black spot plate. A positive response is signalled by the appearance (immediate or after 1–5 minutes) of a white or light yellow precipitate * or turbidity.

Reagent: Potassium periodate solution containing silver nitrate. Add 2 ml of concentrated nitric acid and 2 ml of 10 % silver nitrate solution to 25 ml of 2 % potassium periodate solution. A yellow precipitate sometimes develops when the reagent stands for some time; it may be filtered off.

---

* A yellow precipitate results from the reduction of iodic acid to iodide by many organic compounds with consequent production of yellow silver iodide. The selective reduction of iodic acid on warming with water-soluble organic compounds has been recommended [93] for the detection of simple alcohols, aldehydes, methyl ketones, phenols, and aniline derivatives. This iodate test is not reliable in the form of spot reactions as proved by F. Feigl and D. Goldstein, unpublished studies.

References pp. 148–150

The following attainable identification limits give an idea of the sensitivity of the periodic acid test:

50	γ maltose		5	γ glucose
50	γ tartaric acid		5	γ ascorbic acid
2.5	γ glycerol		5	γ diacetyl
2.5	γ mannitol		2.5	γ o, m-pyridine carboxylic acid hydrazide
5	γ galactose		5	γ p-pyridine carboxylic acid hydrazide

Phenylhydrazine, benzil, benzoin, dimethylglyoxime gave a positive response.

(b) Reduction of phosphomolybdic acid [94]

As pointed out (page 97) in connection with the detection of phosphorus in organic compounds, the molybdenum (VI) in the anions of the complex phosphomolybdic acid $H_3PO_4 \cdot 12MoO_3 \cdot aq$ is much more readily reduced to the so-called molybdenum blue [molybdenum (V)] than in the normal molybdate anions. In mineral acid solutions, this enhanced reactivity appears only toward strong reducing agents (compare detection of ascorbic acid, page 370). However, with proper buffering, weak reductants likewise produce molybdenum blue from phosphomolybdic acid, and this fact provides a simple preliminary test for reducing organic compounds. It is not necessary to establish a particular pH in order to realize this redox reaction. It is sufficient to treat the sample or its acid solution with phosphomolybdic acid and excess ammonia. In this way, the pH region essential to the production of molybdenum blue is traversed. Excess ammonia does not affect the molybdenum blue produced and decomposes, with discharge of color, the yellow phosphomolybdate ion:

$$[PO_4 \cdot 12 MoO_3]^{-3} + 24 OH^- \rightarrow PO_4^{-3} + 12 MoO_4^{-2} + 12 H_2O$$

It is remarkable, and also a sign of the rapidity of the redox reaction, that the latter occurs even before the alkaline decomposition of the phosphomolybdate, which likewise is a very fast reaction.

Procedure. A drop of the neutral or acid test solution is mixed in a depression of a spot plate with a drop of 5 % water solution of phosphomolybdic acid and then a drop of concentrated ammonia is added. A blue to blue-green color indicates the presence of reducing materials.

Molybdenum blue was formed through this procedure by:

10	γ	benzaldehyde	0.1	γ	naphthylamine (1 : 2)
0.10	γ	o-hydroxybenzaldehyde	0.5	γ	dimethylaniline
10	γ	m- ,,	0.1	γ	benzidine hydrochloride
10	γ	p- ,,	0.05	γ	tetrabase
0.05	γ	phenol	0.1	γ	diphenylamine
0.01	γ	resorcinol	0.25	γ	p-phenylenediamine

References pp. 148–150

0.05 γ	hydroquinone	5	γ	semicarbazide
0.05 γ	pyrogallol	0.5	γ	p-methylaminophenol sulfate
0.05 γ	gallic acid	0.05	γ	8-hydroxyquinoline
2.5 γ	aniline	0.5	γ	dithiooxamide
0.5 γ	K-ethyl xanthate	0.2	γ	ascorbic acid
5 γ	thiourea	0.1	γ	uric acid
10 γ	mercaptobenzothiazole	25	γ	barbituric acid
0.05 γ	thiosemicarbazide	0.7	γ	picolinic acid hydrazide
0.5 γ	rhodizonic acid	1	γ	Na-diethyl dithiocarbamate

These data show that this procedure represents a test for neutral, acidic and basic compounds which are oxidizable by phosphomolybdic acid. A degree of selectivity can be attained if the test solution is made alkaline with dilute base and then extracted with ether. The ether is removed and its evaporation residue is tested with phosphomolybdic acid and ammonia. This method will reveal oxidizable aromatic nitrogen bases and also ether-soluble neutral substances. The alkali salts of acidic oxidizable compounds are left in the water layer. They can be tested for by acidifying a drop of the alkaline solution and then adding phosphomolybdic acid and ammonia. A selectivity can also be achieved if the test is restricted to compounds that are volatile with steam. The apparatus shown on page 49 (Fig. 23) can be used for this purpose.

(c) *Reduction of Fehling, Tollens and Nessler reagent*

Fehling reagent intended for the detection of reducing compounds (particularly reducing sugars) [95] is prepared just prior to use by mixing equal volumes of copper sulfate solution (7.5 g crystallized salt in 100 ml water) and an alkaline solution of sodium potassium tartrate (35 g tartrate plus 25 g potassium hydroxide in 100 ml water). The reagent contains anionically bound copper, which is masked against precipitiation by OH⁻ ions.* However, the slight concentration of Cu^{+2} ions in Fehling solution is sufficient to react, on warming, with organic compounds which can function as strong reducing agents in alkaline solution. Copper (I) oxide (or oxyhydrate) is precipitated; its color (yellow to red) depends on the degree of dispersion and the particle size of the precipitate. Sugars (aldoses, ketoses), phenylhydrazine and other organic derivatives of hydrazine (acid hydrazides) react with warm Fehling solution. When conducted as a drop reaction in a micro test tube, the sensitivity of the Fehling test is low; in general, milligram quantities of the reducing substances are needed to produce a decisive result.

* Regarding the mode of bonding of the copper see F. Feigl, Ref. 32, p. 92.

A far more sensitive test of wider applicability to reducing compounds is provided by a solution of silver oxide in ammonia. This so-called Tollens reagent [96] contains $[Ag(NH_3)_2]^+$ and OH^- ions. Solutions of reducing compounds, or the corresponding solids, react with this reagent, in the cold or on warming, to produce elementary silver as a black precipitate, which often forms an adherent shiny mirror on the walls of the reaction vessel. The production of this characteristic silver coating is favored if the vessel, in which the redox reaction with Tollens reagent is to be carried out, is treated beforehand for several minutes with warm 10 % sodium hydroxide solution and then rinsed with distilled water.

The reagent must be prepared just before use and must not be stored, since the solution decomposes on standing and deposits silver fulminate, which is highly explosive when dry. As soon as the test is completed, the mixture should be poured into the drain and flushed down.

Tollens reagent oxidizes sugars, polyhydroxyphenols, hydroxy carboxylic acids, α-diketones, primary ketols, sulfinic acids, aminophenols, alkyl- and arylhydroxylamines, certain aromatic amines, hydrazo compounds, aldehydes, hydrazines, etc.[97]

Procedure. The test is conducted in a micro test tube or in an Emich centrifuge tube. A drop of the test solution is mixed with a drop of the reagent (centrifuge, if necessary) and then placed for 15–30 seconds in water warmed to 70–85°. A deposition of metallic silver indicates reducing compounds. A blank test is essential.

Reagent: Tollens solution: 1 ml of 10 % silver nitrate solution is treated with 1 ml of 10 % sodium hydroxide solution; the precipitate of silver oxide is dissolved by drop-wise addition of ammonia (1 : 1).

An idea of the sensitivity of the test is given by the detection of the following quantities of reducing materials:

0.1	γ formaldehyde	0.5	γ glucose
5	γ m-hydroxybenzaldehyde	0.25	γ isonicotinic acid hydrazide
1	γ galactose	1	γ benzoic acid hydrazide

Compounds which reduce in alkaline solution can be brought to reaction directly with silver oxide, instead of Tollens reagent, and the unused silver oxide dissolved by ammonia.[98] This test can be carried out as a sensitive spot reaction on paper.

Up to the present, relatively little attention has been given to the behavior of reducing compounds toward alkaline solutions of alkali iodide mercuriate (Nessler reagent). Almost all aldehydes [99] precipitate finely divided mercury at room temperature, and aldoses and ketoses likewise give a black or grey color on warming with this reagent [100, 101]. The use of Nessler reagent for spot tests (spot plate or filter paper) is not limited to aliphatic aldehydes, but is capable of far wider application as shown by the following limits of identification.

2.5 γ	hydroquinone	10 γ	m-hydroxybenzaldehyde
5 γ	pyrogallol	500 γ	p- ,,
2 γ	gallic acid	1 γ	formic acid
2.5 γ	benzaldehyde	2 γ	phenylhydrazine hydrochloride
1000 γ	o-hydroxybenzaldehyde	10 γ	nicotinic acid hydrazide

The preparation of Nessler reagent is outlined on page 120.

(d) Reduction of o-dinitrobenzene

The colorless alcoholic-alkaline solution of 1,2-dinitrobenzene turns blue-violet on the addition of certain organic and inorganic reductants (see Volume I, Chapters 3 and 4). It has been found that only those organic compounds are effective which become reducing agents in alkaline solution through delivery of hydrogen. The 1,2-dinitrobenzene thus acts as acceptor for hydrogen, yielding in cooperation with alkali hydroxide blue-violet water-soluble alkali salts of dibasic ortho-quinoidal nitrogen acids. Studies of this color reaction have led to two different reaction paths and reaction products.

(1) The hydrogen is taken up by the dinitrobenzene and then the alkali brings about an enolization of the two NO_2-groups to NO_2H-groups with production of dialkali salts of the o-diaci-dihydronitrobenzene.[102]

(2) The hydrogen reduces 1,2-dinitrobenzene to o-nitrophenylhydrazine

and the *ortho*-quinoidal dialkali salt of the *aci*-form of the o-nitroso-nitrobenzene then forms in the alkaline solution.[103]

After observing and making analytical use of the color reaction of 1,2-dinitrobenzene with reducing sugars (aldoses),[104] the same behavior was found with respect to polyphenols and a series of other reducing organic compounds.[105] These reducing reactions can be conducted within the technique of spot test analysis and provide a selective preliminary test for certain classes of reducing organic compounds.[106]

Procedure. A micro test tube is used. A drop of the aqueous or alcoholic test solution or a grain or two of the solid is treated in succession with one drop of 1% solution of 1,2-dinitrobenzene in alcohol and one drop of 0.5 N sodium hydroxide. The mixture is heated over a free flame for not more than one minute at the most. Depending on the content of reducing substances, a more or less intense violet color appears.

This procedure revealed:

2.5 γ	pyrocatechol		20 γ	benzoic acid hydrazide
10 γ	hydroquinone		25 γ	nicotinic acid hydrazide
5 γ	pyrogallol		5 γ	glucose
10 γ	tannic acid		10 γ	lactose
10 γ	ascorbic acid		10 γ	maltose
5 γ	phenylhydrazine hydrochloride		5 γ	l-sorbose

A positive response was given by: phenylhydroxylamine, benzoin, hydroxybenzenes, adrenaline, glyceric aldehyde, arabinose, rhamnose, xylose, a-galacturonic acid.

This compilation shows that all of these compounds are reductants because of dehydrogenation. Since with the exception of formaldehyde, other aldehydes react only in large amounts with 1,2-dinitrobenzene and then but weakly, the sensitive redox reaction with aldoses must be ascribed to the loss of the H-atoms (designated by *) of the $-\overset{*}{C}H(\overset{*}{O}H)CHO$-group. These are the very hydrogen atoms which are known to bring about the reductive cleavage of phenylhydrazine into aniline and ammonia when the phenylosazones of the aldoses are formed.

Organic derivatives of hydroxylamine and hydrazine reduce 1,2-dinitrobenzene in the same manner as the inorganic parent compounds. Such derivatives can be prepared by "neutral reduction" of aromatic nitro-, nitroso-, azo- and azoxy compounds by warming with zinc dust and ammonium chloride:

$$R-NO_2 \rightarrow RNO \rightarrow RNHOH$$

$$\begin{array}{c} R \\ R_1 \end{array}\!\!\!> N-NO \;\rightarrow\; \begin{array}{c} R \\ R_1 \end{array}\!\!\!> N-NH$$

$$R—N=N—R \rightarrow R—NH—NH—R$$

$$R—\underset{\underset{O}{\overset{\|}{\ }}}{N}=N—R \rightarrow R—NH—NH—R$$

Accordingly, if the original sample does not react with an alcoholic alkaline solution of 1,2-dinitrobenzene, the alcoholic-aqueous solution can be warmed with zinc dust and ammonium chloride and the filtered (if need be) solution again tested with 1,2-dinitrobenzene. If a positive response is then obtained, the color reaction indicates the presence of nitrogen compound,[107] which yield alkyl derivatives of hydroxylamine and hydrazine on treatment with zinc and ammonium chloride as shown in the scheme just given.

21. The Le Rosen Test for Aromatic Compounds[108]

At room temperature, or on gentle warming, concentrated sulfuric acid containing formaldehyde reacts with aromatic hydrocarbons, phenols, polyphenols, thiophen, etc. Red, violet, green precipitates or colorations appear. The same color reactions occur if formaldehyde is added to solutions or suspensions of these organic compounds in concentrated sulfuric acid. The composition of the colored product is not known. Although experimental proof is lacking, it seems likely that the concentrated sulfuric acid, which is both an oxidant and dehydrant, brings about first a condensation of the aromatic compounds with formaldehyde, and then oxidizes the resulting diarylmethylene compounds to colored p-quinoidal compounds. Accordingly, benzene and carbolic acid (phenol) would undergo the reactions:

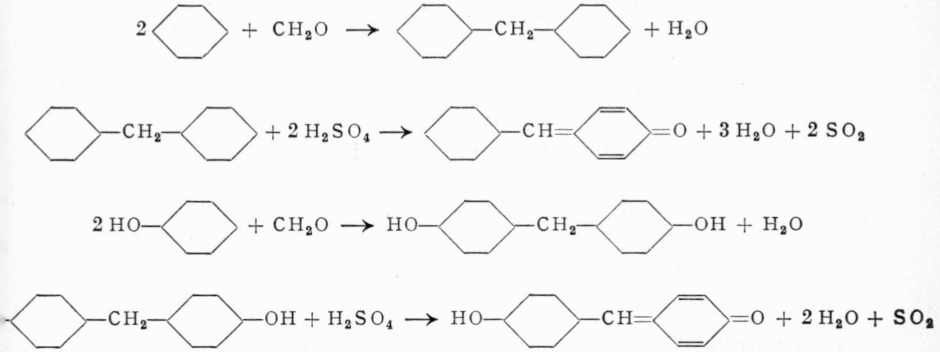

In accord with this tentative explanation, which can also apply to derivatives of benzene and carbolic acid, the color reaction occurs only with those aromatic compounds which condense with formaldehyde to produce such methylene compounds as possess a free *para* position or a *para* OH-group in order that an oxidation to colored *p*-quinoidal compounds can ensue through the action of the concentrated sulfuric acid. These conditions are satisfied in the case of pure aromatic hydrocarbons and also by phenols with a free *para* position. On the other hand, when dealing with substituted aromatic hydrocarbons and phenols, it must be kept in mind that the groups bound to the ring may retard or prevent the condensation with formaldehyde, or it may take place at positions where an oxidation to colored quinoidal products is impossible. A hindering of this kind is probably responsible for the discovery that some aromatic compounds do not react at all with formaldehyde-sulfuric acid, or only after long standing and warming (see page 142). However, even small amounts of so many aromatic compounds do give the color reaction, and the colors are so characteristic, that this rapid test of the behavior of a sample toward formaldehyde-sulfuric acid has considerable orienting value.

When making the test with formaldehyde-sulfuric acid, it must be kept in mind that some organic compounds dissolve in concentrated sulfuric acid with formation of colored products (compare page 143). Possibly, these are colored solvates, but there is also much likelihood that condensation and oxidation reactions have resulted from the action of the concentrated sulfuric acid as a powerful dehydrant and oxidant. Therefore, the behavior of the test material toward concentrated sulfuric acid should be determined in advance. If a color appears, which is altered on the addition of formaldehyde or formaldehyde-sulfuric acid, it may be taken as an indication of the presence of reactive aromatic compounds. When considerable amounts of the colored quinoidal compounds result, the color frequently becomes darker after a while. Possibly this effect is due to a partial carbonization by the concentrated sulfuric acid.

The state of aggregation is not an essential factor when aromatic compounds react with formaldehyde-sulfuric acid, i.e., the sample may be solid, liquid, gaseous, or dissolved in organic liquids, Procedure I will indisputably reveal aromatic hydrocarbons and phenols, which have a distinct vapor pressure at room temperature or when gently warmed. Procedure II is applicable to solid, liquid, or dissolved samples. In this case, however, in contrast to I, a negative result cannot be taken as absolute proof of the absence of aromatic compounds.

Procedure I.[109] (For volatile compounds.) A little of the solid or liquid sample is placed in the bulb of the apparatus pictured on page 48, or a drop of the ether test solution is evaporated there by brief immersion in warm water. A drop of the reagent solution is placed on the knob of the stopper; the apparatus is closed, and placed in hot water (60–80°). After 2–3 minutes, the drop on the knob is transferred (by wiping) to a depression of a white spot plate. A more or less intense color indicates the presence of volatile, reactive aromatic compounds.

If a solution in ether is used, and the solvent evaporated, considerable amounts of benzene, toluene, and phenol are carried along with the ether vapors and removed from the test. Such losses can be prevented by first placing one or two drops of concentrated sulfuric acid in the bulb of the apparatus and then adding the ether solution of the sample. Ether is soluble in concentrated sulfuric acid, and the vapor tension of the ether is thus reduced so much that only benzene, toluene, and the like vaporize at room temperature or on gentle warming.

Reagent: Formaldehyde-sulfuric acid: 0.2 ml of 37 % formaldehyde plus 10 ml concentrated sulfuric acid. The reagent should not be stored longer than a day or two.

This procedure revealed, starting with ether solutions,

2	γ benzene	2 γ	phenol
1.5 γ	toluene	4 γ	o-cresol
5	γ naphthalene	8 γ	benzaldehyde
25	γ anthracene	2 γ	thiophen

If no color reaction with formalin-sulfuric acid is obtained by Procedure I, the absence of volatile aromatic hydrocarbons and phenols is assured. To test for non-volatile reactive aromatic compounds, the test must be carried out on the solid material, or on a solution in alcohol, ether, etc.

Procedure II. (For nonvolatile compounds.) A drop of the non-aqueous test solution, or a little of the solid sample, is treated in a depression of a spot plate with 1 or 2 drops or the reagent solution. A positive reaction is signalled by the development of a color. A parallel trial with concentrated sulfuric acid must be conducted in all cases. If the latter yields a color, a drop of the reagent should be added and any change in the color noted. It is often advisable to conduct the spot reaction with diluted test solutions, in order better to establish the shade of the color.

The following summary contains the findings with various classes of aromatic compounds.*

Anisole	red-violet	Benzildioxime	yellow
Anthracene	yellow-green	Benzoinoxime	yellow
Benzaldehyde		Benzyl alcohol	red
(yellow brown in		Benzyl mercaptan	orange
conc. H_2SO_4)	red	Carbazole	green
Benzene	red	Catechol	violet-red

* The statements are taken from the paper by Le Rosen *et al.* (*loc. cit.*) and the experiments of D. Goldstein.

References pp. 148–150

Chlorobenzene	red	Naphthoresorcinol	
Cinnamic acid	brick red	(brown in conc. H_2SO_4)	green
Cumene	red	Naphthylamine hydro-	
Dibenzyl	dark red	chloride	green
Diphenyl	blue-green	Nitronaphtalene	
Diphenylbenzidine	red	(red in conc. H_2SO_4)	green-blue
Diphenylmethane	red	Phenanthrene	green
Ethylbenzene	red-tan	Phenol	red-violet
Fluorene	green	Phenylarsonic acid	red
Furildioxime		Phenyl ether	violet
(yellow in conc.		Phloroglucinol	brown-red
H_2SO_4)	brown	Pyrogallol	
Gallic acid	yellow-green	(yellow in conc. H_2SO)	red
Hexaethylbenzene	yellow	Resorcinol	red
Hydroquinol	black	Salicylic acid	red
o-Hydroxydiphenyl	red	Sulfosalicylic acid (heating	
p-Hydroxydiphenyl	green	at 110°)	red
Mandelic acid	violet-red	Stilbene	brown
Mesitylene	tan	Tetraline	red
Methyl-2-naphthyl		Thionalide	green
ketone	orange	Thiophen	red-violet
Methyl salicylate	red	Toluene	red
Naphthalene	green	Triethylbenzene	orange
Naphthoic acid		1, 3, 5-Triphenylbenzene	blue
(slightly green in conc.		Triphenylmethane	red
H_2SO_4)	green	o, m, p-Xylene	red
2-Naphthol	brown		

The following develop no color or there is no difference from the color of the solution in concentrated sulfuric acid: amidobenzoic acid, aniline, anthraquinone, azoxybenzene, benzidine, benzil, benzoic acid, benzophenone, dimethylbenzaldehyde, α, α'-dipyridyl, diphenylamine, 8-hydroxyquinoline, mercapto-benzothiazole, o-nitrobenzoic acid, o-nitrophenol, 6-nitroquinoline, pentachlorophenol, phthalic acid, picrolonic acid, salicylaldoxime, salicylaldehyde.

The compilation reveals that diagnostic conclusions can be drawn both from the occurrence of a color reaction and from the actual shade obtained.

When examining mixtures, it is well to make a sublimation trial, and to subject the sublimate (if any) to the action of formaldehyde-sulfuric acid. Since relatively few organic compounds are sublimable at normal pressure, a positive response to this color reaction considerably reduces the number of compounds which need be considered.

References pp. 148-150

22. Ehrlich Diazo Test for Compounds Capable of Coupling

The Ehrlich diazo reaction,[110] which is widely used in biological chemistry for detecting physiologically important substances, especially phenol- and imidazol derivatives, such as histidine and histamine, can serve as a sensitive preliminary test for compounds which are capable of entering into coupling reactions. The chemistry of the test is the same as that of the sensitive Griess test for nitrous acid (Volume I, Chapt. 4). The reagent employed in the diazo reaction is a freshly prepared solution of diazobenzene-sulfonic acid(II) obtained by diazotizing sulfanilic acid (I) with nitrous acid, in the presence of hydrochloric acid:

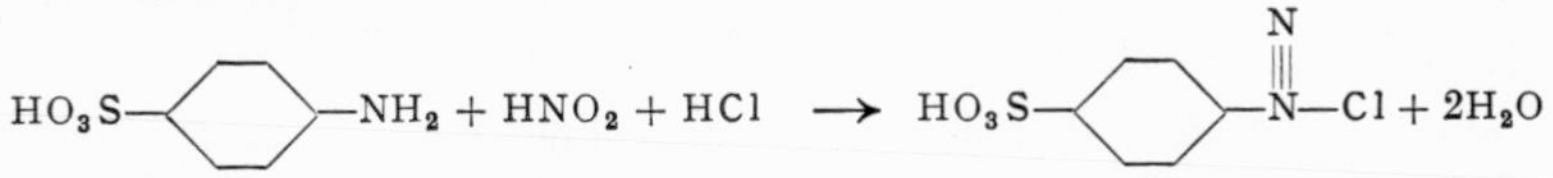

The colorless solution of diazobenzene sulfonic acid couples instantly with solutions of phenols and aromatic amines to produce acid or basic azo dyestuffs. With carbolic acid and aniline, as well as their derivatives with a free *para* position, the coupling proceeds:

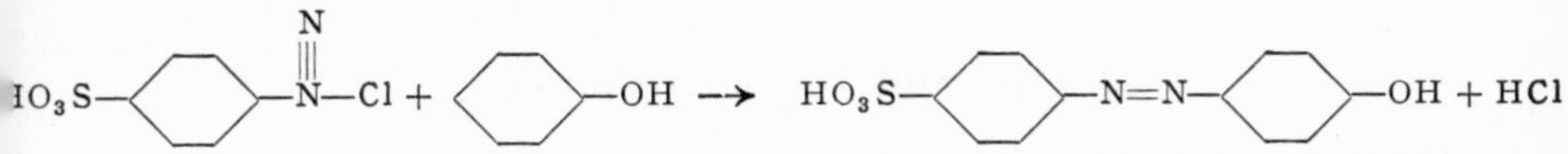

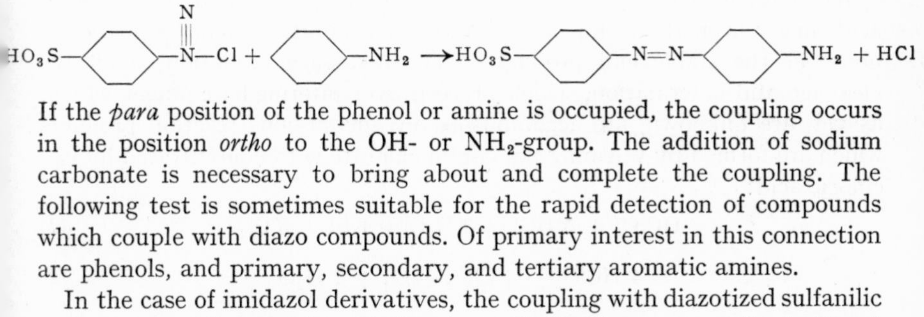

If the *para* position of the phenol or amine is occupied, the coupling occurs in the position *ortho* to the OH- or NH$_2$-group. The addition of sodium carbonate is necessary to bring about and complete the coupling. The following test is sometimes suitable for the rapid detection of compounds which couple with diazo compounds. Of primary interest in this connection are phenols, and primary, secondary, and tertiary aromatic amines.

In the case of imidazol derivatives, the coupling with diazotized sulfanilic acid occurs in the position contiguous to the imide group of the imidazol ring:[111]

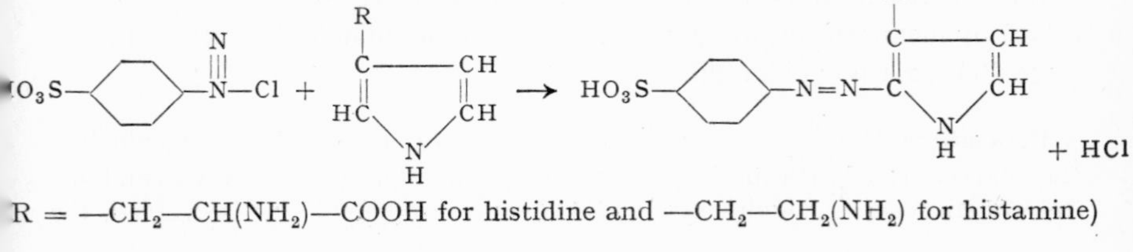

R = —CH$_2$—CH(NH$_2$)—COOH for histidine and —CH$_2$—CH$_2$(NH$_2$) for histamine)

References pp. 148–150

Coupling likewise occurs in the case of a variety of other nitrogen hetero-cycles such as thymine, thiamine (vitamin B_1 etc.)[112]

Procedure. [113] One drop of sulfanilic acid solution and one drop of 0.5% sodium or potassium nitrite solution are mixed in a depression of a spot plate, and then one drop of the test solution is added with stirring. A drop of 10% sodium carbonate solution is then introduced. The immediate production of a color is taken as a positive response. Some compounds are more sluggish and a period of 1–2 minutes waiting is not too long, but a blank test is essential in such cases. Likewise, a blank comparison test is always advisable when alcoholic solutions are being examined.

Reagent: 0.5 % solution of sulfanilic acid in 2 % hydrochloric acid.

This procedure revealed:

0.2 γ phenol	reddish-yellow	5 γ aniline	greenish-yellow
0.8 γ resorcinol	reddish-brown	1.5 γ dimethylaniline	reddish-brown
5 γ p-hydroxy-		2 γ diethylaniline	reddish-brown
biphenyl	red	0.1 γ m-hydroxy-	
2 γ α-naphthol	reddish-brown	benzaldehyde	brown-yellow
5 γ β-naphthol	yellow	50 γ p-hydroxy-	
1.5 γ tyrosine	red	benzaldehyde	orange-red

23. Chloranil Test after Colmant[114]

When warmed with potassium chlorate and concentrated hydrochloric acid, many aromatic compounds form chloranil (tetrachloro-*p*-benzoqui-none) as the stable end product.[115] The necessary oxidation, oxidative cleavage and chlorination, which proceed over intermediate stages which, as yet, are unknown, are accomplished by the gaseous reaction products which are formed by warming potassium chlorate with concentrated hydro-chloric acid:

$$HClO_3 + 5\ HCl \rightarrow 3\ H_2O + KCl + 3\ Cl_2 \qquad (1)$$

$$4\ HClO_3 \rightarrow 4\ ClO_2 + O_2 + 2\ H_2O \qquad (2)$$

Since chlorate or chloric acid is completely destroyed by (*1*) and (*2*), any chloranil that may have been formed can be detected by adding potassium iodide (liberation of iodine) or still more conclusively (after extraction with ether) by means of tetrabase (formation of a blue quinoidal compound). See page 433 regarding chloranil.

Procedure.[116] A micro test tube is used. A drop of the test solution or a pinch of the solid is warmed with one drop of saturated potassium chlorate solution and one drop of concentrated hydrochloric acid. After no more chlorine is evolved, the solution is cooled, 2 or 3 drops of water added, and shaken with 5–10 drops of ether. After the layers have separated, a drop or two of the ethereal solution is placed on filter paper and spotted with one drop of a 1% ether solution of tetrabase. After the ether has evaporated (air blast) a blue stain is left indicating the presence of aromatic compounds that are oxidatively decomposed to form chloranil.

Milligram quantities of the following compounds were tested. The identification limit is given in those cases in which the response was particularly strong.

I. Strong response to the chloranil test:

acetanilide, benzidine (0.5 γ); p-chloroaniline (0.5 γ); coumarin; diphenylamine (0.25 γ); emetine; p-hydroxybenzaldehyde (0.25 γ); m-hydroxybenzaldehyde; 8-hydroxyquinoline; p-hydroxydiphenyl; α-naphthol (10 γ); β-naphthol (10 γ); isatin (1 γ); methylene blue (1 γ); mercaptobenzothiazole (10 γ); naphthylamine (5 γ); naphthylamine hydrochloride; sodium dihydroxybenzene-sulfonate; p-nitrophenol (0.5 γ); papaverine hydrochloride; pentachlorophenol; phenolphthalein (1 γ); phenylurea (10 γ); picric acid (5 γ); quinone; tryptophan; salicin (2.5 γ); salicilic acid (1 γ); sulfametazine; sulfanilic acid (0.5 γ); sulfapyridine; sulfathiazole; sulfosalicylic acid (1 γ);

II. Weaker response to the chloranil test (in milligram quantities):

azobenzene; ephedrine; isoquinoline; Congo red; nitrobenzene; o-nitrobenzoic acid; quinoline; tetrabase; toluene:

III. No response to the chloranil reaction:

alizarin; anthraquinone; anthracene; benzoic acid; chromotropic acid; codein; curcumin; ellagic acid; hexachlorobenzene; morin; morphine hydrochloride; naphthalene; α-nitroso-β-naphthol; phthalic acid; pyrogallol; quinalizarin; quinine hydrochloride; saccharin; Sudan III.

These findings show that many but by no means all aromatic compounds yield chloranil when warmed with potassium chlorate and concentrated hydrochloric acid. Consequently, the procedure given here is not a decisive preliminary test for aromatic compounds. However, the results of the chloranil test are useful if they are correlated with the findings of the Le Rosen preliminary test for aromatic compounds (see page 133). It is remarkable that polyphenols, hydroxyanthraquinone and flavanols, and also such simply constructed compounds as benzoic acid and phthalic acid, yield no chloranil when warmed with chlorate and hydrochloric acid. Therefore, certain groups and structural factors are probably responsible for the formation of chloranil. This is shown plainly in the behavior of naphthol- and naphylamine sulfonic acids, which can be characterized with the aid of the chloranil test

24. Fuming-off Test with Concentrated Nitric Acid[117]

Characteristic alterations may ensue from the warming of non-volatile organic compounds with concentrated nitric acid. Of interest are: nitrations, oxidation of particular groups, oxidative cleavage, as shown in the following assembly:

1. Aromatic hydrocarbons are nitrated.
2. Phenols are converted to mono- and dinitrophenols, which are more acidic than the initial compounds. Aci-nitro compounds are formed if the nitro group enters *para* to an OH group.
3. Thiophenols, mercaptans, and disulfides are oxidized to sulfonic acids. Nitration may occur in addition.
4. Aromatic amines are oxidized and nitrated, i.e., acidic nitrophenols are produced.
5. Certain cyclic nitrogen bases, and also alkaloids, are split with production of carboxylic acids.*
6. Aliphatic polyhydroxy compounds are converted into the corresponding dicarboxylic acids by oxidation of the terminal CH_2OH- and CHO-groups.
7. Glucosides, which are esters of phenols and alcohols with various sugars, are first split hydrolytically and the sugars are then oxidized as per 6. Any liberated phenol is nitrated.

Since nitric acid can be completely removed by evaporation, the changes may be readily detected by testing the evaporation residue, and useful conclusions may sometimes be drawn concerning the nature of the test material from such examinations. The following may be detected:

    I. Carboxylic and sulfonic acids by the iodide-iodate reaction (page 116).
   II. Benzene-soluble carboxylic acids through the color reaction with uranyl acetate and rhodamine B (page 120).
 III. Aci nitro compounds through the color reaction with rhodamine B (page 166).
 IV. Polynitro compounds through saponification to alkali nitrite (page 165).

Procedure. A micro crucible is used. A little of the solid or a drop of the test solution is treated with a drop of two of concentrated nitric acid (sp.gr. 1.4) and taken to dryness in the water bath. The residue is then kept at 120° for 5–10 minutes to assure complete removal of the nitric acid. The residue may then be subjected to the subsequent tests.

---

  * Familiar instances include: cleavage of pyrrole to oxalic acid, piperidine to aminobutyric acid, narcotine to opianic acid, nicotine and alkaloids of the pyridine series to pyridine carboxylic acids.

SOLUBILITY TESTS

The following gave positive reactions:

2.5	γ	mannite by I	50	γ	α- and β-naphthol by III
2.5	γ	glucose by I	5	γ	sedulene by III
5	γ	8-hydroxyquinoline by I	2	γ	salicylic acid by IV
200	γ	narcotine by II	5	γ	naphthylamine by IV
5	γ	α- and β-naphthol by II			

25. Solubility Tests

The behavior of solid, liquid, and gaseous materials and mixtures toward water, dilute acids and alkalies, as well as toward non-aqueous solvents, is of analytical importance for two reasons: 1) such tests give valuable guides regarding the preparation of suitable reaction milieus in which to carry out analytical reactions; 2) the solubility behavior *per se* can be characteristic for certain compounds or types of compounds.

Ordinarily, a distinction is made between inert solvents and those which are chemically active (reaction solvents). This practice is sensible with respect to the residues which are left when the solvent is removed by evaporation or displaced by the addition of another solvent. In the case of inert solvents, the dissolved material is always left unchanged, whereas, with reactive solvents the residue consists of the reaction products of the material which had gone into solution. If, however, the solution process as such and the state existing in solution are considered, then the distinction between indifferent and chemically active can no longer be maintained. In every case, addition reactions produce solvates, i.e., compounds made up of molecules of the solvent plus molecules (or ions) of the now dissolved material, which originally was present as solid, liquid, or gas. It is in accord with the chemical nature of solution that the presence and activity of certain groups in the solvent and solute are responsible for the occurrence and extent of these solution processes.* Therefore, it may obviously be expected that analytically useful conclusions concerning the molecular structure and the presence of certain groups can be drawn from the behavior of an (unknown) organic material toward selected solvents. This is true to the greatest extent for the behavior toward reaction solvents, as is shown in Section 4, which deals with the detection of the acidic and basic behavior of organic materials. However, here also there are notable exceptions to the rule that basic compounds are soluble in acids and acidic compounds in alkali hydroxides. Several characteristic instances demonstrate that in

---

* See the very instructive discussion of the analytical significance of this topic in S. M. McElvain, *The Characterization of Organic Compounds*, New York, 1945, Chapter II; N. D Cheronis and J. B. Entrikin, *Semimicro Qualitative Analysis*, New York, 1947, Chapter 4.

References pp. 148–150

organic compounds the point of attack by acids and bases can be blocked as well as activated by the remainder of the molecule. For example, 8-hydroxyquinoline (oxine) is easily soluble in dilute mineral acids, whereas its halogenated derivatives, e.g. tribromo- and trichlorooxine, are not soluble. Carbolic acid (phenol) does not dissolve in aqueous ammonia or in alkali bicarbonate, but this fact does not permit the generalization that all phenols are insoluble in ammonia or alkali bicarbonates. The behavior of nitroso- and nitrophenols, hydroxyanthraquinones, and hydroxyaldehydes shows clearly that certain compounds which are thoroughly phenolic in constitution may be soluble in ammonia and alkali bicarbonate solutions. But instances are known of phenols which, in opposition to the general rule, are not soluble in caustic alkalis.[118] For instance the phenolic azo dyestuff Sudan III (tetrazobenzene β-naphthol) does not dissolve in caustic alkali solutions.

With regard to divergences from general solubility rules involving reacting solvents, it is very instructive to examine the behavior of alizarin blue (I), which contains not only the characteristic functional groups of alizarin (II) but also of 8-hydroxyquinoline (III).

                (I)   (II)   (III)

Contrary to expectation, this dyestuff, which is an exceedingly sensitive and specific reagent for the detection and gravimetric determination of copper,[119] is soluble neither in alkalis as are (II) and (III) nor in dilute acids as is (III). Consequently, the results of these particular solubility tests with bases and acids would not justify any statement about the presence of acidic phenolic groups or of the basic nitrogen atom in the dyestuff.

Cold concentrated sulfuric acid is a solvent for unsaturated hydrocarbons, polyalkylated aromatic hydrocarbons and many oxygen-containing organic compounds. Sulfonation, esterification, oxidation, removal of water, isomerization, polymerization, hydrolytic splitting, or formation of addition compounds may occur when concentrated sulfuric acid acts; the nature of the action depends on the kind of compound involved. In the case of oxygen-containing organic compounds, the result is often the production of addition compounds which are soluble in concentrated sulfuric acid. Sometimes, the solvates of oxygen-containing compounds in concentrated sulfuric acid are colored or the solutions show a deeper color than the solute itself. Examples are unsaturated ketones [120] and phenazines (condensation products of o-phenylenediamine with 1,2-diketones). This effect is known as halochromy or halochromism. In general, the addition products with concentrated sulfuric acid are decomposed on the addition of water and the initial compounds come out of solution. Consequently, the close relation between reactive and inert solvents is shown particularly well in the behavior of concentrated sulfuric acid.* However, there is no universal rule that all organic compounds behave in this manner toward concentrated sulfuric acid. For example, many aromatic hydrocarbons (benzene, toluene, etc.), and their halogen derivatives are not soluble in concentrated sulfuric acid. Likewise the diaryl ethers constitute a class of oxygen-containing compounds which are insoluble in sulfuric acid. Solubility in concentrated sulfuric acid may therefore be viewed only as an indication of the presence of oxygen-containing organic compounds; perhaps also as a guide in the separation and isolation of a particular organic compound.

Syrupy (85 %) phosphoric acid has been recommended as an inert solvent for differentiating water-insoluble organic oxygen compounds.[121] It dissolves alcohols, aldehydes, methyl ketones, cyclic ketones and esters of less than nine carbon atoms, but there are numerous exceptions in these groups. Some olefines, amylene for example, are also soluble in syrupy phosphoric acid.

Syrupy phosphoric acid behaves much as does concentrated sulfuric acid with respect to dehydration and removal of water from organic compounds, but in contrast, phosphoric acid never acts as oxidant.

Since there are marked departures from solubility rules even with respect to both chemically active and inert inorganic solvents, it is not strange that this is still more true of the behavior of organic compounds toward inert organic solvents. Consequently, the results of preliminary tests of the behavior of organic materials toward such solvents must always be accepted with caution. Insolubility or slight solubility must especially not be taken as a sure indication of the presence or absence of certain groups or members of particular types of compounds. These reservations must be kept in view when applying the following statements, which are intended to give an orientation concerning the solubility behaviors of the most important classes of organic compounds, and which in addition furnish the basis for

* The production of color or the change in color that accompanies solution in concentrated sulfuric acid in many cases, is probably due in large measure to the fact that the concentrated acid can function as dehydrant as well as strong oxidant. Compare in this connection the Le Rosen formalin reaction (page 133) and the test for organic sulfonic acids (page 254).

separations of the constituents of organic mixtures.* Before making solubility tests, it is recommended to carry out the preliminary tests described in
the previous sections, and to take the findings into account along with the
results of the solubility tests.

I. Compounds soluble in water, insoluble in ether

Only carbon, hydrogen, oxygen present:	Dibasic and polybasic acids
	Hydroxy acids
	Polyhydroxy phenols
	Simple carbohydrates
Metals present:	Salts of acids and phenols
	Miscellaneous metallic compounds
Nitrogen present:	Ammonium salts
	Amine salts of organic acids
	Amino acids
	Amides
	Amines (aliphatic-aromatic, polyamines, oxy-amines)
	Amino phenols
	Nitro acids
	Nitro phenols
	Semicarbazides
	Semicarbazones
	Ureas
Halogens present:	Halo acids
	Halo alcohols, aldehydes, etc.
	Acyl halides (by hydrolysis)
Sulfur present:	Sulfonic acids
	Mercaptans
Nitrogen and halogen present:	Amine salts of halogen acids
Nitrogen and sulfur present:	Amino sulfonic acids
	Bisulfates of weak bases
	Cyano sulfonic acids
	Nitro sulfonic acids

II. Compounds soluble in water and ether

Only carbon, hydrogen, oxygen present:	Carboxylic acids
	Alcohols
	Aldehydes and ketones
	Anhydrides
	Esters
	Ethers
	Polyhydroxyphenols

* Consult H. Staudinger, *Anleitung zur organischen qualitativen Analyse*, 6th edition, Berlin
1955, concerning the data indispensable to such separations.

References pp. 148-150

Nitrogen present: Amides
                                     Amines
                                     Amino acids and phenols
                                     Nitro acids and phenols
Halogens present: Halo acids and phenols
Sulfur present: Hydroxy heterocyclic sulfur compounds
                                     Mercaptans
                                     Thiophenols

III. Compounds insoluble in water, soluble in ether

Only carbon and hydrogen pre-   Liquid and solid aliphatic and aromatic hydro-
  sent: carbons
Only carbon, hydrogen, oxygen   Esters and lactones
  present: Higher lactones, alcohols and aldehydes
                                  Ethers
                                  Higher fatty acids
                                  Aromatic carboxylic acids
                                  Phenols and enols
Nitrogen present: Nitro compounds
                                Aromatic nitrocarboxylic acids and nitrophe-
                                  nols
                                Esters of nitrous acid
                                Aromatic bases
                                Hydrazine derivatives
                                Acid amides, -imides, anilides
                                Aromatic amino acids
                                Azo compounds
Halogen present: Aliphatic and aromatic halogen compounds
                                Halogen substituted-alcohols, aromatic alde-
                                  hydes, phenols, carboxylic acids, esters
                                Halogen nitro compounds
Sulfur present: Thiol compounds
                                Thio acid amides and anilides
                                Thio ethers
                                Esters of aliphatic and aromatic sulfonic acids
                                Disulfides

IV. Compounds insoluble in water and ether

Only carbon, hydrogen, oxygen   Aliphatic, alicyclic and certain aromatic poly-
  present: carboxylic acids (gallic acid, phthalic acid,
                                  etc.)
                                Hydroxyanthraquinones
                                High molecular ketones (anthraquinones, etc.)
                                Polymerization products of aldehydes (para-
                                  formaldehyde, etc.)

Nitrogen present: Aminoanthraquinones
                                      High molecular aromatic bases (benzidine and
                                         benzidine derivatives)
                                      Acid amides and anilides
                                      Phenylhydrazones of aldehydes and ketones
                                      Salts of inorganic and organic acids with or-
                                         ganic bases
Sulfur present: Sulfones
                                      Polymeric thioaldehydes
                                      Sulfamide derivatives of secondary amines

V. Compounds insoluble in water, soluble in 10 % hydrochloric acid

                                      Amines
                                      Amino acids
                                      Aryl substituted hydrazines
                                      N-dialkyl amines
                                      Amphoteric compounds

*VI. Compounds insoluble in water, soluble in 10 % sodium
hydroxide and in 10 % sodium bicarbonate solutions*

Only carbon, hydrogen, oxygen   Acids and anhydrides
  present: Hydroxyanthraquinones
Nitrogen present: Amino aromatic acids
                                      Nitro acids
                                      Cyano acids
                                      Polynitrophenols
Halogens present: Halo acids
                                      Polyhalo phenols
Sulfur present: Sulfonic acids
                                      Sulfinic acids
                                      Mercaptans
Nitrogen and sulfur present: Nitro thiophenols
                                      Sulfates of weak bases
                                      Sulfonamides
Sulfur and halogens present: Sulfonhalides

*VII. Compounds insoluble in water and 10 % sodium bicarbonate
solution; soluble in 10 % sodium hydroxide solution*

Only carbon, hydrogen, oxygen   Phenols
  present: Enols

References pp. 148–150

Nitrogen present: Amino acids
Nitro phenols
Amides
Amino phenols
Cyano phenols
N-monoalkyl aromatic amines
N-substituted hydroxylamines, prim. and sec. nitroparaffins
Trinitro aromatic hydrocarbons
Oximes
Ureides

Halogens present: Halo phenols

Sulfur present: Mercaptans
Thiophenols

Nitrogen and halogen present: Polynitro halogenated aromatic hydrocarbons
Substituted phenols

Nitrogen and sulfur present: Alkyl sulfonamides
Aryl sulfonamides
Amino thiophenols
Amino sulfonic acids
Thioamides

VIII. Compounds insoluble in all previously employed solvents

Nitrogen present: Anilides and toluidides
Amides
Nitro arylamines
Nitro hydrocarbons
Diarylamines
Azo-, hydrazo-, and azoxy-compounds
Dinitro phenylhydrazines
Nitriles
Amino phenols

Sulfur present: Sulfides
Sulfones
N-dialkyl sulfonamides
Thio esters
Thiourea derivatives

IX. Compounds soluble in concentrated sulfuric acid, insoluble in all other solvents previously tried

Alcohols
Aldehydes and ketones
Esters
Ethers
Unsaturated hydrocarbons
Anhydrides

References pp. 148–150

X. Compounds containing no nitrogen or sulfur, insoluble
in all other solvents tried previously

Hydrocarbons
Halogen derivatives of hydrocarbons

The differentiation between soluble, difficulty soluble, and insoluble in the behavior of organic compounds towards the solvents cited in I–IX is not sharp. Accordingly, certain types of compounds are included in various solubility classes.

REFERENCES

1. For example, R. Kempf and F. Kutter, *Schmelzpunkttabellen zur organischen Molekular-analyse* (1928), Photostatic reproduction, Ann Arbor, 1944; W. Utermark, *Schmelzpunkt-tabellen organischer Verbindungen*, Berlin, 1953.
2. Comp. L. Rosenthaler, *Mikrochemie ver. Mikrochim. Acta*, 35 (1950) 164.
3. See J. de Ment, *Fluorochemistry*, New York, 1945, Chapter XII regarding fluorescence colors of organic compounds.
4. Ch. Dhéré and L. Laszt, *Compt. rend.*, 226 (1948) 809.
5. Comp. M. Pesez and R. Poirier, *Méthodes et Réactions de l'Analyse Organique*, Vol. III, Chap. IX, Paris, 1954.
6. H. Kunz-Krause, *Apoth. Ztg.*, 31 (1916) 903.
7. N. D. Cheronis and J. B. Entrikin, *Semimicro Qualitative Organic Analysis*, New York, 1947, p. 85.
8. J. Drost, *Z. anal. Chem.*, 71 (1927) 144.
9. F. Feigl, unpublished studies.
10. F. Feigl and C. P. J. da Silva, *Ind. Eng. Chem., Anal. Ed.*, 14 (1942) 316.
11. F. Feigl and G. B., Heisig, *Anal. Chim. Acta*, 3 (1949) 561.
12. F. Emich, *Z. anal. Chem.*, 56 (1917) 1.
13. F. Feigl and D. Goldstein, *Mikrochim. Acta*, (1956) 1317.
14. F. Feigl, D. Goldstein and M. Steinhauser, unpublished studies.
15. Ö. Schewket, *Biochem. Z.*, 224 (1930) 329.
16. H. Král, *Z. anal. Chem.*, 36 (1897) 696.
17. F. Foerster and K. Kubel, *Z. physik. Chem.*, 139 (1924) 261.
18. L. Rosenthaler, *Z. anal. Chem.*, 109 (1937) 32.
19. F. Feigl and E. Silva, unpublished studies.
20. E. Paterno and A. Mazzucchelli, *Gazz.*, 38 (1908) 137.
21. W. Ostwald, *Kolloid-Beih.*, 2 (1911) 409; P. P. v. Weimarn, *ibid.*, 22 (1926) 38; H. Sommer, *Ind. Eng. Chem., Anal. Ed.*, 12 (1940) 368.
22. F. Feigl and A. Caldas, unpublished studies.
23. H. E. Feigl, unpublished studies.
24. F. Beilstein, *Ber.*, 5 (1872) 620.
25. See H. Meyer, *Analyse und Konstitutionsermittlung organischer Verbindungen*, I, 5th ed., Berlin, 1931, p. 132, and J. van Alphen, *Rec. Trav. Chim.*, 52 (1933) 567.
26. H. Jurány, *Mikrochim. Acta*, (1955) 135.
27. F. Feigl, unpublished studies.
28. W. H. Rauscher, *Ind. Eng. Chem., Anal. Ed.*, 9 (1937) 296.
29. F. Feigl, *Anal. Chem.*, 27 (1955) 1318.
30. F. Vieboeck *et al.*, *Ber.*, 63 (1930) 2819, 3207.
31. J. H. de Boer, *Chem. Weekblad*, 21 (1924) 404.
32. Compare F. Feigl, *Chemistry of Specific, Selective and Sensitive Reactions*, New York, 1949, p. 560.

33. F. Feigl and L. Badian, unpublished studies.
34. B. Fetkenheuer, *Chem. Abstr.*, **17** (1923) 1938.
35. Comp. G. Canneri and A. Cozzi, *Anal. Chim. Acta*, **2** (1948) 321.
36. S. K. Hagen, *Mikrochemie*, **15** (1934) 313.
37. F. Feigl and D. Goldstein, unpublished studies.
38. J. L. Lassaigne, *Ann.*, **48** (1843) 367.
39. See G. Kainz and A. Resch, *Mikrochemie ver. Mikrochim. Acta*, **39** (1952) 75.
40. F. Feigl, *Z. anal. Chem.*, **74** (1928) 369; compare F. Raschig, *Ber.*, **48** (1915) 2088.
41. F. Feigl and L. Badian, unpublished studies.
42. F. L. Hahn, *Ind. Eng. Chem., Anal. Ed.*, **17** (1945) 199.
43. C. A. Vournasos, *Ber.*, **43** (1910) 2269.
44. F. Feigl and Cl. Costa Neto, unpublished studies.
45. F. Feigl, *Mikrochemie*, **13** (1933) 132.
46. F. Feigl and L. Badian, unpublished studies.
47. J. L. Lassaigne, *Ann.*, **48** (1843) 367.
48. R. H. Baker and C. Barkenbus, *Ind. Eng. Chem., Anal. Ed.*, **9** (1937) 135.
49. H. Middleton, *Analyst*, **60** (1935) 154.
50. C. L. Wilson, *Analyst*, **63** (1938) 332.
51. See G. Kainz and A. Resch, *Mikrochemie ver. Mikrochim. Acta*, **39** (1952) 75, as well as G. Kainz and F. Schoeller, *Mikrochim. Acta*, (1954) 327, regarding the reaction of fused potassium with organic substances.
52. Comp. F. J. Smith and E. Jones, *A Scheme of Qualitative Organic Analysis*, London, 1953, p. 13.
52a.W. Schlenk, *Ann.*, **363** (1908) 313.
53. F. Feigl and L. Badian, unpublished studies.
54. For an improved procedure compare G. Kainz and F. Schoeller, *Mikrochim. Acta*, (1954) 333.
55. F. Feigl and D. Goldstein, unpublished studies.
56. F. Feigl, *Z. anal. Chem.*, **61** (1922) 454; **74** (1928) 386; **77** (1929) 299.
57. Compare S. A. Hall, *Advances in Chemistry*, Series 1 (1950) 150; S. A. Hall *et al., Anal. Chem.*, **23** (1951) 1830; **23** (1951) 1866.
58. F. Feigl and W. A. Mannheimer, unpublished studies.
59. A. Bettendorf, *Z. anal. Chem.*, **9** (1870) 105.
60. P. Arthur, T. E. Moore and J. Lambert, *J. Am. Chem. Soc.*, **71** (1949) 3260.
61. J. Golse, *Bull. Soc. Pharm. Bordeaux*, **67** (1929) 84.
62. F. Feigl and R. Moscovici, unpublished studies.
63. F. Feigl and A. Schaeffer, *Anal. Chim. Acta*, **7** (1952) 507.
64. D. Davidson, *Ind. Eng. Chem., Anal. Ed.*, **12** (1940) 40.
65. Compare F. Feigl, Ref. 32, page 121.
66. J. Goerdeler and H. Domgoergen, *Mikrochemie ver. Mikrochim. Acta*, **40** (1953) 212.
67. F. Feigl and A. Schaeffer, *Anal. Chim. Acta*, **4** (1950) 458.
68. H. Marshall, *Chem. News*, **83** (1901)76; *Z. anal. Chem.*, **43** (1904) 4181.
69. O. Kempf, *Ber.*, **38** (1906) 3963.
70. O. Kempf, *Ber.*, **39** (1907) 3717, 3726.
71. G. F. Smith, *Anal. Chim. Acta*, **8** (1953) 397.
72. F. Feigl and A. Caldas, *Anal. Chim. Acta*, **13** (1955) 526.
73. A. Merget, *Compt. rend.*, **73** (1871) 1356.
74. J. Stone, *Ind. Eng. Chem., Anal. Ed.*, **5** (1933) 220.
75. F. Feigl, *J. Chem. Education*, **22** (1945) 344.
76. G. Sachs, *Analyst*, **78** (1953) 185.
77. F. C. Philips, *Z. anorg. Chem.*, **6** (1894) 237.
78. P. Artmann, *Z. anal. Chem.*, **60** (1921) 81.
79. D. Davidson, *J. Chem. Education*, **19** (1942) 221, 532.
80. C. S. Marvel and F. E. Smith, *J. Am. Chem. Soc.*, **45** (1923) 2696.
81. F. Feigl, Cl. Costa Neto and J. E. R. Marins, unpublished studies. See also F. Feigl and C. P. J. Silva, *Ind. Eng. Chem., Anal. Ed.*, **14** (1942) 316; L. Velluz and M. Pesez, *Ann. Pharm. France*, **4** (1946) 10.

82. F. Feigl and V. Gentil, unpublished studies.
83. F. Feigl, V. Gentil and D. Goldstein, unpublished studies.
84. F. Feigl, V. Gentil and J. E. R. Marins, unpublished studies.
85. F. Feigl, V. Gentil and D. Goldstein, unpublished studies.
86. F. Feigl and V. Gentil, *Mikrochim. Acta*, (1954) 435.
87. W. M. Hearon and R. G. Gustavson, *Ind. Eng. Chem., Anal. Ed.*, 9 (1937) 352.
88. F. Feigl and D. Goldstein, unpublished studies.
89. R. L. Shriner and R. C. Fuson, *Identification of Organic Compounds*, 3rd edition, New York, 1948, p. 115; see also L. Malaprade, *Compt. rend.*, 186 (1928) 382; P. Fleury and S. Boisson, *ibid.*, 204 (1937) 1264.
90. Compare G. Hughes and T. P. Newell, *Trans. Faraday Soc.*, 44 (1948) 941.
91. R. Fuchs, R. C. Waters and C. A. van der Werf, *Anal. Chem.*, 24 (1952) 1514.
92. F. Feigl and V. Gentil, unpublished studies.
93. R. J. Williams and M. A. Woods, *J. Am. Chem. Soc.*, 59 (1937) 1408.
94. F. Feigl, W. A. Mannheimer and L. Vokac, unpublished studies.
95. H. Fehling, *Ann.*, 72 (1849) 106; see also B. Herstein, *J. Am. Chem. Soc.*, 32 (1910) 779.
96. B. Tollens, *Ber.*, 14 (1881) 1950; 15 (1882) 1635, 1828.
97. Compare G. T. Morgan and F. M. G. Micklethwait, *J. Soc. Chem. Ind.*, 21 (1902) 1375.
98. F. Feigl, *Chemistry and Industry*, 16 (1938) 1161.
99. L. Rosenthaler, *Pharm. Acta Helv.*, 29 (1954) 23.
100. T. H. Lee, *Chem. News*, 72 (1895) 153.
101. L. Crismer, *Chem. Ztg.*, 4 (1889) 81.
102. J. Meisenheimer, *Ber.*, 36 (1903) 4174; J. Meisenheimer and E. Patzig, *Ber.*, 39 (1906) 2526; *Ber.*, 50 (1919) 1161. Comp. also R. D. Block and D. Bolling, *J. Biol. Chem.*, 129 (1939) 1.
103. R. Kuhn and F. Weygand, *Ber.*, 69 (1936) 1969.
104. P. K. Bose, *Z. anal. Chem.*, 87 (1932) 110.
105. Comp. M. Pesez and P. Poirier, *Méthodes et Réactions de l'Analyse Organique*, Paris, 1954, pp. 7, 10, 21.
106. F. Feigl and L. Vokac, *Mikrochim. Acta*, (1955) 101.
107. M. Pesez and P. Poirier, *loc. cit.*, p. 22.
108. A. L. Le Rosen, R. T. Moravek and J. K. Carlton, *Anal. Chem.*, 24 (1952) 1335. Comp. G. Denigès, L. Chelle and A. Labat, *Précis de Chimie Analytique*, 7e ed., Paris, 1930, p. 176.
109. F. Feigl and Cl. Costa Neto, unpublished studies.
110. P. Ehrlich, *Z. klin. Medizin*, 5 (1882) 285.
111. R. Burian, *Ber.*, 37 (1904) 696; H. Pauly, *Z. physiol. Chem.*, 44 (1905) 159.
112. Comp. M. Pesez and P. Poirier, *Méthodes et Réactions de l'Analyse Organique*, Vol. III, Paris, 1954, p. 82.
113. A. Bondi (Rehovot), unpublished studies.
114. R. L. Pr. Colmant, *Chem. Zbl.*, 1931, I, 3705.
115. Comp. P. Karrer, *Organic Chemistry*, 4th Engl. Ed., New York, 1950, p. 580.
116. F. Feigl, V. Gentil and J. E. R. Marins, *Anal. Chim. Acta*, 13 (1955) 210.
117. F. Feigl and V. Gentil, unpublished studies.
118. R. Adams, *J. Am. Chem. Soc.*, 41 (1919) 247.
119. F. Feigl and A. Caldas, *Anal. Chim. Acta*, 8 (1953) 117, 339.
120. G. Reddelien, *Ber.*, 35 (1903) 2904.
121. R. L. Shriner and R. C. Fuson, *Identification of Organic Compounds*, 2nd edition, New York, 1940, page 23.

Chapter 4

Detection of Characteristic Functional Groups in Organic Compounds

The tremendous number of organic compounds would present a vast chaos of materials if there were no possibility of arranging them into classes (alcohols, carboxyl compounds, amines, etc.) whose members can be characterized with respect to their structural constitution, since they contain certain identical groups of atoms within the framework of their molecules. Accordingly, one of the most important tasks of qualitative organic analysis is to recognize with certainty such typical groups. When attempting this task, it must be kept in mind that in many cases there exist distinct relations between atom groups and the chemical and physical properties of an organic compound. The same group whose presence constitutes the basis for the classification of an organic compound is often the place in the molecule where chemical reactions are likely to occur. It has become customary to designate such groups as functional groups. It is clear that organic compounds may include not merely one but two or even more different functional groups in their molecule.

Comparatively few characteristic functional groups can be detected directly, that is by rapid reaction with suitable reagents which produce compounds having an appropriate insolubility, a distinctive color in day- or ultraviolet light, or other properties which may be the basis for identification by means of spot reactions. Usually it is necessary to subject the sample to condensation, oxidation, etc. reactions, to arrive at products which, in their turn, can be detected easily by appropriate reagents in the form of a spot reaction. These are known as indirect tests, in contrast to the direct tests referred to previously. In spot test analysis the preliminary operations on the starting material, which are necessary for the production of characteristic and sensitive reacting compounds, must be such as can be successfully conducted on a micro- or semimicro scale without too great loss of the prime material and with little expenditure of time. Because of these requirements, it is by no means possible to employ in spot test analysis all of the tests which are of use in organic macroanalysis.

The objectives of the examination for functional groups in organic compounds correspond somewhat to the testing for certain cationic or anionic constituents in inorganic compounds. However, the literature of inorganic analysis contains much observational material concerning the influence on and impairment of analytically usable reactions by accompanying materials, but as yet such records exist to only a limited extent with respect to organic analysis. This lack or paucity of information must be taken into account when applying the tests described in this chapter. When testing for functional groups in organic compounds, account must be taken not only of the behavior of organic accompanying materials toward the reagents being employed, but also of a special circumstance that plays no part in inorganic analysis. In contrast to ions, functional groups are not independent participants but they represent only the active portions of the molecular species taking part in the reaction. Consequently, the remainder of the molecule has an influence on the solubility of the particular compound and its reaction products in either water or organic liquids, on the speed and extent of the reactions, and also on the color of the reaction products in daylight or ultraviolet light. In isolated cases, these influences can be so extensive that certain compounds do not respond at all to tests for functional groups even though these tests are known to be applicable to other materials containing these groups. Sometimes such departures from the general rules are so characteristic that the failure to give a particular reaction picture can be of real diagnostic value. As a rule, deviations of this kind are only a matter of degree. This shows itself in the finding that the values for the limit of identification vary widely at times when compounds containing the same functional group are tested under the same circumstances. In this respect, see the Tables included in Chapter 8.

Tests for functional groups do not necessarily demand that the test material be in solution. Sometimes fusion or sintering reactions can be made with the solid sample. In such cases, reactions may sometimes be realized which do not occur al all in solution. Spot test analysis also makes use of the reactions of gaseous thermal fission products, which are brought into contact in the vapor phase with suitable reagents, and thus reveal the presence or absence of particular functional groups. Reactions in the vapor phase deserve special attention when testing for functional groups in compounds which are volatile at room temperature or on gentle warming, i.e. in compounds, which have a notable vapor pressure. If this is the case, a test which is merely selective when conducted in solution, can be rendered specific for an individual compound. Examples are given in Chapter 5.

Because of their importance, many organometallic compounds can be the subject of qualitative organic analysis. Sometimes it is possible to test them directly for functional groups. The more reliable method, however, is first to decompose the material being tested in such manner that the organic constituent remains intact and can be isolated. Although no general procedure can be advocated, this goal is often achieved by treating organometallic compounds with acids, hydrogen sulfide, alkali hydroxide and the like, and then taking up the liberated organic compounds in solvents which are not miscible with water.

It is not good practice to start the chemical examination of organic materials with tests for typical groups of atoms. Rather, as in qualitative inorganic analysis, a series of preliminary tests should be made which will often afford valuable clues as to which atomic groups are likely to be present or absent. Directions for carrying out such exploratory tests have been given in Chapter 3. On the other hand, tests to establish the presence of functional groups should invariably precede the testing for particular organic compounds (Chapter 5). When testing for functional groups it is always advisable (particularly for beginners) to set up "model tests". In these, trials are made with a compound which contains the functional group in question, and at various concentrations. In this way, the operator becomes acquainted with the typical reaction picture. If more than one test is available, the trials should not be limited to a single selected test. Such comparative tests are no great handicap in spot test analysis since but little time and material are consumed and the same conditions apply to repetitions of a procedure. Not only is a greater certainty thus secured in judging the results of an examination of a material but in addition the intensity of the response yields an orientation concerning the possible amounts of active material present. This semi-quantitative testing is particularly valuable if tests of different sensitivities are applied to equal amounts of the sample.

1. Nitroso Compounds (NO-group)

Nitroso compounds may be divided into two classes: (a) the N-nitroso compounds know as nitrosamines, in which the NO-group is attached to nitrogen as in $\begin{matrix} R \\ R_1 \end{matrix}$N—NO (R and R_1 = alkyl or aryl radical) and (b) the C-nitroso compounds in which the NO-group is attached to a carbon atom in an alkyl or aryl radical. The second class also includes the iso-nitroso compounds in which the NO-group is enolized to an NOH-group.

An indication of the presence of C-nitroso compounds is furnished by the fact that frequently they are green, or if colorless in the crystalline state (e.g. nitrosobenzene) they assume a green or blue color when fused or vaporized. Furthermore, freshly prepared solutions in benzene, alcohol, ether, etc.

turn blue on standing and especially when warmed. Nitroso compounds, which form salts because of basic groups in the molecule, show this color change only after they are liberated from their salts by the addition of caustic alkali. In contrast, N-nitroso compounds are yellow liquids or solids, which show no color change when the state of aggregation is changed.

There is a fundamental difference between the two classes of nitroso compounds in their behavior toward hydrazoic acid. Even when warmed C-nitroso compounds give no reaction with sodium azide and dilute hydrochloric acid, whereas N-nitroso compounds are quickly denitrosated even at room temperature: [1]

$$\text{>N—NO} + HN_3 \rightarrow \text{>NH} + N_2O + N_2$$

(Trials were run on p-nitroso-diphenylamine and acylnitrosamines.) Alkyl nitrites (compare page 168) are likewise decomposed by hydrazoic acid. This process, together with the following tests may be of value in characterizing C-nitroso compounds.

(1) *Test with phenol and sulfuric acid (Liebermann test)* [2]

When warmed with phenol and concentrated sulfuric acid, aliphatic nitroso and *iso*-nitroso compounds and aromatic nitroso compounds give a red color, which turns blue with alkalis. The sulfuric acid probably saponifies nitroso compounds with production of nitrous acid, which nitrosates the phenols in the unoccupied p-position. The resulting nitroso-phenols condense in their isomeric NOH (oxime) form with excess phenol to produce quinoid indophenol dyes (compare tests (1) and (2) for phenol, page 182.

The following test is characteristic for nitroso-compounds, provided alkyl nitrites are absent, since the latter, as derivatives of nitrous acid, likewise show the Liebermann reaction.

Procedure. [3] A little of the powdered substance is melted in a microcrucible along with a particle of phenol. After cooling, a few drops of pure concentrated sulfuric acid are added. The sample turns dark cherry-red. After diluting with a little water, the solution is made alkaline with a few drops of 4 N sodium hydroxide. The solution then turns deep blue. A solution of the sample in ether, which evaporates readily, may be used instead of the solid.

Limits of identification attainable by means of this test are given in Table 7.

(2) *Test with sodium pentacyanoammine ferroate* [3]

Nitroso compounds form brightly colored complex compounds with the prussic salts: sodium pentacyanoaquo ferroate $Na_3[Fe(CN)_5H_2O]$ and sodium pentacyanoammine ferroate $Na_3[Fe(CN)_5NH_3]$. This color reaction [4] depends on the exchange of the water or ammonia molecule of the prussic salt for a molecule of the nitroso compound:

$$Na_3[Fe(CN)_5NH_3] + RNO \rightarrow NH_3 + Na_3[Fe(CN)_5RNO]$$

$$Na_3[Fe(CN)_5H_2O] + RNO \rightarrow H_2O + Na_3[Fe(CN)_5RNO]$$

It is noteworthy that the entrance of the RNO molecule into the inner sphere of the prussic salt, with expulsion of the NH_3 or H_2O molecule, occurs only in the light. In the dark, the exchange proceeds at an immeasurably slow rate. This is one of the very rare examples of the direct application in spot test analysis of a photo reaction. Other instances may be found in the test for primary aromatic amines (page 272) and of coumarin (page 419).

TABLE 7. NITROSO COMPOUNDS

Name	Formula	Test with			
		$C_6H_5OH + H_2SO_4$		$Na_3[Fe(CN)_5NH_3]$	
		Limit of identification	Color	Limit of identification	Color
p-Nitrosodimethylaniline	$(CH_3)_2NC_6H_4NO$	$0.5\,\gamma$	Pink-yellow-green	0.15γ	Emerald green
p-Nitrosophenol	HOC_6H_4NO	$0.4\,\gamma$	Red-blue	0.15γ	Dark green
α-Nitroso-β-naphthol	$C_{10}H_6(NO)(OH)$	$0.5\,\gamma$	Red-blue	$1\,\gamma$	Olive green
β-Nitroso-α-naphthol	$C_{10}H_6(NO)(OH)$	$0.6\,\gamma$	Red-green	$1\,\gamma$	Olive green
Tetrahydro-β-nitroso-α-naphthol	$C_{10}H_{10}(NO)(OH)$	$0.5\,\gamma$	Red-green	—	No reaction
Isonitroso acetylacetone	$CH_3COCH_2COCH:NOH$	$1\,\gamma$	Dark red to green-yellow	$2.5\,\gamma$	Brown lilac
Isonitroso acetophenone	$C_6H_5COCH:NOH$	$1\,\gamma$	Brick-red to yellow	$3\,\gamma$	Green

Aromatic thioaldehydes and a few thioketones[5] also react with prussic salts to give a blue color; certain aromatic hydrazines give a red or violet color. This result probably likewise involves an exchange reaction with NH_3 and

H_2O molecules of the prussic salts. Interference due to hydrazines may be prevented by the addition of a few drops of formaldehyde; formhydrazone is formed at once and it does not react with prussic salts.

The following compounds give blue or blue-green products with sodium pentacyanoammine ferroate [6]: thiourea, phenylthiourea, formamidine disulfide, thiouracil. A reddish color is produced with isonicotinic acid (in contrast to nicotinic acid and picolinic acid, which do not react).

It is noteworthy that pyridine (contrary to picoline) hinders the color reaction of nitroso compounds with sodium pentacyanoammine ferroate [7]; this masking is based probably on the formation of sodium pentacyanopyridine ferroate.

Procedure. A drop of the test solution or a small amount of the not dissolved sample is mixed on a spot plate with several drops of a freshly prepared 1 % solution of sodium pentacyanoammine ferroate. After a little while, an intense green color, or more rarely, a violet color, is formed.

Limits of identification attainable by means of this test are given in Table 7.

(3) *Detection of N-nitroso compounds (nitrosamines) by hydrolytic splitting off of nitrous acid* [8]

The decomposition of nitrosamines by hydrazoic acid (see page 154) does not rest exclusively on a direct denitrosation. It may also result from the constant removal of nitrous acid from the equilibrium, in an acid medium,

$$\text{>N—NO} + H_2O \rightleftharpoons \text{>NH} + HNO_2$$

through the irreversible redox reaction

$$HNO_2 + HN_3 \rightarrow H_2O + N_2O + N_2$$

Consequently, even a minor hydrolytic splitting can thus run to completion. In harmony with this viewpoint is the fact that N-nitroso compounds, at suitable pH values, show the reactions of nitrous acid which is not true at all or only to a slight extent of C-nitroso compounds, which do not undergo an adequate primary hydrolytic cleavage.

The nitrous acid resulting from nitrosamines can be detected by means of the Griess reagent, which yields a red color (Procedure I). Certain N-nitroso compounds give this color reaction even on slight warming with this acetic acid solution of sulfanilic acid and α-naphthylamine. For the general test, it is best to warm the sample plus the reagent solution in the presence of strong hydrochloric acid. The chemistry of this test is discussed on page 165.

The nitrous acid furnished by the hydrolysis equilibrium may also be caused to react with sulfamic acid:

$$HNO_2 + NH_2SO_3H \rightarrow H_2SO_4 + H_2O + N_2$$

This procedure is less sensitive but is satisfactory in many cases. Since the barium salt of sulfamic acid is soluble in water, the redox reaction may be revealed by the precipitation of barium sulfate if Ba^{+2}-ions are present. The reaction is obviously the inorganic counterpart of the familiar exchange of NH_2-groups bound to C-atom for OH-groups which is brought about by nitrous acid. This exchange, which is the basis of a macro test and also a gravimetric method for determining nitrite,[9] can be translated into the technique of spot test analysis (Procedure II).

In both I and II, the hydrolytic splitting of N-nitroso compounds can be accomplished in the wet way by acid. In conformity with its stoichiometric representation, this hydrolysis should also be realizable in the absence of acid. Actually, if dry mixtures of nitrosamines with hydrated manganese sulfate or zinc sulfate are heated the following sequence occurs. The sulfates lose their water and the resulting superheated steam accomplishes the hydrolysis to yield volatile nitrous acid, which can then be detected in the vapors by means of the Griess reagent (procedure III). If C-nitroso compounds are subjected to this treatment, they yield no nitrous acid.

Procedure I. A micro test tube is used. One drop of the test solution is treated with a drop of the Griess reagent and one drop of 1 : 1 hydrochloric acid and the mixture is warmed in a water bath. If nitrosamines are present, a more or less intense red-violet develops within several minutes.

Reagents: 1) 1% solution of sulfanilic acid in 30% acetic acid
2) 0.1% solution of α-naphthylamine in 30% acetic acid

The Griess solution is prepared by mixing equal volumes of 1 and 2 just prior to use.

This procedure revealed:

10	γ N-nitroso-dibenzylamine	0.4 γ	N-nitroso-methylurea
9	γ N-nitroso-dicyclohexylamine	4 γ	N-nitroso-piperazine
1	γ N-nitroso-diphenylamine		

Procedure II. A drop of the aqueous, alcoholic, etc. test solution and a drop of the reagent solution are mixed in a micro test tube and then heated gently, if necessary, by plunging the test tube into warm water. A precipitate or turbidity appears if nitrosamines are present. A blank is advisable when slight amounts are suspected.

Reagent: 5 grams $BaCl_2 \cdot 2 \ H_2O$ and 5 grams sulfamic acid (amidosulfonic acid) are dissolved in 100 ml of a mixture of equal volumes of water and dioxan. Any precipitate should be filtered off (Pyrex filtering crucible). The reagent solution becomes turbid on standing and should be filtered before use. The procedure revealed:

10 γ   N-nitroso-methylurea
10 γ   N-nitroso-diphenylamine

Procedure III. A micro test tube is used. One drop of the test solution or a little of the solid is mixed with several centigrams of $MnSO_4$.aq. and, if necessary, taken to dryness. The mouth of the test tube is covered with a disk of filter paper moistened with Griess reagent (see Procedure I). The heating over a micro flame is continued until strong caramelization has occurred. In the presence of nitrosamines, a red-violet stain appears on the colorless paper.

The procedure revealed:

20 γ N-nitroso-dicyclohexylamine
5 γ N-nitroso-diphenylamine
15 γ Di-N-nitroso-piperazine

(4) Detection of aliphatic nitrosamines [9a]

Aliphatic nitrosamines are denitrosated by hydrazoic acid to yield secondary amines (comp. page 154) which react in characteristic manner with carbon disulfide and ammoniacal copper solution. Brown copper dithiocarbamates result which give brown solutions in benzene. The salts are formed directly from the components:

$$CS_2 + NHRR_1 + \tfrac{1}{2}Cu^{+2} + NH_3 \rightarrow S\,C \overset{\displaystyle S-Cu/_2}{\underset{\displaystyle NRR_1}{\diagdown}} + NH_4^+$$

The procedure given here is reliable, of course, only in the absence of secondary aliphatic amines. After denitrosation with hydrazoic acid, aromatic and aryl-aliphatic nitrosamines, and likewise N-nitrosated acylamides, do not react.

Procedure. The test is conducted in a micro test tube. The solid or the evaporation residue from a solution is treated with a little solid sodium azide and several drops of dilute hydrochloric acid. The mixture is gently warmed until no more gas is evolved. One drop of 5% solution of copper sulfate is then introduced and an excess of ammonium hydroxide is added. The blue solution is then shaken with 2 drops of a mixture prepared from 3 parts benzene and 1 part carbon disulfide. A positive response is signalled by the benzene layer becoming yellow or brown.

The test revealed:

1 γ N-nitroso-dibenzylamine
500 γ N-nitroso-dicyclohexylamine
10 γ Di-N-nitroso-piperazine

2. p-Nitroso-aromatic Amines $\left(>\!N\!-\!\!\left\langle\;\right\rangle\!\!-\!NO\text{-group}\right)$

Test with palladium chloride

A very selective and sensitive test for palladium (and a colorimetric determination of this metal) is based on the formation of a colored pre-

References pp. 314–319

cipitate when an alcoholic solution of a *p*-nitroso-aromatic amine is added to weakly acidic solutions of palladium salts [10].

The product is an addition compound of the two components. The possible coordination centers [11] are indicated in (I), (II) and (III).

$$\overset{>}{N}\!-\!\langle\ \rangle\ N{=}O \qquad \overset{>}{N}\!-\!\langle\ \rangle\!-\!N{=}O \qquad \overset{>}{N}\!-\!\langle\ \rangle\!-\!N{=}O$$

$$\underset{2}{\underline{PdCl_2}} \qquad\qquad\qquad \underset{2}{\underline{PdCl_2}} \qquad\qquad\qquad \underset{2}{\underline{PdCl_2}}$$

$$\text{(I)} \qquad\qquad\qquad \text{(II)} \qquad\qquad\qquad \text{(III)}$$

The formation of the colored addition products can also be used as the basis for a sensitive and highly selective test for *p*-nitroso-aromatic amines [12].

The following facts should be kept in mind when carrying out this test. Many amines and amino phenols form addition compounds with palladium chloride. Although nearly all of them are yellow and cannot be confused with the red nitrosopalladium compounds, they may consume all of the reagent and hence small amounts of nitroso amines may escape detection.

1,2- and 2,1-nitroso-naphthols and their derivatives react with $PdCl_2$, forming insoluble, brown-violet inner complex palladium salts. Such phenols can be removed if the material to be tested is treated with an aqueous solution of potassium or sodium hydroxide and extracted with ether. The nitrosoamines are taken up by the ether, whereas the phenols remain in the aqueous layer as alkali phenolates.

Procedure. One drop of the test solution or a small amount of the solid and one drop of the palladium chloride solution are mixed in a depression of a spot plate. The immediate production of a colored precipitate or a color is taken as a positive response. Small amounts require a blank test.

Reagent: Palladium chloride solution: 0.1 g $PdCl_2$ and 0.2 g NaCl in 100 ml water.

This procedure revealed:

    0.05 γ *p*-Nitroso-aniline (brown)
    0.05 γ *p*-Nitroso-dimethylaniline (bright red)
    0.05 γ *p*-Nitroso-diethylaniline (bright red)
    0.05 γ *p*-Nitroso-diphenylamine (bright red)

3. *o*-Nitroso-phenols $\left(\ \rangle\!-\!\overset{-OH}{_{-NO}}\text{-group}\ \right)$

Test by formation of cobalt (III) chelate compounds [13]

When dissolved, *o*-nitroso-phenols (I) give an equilibrium with their tautomeric *o*-quinone oxime forms (II):

$$\begin{array}{ccc} \diagdown\!\!-OH & \diagdown\!\!=O & \diagdown\!\!=O\diagdown \\ \diagup\!\!-NO & \rightleftharpoons \diagup\!\!=NOH & \diagup\!\!=N\diagup \hspace{-0.3em}Co/_3 \\ (I) & (II) & (III) \end{array}$$

The quinone oxime group combines with a number of metal ions to produce water-insoluble inner complex salts or water-soluble complex compounds yielding inner complex metal-containing anions, provided the molecule also contains hydrophilic groups such as CO_2H, SO_3H, etc. The most familiar of such salts are those of trivalent cobalt, which contain this metal in the chelate ring (III).

The water-insoluble inner complex salts of trivalent cobalt are brown-red. They dissolve in chloroform, carbon tetrachloride, etc. to give brown-red solutions, a fact first noted with the classic instance of α-nitroso-β-naphthol.[14] The water-soluble salts containing inner complex bound cobalt (III) have this same color; they cannot be taken up in chloroform. Organic compounds containing the groups (I) and (II) are widely used as reagents in inorganic qualitative and quantitative analysis.[15]

The ability to form chelate compounds of trivalent cobalt (compounds of divalent cobalt are also producted in isolated instances [16]) can be utilized for the selective detection of o-nitroso-phenols. In this connection, information concerning the presence or absence of hydrophilic groups in the nitroso-phenol molecule is furnished by the behavior toward organic solvents that are not miscible with water.

Procedure. A drop of the test solution is placed on filter paper along with a drop of 0.1% cobalt nitrate solution and the paper is then held over ammonia water. A positive response is signalled by a brown-red to yellow stain, which is resistent to 2 N sulfuric acid.

The test revealed:

1 γ	α-nitroso-β-naphthol	5 γ	nitroso R salt
1 γ	β-nitroso-α-naphthol	0.25 γ	dinitroso-resorcinol

4. Nitro Compounds (NO₂-group)

(1) Detection by fusion with tetrabase or diphenylamine [17]

If nitro compounds are added to molten tetrabase (m.p. 91°) or molten diphenylamine (m.p. 53°), or if their solid mixtures with these bases are heated to 100°, colored, usually orange-red, melts are obtained. These color reactions are based on the formation of colored molecular compounds between nitro compounds and tetrabase or diphenylamine. They have the respective general structures:

$$R-N=O \ldots \overset{\overset{\displaystyle CH_3}{|}}{\underset{\underset{\displaystyle CH_3}{|}}{N}}-C_6H_4-CH_2-C_6H_4-\overset{\overset{\displaystyle CH_3}{|}}{\underset{\underset{\displaystyle CH_3}{|}}{N}} \qquad \overset{\overset{\displaystyle C_6H_5}{|}}{\underset{\underset{\displaystyle C_6H_5}{|}}{HN}} \ldots O=N-R$$

References pp. 314–319

The addition compounds are soluble in the molten bases (solvation). The postulate of solvate formation is supported by the finding that in the case of some nitro compounds the colored melts become colorless when cooled or take on the color of the dry mixture. This signifies that the molecular compounds in these instances are stable only in the form of their solvates and dissociate into their components on cooling.

Mono- and polynitro compounds behave alike with respect to the formation of molecular compounds and their solvation in the melts of these bases. In general, the molecular compounds of the poly compounds are more intensely colored and more stable than the mono compounds. The presence of p-quinoid compounds interferes with the test because they yield red solvates of the respective molecular compounds when fused with tetrabase or diphenylamine. The melts with quinoid compounds lose their color on cooling.

Procedure. The test is conducted in a micro conical tube (Emich centrifuge tube). One drop of the ether or benzene solution of the sample, and one drop of a 5% solution of tetrabase or diphenylamine in benzene are introduced and the tube then dipped into boiling water. After the solvent has evaporated, a melt remains in the narrow part of the tube; it is more or less yellow depending on the quantity of nitro compound present. It is best to run comparison tests with a drop of the reagent solution alone if slight amounts of nitro compounds are to be detected.

The procedure revealed:

50	γ	nitromethane	0.2 γ	p-nitrophenetol	
0.5	γ	tetranitromethane	1 γ	o-nitrobenzaldehyde	
0.8	γ	nitrobenzene	3 γ	o-nitrobenzoic acid	
1	γ	p-(o)-dinitrobenzene	0.1 γ	2,4-dinitrochlorobenzene	
0.25	γ	p-nitrobenzonitrile	2.5 γ	3-nitro-4-hydroxybenzyl alcohol	
2	γ	p-nitraniline	0.2 γ	1,2,4-dinitrophenol	
2	γ	p-(m)-nitrophenol	0.1 γ	2,4-dinitroresorcinol	
1	γ	1-nitronaphthalene	5 γ	chloromycetin	

(2) Test by reaction with sodium pentacyanoammine ferroate after reduction to nitroso compounds [18]

The color reaction of nitroso compounds with sodium pentacyanoammine ferroate, described on page 154, can also be applied to the detection of nitro compounds, if the nitro group is reduced to the nitroso group. This reduction can be carried out electrolytically in a drop of the test solution. The electrolysis is accomplished in neutral or alkaline solution, in the presence of the reagent, and between a nickel and a lead electrode. [19]

Procedure. A drop of the alcoholic or aqueous test solution is mixed in a microcrucible with a drop of a freshly prepared solution of 1% sodium pentacyanoammine ferroate and a drop of 4 N alkali. If the addition of alkali causes a coloration, a drop of 4% sodium sulfate solution should be used instead as the electrolyte.

The current is then allowed to pass through the solution in the microcrucible, using a nickel wire as cathode and a lead wire as anode. The current can be drawn from a flashlight battery or a 4-volt storage battery. The electrolysis should continue for at least 10 minutes; for small amounts of test substance, up to half an hour. The liquid becomes colored during the electrolysis. The color, which deepens on standing, is usually green, more seldom violet.

A blank test with sodium sulfate shows no alteration in the pale yellow color, but with alkali there is a slight deepening in the yellow shade.

The *limits of identification* for different nitro compounds attained with this test are given in Table 8.

If sufficient sample is available, it is well to make the reduction of nitro to nitroso groups by warming with calcium chloride and metallic zinc.[20]

Procedure. A few milligrams of sample is dissolved in 3 ml of hot alcohol in a test tube and 6–7 drops of 10% calcium chloride solution added. After introducing 50 mg zinc dust, the mixture is heated to strong boiling in a water bath. The liquid is filtered and the cooled filtrate is treated with one drop of 1% $Na_3[Fe(CN)_5NH_3]$. If nitro compounds are present, the color becomes purple, blue, or green.

This procedure revealed not only the compounds included in Table 8 but also: 3-nitro-4-amino-anisol, 2-amino-4-nitro-phenetol, 4-nitro-veratrol, 4-nitro-5-amino-veratrol, 3-nitro-4-acetamino-veratrol, o-nitraniline, p-nitroacetanilide, 1-nitro-2-naphthol, 4-nitropyridine-N-oxide, 4-nitroquinoline-N-oxide, 6-methoxy-8-nitroquinoline, 5-nitro-furfural semicarbazone, 2,4-dinitro-chlorobenzene, 2,4-dinitrotoluene, 2,4-dinitrophenol, 2,4-dinitro-phenylhydrazine, 3,5-dinitrotoluene, 2,4-dinitro-1-naphthol-7-sulfonic acid (sodium salt), trinitrobenzene, 2,4,6-trinitrotoluene.

Chloromycetin can likewise be detected by this procedure. Therefore, it is likely that the procedure for the detection of this compound given on page 499 can also be used for the detection of other nitro compounds.

(3) Test for m-dinitro compounds by reaction with potassium cyanide [21]

If *m*-dinitro compounds are warmed with a solution of alkali cyanide, a red-brown to violet color or precipitate is formed. The color is permanent in the presence of dilute acids. This behavior is in contrast to that of nitrophenols, whose color change is reversed when acids are added. The constitution of these products of the cyanide reaction is only partly known.

TABLE 8. NITRO COMPOUNDS

Name	Formula	Limit of identification	Color
Nitrobenzene	$C_6H_5NO_2$	1.5 γ	Dark violet
o-, m-, p-Chloronitro-benzene	$ClC_6H_4NO_2$	2 γ 3 γ 15 γ	Green
m-Dinitrobenzene	$C_6H_4(NO_2)_2$	3 γ	Brown-violet
o-, p-Nitrotoluene	$CH_3C_6H_4NO_2$	7 γ 8 γ	Violet-red
o-, p-Nitrophenol	$C_6H_4(OH)NO_2$	0.4 γ 0.4 γ	Dark green
Picric acid	$C_6H_2(OH)(NO_2)_3$	8 γ	Dark olive green
o-, m-, p-Nitrobenzal-dehyde	$C_6H_4(CHO)NO_2$	4 γ	Olive green
m-, p-Nitrobenzoic acid	$C_6H_4(COOH)NO_2$	8 γ 2.5 γ	Lilac dark green
o-, m-, p-Nitrocinnamic acid	$NO_2C_6H_4CH{=}CHCOOH$	3 γ 4 γ 3 γ	Green
o-, m-, p-Nitraniline	$C_6H_4(NH_2)NO_2$	4 γ 4 γ 0.25 γ	Green
1,5-Nitronaphthyl-amine	$C_{10}H_6(NH_2)NO_2$	0.3 γ	Dark brown
o-, m-, p-Nitrophenyl-hydrazine	$NH_2NHC_6H_4NO_2$	0.5 γ 1.5 γ 0.5 γ	Green
6-Nitroquinoline	$C_9H_6N{\cdot}NO_2$	5 γ	Light green

References pp. 314-319

Presumably they are substituted phenylhydroxylamines.[22] [23] For example, 2,4-dinitrophenol (I) reacts with potassium cyanide to produce the potassium salt (II) of 4-nitro-2-hydroxylamino-3-cyanophenol (meta-purpuric acid):

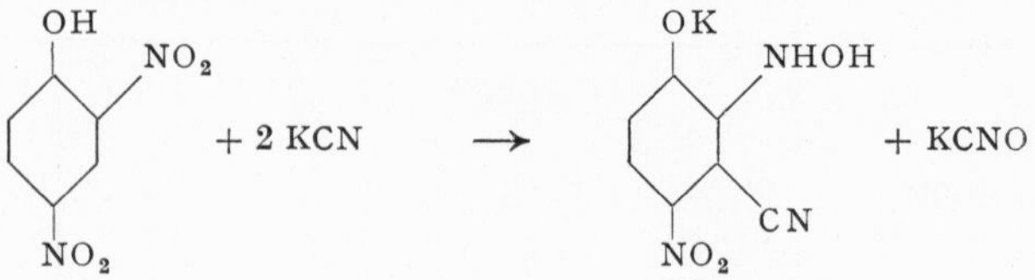

TABLE 9. m-DINITRO COMPOUNDS

Name	Formula	Limit of identification	Color
m-Dinitrobenzene	$C_6H_4(NO_2)_2(1, 3)$	10 γ	Violet
Chlorodinitrobenzene	$C_6H_3Cl(NO_2)_2(1, 2, 4)$	1 γ	Red
Picryl chloride	$C_6H_2Cl(NO_2)_3(1, 2, 4, 6)$	2 γ	Red-brown
Dinitrophenol	$C_6H_3(OH)(NO_2)_2(1, 2, 4)$	1 γ	Red
Picric acid	$C_6H_2(OH)(NO_2)_3(1, 2, 4, 6)$	2 γ	Red-brown
Dinitraniline	$C_6H_3(NH_2)(NO_2)_2(1, 2, 4)$	1 γ	Red
Picramine	$C_6H_2(NH_2)(NO_2)_3(1, 2, 4, 6)$	2 γ	Red-brown
Dinitrochlorobenzoic acid	$C_6H_2Cl(COOH)(NO_2)_2(1, 4, 2, 6)$	2 γ	Red-brown
Dinitroaminobenzoic acid	$C_6H_2(NH_2)(COOH)(NO_2)_2(1, 4, 2, 6)$	1 γ	Red-brown
1,8-Dinitronaphthalene	$C_{10}H_6(NO_2)_2(1, 8)$	10 γ	Brown
Dinitro-α-naphthol	$C_{10}H_5(OH)(NO_2)_2(1, 2, 4)$	2 γ	Dark brown

1,8-Dinitronaphthalene is different from the other peri-naphthalene derivatives and behaves like a m-dinitronaphthalene with potassium cyanide. Mononitrobenzene and o-dinitrobenzene derivatives and also 1,5-dinitronaphthalene do not react; therefore m-dinitro compounds may be detected even in the presence of other nitro compounds.

References pp. 314–319

Procedure. A drop of a solution or a few grains of the solid is mixed with a drop of 10 % potassium cyanide solution in a microcrucible and heated gently over a microburner. In the presence of *m*-dinitro compounds, a violet or red color appears. It remains unchanged even on the addition of a few drops of 2 *N* hydrochloric acid.

The *limits of identification* attained with this test are shown in Table 9.

(4) Detection of aromatic polynitro compounds through saponification to alkali nitrite [24]

Aliphatic and aromatic mono- and polynitro compounds exhibit characteristic differences in their behavior toward alkali hydroxide. Whereas, aliphatic nitro compounds are saponified by dilute alkali even in the cold, aromatic mononitro compounds, with a few exceptions, remain unaltered even after prolonged boiling with concentrated alkali. On the other hand, aromatic polynitro compounds produce considerable quantities of alkali nitrite after even brief warming with concentrated alkali. Accordingly, at least one of the nitro groups in the molecule undergoes the reaction:

$$R\text{—}NO_2 + 2\ KOH \rightarrow R\text{—}OK + KNO_2 + H_2O$$

This difference in the behavior of alkali hydroxide toward mono- and polynitro compounds (with the nitro groups in the *ortho* and *para* positions) is in accord with the rule, which applies throughout the entire aromatic series, that negative substituents always activate and render groups in the *ortho* and *para* position mobile. Strangely enough, *meta* dinitro compounds likewise react under the conditions given here.

The alkali nitrite produced by the saponification of aromatic polynitro compounds can be detected by means of the Griess test [25]. This very sensitive reaction involves the diazotization of sulfanilic acid (I) and the coupling of the resulting diazonium compound or its cation (II) with α-naphthylamine (III) to produce the red water soluble azo dye (IV):

If aryl and alkyl nitrites and aliphatic nitro compounds are absent, the following procedure is characteristic for aromatic polynitro compounds. No nitrite is formed when C- and N-nitroso compounds are warmed with alkali solutions; an exception is N-dinitrosopiperazine.

Procedure.[26] A micro test tube is used. A tiny particle of the solid or a drop of its alcohol solution is treated with a drop of 1 N alkali and taken to dryness. The cooled residue is then treated with one drop of an acetic acid solution of sulfanilic acid and one drop of an acetic acid solution of a-naphthylamine. Depending on the amount of polynitro compound present, a pink or red color appears.

Reagents: *1*) 0.5% solution of sulfanilic acid in 1 : 1 acetic acid.
          2) 0.3% solution of a-naphthylamine in 1 : 1 acetic acid.

After saponification, the following gave a strong nitrite reaction:

Dinitrobenzene (1,2; 1,3; 1,4)	Dinitro-o-cresol (3,5; 3,4)
2,4-Dinitrochlorobenzene	2,4-Dinitro-1-naphthol-7-sulfonic acid
Dinitrotoluene (1,2,4; 1,2,6)	Dinitronaphthalene (1,5; 1,8)
4-Chloro-1-bromo-dinitrobenzene	2,4-Dinitrophenylhydrazine
Dinitrophenol (1,2,4)	Trinitrobenzene (1,3,5)
Dinitroaniline (1,2,4)	Trinitrophenol (2,4,6)
Dinitrobenzoic acid (1,2,4; 1,3,5)	Trinitrotoluene (2,4,6)
Dinitroxylene (1,2,4,6; 1,2,3,4)	Trinitro-m-cresol (2,4,6)
3,5-Dinitrosalicylic acid	Hexanitrodiphenylamine

The sensitivity of this test is shown by the following identification limits:

0.5 γ	o,p-Dinitrobenzene	1	γ	2,4-Dinitroresorcinol
1	γ	2,4-Dinitrochlorobenzene	0.1 γ	Trinitrophenol (2,4,6)
1	γ	Dinitrophenol (1,2,4)	0.5 γ	Hexanitrodiphenylamine
0.5 γ	3,5-Dinitrosalicylic acid			(dipicrylamine)

(5) Acidic polynitro compounds

Detection with rhodamine B[27]

In the absence of other acidic groups, the acidic character of organic nitro compounds is due to the enolization of the NO_2 to the NO_2H group. In the case of aliphatic primary and secondary nitro compounds, there is an equilibrium between the tautomeric forms:

$$—CH_2—NO_2 \rightleftharpoons —CH=NO_2H$$
$$CH—NO_2 \rightleftharpoons C=NO_2H$$

In the case of aromatic nitro compounds, the acidification results from the rearrangement into quinoidal compounds with development of NO_2H groups.

For example, the following equilibria are established in the case of p-nitro-phenol and hexanitrodiphenylamine, respectively:

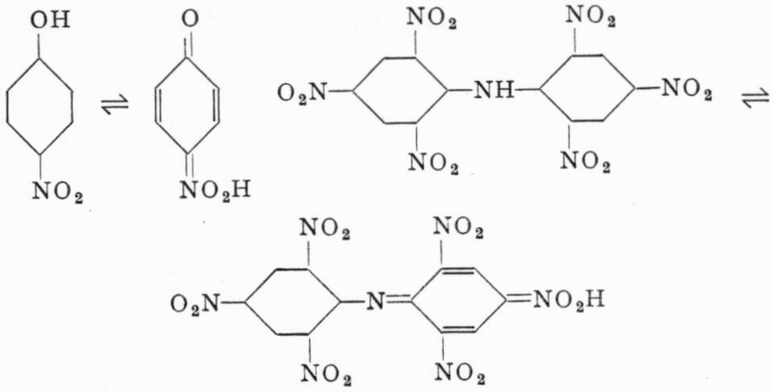

Enolizable aliphatic and aromatic nitro compounds give yellow solutions in caustic alkali because formation of the water-soluble alkali salts removes the *aci*-form from the equilibrium.

Such equilibrium disturbances can be effected even in the absence of water by forming salts with rhodamine B. This is shown by the fact that the color-less solution of rhodamine B in benzene (toluene), which contains the *lacto*-form of the dyestuff, immediately turns red on the addition of nitro com-pounds which are able to produce nitroxy acids on enolization. This salt formation, beginning with the *lacto*-form, can be represented schematically as:

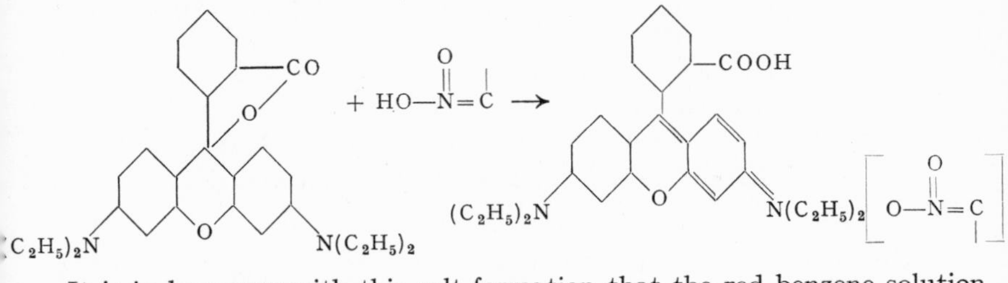

It is in harmony with this salt-formation that the red benzene solution shows the same orange fluorescence in ultraviolet light as the benzene solu-tion of salts of rhodamine B with complex metal halogeno acids (see Volume I, Chapter 3).

Many enolizable nitro compounds can be detected directly through the salt formation on treatment with a benzene solution of rhodamine B.* How-

* The following mononitro compounds, which are capable of enolization, were tested with the colorless reagent solution: nitromethane, nitroethane, the 3 isomeric nitrophenols, p-nitraniline, 5-nitrosalicylic acid. With the exception of the last compound, the color and fluorescence reac-tion were not evident with amounts less than $2500\,\gamma$. No reaction is given by o-nitrophenol below 0.5 gram. In contrast to mononitro compounds, polynitro compounds give a decided reaction in γ-quantities. Consequently, nitro and carboxyl groups in enolizable compounds seem to exert a positive influence on the occurrence of the reaction with rhodamine B.

References pp. 314-319

ever, this procedure is not reliable. Certain phenols, mercapto compounds, carboxylic acids, and sulfonic acids yield red solutions, while others are made red through treatment with a benzene solution of rhodamine B. Salts of the latter are obviously formed in these cases.

Red benzene-soluble dyestuff salts are likewise formed by bringing together alkaline solutions of *aci*-nitro compounds and a mineral acid solution of rhodamine B and then shaking out with benzene. If an ether-benzene mixture is used for the extraction, the reaction picture remains unchanged in the case of acidic polynitro compounds. In contrast, the color (fluorescence) reaction is considerably weakened for enolizable mononitro compounds, and it disappears entirely for phenol, and carboxylic and sulfonic acids. This is in line with the observation that the red color of a benzene solution of rhodamine B which has reacted with phenol is discharged on the addition of ether, obviously because of the dissociation of the rhodamine phenolate.

Trials with about 80 acidic compounds (in amounts of 5–10 mg per drop) have shown that the thio compounds (mercaptobenzothiazole, thionalide as well as benzimidazole) react in a fashion analogous to that of acidic polynitro compounds. Therefore, a positive response to the rhodamine B reaction is not entirely decisive. However, it is of value in detecting enolized polynitro compounds in the presence of enolized mononitro compounds.

Procedure. One drop of the weakly alkaline solution is placed in a micro test tube and five drops of rhodamine B solution added. Five drops of ether-benzene mixture is introduced and the mixture vigorously shaken. The presence of enolizable polynitro compounds is indicated by a pink or yellow color in the upper layer along with an orange fluorescence in ultraviolet light.

Reagents: 1) 0.1% solution of rhodamine B in 4% hydrochloric acid.
            2) Mixture of equal volumes of benzene and ether.

This procedure revealed:

0.25	γ	dipicrylamine (2,4,6,2′,4′,6′-hexanitrophenylamine)
0.5	γ	picric acid (2, 4, 6-trinitrophenol)
1	γ	picrolonic acid [3-methyl-4-nitro-1-(*p*-nitrophenyl)5-pyrazolone]
4	γ	5-nitrosalicylic acid
10	γ	Martius yellow (alkali salt of 2,4-dinitrophenol)
10	γ	naphthol yellow (alkali salt of 2,4-dinitro-1-naphtholsulfonic acid)
500	γ	2,4-dinitrophenol
2000	γ	*p* (*m*)-nitrophenol

5. Nitrites and Nitrates (—O—NO and —O—NO$_2$-groups)

Test through oxidation of diphenylamine or diphenylbenzidine [28]

Among the organic nitrates are the salts of nitric acid with organic nitrogen bases (B) which as B·HNO$_3$ represent organic derivatives of ammonium nitrate (NH$_3$·HNO$_3$). As solids or in solution they contain the NO$_3^-$ anion, and with few exceptions are water-soluble. The best known exception is nitron nitrate.[29] The —O—NO$_2$-group occurs in non-ionogenic form in the alkyl nitrates R—O—NO$_2$, which are alcohol esters of nitric acid. These esters of the lower C-numbers are sweet smelling, mobile liquids, which explode violently when heated. The nitric esters of polyhydric alcohols (nitroglycerine, nitrocellulose, etc.) are solids if the parent alcohols are solid.

Salts of the nitrous acids with organic bases cannot be isolated. The nitrous esters (R—O—NO) are isomeric with the corresponding nitro compounds (R—NO$_2$), but differ from these stable materials in the ease with which they are saponified into nitrous acid and the respective alcohol.

The test for all organic nitrates and nitrites is based on the fact that they oxidize diphenylamine and diphenylbenzidine (dissolved in concentrated sulfuric acid) to intensely blue quinoidal compounds.[30] This oxidation of diphenylamine or diphenylbenzidine is brought about by the nitric or nitrous acid produced on saponification of alkyl nitrates or nitrites:

(I) Diphenylamine (colorless)

↓ + (HNO$_3$, HNO$_2$)

(II) N,N'-diphenylbenzidine (colorless)

↓ + (HNO$_3$, HNO$_2$)

(III) Quinoidimonium salt of (II) (blue)
X = $^1/_2$ S O$_4$$^{-2}$, Cl$^-$, etc.

It is apparent from this series of reactions that the use of diphenylbenzidine instead of diphenylamine has the advantage of making more effective use of the oxidizing action of the nitric or nitrous acid, and consequently the sensitivity of the test for the —O—NO- and —O—NO$_2$-groups is raised.

Certain aliphatic nitro compounds are resistant to diphenylamine (and probably diphenylbenzidine).[31] The test gives a negative result with RCH$_2$NO$_2$, R$_2$C(NO$_2$)$_2$ and R'''C(NO$_2$)$_3$ when R =alkyl and R''' =alkyl or NO$_2$. The result is positive with RCH(NO$_2$)R' and RC(NO$_2$)R$_2$'' when R =alkyl, R' =alkyl, NO$_2$ or halogen and R'' =alkyl or halogen.

Procedure. About 0.5 ml of the reagent solution is placed on a spot plate and a little of the test material (fragment of a solid or a drop of a solution or suspension) is added. A blue ring is formed; the intensity of the color depends on the nitrate or nitrite content.

(a) with diphenylamine (b) with diphenylbenzidine

Limit of Identification: 0.5 γ nitric acid 0.07 γ nitric acid

Reagent: Several crystals of diphenylamine or diphenylbenzidine are covered with concentrated sulfuric acid. A little water is added. After solution is complete, more concentrated sulfuric acid is added. About 1 mg of the solute should be present in 10 ml of the finished reagent solution.

$$\overset{\text{O}}{\underset{\|}{}}$$

6. Azoxy Compounds (—N=N-group)

Test by conversion into hydroxydiazo compounds [32]

If aromatic azoxy compounds, which contain this group in open chains, are allowed to stand in contact with concentrated sulfuric acid or are gently warmed with it, they are converted into the isomeric azo-hydroxy compounds (hydroxydiazo compounds). For example:

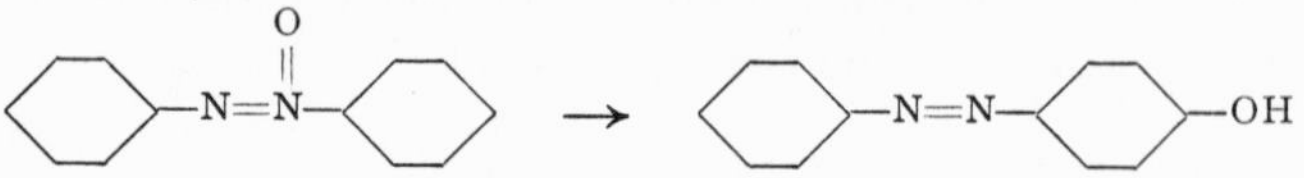

This so-called Wallach transformation [33] is accompanied by a color change because the resulting hydroxydiazo compounds in sulfuric acid solution are not so highly colored as the isomeric azoxy compounds. The rearrangement apparently occurs via less stable, intensely colored intermediate compounds, probably of quinoidal character. These products, which are usually deep red or red-brown, appear within 3 seconds when the temperature is raised to 95°. The color deepens within 30 seconds and then fades somewhat because of the formation of the hydroxydiazo compounds. Polynitroazoxy compounds present an exception; their sulfuric acid solutions require longer or more intense heating to develop the optimum color intensification. The darkening observed when such solutions are boiled cannot be mistaken for charring (of a compound not containing an azo group) since the solution rapidly loses its color on further heating. Azo compounds which contain only the —N=N—group do not exhibit this behavior, the color of their concentrated sulfuric acid solutions remains unchanged even on boiling. On the other hand, aromatic compounds containing iodine directly attached to the nucleus (p-iodophenol, o-iodoaniline, etc.) show a similar behavior, but the color deepening occurs more slowly.

Procedure. A drop of the test solution (in a volatile solvent) is evaporated to dryness on a watch glass. A drop of concentrated sulfuric acid is added and the temperature raised to 95°. Comparison is made with an unheated blank.

The behavior of a number of azoxy compounds when warmed with concentrated sulfuric acid is given in Table 10.

TABLE 10

BEHAVIOR OF AZOXY COMPOUNDS WITH CONCENTRATED SULFURIC ACID

Azoxybenzenes	Color			
	Initial	3 sec 95° C	30 sec 95° C	boiled
Azoxybenzene	lemon yellow	very deep red	very deep red	—
3,3'-Difluoro	,,	orange	deep orange-red	—
3,3'-Dichloro	,,	orange-red	deep orange-red	—
4,4'-Dichloro	yellow	orange-red	bright blood red	—
3,3'-Dibromo	lemon yellow	orange-red	bright red	—
3,3'-Diiodo	yellow	dark red	intensely dark red-brown	—
α-4-Bromo	yellow-orange	deep red-brown	,,	—
β-4-Bromo	yellow	deep red-brown	,,	—
2,4,6,2',4',6'-Hexabromo	very pale brown	yellow-brown	deep rose-red	—
3,3'-Dinitro	yellow	yellow	yellow	red-brown very light brown
3,5,3,5'-Tetranitro	pale yellow	pale yellow	light yellow-brown	red-brown very pale
α-4-Nitro	greenish yellow	greenish yellow	orange-red	—
β-4-Nitro	pale yellow	orange-red	deep blood red	—
2,2'-Dimethyl	orange-brown	chocolate brown	intensely dark brown	—
4,4'-Dimethyl	orange	intensely dark blood red	deep red-brown	—
4,4'-Diphenyl	deep red	deep tyrian purple	purplish brown	—
2,2'-Dimethoxy	yellow-brown	olive green deep green very dark royal blue	deep bluish purple	—
4,4'-Dimethoxy	yellow-brown	deep red-brown	deep chocolate brown	—

7. Alcohols

(1) Detection of primary, secondary and tertiary alcohols with vanadium oxinate [34]

The black-green vanadium compound (I) of 8-hydroxyquinoline (oxine) can be precipitated from acetic acid solution. It is soluble in ethyl alcohol to yield a red solution, whereas in solvents such as benzene, toluene, trichlorethylene, that are not miscible with water, its solutions are grey-green. On addition of alcohol, these green solutions become red. If a water suspension of this phenol ester of orthovanadic acid [35] is treated with some alcohol and then shaken with benzene, etc., the second layer is not green but red. These findings indicate that the formation-tendency and stability of the red solvates of (I) are greater than those of the grey-green solvate. Probably these effects involve alcoholates, in which, as shown in (II), the OH-group of the ester acid takes over the binding of the alcohol molecules. This is corroborated by the fact that the orange oxine esters of molybdic and tungstic acids, for example (III), which contain no free OH groups, are not soluble in alcohol and organic liquids.

$$\text{(I)} \qquad \text{(II)} \qquad \text{(III)}$$

The color change of the grey-green benzene solution of vanadium oxinate is brought about by primary, secondary and tertiary alcohols, and also by some compounds containing alcoholic OH groups provided certain conditions are met. One of these requirements appears to be a slight solubility in benzene, toluene, etc. Accordingly, glycerol and esters of lactic acid bring about the color change, while sugars are ineffective. No effect is obtained with compounds which, in addition to alcohol groups, also contain carboxyl-, phenol groups, or basic nitrogen atoms. This is shown by the behavior of lactic-, tartaric-, citric,- and mandelic acid, and choline chloride.

Only grey-green solvates are formed by vanadium oxinate with phenols, ketones and ether, and when they are added to solutions of (I) in benzene, toluene, etc. there is no change in color.

The formation of red solvates of vanadium oxinate makes possible the detection of lower (water-soluble) and higher (benzene-soluble) alcohols. It is advantageous to use a benzene solution of vanadium oxinate as reagent.

References pp. 314–319

Procedure.[36] One drop of the test solution (in water, benzene, or toluene) is treated in a micro test tube with four drops of the grey-green reagent solution. The mixture is heated, with intermittent shaking, in a water bath at 60°. A color change to red after 2–8 minutes is easily visible. Slight color changes are best detected by conducting a comparison blank when only small amounts of alcohol are involved.

Reagent: Benzene solution of vanadium oxinate: One ml of a solution that contains 1 mg of vanadium is treated with 1 ml of 2.5% solution of 8-hydroxyquinoline in 6% acetic acid. The mixture is then shaken with 30 ml benzene. The reagent solution will keep for about one day.

The procedure revealed:

20 γ methyl alcohol	500 γ glycerol
20 γ ethyl alcohol	5 γ benzyl alcohol
20 γ *n*-butyl alcohol	10 γ 3-nitro-4-hydroxybenzyl alcohol
20 γ *iso*propyl alcohol	3 γ salicyl alcohol (violet)
5 γ amyl alcohol	10 γ cyclohexanol
6.5 γ cetyl alcohol	5 γ menthol
20 γ 2,4-dichlorophenoxyethyl alcohol	10 γ chloromycetin
100 γ glycol	5 γ borneol

The following gave a positive response: hexyl alcohol, octyl alcohol, methylcyclohexanol, benzoin (hot, yellow; on cooling, red), terpineol, terpenes, vitamin A, vitamin D_2, cinchonine, sitosterol, tropine, atropine, the insaponifiable residues of carnauba wax.

Xanthydrol, which is soluble in benzene, showed no reaction.

When using the test, it should be noted that thiols and amines give a green or yellow color, respectively, under the prescribed conditions.[36a]

(2) Test for primary and secondary alcohols by conversion into alkali-alkyl xanthates [37]

At room temperature, and in the presence of alkali hydroxides, primary and secondary alcohols react rapidly with carbon disulfide to give water-soluble alkali-alkyl xanthates:

$$ROH + CS_2 + NaOH \rightarrow CS(OR)(SNa) + H_2O$$
$$RONa + CS_2 \rightarrow CS(OR)(SNa)$$

All alkali-alkyl xanthates form violet products with molybdates in solutions containing an excess of mineral acid. (Compare the sensitive test for molybdenum with potassium-ethyl xanthate, Vol. I, Chap. 3.) The colored products, whose composition is $MoO_3 \cdot 2CS(OR)SH$,[38] are soluble in organic liquids, such as benzene, carbon disulfide, ether, chloroform. Primary and secondary alcohols can be detected by conversion to the respective xanthates followed by the molybdate reaction.

The xanthate-molybdate test for alcohols is not very sensitive, because the condensation of alcohols or alcoholates to alkali-alkyl xanthate is not quantitative. Furthermore, when xanthate solutions are acidified even in the presence of molybdate, there is an unavoidable partial decomposition of xanthates with regeneration of CS_2 and ROH.

Esters react similarly to alcohols since, under the conditions of the test, they are partially saponified to alcohols. Compounds containing the CH_2COCH_2 group also react with carbon disulfide and alkali. They form orange-red compounds [39] which on treatment with molybdates give chocolate-brown precipitates insoluble in chloroform. They therefore interfere with the detection of small amounts of alcohols by the xanthate test.

Procedure. [40] A drop of the test solution (in ether, if possible) is placed in a small test tube along with a drop of carbon disulfide and a few centigrams of powdered sodium hydroxide. The mixture is shaken for about 5 minutes. One or 2 drops of 1% ammonium molybdate solution are then added, and as soon as the alkali has dissolved, the solution is carefully acidified with 2 N sulfuric acid and shaken with 2 drops of chloroform. When primary or secondary alcohols are present in the test solution, the chloroform layer is violet.

The following amounts were detected:

1 mg ethyl alcohol	0.5 mg isoamyl alcohol
1 mg methyl alcohol	1.0 mg allyl alcohol
1 mg propyl alcohol	0.5 mg cyclohexanol
1 mg butyl alcohol	0.1 mg phenylethyl alcohol
1 mg isobutyl alcohol	

(3) Detection of secondary alcohols by heating with sulfur [41]

If nonvolatile compounds which contain secondary alcohol groups are fused for a short time with sulfur (m.p. 119°), hydrogen sulfide results from the redox reaction:

$$\overset{|}{\underset{|}{C}}HOH + S° \rightarrow \overset{|}{\underset{|}{C}} = O + H_2S$$

This reaction seems to be especially realizable with compounds which melt at temperatures between 120–180° or whose boiling points lie above this temperature range.

The procedure described here for the detection of secondary alcohols is not very sensitive but it has value if used in conjunction with tests (1) and (2).

Fatty acids with long chains, e.g., palmitic-, stearic-, and oleic acid, as well as fats and waxes likewise yield hydrogen sulfide when heated with elementary sulfur, a result that probably is related to a dehydrogenation of $-CH_2-CH_2$-to $-CH=CH$-groups. However, these reactions are sluggish even when much sulfur is used, while secondary alcohols rapidly give hydrogen sulfide when they are heated with even slight amounts of sulfur.

Procedure. A micro test tube is used. A little of the solid or a drop of its solution in alcohol, ether, etc., is treated with a drop of a 2% solution of sulfur in carbon disulfide. The mixture is brought to dryness by brief heating. The mouth of the test tube is covered with a disk of lead acetate paper and the tube is suspended in a glycerol bath previously heated to 150°. If necessary, the temperature is raised to 180°. If secondary alcohols are present, a black or brown stain (lead sulfide) appears on the paper within two or three minutes, the time depending on the amount present.

The procedure revealed: heated at

10 γ Benzoin $C_6H_5COCHOHC_6H_5$ 135–140 °

20 γ Benzoin oxime $C_6H_5C(NOH)CHOHC_6H_5$ 150–160 °

50γ Furoin   135°–150 °

20γ Xanthydrol   155 °

2γ Codeine   154°–160 °

50γ Chloromycetin $O_2N-\text{—}-CHOHCHCH_2OH$ 175 °
$\qquad\qquad\qquad\qquad\qquad\qquad\qquad NHCOCHCl_2$

200γ Ephedrine hydrochlorid $C_6H_5.CHOH.CHCH_3$ 180 °
$\qquad\qquad\qquad\qquad\qquad\qquad\qquad NHCH_3.HCl$

References pp. 314–319

200γ Menthol   H₃C, H, H₂ H₂, CH₃ CH₃   200 °

25γ Cholesterol   H₃C, CH₃, CH₃, CH₃, CH₃, HO   180 °

100γ Cholic acid   H₃C, OH, CH₃, COOH, CH₃, H, HO, H, OH   180 °

40γ Borneol   CH₃, H₃CCCH₃, —OH   200–210 °

Cyclohexanol (180 °), cinchonine (180–190 °), morphine (180–190 °), adrenaline (170 °), tropine (150–155 °) give also a positive response.

(4) Test for polyhydric alcohols by oxidation with periodic acid

Polyhydroxy alcohols, such as glycol, glycerol, erythritol, mannitol, etc., can be broken down to formaldehyde and formic acid by excess periodic acid in the cold; the periodic acid is reduced to iodic acid.[42, 43] The reaction can be expressed:

$$\text{CH}_2\text{OH} - [\text{CHOH}]_{n-1} - \text{CH}_2\text{OH} + n\ \text{HIO}_4 \rightarrow 2\ \text{CH}_2\text{O} + (n-1)\ \text{HCOOH} + n\ \text{HIO}_3 + \text{H}_2\text{O}$$

Sensitive tests are available for the organic products of this oxidation. Accordingly, the presence of polyhydroxy compounds can be established

References pp. 314–319

by treating the sample with periodate and then testing for (a) formaldehyde or (b) formic acid. The test described under (b), which is based on the detection of the formic acid, is more sensitive than that for formaldehyde (a), since, as the reaction shows, 1 molecule of a polyvalent alcohol furnishes only 2 molecules of CH_2O as against (n—1) molecules of HCOOH.

The reaction is given by almost all glycols and also by many carbohydrates that do not normally react with fuchsin–sulfurous acid; monosaccharides also give a positive reaction. Cane sugar gives the reaction only after boiling, when the acid probably breaks up the disaccharide into the two monosaccharides, which in turn give the glycol reaction.

The oxidation with periodic acid also permits a differentiation between tartaric and citric acid or their salts. Tartaric acid, which has two adjacent hydroxyl groups, is probably oxidized to glyoxylic acid, and reacts with fuchsin–sulfurous acid due to decomposition to formaldehyde, while citric acid shows no visible change.

(a) Oxidation with periodate and detection of formaldehyde [44]

The reaction with fuchsin-sulfurous acid (see page 208) can be used to detect the formaldehyde after destroying the excess periodate and iodate. Most polyhydroxy alcohols can then be detected, provided aldehydes are absent.

Procedure. A drop of the aqueous or alcoholic solution of the polyhydroxy alcohol is mixed in a microcrucible with a drop of 5% potassium periodate solution and a drop of 10% sulfuric acid and allowed to stand for 5 minutes. The excess periodic acid is then reduced with a few drops of saturated sulfurous acid, and the sample is treated with a drop of fuchsin-sulfurous acid. After a short time, at longest half an hour, a red to blue color appears. When testing for polysaccharides, the procedure is similar except that the contents of the covered crucible are heated to boiling and then likewise left to stand for about 5 minutes.

The following amounts were detected:

5	γ ethylene glycol	25	γ arabinose
2.5	γ glycerol	25	γ saccharose (with boiling)
5	γ mannitol	12.5	γ dextrose (with boiling)
25	γ glucose	50	γ starch (with boiling)
12.5	γ levulose	100	γ tartaric acid
25	γ lactose	100	γ mucic acid (dissolved in dioxan)

The following gave a positive reaction: erythritol, cherry gum, gum arabic.
The following did not react: citric acid, 1,10-decanediol, inositol, pentaerythritol, pentaacetylglucose, and acetylcellulose.

(b) *Oxidation with periodate and detection of formic acid* [45]

The detection of the formic acid produced when polyhydric alcohols are oxidized with periodic acid is based on the oxidation of formic acid with free bromine:

$$HCOOH + Br_2 \rightarrow 2\,HBr + CO_2$$

The carbon dioxide formed can be detected by passing the gas into baryta water (precipitation of $BaCO_3$). The formaldehyde produced along with formic acid by the action of periodic acid is also oxidised by bromine first to formic acid and then to carbon dioxide, so that all of the carbon of the polyhydroxy compound is converted into carbon dixode.

Procedure. The microdistillation apparatus (Fig. 29, page 50) is used. A little of the sample is treated with 2 drops of 5 % potassium periodate and 2 drops of 1 N sulfuric acid and warmed slightly. Bromine water is then added, drop by drop, until a distinct yellow is obtained. A glass bead is introduced and the stopper put in place. The distillation tube is inserted into a small test tube containing baryta water. (The reagent is protected against the carbon dioxide of the air by a layer of a paraffin oil.). The distillation apparatus is gently warmed. If the liquid in the receiver becomes turbid, polyhydroxy compounds are indicated.

The following quantities were detected by this procedure:

2.5 γ	glycerol	2.5 γ	maltose
3 γ	mannitol	7 γ	saccharose
5 γ	glucose	6 γ	lactose
5 γ	levulose	6 γ	dextrin
5 γ	arabinose	3 γ	mucic acid
2.5 γ	mannose	20 γ	starch

(5) *Other test for alcohols*

The conversion of $[Ce(NO_3)_6]^{-2}$ into $[Ce(OR)(NO_3)_5]^{-2}$ is accompanied by a color change (yellow to red) which can be used for the detection of primary, secondary and tertiary alcohols.[46] One ml of a solution containing 40 g $(NH_4)_2Ce(NO_3)_6$ in 100 ml 2 N nitric acid is diluted with 2 ml water or dioxan. To this is added a drop of a solution prepared by dissolving the material to be tested in as little water or dioxan as possible (*Idn. Limit:* about 400 γ). Aliphatic bases interfere by forming precipitates; oxidizable compounds (phenols and aromatic amines) by giving colored products.

References pp. 314–319

8. O- and N-Methyl Compounds (—OCH$_3$ and $>$NCH$_3$-groups)

Detection through oxidative cleavage with molten benzoyl peroxide [47]

Compounds containing the above groups are oxidatively split when they are heated to 120° with benzoyl peroxide (m.p. 103°):

$$\geq\!C\!-\!OCH_3 + (C_6H_5CO)_2O_2 \rightarrow \geq\!C\!-\!OH + (C_6H_5CO)_2O + CH_2O \qquad (1)$$

$$\geq\!NCH_3 + (C_6H_5CO)_2O_2 \rightarrow \geq\!NH + (C_6H_5CO)_2O + CH_2O \qquad (2)$$

The gaseous formaldehyde produced in (1) or (2) can be detected by bringing it into contact with a solution of chromotropic acid in concentrated sulfuric acid; a violet color appears. The chemistry of this very sensitive color reaction is discussed on page 331. Accordingly, the fusion reaction with benzoyl peroxide permits the reliable detection of methoxy and N-methyl groups in the absence of compounds, which give the formaldehyde reaction under the conditions of the test. Such materials include hexamethylenetetramine and its salts because of the distinct volatility at 120°. Vinyl compounds are likewise oxidatively split:

$$R\!-\!CH\!=\!CH_2 + 2\ (C_6H_5CO)_2O_2 \rightarrow (C_6H_5CO)_2O + RCHO + CH_2O$$

but as yet no extensive study has been made of the analytical use of this decomposition for the detection of vinyl compounds.

If O- and N-methyl compounds are dissolved in ether, they may readily be separated by shaking with dilute hydrochloric acid. The N-methyl compounds pass into the water layer as hydrochlorides, and may be extracted from this solvent with ether after the bases are liberated by alkali. The evaporation residues of such ether solutions can then be subjected to the benzoyl peroxide fusion. This procedure gives a reliable recognition of N-methyl compounds and even in the presence of ether-soluble vinyl compounds.

Procedure. The apparatus shown in Fig. 23, page 49 is used. A little of the solid or liquid sample, or a drop of its solution in benzene, ether or chloroform, is placed in the bulb. Two drops of a 10% solution of benzoyl peroxide in benzene are added. The solvent is evaporated. The apparatus is placed in a glycerol bath that has been heated to 120–130°. The knob of the stopper is charged with chromotropic acid solution and the stopper put in place. A positive result is given if the hanging drop becomes violet within several minutes. If care is used, the fusion may be accomplished without fulmination.

Reagent: Chromotropic acid-sulfuric acid mixture: Several mg of pure chromotropic acid is stirred with 2 ml of concentrated sulfuric acid. The reagent must be freshly prepared at not too long intervals.

A positive result was obtained with the following compounds; some of them have rather complicated structures:

O-methyl compounds: anisol, veratrol, *p*-methoxybenzhydrol, *p,p*-dimethoxybenzhydrol, methyl cellulose, codeine, brucine, papaverine.

N-methyl compounds: choline chloride, *m*-dimethylaminophenol, N-methyldiphenylamine, antipyrine, pyramidone, caffein, theobromine, theophylline, pilocarpine, methyl orange, methyl red, methyl violet, malachite green.

The usefulness of the procedure is shown its giving positive results with:

20 γ pyramidone	40 γ codeine
40 γ caffein	100 γ antipyrine
20 γ brucine	10 γ methyl orange

9. N-Ethyl Compounds ($>$NC$_2$H$_5$-group)

Detection through oxidative cleavage with molten benzoyl peroxide [47]

When heated to 120–130° with benzoyl peroxide, N-mono and N-diethyl compounds form acetaldehyde:

$$>NC_2H_5 + (C_6H_5CO)_2O_2 \rightarrow >NH + (C_6H_5CO)_2O + CH_3CHO$$

Consequently this oxidative splitting is analogous to that of O- and N-methyl compounds described in **8**.

The gaseous acetaldehyde yielded by the reaction can be detected by the blue color it gives when placed in contact with a solution of sodium nitroprusside containing morpholine (see page 334). This thus constitutes an indirect test for N-ethyl compounds.

With mild heating some ethoxy compounds are distinctly resistant to fused benzolyl peroxide. The splitting off of acetaldehyde is detectable only at higher temperature but then there is danger of explosive reaction.

Propenyl compounds likewise yield acetaldehyde when melted with benzoyl peroxide (see page 310).

To detect N-ethyl compounds with certainty it is best to start with a readily prepared aqueous mineral acid solution and to extract this with ether after it has been made alkaline. In this manner, ether solutions of the bases are obtained and the test is run on the latter.

Procedure. A micro test tube is used. A little of the solid or the evaporation residue of a drop of a solution is treated with 2 drops of a 10% solution of benzoyl peroxide in benzene and the mixture taken to dryness. The open end of the test tube is covered with a piece of filter paper that has been moistened with a drop of sodium nitroprusside-morpholine reagent. The tube is hung in a glycerol bath at 120–130°. Depending on the amount of N-ethyl compounds present, a more or less intense blue stain appears.

References pp. 314–319

Reagents: (a) 20% aqueous solution of morpholine.

(b) 5 % aqueous solution of sodium nitroprusside.

Equal volumes of (a) and (b) are united just before use.

A positive response was given by the following compounds; some of them have complicated structures:

Mono- and di-ethylaniline, N-ethyl-4-aminocarbazol, brilliant green, ethyl orange, coelestine blue, rhodamine B, procaine hydrochloride, procaine penicillin G, coramine (N,N-diethylnicotinamide), quinadrine hydrochloride (3-chloro-7-methoxy-9-(1-methyl-4-diethylaminobutylamino) acridine dihydrochloride dihydrate), chloroquine phosphate (7-chloro-4-(4-diethylamino-1-methylbutylamino) quinoline diphosphate).

The value of the procedure is indicated by its revealing: 25 γ Brilliant green, 50 γ rhodamine B, 15 γ ethyl orange.

The test is especially useful for the distinction of N-methyl and N-ethyl compounds which up to now was almost impossible. Examples are: coelestine blue-gallamine blue and brilliant green-malachite green.

10. Ethoxy Compounds (—OC₂H₅-group)

Detection by formation of acetaldehyde [47]

Acetaldehyde is produced if ethoxy compounds are treated with a solution of alkali bichromate in sulfuric acid. Probably, the initial step is hydrolysis to ethanol, followed by oxidation to acetaldehyde:

$$R—OC_2H_5 + H_2O \rightarrow ROH + C_2H_5OH$$
$$C_2H_5OH + O \rightarrow CH_3CHO + H_2O$$

This assumption is supported by the fact that many ethoxy compounds are promptly oxidized in the wet way to yield acetaldehyde, whereas the direct oxidation with benzoyl peroxide (see 9) does not succeed in all cases.

The acetaldehyde in the vapor phase can be detected by the bluing of sodium nitroprusside-morpholine solution.

The behavior of N-ethyl compounds toward chromic acid is not uniform; many compounds are not attacked. Consequently, it is advisable when testing for ethoxy compounds to remove any N-ethyl compounds. This is readily accomplished by shaking the chloroform test solution with dilute hydrochloric acid (formation of water-soluble hydrochlorides).

Procedure. A drop of the test solution * or better still a small amount of the not-dissolved sample is treated in a micro test tube with a drop of acidified bichromate solution. The mouth of the tube is covered with filter paper moistened with a drop of sodium nitroprusside-morpholine solution (for preparation see 10).

* Alcohol or ether may not be used as solvent because these ethoxy compounds produce acetaldehyde under the prescribed conditions.

References pp. 314–319

The test tube is placed in boiling water. If ethoxy compounds are present, a more or less intense blue fleck appears.

Reagent: Bichromate solution: 1 gram potassium bichromate is dissolved in 60 ml water and poured into 7.5 ml concentrated sulfuric acid (caution).

The procedure revealed:

30 γ phenetole $C_6H_5\text{-}OC_2H_5$
50 γ phenacetin $CH_3CONH\text{-}C_6H_4\text{-}OC_2H_5$
200 γ ethylmorphine hydrochloride dihydrate (dionin) $C_{19}H_{23}O_3N\cdot HCl\cdot 2\ H_2O$

A positive response was obtained with: ethyl benzoate, ethylamino benzoate (anesthesin), ethyl butyrate, ethyl lactate, diethyl phthalate, ethyl cellulose, and with the ethyl esters of phosphoric and thiophosphoric acids given on page 97.

It must be noted that ethylurethane and 3-ethoxy-4-methoxybenzylcyanide when treated with chromic acid, form no acetaldehyde, whereas this occurs when fused with benzoyl peroxide. Probably the two mentioned ethoxy-compounds are not hydrolyzed to ethanol, which is essential for the oxidation into acetaldehyde in the wet way.

11. Phenols

(1) Test with nitrous acid [48]

Many phenols form *p*-nitroso derivatives (I) with nitrous acid and these products, by reacting in the isomeric *p*-quinoid oxime form (II) condense with the excess phenol in the presence of concentrated sulfuric acid to yield the intensely colored indophenols (III): [49]

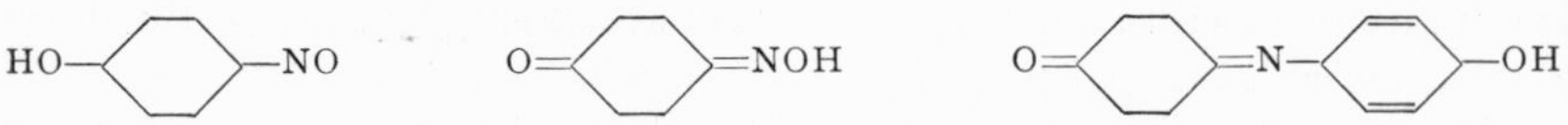

(I)   (II)   (III)

p-Substituted phenols and nitrophenols do not react; phenol ethers and thiophene give an intense phenol reaction.

Procedure. [50] A drop of the test solution (in ether) is allowed to evaporate to dryness in a microcrucible, then treated with a drop of concentrated sulfuric acid containing a little nitrous acid, swirled, and left for a few minutes. The sample is then cautiously diluted with a drop of water. Sometimes the color deepens. After cooling, the mixture is made alkaline with 4 *N* sodium hydroxide, when a further color change often results.

Reagent: Concentrated sulfuric acid containing 1% sodium nitrite (freshly prepared).

Table 11 gives the limits of identification obtained with this procedure.

References pp. 314–319

(2) Test with 5-nitroso-8-hydroxyquinoline [51]

The *Liebermann reaction*, described in Test *1*, is based on the conversion of a portion of the phenol present (with free *para* position) into *p*-nitrosophenol by action of nitrous acid and condensation of the resulting nitrosophenol (in its oxime form) with unchanged phenol to produce colored indophenols. An alternative method to obtain indophenol dyes is to use an appropriate *p*-nitrosophenol directly as the reagent. A light yellow solution of 5-nitroso-8-hydroxyquinoline (I) in concentrated sulfuric acid has been found suitable. Its oxime form, which reacts with phenols, is shown in (II). The condensation product of the oxime with carbolic acid is shown in the indophenol compound (III). Other phenols yield analogous indophenol dyes.

HO—⟨ ⟩—NO   O=⟨ ⟩=NOH   O=⟨ ⟩=N—⟨ ⟩—OH

(I)　　　　　　(II)　　　　　　(III)

Procedure. A drop of the alcoholic or alkaline–water solution of the test solution is evaporated to dryness in a microcrucible, and a drop of the reagent is added to the cold residue. The indophenol dyestuff is formed on gentle warming. A blank is recommended if only small amounts of phenol are suspected.

Reagent: 1% solution of 5-nitroso-8-hydroxyquinoline in concentrated sulfuric acid.

This procedure revealed:

1 γ phenol (dark brown)	5 γ *o*-nitrophenol (green-yellow)
2 γ resorcinol (red-violet)	5 γ *o*-cresol (dark brown)
7 γ pyrogallol (black)	5 γ xylenol (violet)
4 γ pyrocatechol (greenish black)	10 γ α-naphthol (dark brown)

(3) Test with nitrous acid and mercuric nitrate [52]

Nitrous acid solutions containing mercuric nitrate react with phenols, either in the cold or on slight warming, producing red colors or yellow precipitates, which dissolve in nitric acid to form red solutions. The reaction probably depends on the formation of a nitro compound, which then reacts with the phenol. Both aniline and phenol ethers also show this reaction, since they produce phenol on boiling with nitrous acid.

Di-*o*- and di-*m*-substituted phenols,[53] such as picric acid, do not react; neither do hydroxyanthraquinones. This *Millon test* is especially recommended for *p*-substituted phenols, which do not respond to Tests *1* and *2*.

Procedure. [54] A drop of the aqueous, alcoholic or ether solution is mixed in a microcrucible with a drop of the reagent solution and left for a few minutes. If

References pp. 314–319

no change occurs, the mixture is briefly heated to boiling over a microburner.
A red color forms in the presence of phenols.

Reagent: One part mercury is dissolved in one part fuming nitric acid and
diluted with 2 parts water.

The *limits of identification* and the colors for the different phenols are given in
Table 11.

TABLE 11.   PHENOLS

Name	Formula	Test with		
		Liebermann's reagent		Millon's reagent
Phenol	C_6H_5OH	1 γ	Blue-red-green	1 γ
Resorcinol	$C_6H_4(OH)_2$	5 γ	Red-blue	0.5 γ
Pyrocatechol	,,	5 γ	Green-red-blood-red	5 γ
Hydroquinone	,,	10 γ	Green-red	10 γ	Heating
Orcinol	$C_6H_3(OH)_2CH_3$	5 γ	Yellow-red-purple	5 γ
Phloroglucinol	$C_6H_3(OH)_3$	10 γ	Blood-red	5 γ
Pyrogallol	,,	10 γ	Violet-brown	5 γ
Thymol	$C_6H_3(CH_3)(C_3H_7)OH$	5 γ	Green-red-blue	
p-Nitrophenol	$C_6H_4(OH)NO_2$		No reaction	2 γ	Heating
o-Hydroxybenz-aldehyde	$C_6H_4(CHO)(OH)$	2 γ	Red-light green	5 γ
m-Hydroxy-benzalde-hyde	,,			10 γ
p-Hydroxybenz-aldehyde	,,		No reaction	1 γ	Heating
Protocatechuic aldehyde	$C_6H_3(CHO)(OH)_2$		No reaction	4 γ
Vanillin	$C_6H_3(CHO)(OCH_3)OH$		No reaction	4 γ

(continued)

References pp. 314–319

TABLE 11. PHENOLS (CONTINUED)

Name	Formula	Test with			
		Liebermann's reagent		Millon's reagent	
Methyl salicylate	$C_6H_4(OH)COOCH_3$			$1\,\gamma$	
Phenyl salicylate	$C_6H_4(OH)COOC_6H_5$	$4\,\gamma$	Green-red-blue		
p-Hydroxybenz-oic acid	$C_6H_4(OH)COOH$		No reaction	$2\,\gamma$	Heating
Methyl p-hy-droxy benzo-ate	$C_6H_4(OH)COOCH_3$		No reaction	$1\,\gamma$	Heating
α-Naphthol	$C_{10}H_7OH$		Green	$1\,\gamma$	
β-Naphthol			Dark green	$1\,\gamma$	
o-Hydroxy-quinoline	$C_9H_6(OH)N$		No reaction	$0.5\,\gamma$	
m-Hydroxy-cinnamic acid	$C_6H_4(OH)CH{:}CHCO_2H$			$5\,\gamma$	Do not heat

(4) Test by conversion into o-hydroxyaldehyde [55]

Phenols with free *ortho* position can be converted into o-hydroxyaldehydes by the long known Reimer-Tiemann synthesis.[56] This process, which is frequently employed in preparative organic chemistry, consists in protracted refluxing of the alkaline phenolate solution with chloroform. The conversion of phenols into phenol aldehydes can be represented by the net reaction:[57]

$$\begin{array}{c}\text{C—OK}\\\|\\\text{C—H}\end{array} + CHCl_3 + 3\,KOH \longrightarrow \begin{array}{c}\text{C—OK}\\\|\\\text{C—CHO}\end{array} + 3\,KCl + 2\,H_2O \qquad (1)$$

This reaction in general gives low yields. However, it can be utilized in the detection of many phenols, because aromatic aldehydes condense with hydrazine, in weakly alkaline, neutral, or weakly acid solution, to produce water-insoluble aldazines. The aldazines formed from o-hydroxyaldehydes:

$$2\;\begin{array}{c}\text{C—OH}\\\|\\\text{C—CHO}\end{array} + H_2N{-}NH_2 \longrightarrow \text{(aldazine)} + 2\,H_2O \qquad (2)$$

are distinguished by especially low water-solubility and without exception they display a yellow to orange fluorescence in ultra violet light. Both characteristics are probably related to the chelate nature of the aldazines. The fluorescence reaction between o-hydroxyaldehydes and hydrazine is very sensitive (see page 220), so that reaction (1) on the spot test scale produces sufficient o-hydroxyaldehyde to be detectable by (2).

Procedure. A drop of the alkaline test solution is evaporated to dryness in a microcrucible. The residue is treated with 10–20 drops of chloroform and taken to dryness in an oven. This treatment with chloroform is repeated once or twice. The residue is taken up in a drop of 6 N acetic acid, a drop of hydrazine solution is added, and the contents of the crucible transferred to filter paper (S & S 589). If phenols were present, a yellow to orange fluorescing fleck is seen on the paper under ultraviolet light. To avoid a false conclusion due to the self-fluorescence of phenols in acetic acid solution, it is well to conduct a blank with a drop of water in place of the hydrazine solution. In contrast to the fluorescence of the acid-stable aldazines, the fluorescence of phenols can usually be made to disappear by bathing the fleck in alcohol or 2 N hydrochloric acid.

Reagent: Hydrazine, solution: 10 g hydrazine sulfate boiled with 10 g sodium acetate in 100 ml water. Filter after cooling.

Table 12 gives the *limits of identification* attainable by the foregoing procedure.

(5) *Detection by conversion to cobalt (III) salts of* o-*nitrosophenols* [58]

Compounds, which have a free position ortho to a phenolic OH-group, can be converted by nitrous acid into o-nitrosophenols. As shown on page 159, the latter can be detected by means of the brown cobalt (III) chelate compounds. It is not necessary to conduct a separate nitrosation of the phenols and reaction of the isolated nitroso compounds with cobalt salts in acetic acid solution. It is perfectly feasible to start with phenols (solid or dissolved) and to arrive directly at the colored cobalt chelated compounds by warming with an acetic acid solution of sodium cobaltinitrite. This provides the most favorable conditions for the production of cobalt (III) chelate compounds, which then result from the following succession of reactions:

$$Co(NO_2)_6{}^{-3} + 6\ H^+ \rightarrow Co^{+3} + 6\ HNO_2 \qquad (1)$$

$$\qquad (2)$$

$$\qquad (3)$$

TABLE 12. PHENOLS

Name	Formula	Fluorescence color	Limit of Identification (γ)
Phenol	C_6H_5OH	Yellow	12
α-Naphthol	$C_{10}H_7OH$	Yellow	7
β-Naphthol	$C_{10}H_7OH$	Yellow	6
Di-β-naphthol	$[C_{10}H_6OH]_2$	No reaction	—
o-Hydroxydiphenyl	$C_{12}H_9OH$	Orange	20
p-Hydroxydiphenyl	$C_{12}H_9OH$	Orange	2,5
2,7-Dihydroxynaphthalene	$C_{10}H_6(OH)_2$	Yellow	50
1,8-Dihydroxynaphthalene-3,6-disulfonic acid	$C_{10}H_4(OH)_2(SO_3H)_2$	No reaction	—
Resorcinol	$C_6H_4(OH)_2$	Yellow	3
Naphthoresorcinol	$C_{10}H_6(OH)_2$	No reaction	—
Salicylic acid	$C_6H_4OHCOOH$	Yellow	5
Acetylsalicylic acid	$C_6H_4OCOCH_3COOH$	Yellow	5
Phenylsalicylate	$C_6H_4OHCOOC_6H_5$	Yellow	5
2,4-Dinitroresorcinol	$C_6H_2(OH)_2(NO_2)_2$	No reaction	—
m-Hydroxybenzoic acid	$C_6H_4OHCOOH$	Yellow	10

It seems that the o-nitrosation of phenols is favored by the occurrence of (1)–(3) and likewise the related chelation with a cobalt atom. This is shown by the finding that carbolic acid, which yields p-nitrosophenol almost exclusively with nitrous acid, gives notable amounts of the cobalt salt of o-nitrosophenol when an acetic acid solution of cobaltinitrite is employed as nitrosating agent. On the other hand, the groups contained in the molecule of the phenol also exert an influence on the nitrosation. For example, reactions (2) and (3) cannot be realized in the case of salicylic acid or the three isomeric hydroxybenzaldehydes.

When the test described here is used, the absence of primary aromatic amines should be assured. Under the conditions specified by the procedure, these amines exchange the NH_2 for an OH group and then of course show the phenol reaction. If necessary, the amines can be removed by extracting the alkaline solution or suspension with ether, whereby phenols remain in the aqueous phase.

Procedure. The test is made in a micro test tube. One drop of the test solution or a very little of the solid being examined is treated with one drop of sodium cobaltinitrite solution and one drop of glacial acetic acid. At the same time, a blank test is set up in a second test tube with a drop of water. The two tubes are heated over a free flame until the blank has acquired a pink color. A positive response is given by a brown to yellow color or brown precipitate. The cobalt chelate compounds formed are insoluble in water and soluble extractable in chloroform when the phenols in question do not contain hydrophylic groups.

Reagent: Freshly prepared 5% water solution of sodium cobaltinitrite.

The procedure revealed:

1	γ	α-naphthol	0.5 γ	resorcinol	
5	γ	1,4-naphtholsulfonic acid	2 γ	elagic acid	
1	γ	sulfosalicylic acid	0.5 γ	morin	
5	γ	chromotropic acid	0.5 γ	2,4-dihydroxy benzaldehyde	

A positive response was given by: pyrogallol, eugenol, hydroquinone, pyrocatechol disulfonic acid, *p*-hydroxdiphenyl, *o*-hydroxydiphenyl, adrenaline, gallic acid, tropeolin 0, morphine, thymol, arbutin, 2,4-dihydroxybenzaldehyde, *o*-hydroxyacetophenone, stovarsol.

12. 8-Hydroxyquinoline and Derivatives $\left(\begin{array}{c} \text{—OH} \\ \text{-group} \end{array} \right)$

Test through fluorescence by chemical adsorption on magnesium hydroxide [59]

The group in question is present in 8-hydroxyquinoline (I) and its derivatives (II–VIII). As shown by the acidic phenolic OH group and the basic tertiary N-atom in the quinoline ring system, 8-hydroxyquinoline* and its derivatives are ampholytes, which can be brought into solution by either acids or bases. (The acidic character is strengthened in the halogen substituted derivatives as well as in the sulfonic acids.)

OH   OH   OH   OH   OH
(I)   (II)   (III)   (IV)   (V)

* This compound, which is widely used as a reagent in inorganic analysis, has the trivial name "oxine".

(VI)   (VII)   (VIII)

Alcohol solutions of (I)–(IV) produce quantitative precipitations of numerous metal ions from neutral, ammoniacal-tartrated, and acetate-buffered solutions.[60] The precipitates consist of inner complex salts in which, as shown by (IX) and (X), the hydrogen of the phenol group is replaced by one equivalent of metal with coordinative bonding on the cyclic N-atom:

(IX)   (X)

The yellow precipitates produced by (I)–(IV) with Al^{+3}, Zn^{+2}, and Mg^{+2} ions give an intense yellow-green or bluish-white fluorescence if the solids or their solutions in organic liquids (immiscible with water) are viewed in ultraviolet light. The 8-hydroxyquinoline derivatives (V)-(VIII) are not precipitants, because of the solubilizing influence of the SO_3H-group. 8-Hydroxyquinaldine (VIII) has no precipitating power toward Al^{+3} ions, presumably because of steric hindrance by the CH_3-group.[61] However, a binding of the reactive group (IX) to metal atoms as pictured in (X) is established not only in the production of stoichiometrically defined salts through ionic reactions in aqueous solution, but also when 8-hydroxyquinoline and its derivatives are adsorbed on the surface of water-insoluble oxides(oxyhydrates, hydroxides) of the metals just mentioned. Proof is provided by the fact that products with the same fluorescence color result in both cases, i.e., when there is salt-formation as an independent phase and also when chemical adsorption occurs in which no new phase is produced.* The latter is the case with (V)–(VIII), which do not enter into precipitation reactions with the parent metal ions of the oxides. The fluorescence resulting when there is salt-formation or chemical adsorption on contact with metal oxides can therefore be utilized for the general test to detect the group (IX). Magnesium oxide or hydroxide are suitable adsorbents.

* A schematic representation of the surface reaction for the chemical adsorption of oxine on alumina is shown on page 379.

Procedure. About 0.2 g of magnesium oxide is placed on a watch glass or in a depression of a spot plate. A drop of the test solution (water, alcohol, ether, etc.) is added. The suspension is placed under a quartz lamp. Depending on the quantity of active material present, a light yellow or whitish blue fluorescence appears at once or in a short while. A blank with magnesium oxide and the particular solvent is advisable when small amounts of the hydroxyquinoline are suspected. A water suspension of freshly prepared magnesium hydroxide may be used in place of magnesium oxide.

Limits of Identification:

I 8-Hydroxyquinoline: 0.5 γ (aqueous alcohol solution)
II 7-Chloro-8-hydroxyquinoline: 0.6 γ (acetone)
III 5, 7-Dichloro-8-hydroxyquinoline: 0.8 γ (acetone)
IV 5, 7-Dibromo-8-hydroxyquinoline: 1 γ (acetone)
V 8-Hydroxyquinoline-5-sulfonic acid: 0.5 γ (water)
VI 8-Hydroxyquinoline-7-sulfonic acid: 0.5 γ (water)
VII 7-Iodo-8-hydroxyquinoline-5-sulfonic acid: 1 γ (water)
VIII 2-Methyl-8-hydroxyquinoline (8-hydroxyquinaldine): 0.4 γ (alcohol)

This recommended procedure can also be applied to acid aqueous solutions of 8-hydroxyquinoline or its derivatives, but of course more magnesium oxide must be used. The latter acts as neutralizer, and produces Mg^{+2} ions, which then form insoluble fluorescing magnesium salts with 8-hydroxyquinoline or such of its derivatives as may form inner complex magnesium salts. Otherwise, the fluorescence is due to a chemical adsorption as mentioned previously.

13. *o*-Diphenolmethylene Ether $\left(\begin{array}{c} \text{—O} \\ \text{—O} \end{array} \hspace{-0.3cm} \diagdown \text{CH}_2 \text{ -group} \right)$

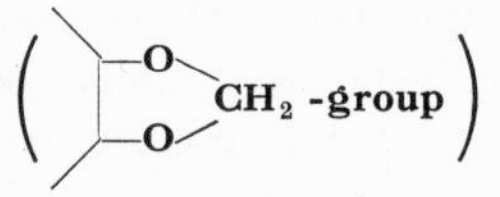

Detection through hydrolytic splitting out of formaldehyde [62]

When cyclic methylene ethers of *o*-diphenols are heated alone or along with concentrated sulfuric acid, to 170–180°, formaldehyde results:

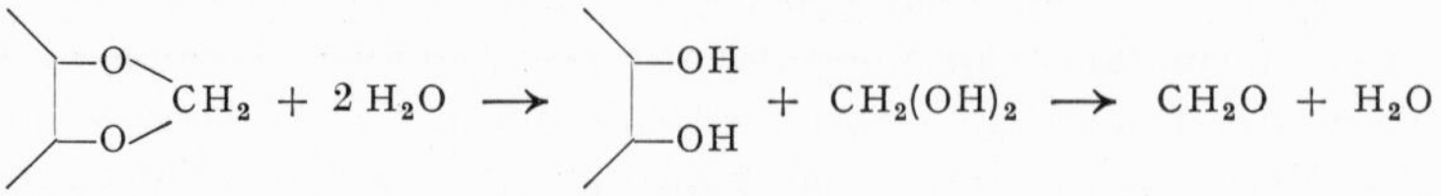

$$\text{—O}\diagdown\text{CH}_2 + 2\,H_2O \longrightarrow \text{—OH} \quad \text{—OH} + CH_2(OH)_2 \longrightarrow CH_2O + H_2O$$

In the case of dry heating, this hydrolysis is brought about by the water split out of the test material which then acts as superheated steam at the locale of its production and accomplishes hydrolyses which cannot be brought about by boiling water, and which are realized but slowly by warming with dilute acids or alkalis. Also when the material is heated with concentrated sulfuric acid, it is the water in the acid which, so to speak brought into the state of superheated steam, is responsible for the hydrolysis shown above. The resulting formaldehyde can be easily detected in the vapor phase by means of the color (violet) that appears when this product is brought into contact with chromotropic acid and concentrated sulfuric acid. The chemistry of this color reaction is discussed on page 331.

A study of the detection of cyclic bound —O—CH$_2$—O— groups by means of the formaldehyde reaction showed that the same limits of detection are obtained when the material is heated dry or in contact with concentrated sulfuric acid. However, only the latter procedure is recommended because it was found that the alkaloids codeine and corydaline, which only contain one and two methoxy groups, respectively, give a decided formaldehyde reaction when heated dry to 170°, but this is by no means the case when they are heated to this temperature with concentrated sulfuric acid.*

When testing for cyclic bound —O—CH$_2$—O— groups, it is best to start with ether solutions of the sample because then interferences from water-soluble compounds, which yield formaldehyde under the conditions of the test, are averted. Such materials include: hexamethylenetetramine and its salts, glycolic acid, monochloroacetic acid, pyramidone, organic sulfoxyl compounds.

Procedure. The apparatus shown in Fig. 49, page 23 is used. A little of the solid or a drop of the test solution is placed in the bulb and taken to dryness if necessary. One or two drops of concentrated sulfuric acid is introduced. The knob of the stopper is charged with a drop of reagent solution and the stopper is put in place. The apparatus is immersed to a depth of 0.5 cm in an oil or glycerol bath previously heated to 170°. At this temperature, after 1–10 minutes, depending on the amount of formaldehyde generated, a more or less intense violet color develops in the suspended drop. If the latter is wiped onto a spot plate, even slight colors are easily visible. A blank is advised in doubtful cases.

    Reagent: Chromotropic acid-sulfuric acid mixture: A pinch (tip of knife blade), of the purest available chromotropic acid is placed in a centrifuge tube and well stirred with 2 or 3 ml of concentrated sulfuric acid. The suspension is then centrifuged. The supernatant liquid, which usually is turbid, serves for the test. It is best to prepare fresh reagent occasionally.

The following compounds were tested and their limits of identification determined.

* The natural assumption that a splitting off of formaldehyde on dry heating rests on a disproportionation of methoxy groups, namely >C—OCH$_3$ → >CH + CH$_2$O, cannot be valid or hold in general. It has been found that quinine and veratrol, containing respectively, one and two methoxy groups, show no splitting out of formaldehyde, and papaverine, with four methoxy groups exhibits no more than a slight effect of this kind. The discovery of compounds which give off formaldehyde when they are thermally decomposed would be of interest with respect to analytical utilization.

Piperine	(structure: CH=CHCH=CHCO piperidine amide of methylenedioxyphenyl)	0.1 γ
Narcotine	(structure)	0.2 γ
Hydrastine	(structure)	0.2 γ
Berberine	(structure)	0.1 γ
Chelidonine	(structure)	0.1 γ
Narceine	(structure)	0.5 γ

| Safrole | $CH_2CH=CH_2$ structure | 0.4 γ |

A positive response was given also by heliotropine, piperonyl acid, iso-safrole, and apiole.

The procedure may also be used with the insoluble salts of the alkaloids referred to above. This was established with the molybdates. The precipitations can be made in the bulb of the apparatus and the precipitate collected on the bottom of the vessel by centrifuging. (It is not necessary to wash the precipitate.) After drying at 110°, one or two drops of concentrated sulfuric acid is introduced and the vessel warmed as prescribed. The procedure may be employed in the study of alkaloids.

14. Polyhydroxyanthraquinones

Detection by formation of zirconium color lakes [63]

If alizarin or alizarin sulfonic acid is added to acid solutions of zirconium salts, red-violet precipitates or colorations result. This fact is the basis of sensitive tests for zirconium and fluorine (comp. Vol. I, Chap. 3 and 4). In conformity with the principle of group action of organic reagents,[64] the color reaction with zirconium is not restricted to alizarin but represents a special case of the activity of certain anthraquinones. All polyhydroxy-anthraquinones with two hydroxyl groups in the *ortho* position behave similarly to alizarin, but those lacking this relative placing of the OH groups do not react with acid solutions of zirconium salts. The conditions are quite different when alkaline solutions of polyhydroxyanthraquinones are allowed to react with solutions of zirconium salts. Colored precipitates are obtained in every instance and these are not altered even by prolonged washing with hot water. If washed with dilute hydrochloric acid, these precipitates leave colored products only if polyhydroxyanthraquinones with OH groups in the *ortho* position were present. Consequently, the divergent reaction picture presented by polyhydroxyanthraquinones toward zirconium salts in acid and basic surroundings makes possible a general test for these compounds and also provides information regarding the relative position of the OH groups in the molecule.

The colored products of the reaction between zirconium salts and polyhydroxyanthraquinones in acid medium are stoichiometrically definable phenolates only in extreme cases [65] and at high dilutions. In concentrated solutions of zirconium salts, which contain hydrolysis products in the sol form, and also in alkaline gels of Zr $(OH)_4$ precipitates, there exists the possibility of forming zirconium color lakes with polyhydroxyanthraquinones. The lakes are not definite "Daltonian compounds" but are adsorption complexes of the polyhydroxyanthraquinones with the sol or gel particles in which zirconium atoms take over the salt-like bonding without leaving the phase association of the sol or gel.[66] The bonding scheme (I) may well be considered for the acid-resistant color lakes, and (II) for the acid-labile lakes:

(I)   (II)

In the general test for polyhydroxyanthraquinones, the alkaline solution should be treated with dilute zirconium salt solution, the mixture warmed gently, the precipitate isolated by centrifuging or filtering, and washed with water. If a violet or red residue is left, the presence of polyhydroxyanthraquinones is indicated. Should dilute hydrochloric acid turn the residue yellow or discharge its color, the polyhydroxyanthraquinone did not have OH groups ortho to each other, but if the color is not altered polyhydroxyanthraquinones with OH groups ortho to each other are present. These tests can be accomplished within the technique of spot test analysis and with small amounts of the test material. The following procedure is recommended for the direct detection of polyhydroxyanthraquinones with OH groups in the *ortho* position.

Procedure. A drop of the test solution (in acetone) and a drop of a 4% solution of zirconium nitrate in dilute hydrochloric acid are mixed on a spot plate. When the response is positive, a colored precipitate appears or there is a characteristic color change.

The following compilation presents the results obtained with a variety of polyhydroxyanthraquinones and the respective limits of identification.

O OH ─OH O Alizarin (1,2-dihydroxyanthra- quinone)	yellow- purple 0.7 γ	O OH ─OH ─OH O Anthragallol (1,2,3-trihydroxyanthra- quinone)	orange- brown 2.5 γ
O OH ─OH O OH Purpurin (1,2,4-trihydroxyanthra- quinone)	orange- reddish 0.1 γ	O ─OH ─OH O Histazarin (2,3-dihydroxyanthra- quinone)	orange- red 2.0 γ
O OH HO─ ─OH HO─ ─OH OH O Rufigallic acid (1,2,3,5,6,7-hexahydroxy- anthraquinone)	yellow- violet 1.0 γ	OH O OH ─OH OH O Quinalizarin (1,2,5,8-tetrahydroxy- anthraquinone)	red- violet 0.8 γ

The following gave no color change in acid solution, but orange to red-violet precipitates in alkaline solution:

OH O OH ─CH₃ O 1,8-Dihydroxy-3-methylanthraquinone	O OH ─CH₃ ─OH O 1,3-Dihydroxy-2-methylanthraquinone

1,8-Dihydroxy-3-methyl-6-methoxy-
anthraquinone

1-Hydroxy-2-methylanthraquinone

1,8-Dihydroxy-3-hydroxymethyl-
anthraquinone

1,8-Dihydroxy-2-methylanthraquinone

1,8-Dihydroxyanthraquinone-3-
carboxylic acid

1,4-Dihydroxy-2-methylanthraquinone

1,6,8-Trihydroxy-3-methyl-
anthraquinone

1,3,6,8-Tetrahydroxyanthraquinone

15. Enols

Test with bromine and potassium iodide

Ketones in which the CO-group is adjacent to a CH_2-group have acid character because in solution there is an equilibrium between the keto form and a tautomeric unsaturated alcohol form, the so-called enol form. In the case of ethyl acetoacetate, the keto-enol equilibrium is:

$$CH_3—CO—CH_2—COOC_2H_5 \rightleftarrows CH_3—C = CH—COOC_2H_5$$
$$\underset{OH}{|}$$

References pp. 314–319

All enols take up bromine instantaneously with intermediate formation of dibromoenols, which form labile α-bromoketones on elimination of hydrogen bromide. These α-bromoketones oxidize hydrogen iodide and liberate iodine, the enols being regenerated.[67] Enols can therefore be detected by treating the sample with excess bromine, removing the unused bromine, and adding potassium iodide to the acid solution. A liberation of iodine indicates the presence of enols.

In the case of the enol form of ethyl acetoacetate, the equations relating to the bromination and the liberation of iodine are:

$$CH_3C(OH) = CHCOOC_2H_5 + Br_2 \rightarrow CH_3C(OH)Br \cdot CHBr \cdot COOC_2H_5 \quad (1)$$

$$CH_3C(OH)Br \cdot CHBr \cdot COOC_2H_5 \rightarrow CH_3CO \cdot CHBr \cdot COOC_2H_5 + HBr \quad (2)$$

$$CH_3COCHBr \cdot COOC_2H_5 + 2 HI \rightarrow CH_3COCH_2COOC_2H_5 + HBr + I_2 \quad (3)$$

After the α-bromoketone has been formed, the excess bromine is best removed by adding sulfosalicylic acid. The free bromine is consumed to form bromosulfosalicylic acid:

$$C_6H_3(OH)(COOH)(SO_3H) + Br_2 \rightarrow HBr + C_6H_2Br(OH)(COOH)(SO_3H)$$

and the color is discharged immediately. It should be noted that the bromine is taken up according to (1) and (2) at once, whereas the action of the α-bromoketone on hydrogen iodide (3) is slow. Iodine has no action on sulfosalicylic acid.

Procedure.[68] Saturated bromine water is added to a drop of the test solution until a permanent yellow color forms, and then a saturated solution of sulfosalicylic acid until the solution is decolorized. The solution is then treated with a few drops of 5% potassium iodide solution and starch solution. A blue color indicates the presence of enols.

A positive reaction was given by: 60 γ acetoacetic ester, 40 γ malonic ester, 100 γ benzoylacetic ester.

16. Carbonyl Compounds ($>$CO-group)

Test for aldehydes and aliphatic methyl ketones by interaction with bisulfite

Approximately neutral solutions of aldehydes and aliphatic methyl ketones combine with sodium bisulfite to form well crystallized water-soluble products [69] known as "aldehyde bisulfite" and "ketone bisulfite", respectively. These products are the alkali salts of α-hydroxysulfonic acids: [70]

$$\begin{array}{c} R \\ \diagdown \\ C=O \ + \ NaHSO_3 \ \rightarrow \\ H \diagup \end{array} \qquad \begin{array}{c} R \diagdown \diagup OH \\ C \\ H \diagup \diagdown SO_3Na \end{array}$$

$$\begin{array}{c} R \\ \diagdown \\ C=O \ + \ NaHSO_3 \ \rightarrow \\ H_3C \diagup \end{array} \qquad \begin{array}{c} R \diagdown \diagup OH \\ C \\ H_3C \diagup \diagdown SO_3Na \end{array}$$

An excess of aldehyde or methyl ketone rapidly consumes the bisulfite and converts it into compounds which, unlike free bisulfite, no longer react with iodine.[71] Consequently, the familiar redox reaction:

$$SO_3^{-2} + I_2 + H_2O \rightarrow SO_4^{-2} + 2\ I^- + 2\ H^+$$

may be masked through the formation of aldehyde- or ketone bisulfite. Therefore, when a solution of aldehyde or methyl ketone is mixed with a dilute solution of bisulfite followed by a blue starch-iodine solution, and the color is not discharged, it indicates the presence of aldehydes or ketones. Obviously, no other substance which will consume iodine may be present; furthermore the solution must be neutral.

Procedure. [72] A drop of the alcoholic or aqueous test solution is mixed with a drop of approximately 0.001 N sodium bisulfite. If the original solution is alcoholic it is advisable to dilute with 4 or 5 drops of water. After about 5 minutes, a drop of approximately 0.001 N iodine in potassium iodide is added, and also a drop of a 1% starch solution made very faintly blue with iodine. If the blue color remains, the test is positive, indicating the presence of aldehyde or ketone. A blank test is advisable in the detection of very small amounts.

Reagent: 1% starch solution faintly colored with iodine.

The dilutions should be so adjusted that 10 drops of the bisulfite solution require 11 or 12 drops of the iodine solution to give a permanent blue.

The following were revealed:

0.05	γ formaldehyde	1 γ	m-nitrobenzaldehyde
0.5	γ acetaldehyde	1 γ	p-aminobenzaldehyde
5	γ oenanthal	20 γ	vanillin
5	γ furfural	15 γ	anisaldehyde
2	γ benzaldehyde	500 γ	glucose
4	γ benzaldehyde-o-sulfonic acid	500 γ	levulose
4	γ o-hydroxybenzaldehyde	500 γ	lactose
1	γ m-hydroxybenzaldehyde	50 γ	acetone
10	γ p-hydroxybenzaldehyde	20 γ	methyl ethyl ketone
4	γ o-nitrobenzaldehyde	20 γ	acetophenone

No reaction was given by: cane sugar, benzophenone, benzil, ethyl alcohol, purified dioxan (boiling with hydrochloric acid and distillation over sodium).

References pp. 314–319

17. o-Dioxo and Oxomethylene Compounds
(—CO—CO— and —CH₂—CO— groups)

(1) Test for aliphatic and aromatic dioxo compounds through the benzilic acid transformation [73]

When benzil (I), which is neutral, is fused or sintered with an alkali it undergoes a characteristic rearrangement. Probably the initial step is the addition of a molecule of alkali, which then transforms into the alkali salt of benzilic acid (II):

$$
\begin{array}{c}
C_6H_5{-}CO \\
| \\
C_6H_5{-}CO \\
(I)
\end{array}
+ KOH \rightarrow
\begin{array}{c}
\quad\quad\quad {/}OH \\
C_6H_5{-}C \\
\quad\quad | \,{}^{\backslash}OK \\
C_6H_5{-}CO
\end{array}
\rightarrow
\begin{array}{c}
C_6H_5{\backslash}\quad{/}OH \\
\quad\quad C \\
C_6H_5{/}\quad{\backslash}COOK \\
(II)
\end{array}
$$

This intramolecular change, which occurs rapidly, is known as the "benzilic acid rearrangement"[74]. Analogous transformations leading to akyl and aryl derivatives of glycolic acid seem to occur with all dioxo compounds [75]; not merely the simple aliphatic diacetyl but likewise the more complicated cyclic phenanthraquinone undergo this type of rearrangement, i.e., transformation into alkali salts of disubstituted glycolic acid:

$$
\begin{array}{c}
CH_3{-}CO \\
| \\
CH_3{-}CO
\end{array}
+ KOH \rightarrow
\begin{array}{c}
CH_3{\backslash}\quad{/}OH \\
\quad\quad C \\
CO_3{/}\quad{\backslash}COOK
\end{array}
$$

It has been found that one evaporation of dioxo compounds with an alkali hydroxide is sufficient to bring about the benzilic acid rearrangement to an extent that can be easily recognised. When the residue from the evaporation is treated with hydrochloric acid, the respective disubstituted glycolic acid is liberated and can be detected by means of the color reaction for benzene-soluble carboxylic acids (page 120) involving uranyl nitrate and rhodamine B.

The following test based on the benzilic acid rearrangement assumes the absence of benzene-soluble organic acids. Dioxo compounds can be separated from such acids by shaking the ether test solution with aqueous alkali hydroxide.

Procedure. A micro test tube is used. A little of the solid (or residue from drops of its ether solution) is taken to dryness with a drop of 1N caustic alkali. A drop of hydrochloric acid is added to the residue and the evaporation is repeated. The residue is treated with a drop of 2% uranyl nitrate solution and five drops of a saturated benzene solution of rhodamine B. If dioxo compounds were present the benzene layer turns red or pink after shaking and gives an orange fluorescence in ultraviolet light.

The procedure revealed: 1 γ diacetyl and 2.5 γ benzil.

(2) Test for aliphatic 1,2-dioxo compounds by conversion into colored inner complex nickel dioxime salts [76]

Aliphatic and monocyclic hydroaromatic *o*-dioxo compounds react with hydroxylamine or with hydroxylamine hydrochloride plus alkali and produce 1,2-dioximes which form water-insoluble red or yellow inner complex nickel salts.[77] These salts are also formed directly from the components: [78]

$$
\begin{array}{l}
-\text{C}=\text{O} \\
| \quad\quad + 2\ \text{NH}_2\text{OH} + {}^{1}/_{2}\ \text{Ni}^{++} + \text{OH}^{-} \longrightarrow \\
-\text{C}=\text{O}
\end{array}
\quad
\begin{array}{l}
\overset{\overset{\text{O}}{\|}}{-\text{C}=\text{N}} \\
\quad\quad\quad\quad\text{Ni}/2 + 3\ \text{H}_2\text{O} \\
-\text{C}=\text{N} \\
\quad | \\
\quad \text{OH}
\end{array}
$$

Through this reaction, it is possible to distinguish aliphatic (or monocyclic) hydroaromatic dioxo compounds from aromatic dioxo compounds, such as benzil, phenanthraquinone, camphor quinone, etc. The latter are orthoquinoidal in character and hence are not oximated but reduced by hydroxylamine.

Procedure. A drop of the test solution is treated in a centrifuge tube with a drop of hydroxylamine solution and warmed briefly on the water bath. A drop of the clear solution is then placed on filter paper and spotted with a drop of 5% nickel acetate solution. A more or less intense yellow or red appears, either at once or after fuming over ammonia.

Reagent: Hydroxylamine solution: 1 g hydroxylamine hydrochloride plus 1 g sodium acetate in 2 ml water.

The *identification limits* for the detection of aliphatic 1,2-dioxo compounds are given in Table 13.

(3) Test for oxomethylene compounds by conversion into 1,2-diketones [79]

The conversion of aliphatic 1,2-diketones into red or orange 1,2-dioxime nickel salts as described in (2) can also be used for the detection of oxomethylene compounds, due to the fact that the CH$_2$ group adjacent to the CO group can be oxidized to a CO group. Selenium dioxide (selenic acid) is a

suitable oxidant for the transformation of the —CH₂—CO— group into the
—CO—CO— group.[80] Elementary selenium is formed.

The test is not completely decisive for the —CH₂—CO—group, since the
o-dioxo compounds, which finally enter the test reaction sometimes originate
in other groupings which produce them when oxidized by selenious acid.
Instances are:

a) Compounds of the acyloin type, R₁—CO—CH(OH)—R₂, which can be
oxidized, just as the oxomethylene groups, to the corresponding dioxo
compounds. This grouping, in distinction to the oxomethylene grouping, is
easily oxidized to *o*-diketones by other oxidizing agents also (chromic acid,
potassium ferricyanide, etc.).

b) Selenious acid is also capable of oxidizing unsaturated hydrocarbons
to the corresponding α, β-unsaturated ketones [81] which then, in turn, may
be further oxidized, as in *a*), to diketones.

c) The grouping —CHOH—CH₂— also can be oxidized to diketone by
the action of selenious acid.

Procedure. One drop of the alcoholic test solution is placed in a capillary
tube along with several grains of selenious acid. The capillary is fused shut and
heated for 20 minutes at 150° to 170° C. When cool, the reaction mass is transferred to a centrifuge tube, and warmed briefly with 2 drops of the hydroxylamine
solution just described. The oxime is formed and the excess selenious acid is reduced to selenium. A little animal charcoal is added and the selenium is separated
by centrifuging. One drop of the clear supernatant solution is spotted on filter
paper with a drop of 5% nickel acetate solution. A yellow or red fleck appears
if the oxomethylene group is present.

The *identification limits* for the detection of oxomethylene compounds are
given in Table 13.

(4) Test for aromatic o-dioxo compounds by conversion into oxazine dyes [82]

The action of 2-amino-5-dimethylaminophenol (I) on aromatic *o*-diketones,
such as phenanthraquinone (II), involves first a mutual reduction and
oxidation to the system of compounds (III) and (IV). The interaction continues as a condensation between (III) and (IV), and the deep blue oxazine
dyestuff with the quinoidal cation (V) results:

(I)   (II)

TABLE 13. DIOXO- AND OXO-METHYLENE COMPOUNDS; ALIPHATIC 1,2-DIOXO- AND OXOMETHYLENE COMPOUNDS

Name and Formula	Oxidation product	Color	Limit of identification (in γ)
Acetoin $CH_3CH(OH)COCH_3$	—	Red	0.5
Acetone CH_3COCH_3	CH_3COCHO	Red	50
Methyl ethyl ketone $C_2H_5COCH_3$	$CH_3COCOCH_3$ and C_2H_5COCHO	Brown-red	25
Cyclopentanone 		Orange	5
Cyclohexanone 		Red	2.5
Methylheptenone 		Yellow-orange	2.5
Phenylacetaldehyde $C_6H_5-CH_2-CHO$	$C_6H_5-CO-CHO$	Orange	5
Hydrindone (α) 		Orange	10
o-Tetralone 		Orange	10

References pp. 314–319

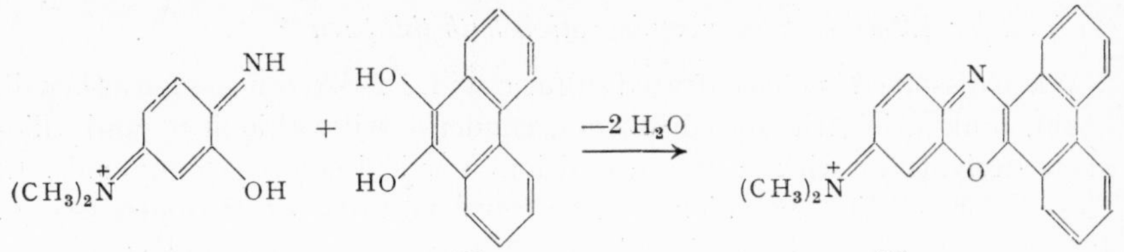

The formation of this dye occurs only with aromatic dioxo compounds which are not oximated when subjected to the procedure described in (2). Accordingly, aliphatic 1,2- and aromatic o-dioxo compounds can be distinguished from each other by the dioxime formation on the one hand, and through the oxazine formation on the other.

Care must be taken that the sample contains no oxidizing agent, since the latter will react with the reagent and form colored quinoidal compounds.

Procedure. One drop of the test solution is treated in a micro test tube with 2 drops of freshly prepared reagent solution. A more or less intense blue appears either immediately or after gentle warming, depending on the quantity of dioxo compound present. When dealing with small quantities it is well to run a blank and to view the color against a white background.

Reagent: 0.05 g 2-nitroso-5-dimethylaminophenol is suspended in 5 ml glacial acetic acid; and shaken with zinc dust (with cooling) until decolorized, filtered, and the filtrate diluted to 10 ml with glacial acetic acid. The reagent must always be freshly prepared because it turns light blue on standing in contact with the air.

The reaction revealed: 2 γ benzil; 1 γ camphorquinone; 0.25 γ phenanthraquinone.

(5) *Test for aromatic and aliphatic diketones through formation of dihydropyrazines* [83]

Aromatic and aliphatic diketones condense easily and quickly with ethylenediamine to form dihydropyrazines:

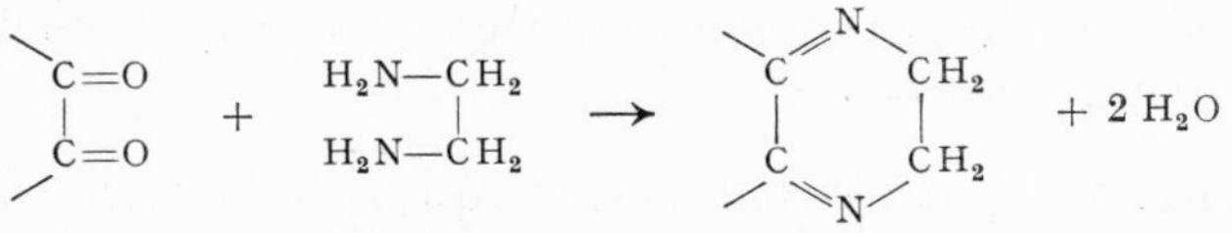

Therefore, the consumption of ethylenediamine can be used to reveal the presence of diketones of the types named. This test is described on page 257 in connection with a test for primary and secondary aliphatic amines, which is based on their reaction with carbon disulfide to produce dithiocarbamates of the respective amines.

References pp. 314–319

(6) Test for 1,2-diketones by condensation with thiophen [84]

When dissolved in concentrated sulfuric acid, 1,2-diketones, such as benzil, isatin, ninhydrin (triketohydrindene), condense with thiophen (and thiophen derivatives with a free α-position) to yield colored compounds. In these color reactions,[85] which provide sensitive tests for thiophen (see p. 425), the sulfuric acid functions both as dehydrating agent and as oxidant. The condensation of diketones and thiophen can be represented by the general scheme:[86]

$$2 \;\; \underset{C=O}{\overset{C=O}{|}} + 2 \;\; \underset{HC \quad CH}{\overset{HC \text{---} CH}{\underset{S}{\parallel \quad \parallel}}} \rightarrow \;\; \underset{C=O \quad S \quad O=C}{\overset{HC == CH}{C=C \quad C=C}} + 2\,H_2O$$

The term indophenine has become a generic expression and refers to the colored product (red, violet, blue) obtained by condensation of thiophen or thiophen compounds that contain two nuclear hydrogen atoms in the 2,5- or 2,3-position with 1,2-dicarbonyl compounds.

The test based on the formation of indophenine leads to the desired goal only with those diketones whose solutions in concentrated sulfuric acid are stable and colorless or almost without color. For instance, diacetyl is excluded because it is carbonized by concentrated sulfuric acid. Attention must be given to the fact that cold concentrated sulfuric acid produces a variety of colors with many (even colorless) compounds, particularly those which are polycyclic or highly substituted.[87] To detect 1,2 diketones in the presence of such compounds, a comparison test with a solution of the sample in concentrated sulfuric acid should be conducted without addition of thiophen.

In concentrated sulfuric acid, mercaptans react with thiophen to yield a green coloration.[88] Since disulfides show no reaction, it is necessary when mercaptans are present to convert them into disulfides by evaporation with hydrogen peroxide. The presence of mercaptans is easily established by the test given on page 228.

Procedure. A drop of the solution to be tested (if possible in alcohol) is placed in a micro test tube and evaporated to dryness in a water bath. Alternatively, fractions of a milligram of the solid may be taken. The material or residue is dissolved or suspended in three drops of concentrated sulfuric acid and treated with two drops of thiophen solution. Depending on the quantity of 1,2 diketone present, a characteristic color appears at once or within fifteen minutes at most. A blank test, without addition of thiophen, is advisable in all cases.

Reagent: 0.3% solution of thiophen in purest benzene.

The foregoing procedure revealed

    5   γ benzil (violet to pink)
   10   γ phenanthraquinone (blue to blue-green)
    5   γ isatin (blue to blue-green)
  1.5 γ triketohydrindene (violet to pink)
    4   γ rhodizonic acid (blue-green)

Alloxan in amounts up to 25 γ gives a blue color; smaller quantities yield pink colorations.

A color reaction is also given by esters of phenylglyoxylic and mesoxalic acid which contain a 1,2-dicarbonyl group in their molecule.

18. 1,2 (*o*)-Diketones and Quinones

Detection through catalytic hastening of the formaldehyde-o-dinitrobenzene reaction [89]

Formaldehyde is among the organic compounds which function as hydrogen donors in alkaline solution and therefore reduce *o*-dinitrobenzene to the violet alkali salt of the *aci*-form of *o*-nitroso nitro benzene (see page 131). However, the reaction

$$\text{C}_6\text{H}_4(\text{NO}_2)_2 + 2\,CH_2O + 4\,OH^- \longrightarrow \text{C}_6\text{H}_4\!\begin{array}{l}=NO^-\\=NO_2{}^-\end{array} + 2\,HCOO^- + 3\,H_2O \qquad (1)$$

proceeds very slowly in alkali carbonate solution even though considerable amounts of aldehyde are present. The reaction is hastened by α-(*o*)-diketones to such an extent that a sensitive test for these diketones can be based on this catalytic effect.

The catalytic acceleration of (*1*) by α-diketones may rest on the fact that in alkaline solution they are reduced by formaldehyde to hydroxyketones as shown in (*2*), and the latter in turn reduce the *o*-dinitrobenzene to the violet *o*-quinoid alkali salt as shown in (*3*). The diketone is thus regenerated and once again enters into (*2*). The redox reactions (*2*) and (*3*) which occur repeatedly proceed faster than the non-catalyzed reaction (*1*) which leads to the same endproduct. Accordingly, the sum of (*2*) and (*3*) is a net reaction identical with (*1*) which does not contain the catalyzing and constantly regenerated diketone as a participant:

$$2\,\begin{array}{l}-CO\\-CO\end{array} + 2\,CH_2O + 2\,OH^- \longrightarrow 2\,\begin{array}{l}-CHOH\\-CO\end{array} + 2\,HCOO^- \qquad (2)$$

$$2 \begin{array}{c} -CHOH \\ | \\ -CO \end{array} + \left\langle \begin{array}{c} -NO_2 \\ -NO_2 \end{array} \right. + 2\,OH^- \longrightarrow \left\langle \begin{array}{c} =NO^- \\ =NO_2^- \end{array} \right. + 2 \begin{array}{c} -CO \\ | \\ -CO \end{array} + 3\,H_2O \qquad (3)$$

$$\left\langle \begin{array}{c} -NO_2 \\ -NO_2 \end{array} \right. + 2\,CH_2O + 4\,OH^- \longrightarrow \left\langle \begin{array}{c} =NO^- \\ =NO_2^- \end{array} \right. + 2\,HCOO^- + 3\,H_2O \qquad (2+3)$$

When this reaction is employed in analysis, the conditions prescribed in the Procedure must be carefully maintained so that the uncatalyzed reaction proceeds slowly enough that there is no difficulty in observing the catalytic effect produced by even microgram amounts of diketones.

The catalysis reaction is not specific for α-diketones because o- and p-quinones likewise act as catalysts. This effect is probably the result of redox reactions analogous to (2), namely

$$O=\left\langle \!\!=\!\! \right\rangle=O + 2\,CH_2O + 2\,OH^- \longrightarrow HO-\left\langle \right\rangle-OH + 2\,HCOO^-$$

$$\left\langle \right\rangle \!\!\begin{array}{c} =O \\ \end{array} + 2\,CH_2O + 2\,OH^- \longrightarrow \left\langle \right\rangle \!\!\begin{array}{c} -OH \\ \end{array} + 2\,HCOO^-$$

in which these quinones lead to hydroxy compounds, which function as hydrogen donors toward o-dinitrobenzene with reformation of the quinones, which then act once more with formaldehyde.

The test for α-, o-, and p-diketones described here is subject to interference by those organic compounds which function per se as hydrogen donors to o-dinitrobenzene and thus lead to the color reaction. Consequently, a test must first be made of the behavior of the sample but without the addition of formaldehyde as prescribed in the Procedure. If no or only a pale violet color results, the absence of interfering compounds is assured and the test can be conducted with the addition of formaldehyde. If the result is now a violet or a more intense shade, it may be concluded that catalytically effective α-diketones or quinones are present.

A simple method for detecting o-diketones in the presence of much reducing organic materials, which give the color reaction in the absence of formaldehyde, consists in oxidizing the sample with alkali hypobromite and then carrying out the catalysis reaction. (Compare the test for inositol in the presence of reducing sugars, page 394.) When using this procedure, it should be remembered that it does not avert the interference due to quinones and polyphenols (which are oxidized to quinones).

References pp. 314–319

Procedure. A micro test tube is used. A drop of the aqueous or benzene test solution is mixed with one drop each of 25% sodium carbonate solution, 4% formaldehyde, and 5% solution of o- dinitrobenzene (in benzene). The mixture is warmed in boiling water and shaken from time to time. Depending on the amount of catalyzing material present, a more or less intense violet color appears within 1–4 minutes. A blank is advisable.*

The procedure revealed:

0.05 γ diacetyl $CH_3CO—COCH_3$

2 γ benzil $C_6H_5CO—COC_6H_5$

2.5 γ furil

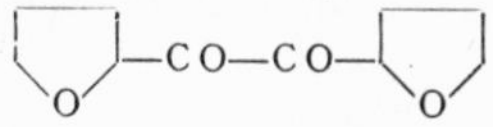

0.002 γ phenanthraquinone

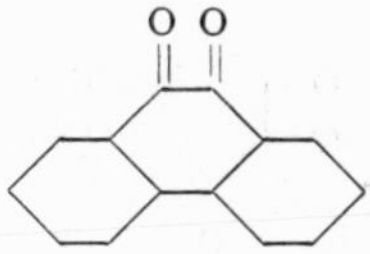

0.002 γ 3-nitrophenanthraquinone

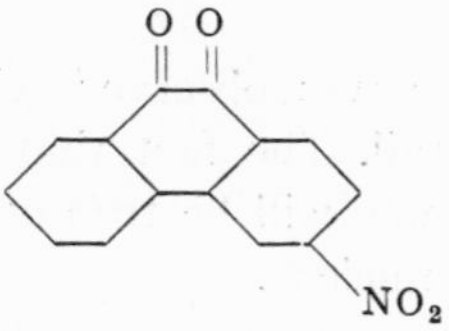

0.5 γ ninhydrin H_2O

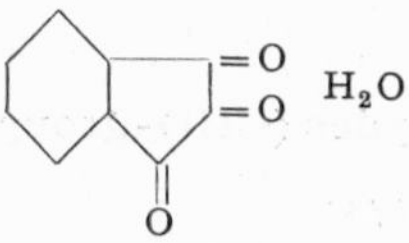

30 γ isatin

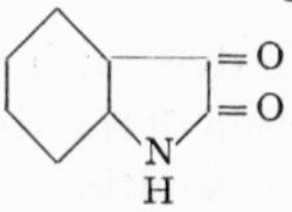

0.01 γ 2-methyl-1,4-naphthaquinone
(Vitamin K_3)

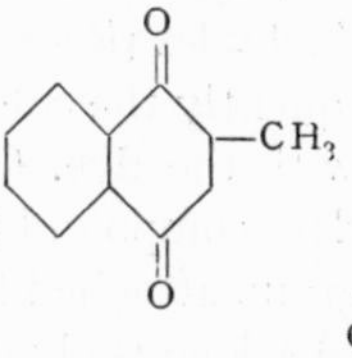

0.5 γ sodium 1,2-naphthaquinone-4-sulfonate

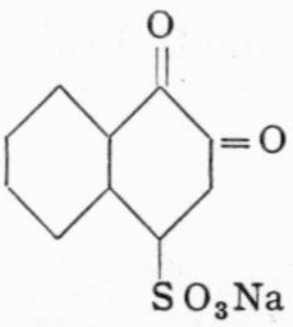

* A red color is produced if p-dinitrobenzene is used. The limits of identification were not determined; they appear to be higher or lower than with o-dinitrobenzene, depending on the nature of the test compound. It is likely that 3,4-dinitrobenzoic acid can be used here with success, since it has recently been employed by Weygand and Hofmann [90] for the chromatographic detection of reducing sugars.

0.05 γ anthraquinone

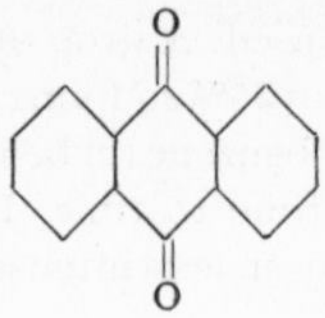

0.5 γ sodium anthraquinone 2-sulfonate

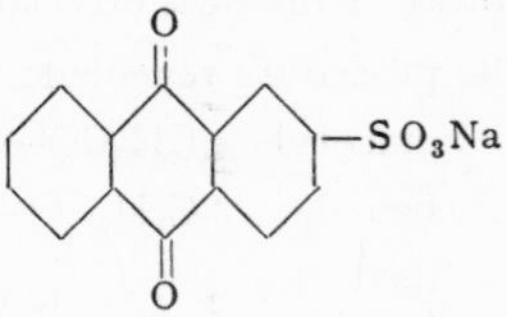

0.5 γ sodium rhodizonate

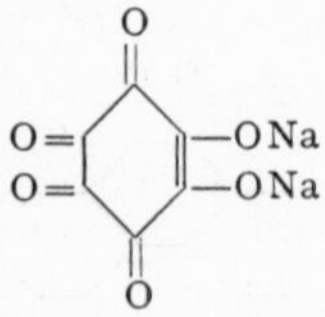

A stronger response was observed with dehydroascorbic acid, p-benzo-quinone and chloranil. The fact that vitamin K_3 catalyzes the reaction suggests that the same will be true of K_1 and K_2, since they too contain a napththaquinone nucleus.

19. Aldehydes (CHO-group)

(*1*) *Test with fuchsin-sulfurous acid* [91]

Sulfurous acid decolorizes tripenylmethane dyes such as p-fuchsin (I) by destroying the quinoid structure with production of the N-sulfinic acid of the leuco sulfonic acid (II). The resulting colorless solutions turn violet to blue on the addition of aldehydes (R—CHO). The aldehyde restores the quinoid structure, and consequently the color, by combining with the sulfurous acid which has reacted with the dye. On the addition of aldehyde, the initial product is the colorless compound (III). The second step involves the loss of the sulfonic acid group attached to the carbon atom and the pink quinoid dye (IV) is formed. Analogous changes occur with other triphenylmethane dyes.[92]

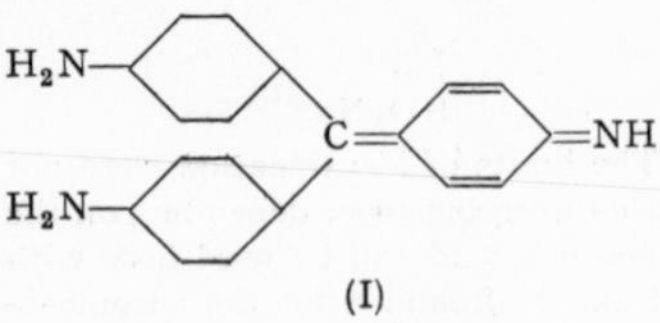

(I)
red

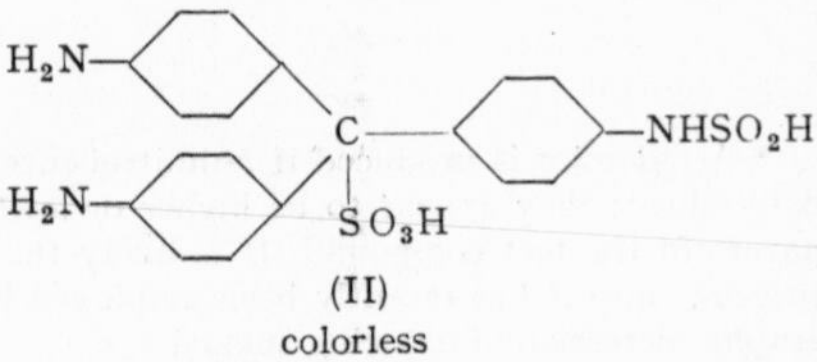

(II)
colorless

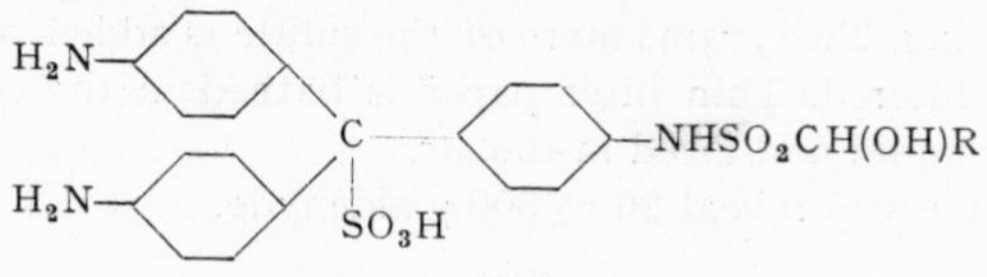

(III)
colorless

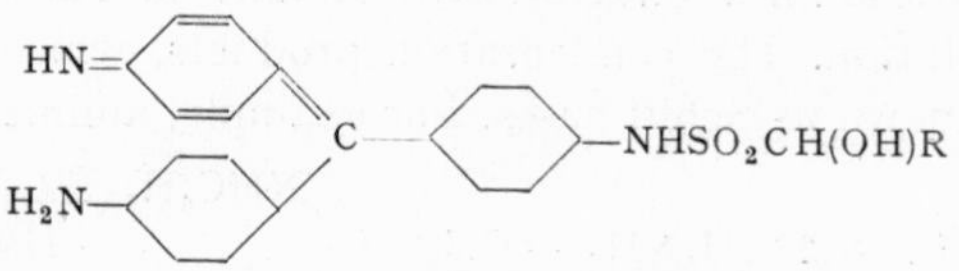

(IV)
pink

The reaction between aldehydes and solutions of fuchsin or malachite green, which have been decolorized by sulfite, can be carried out as a spot reaction (a) on a spot plate, or (b) on filter paper.

Procedure. [93] (a) A drop of the alcoholic or aqueous solution is treated on a spot plate with a drop of sulfurous acid and a drop of fuchsin-sulfurous acid and allowed to stand. The violet to blue color appears in 2–30 minutes according to the amount of aldehyde present.

Reagents: 1) Fuchsin–sulfurous acid: SO_2 is passed through a 0.1 % solution of fuchsin until the color is discharged. *
　　　　　2) 1 % solution of sulfurous acid.

The following were detected:

1 γ formaldehyde	100 γ o-hydroxybenzaldehyde
4 γ acetaldehyde (freshly distilled)	50 γ m-hydroxybenzaldehyde
20 γ furfural (freshly distilled)	1000 γ p-hydroxybenzaldehyde
30 γ benzaldehyde (freshly distilled)	1000 γ anisaldehyde (freshly distilled)
40 γ o-nitrobenzaldehyde	8 γ cinnamaldehyde (freshly
40 γ m-nitrobenzaldehyde	distilled)

Oenanthal gives a slight reaction; vanillin, ethyl vanillin, 2,4-dihydroxybenz-aldehyde, chloral hydrate, p-aminobenzaldehyde, p-dimethylaminobenzaldehyde give none.

Procedure. [94] (b) A drop of a neutral aldehyde solution is placed on filter paper impregnated with a solution of malachite green decolorized with much alkali sulfite. A green spot develops.

Reagent paper: 0.8 g malachite green is suspended in a little water and brought into solution by adding 3 g sodium sulfite, and warm-

* See W. C. Tobie, *Ind. Eng. Chem., Anal. Ed.*, 14 (1942) 405 regarding na improved reagent which also reveals free aldehyde groups in certain aldoses.

ing. Two grams more of the sulfite is added, and the solution filtered. Thin filter paper is bathed in the cooled yellowish liquid and dried in the air.

This color reaction will reveal 20 to 300 γ aldehyde.

(2) Test with o-dianisidine [95]

Primary aromatic amines condense with aliphatic and aromatic aldehydes in acetic acid solution. The condensation products, which are colored in some cases, are known as Schiff bases. For example, aniline reacts:

$$CH_3CHO + 2 C_6H_5NH_2 \rightarrow CH_3CH{\overset{NHC_6H_5}{\underset{NHC_6H_5}{<}}} + H_2O$$

$$C_6H_5CHO + C_6H_5NH_2 \rightarrow C_6H_5CH=NC_6H_5 + H_2O$$

o-Dianisidine (I) is especially suitable for the formation of colored Schiff bases (II):

(I)   (II)

Ketones do not generally interfere as they are rather inactive. However, large amounts of certain ketones may give yellow, green or brown colorations, especially on heating, and so interfere with the detection of very small amounts of aldehydes, or the ketone may be mistaken for an aldehyde. Formation of traces of ketimides is probably responsible for these extraneous colors.

Alicyclic compounds, such as pinenes, camphenes and others, especially in high concentrations, form brown colors with the reagent. They can interfere with the test when the sample is a mixture, such as ethereal oils. The brown reaction products are probably addition compounds.

Procedure. A drop of the sample is mixed with 3 or 4 drops of reagent solution in a microcrucible. A light color usually appears even in the cold, and is intensified by heating, either on an asbestos plate or over a microburner. The reaction may also be carried out on filter paper, by treating a drop of the sample solution with the reagent solution. The color may be deepened by warming over a microburner.

Reagent: Saturated solution of o-dianisidine in glacial acetic acid. The base is purified, when necessary, by heating with adsorbent charcoal and filtering. 2,7-Diaminofluorene may be used in place of o-dianisidine; it forms even brighter colors with some aldehydes.

The colors and the *limits of identification* obtained with this test on heating are listed in Table 14.

TABLE 14. ALDEHYDES

Name	Formula	Color		Limit of identification, γ
		In the cold	On heating	
Formaldehyde	HCHO	Pale yellow	Orange-brown	50
Acetaldehyde	CH_3CHO	Orange	Dark brown	30
Paraldehyde	$(CH_3CHO)_3$	Dark olive green	Dark red-brown	4
Bromal	CBr_3CHO	No reaction	Dark green	40
Acrolein	CH_2CHCHO	Red-brown	Violet-brown	0.1
Crotonalde-hyde	$CH_3CHCHCHO$	Dark red	Dark brown-red	2
Propionalde-hyde	CH_3CH_2CHO	Dark olive green	Red	20
Oenanthal	$CH_3(CH_2)_5CHO$	Red-brown	Red	9
Decylaldehyde	$CH_3(CH_2)_8CHO$	Pale olive	Dark brown	200
Glyoxal	$OHC–CHO$	Brown-green	Yellow-brown	Polymer-ization
a-Hydroxy-n-butyric aldehyde	$CH_3CH_2CHOHCHO$	No reaction	Slight brown	—
Citral	$C(CH_3)=CHCHO$ $\mid$ $CH_2CH_2CHC(CH_3)_2$	Dark red	Red-black	0.1
Citronellal	$CH(CH_3)\cdot CH_2CHO$ $\mid$ $CH_2CH_2CH_2C(CH_2)CH_3$	Deep dark green	Carmine	10
Anisaldehyde	$C_6H_4\big<^{OCH_3\,(4)}_{CHO\,(1)}$	Dark orange	Red	2
p-Aminobenz-aldehyde	$C_6H_4\big<^{NH_2\,(4)}_{CHO\,(1)}$	Orange-brown	Red-brown	0.4

(*continued*)

References pp. 314–319

TABLE 14. ALDEHYDES (CONTINUED)

Name	Formula	Color		Limit of identification, γ
		In the cold	On heating	
Benzaldehyde	C_6H_5CHO	Orange	Red-orange	3
Benzaldehyde o-sulfonic acid	C_6H_4 $<$ SO_3H (2) CHO (1)	Brown-red	Dark red	3
Cumic aldehyde	C_6H_4 $<$ $CH(CH_3)_2$ (4) CHO (1)	Dark carmine	Olive yellow	3
p-Dimethyl-aminobenz-aldehyde	C_6H_4 $<$ $N(CH_3)_2$ (4) CHO (1)	Orange-red	Dark carmine	0.2
Piperonal (heliotropin)	CH_2 $<$ $\overset{O}{\underset{O}{}}$ $>$ C_6H_3CHO	Bright red	Dark red	4
Opianic acid	$C_6H_2(OCH_3)_2COOHCHO$	Olive green	Brown	70
Salicylaldehyde (o-Hydroxy-benzaldehyde)	C_6H_4 $<$ OH (2) CHO (1)	Orange	Orange	5
m-Hydroxy-benzaldehyde	C_6H_4 $<$ OH (3) CHO (1)	Dark brown-red	Dark cherry red	4
p-Hydroxy-benzaldehyde	C_6H_4 $<$ OH (4) CHO (1)	Dark orange-red	Cherry red	5
o-Nitrobenz-aldehyde	C_6H_4 $<$ NO_2 (2) CHO (1)	Green-brown	Red-brown	5
p-Nitrobenz-aldehyde	C_6H_4 $<$ NO_2 (4) CHO (1)	Orange-brown	Red-brown	1
Phenylacet-aldehyde	$C_6H_5CH_2CHO$	Dark brown-red	Dark brown	Always polymer-ization

(continued)

References pp. 314–319

TABLE 14. ALDEHYDES (CONTINUED)

Name	Formula	Color		Limit of identification, γ
		In the cold	On heating	
o-Phthalalde-hyde	$C_6H_4{<}^{CHO\ (2)}_{CHO\ (1)}$	Bright yellow precipitate	Bright yellow precipitate	—
Protocatechuic aldehyde	$C_6H_3{<}^{OH\ \ (4)}_{OH\ \ (3)}{\searrow}_{CHO\ (1)}$	Brown-red	Dark red	7
Tolualdehyde	$C_6H_4{<}^{CH_3\ (2)}_{CHO\ (1)}$	Dark orange-red	Cherry red	5
Vanillin	$C_6H_3{<}^{OH\ \ (4)}_{OCH_3\ (3)}{\searrow}_{CHO\ (1)}$	Bright orange-red	Cherry red	3
Cinnamalde-hyde	$C_6H_5CH{=}CHCHO$	Dark cherry red	Cherry red	0.05
2-Hydroxy-1-naphthalde-hyde	$C_{10}H_6{<}^{OH\ \ (2)}_{CHO\ (1)}$	Orange	Brick red	10
Furfural	$C_4H_3O(CHO)$	Dark red-violet	Deep blue-violet	0.02

(3) Test with azobenzenephenylhydrazine sulfonic acid [96]

The aqueous solution of azobenzenephenylhydrazine sulfonic acid (I) reacts with aldehydes giving deep red or blue solutions. Apparently hydrazones of azobenzenephenylhydrazine (II) are formed:

          (I)   (II)

This color reaction may be applied to the detection of aldehydes. It is carried out in strongly acid solution, with heating, and the product of the reaction is extracted with chloroform in the presence of alcohol. It should be noted that the color of the product differs for aromatic and aliphatic aldehydes; the former are red, the latter blue. Aromatic and aliphatic aldehydes may be differentiated by this color difference.

Ketones react similarly to aldehydes, but much less readily. The following do not react: esters, alcohols, phenols, naphthols, amines, amides, quinones, chloral.

Procedure. A drop of the test solution is mixed with about 7 drops of reagent solution and 4 drops concentrated sulfuric acid in a test tube. The tube is then dipped in a boiling water bath for 30 seconds and allowed to cool. A few drops of alcohol are added and enough chloroform to form a lower layer. About 5 drops of concentrated hydrochloric acid are added and the mixture shaken vigorously. In the presence of aldehyde (ketones) the chloroform layer is colored.

Reagent: Solution of 0.018 g azobenzenephenylhydrazine sulfonic acid in 100 ml water.

The following were detected by this test:

0.25 γ	acetaldehyde	1 γ	protocatechuic aldehyde
0.25 γ	formaldehyde	0.5 γ	m-hydroxybenzaldehyde
0.36 γ	paraldehyde	0.2 γ	p-nitrobenzaldehyde
0.16 γ	oenanthal	0.16 γ	vanillin
4.5 γ	glyceraldehyde	1 γ	piperonal
2 γ	phenylacetaldehyde	0.5 γ	2-hydroxy-1-naphthaldehyde
0.2 γ	benzaldehyde	1.2 γ	dimethylaminobenzaldehyde
0.35 γ	anisaldehyde	0.2 γ	acrolein
0.35 γ	salicylaldehyde	0.1 γ	crotonaldehyde
0.11 γ	cinnamaldehyde	0.35 γ	furfural
0.86 γ	o-benzaldehyde sulfonic acid	40 γ	acetone
0.5 γ	o-nitrobenzaldehyde	130 γ	acetophenone
4.8 γ	o-phthalaldehyde	25 γ	cyclohexanone
0.25 γ	3-nitrosalicylaldehyde	12 γ	benzoin
6.8 γ	5-nitrosalicylaldehyde	55 γ	epichlorhydrin

(4) Test by catalytic acceleration of the oxidation of p-phenylenediamine by hydrogen peroxide [96]

p-Phenylenediamine (I) is oxidized by hydrogen peroxide, in acid or neutral solution, to a black quinoidal compound (II), insoluble in acetic acid, known as Bandrowski's base.[97]

It has been found that the velocity of the oxidation is appreciably increased by aldehydes.[98] This peroxidase reaction may be applied to the detection of aldehydes, if the test is carried out in certain concentrations of reagent and acid, at which the oxidation rate of the uncatalyzed reaction is lowered, while the action of the aldehydes is not appreciably affected.

In neutral solution, all aldehydes form a black color or precipitate (with other preceding transitory colorations) which lasts a little longer when aromatic aldehydes are involved. In acid solution, the aliphatic aldehydes behave in the same way as in neutral solution, but most aromatic aldehydes form a yellow precipitate or color that persists for some time. This difference in behavior is useful in distinguishing between aliphatic and aromatic aldehydes.

Nitriles, aldehyde ammonia, and aldehyde bisulfite compounds behave similarly to aldehydes. Oximes are less reactive; ketones have no catalytic effect.

Procedure. A drop of the reagent solution, 2 drops of 2 N acetic acid, and 2 drops of 3% hydrogen peroxide are mixed with a drop of the test solution on a spot plate. A color appears in the presence of aldehydes; this appears at once when large amounts are present, or after a short time when small amounts of aldehyde are involved. It is advisable always to carry out a blank test on a drop of water, and further to carry out a parallel test omitting the acetic acid since some aldehydes react more rapidly in acid solution and others more rapidly in neutral solution. A yellow color in acid solution indicates the presence of aromatic aldehydes.

Reagent: 2% solution of p-phenylenediamine.

The *limits of identification* obtained with this color reaction are listed in Table 15.

(5) *Test with 1,2-dianilino-ethane (for water-soluble aldehydes)* [99]

1,2-Dianilino-ethane (N,N-diphenylethylenediamine) reacts in methyl alcohol solutions with most aliphatic and aromatic aldehydes:

$$\begin{array}{c} H_2C-NH \underset{\diagdown C_6H_5}{\overset{\diagup C_6H_5}{}} \\ | \\ H_2C-NH \underset{\diagdown C_6H_5}{} \end{array} + OCHR \rightarrow \begin{array}{c} H_2C-N \underset{\diagdown}{\overset{\diagup C_6H_5}{}} \\ | \qquad CHR \\ H_2C-N \underset{\diagdown C_6H_5}{\diagup} \end{array} + H_2O$$

The precipitates are colorless condensation products (2-substituted 1,3-diphenyltetrahydroimidazoles) and come out in very pure condition. The

TABLE 15. ALDEHYDES AND ALDEHYDE DERIVATIVES

Name	Formula	Color In acid solution	Color In neutral solution	Limit of identification, γ
Formaldehyde	HCHO	Green Black	Black Black	0.02
Acetaldehyde	CH_3—CHO	Green Black	Black Black	0.01
Propionalde-hyde	C_2H_5—CHO	Brown Black	Brown Black	35 10
Oenanthal	CH_3—$(CH_2)_5$—CHO	Green Black	Violet Black	0.3
Phenylacet-aldehyde	C_6H_5—CH_2—CHO	Green Black	Violet-black	10 5
Glyceraldehyde	CH_2OH—CHOH—CHO	Violet Black	Greenish Black	12 8
Acrolein	CH_2=CH—CHO	Green Black	Red Black	0.25
Crotonalde-hyde	CH_3—CH=CH—CHO	Light brown Black	Brown Black	0.12
Benzaldehyde	C_6H_5—CHO	Yellow	Brown Black	3.5
o-Benzaldehyde sulfonic acid	$C_6H_4(SO_3H)CHO$ (1, 2)	Green	Red-violet Black	1.6
Phthalaldehyde	$C_6H_4(CHO)_2$ (1, 2)	Yellow	Black	4 1
o-Hydroxy-benzaldehyde	$C_6H_4(OH)CHO$	Orange-yellow	Yellow Black	0.7
m-Hydroxy-benzaldehyde	,,	Yellow	Violet Black	0.5
o-Nitrobenzal-dehyde	$C_6H_4(NO_2)CHO$	Violet	Violet Black	0.6
p-Nitrobenzal-dehyde	,,	Orange-red	Red-brown Black	0.8

       (continued)

TABLE 15. ALDEHYDES AND ALDEHYDE DERIVATIVES (CONTINUED)

Name	Formula	Color		Limit of identification, γ
		In acid solution	In neutral solution	
Anisaldehyde	$C_6H_4(OCH_3)CHO$	Light yellow	Darker	5
Protocatechuic aldehyde	$C_6H_3(OH)_2CHO$ (1, 2, 4)	Orange	Greenish brown	1.2
Vanillin	$C_6H_3(OH)(OCH_3)CHO$ (1, 2, 4)	Yellow	Brown Black	2
Cinnamalde-hyde	$C_6H_5\!-\!CH\!=\!CH\!-\!CHO$	Orange	Violet Black	0.2
5-Nitrosali-cylaldehyde bisulfite	$C_6H_3(OH)(NO_2)CH\!\!<^{OH}_{SO_3Na}$ (2, 5, 1)	Orange	Brown Black	0.15
Salicylalde-hyde bisulfite	$C_6H_4(OH)CH\!\!<^{OH}_{SO_3Na}$ (2, 1)	Orange	Yellow Black	0.78
Anisaldehyde bisulfite	$CH_3O\!-\!C_6H_4\!-\!CH\!\!<^{OH}_{SO_3Na}$ (1, 4)	Light yellow	Brown	6.5
Cinnamalde-hyde bisul-fite	$C_6H_5\!-\!CH\!=\!CH\!-\!CH\!\!<^{OH}_{SO_3Na}$	Yellow	Black	0.8
Furfural bisul-fite	$C_4H_3O\!-\!CH\!\!<^{OH}_{SO_3Na}$	Yellow Darker	Brown Black	0.66
Acetaldehyde ammonia	$CH_3\!-\!CH\!\!<^{OH}_{NH_2}$	Green Black	Green Black	0.06
Hexamethylene-tetramine	$(CH_2)_6N_4$	Violet Black	Violet Black	50
Mandelonitrile	$C_6H_5\!-\!CHOH\!-\!CN$	Yellow Brown	Dark brown	4
Propionaldehyde cyanhydrin	$C_2H_5\!-\!CHOH\!-\!CN$	Violet	Dark brown	34 10

References pp. 314–319

characteristic melting points can serve to identify the initial aldehydes. This condensation is characteristic of the —CHO group of aldehydes; ketones do not react with 1,2-dianilino-ethane.

Since the aldehyde condensation products are quite soluble in methyl alcohol, the precipitation sensitivity of the condensation reaction in methyl alcohol solution is low for a general test for aldehydes in spot test analysis. However, water-soluble aldehydes react not only with the methyl alcohol solution of the reagent but also with the water solution of its hydrochloride and the precipitation sensitivity attained in the latter case is adequate for the purposes of spot test analysis. This is particularly true of the test for formaldehyde and its derivatives (hexamethylenetetramine, formaldehyde bisulfite, etc.). Chloral and glucose do not react.

Procedure. One drop of the neutral or weakly acid test solution is treated in a micro test tube with a drop of reagent solution. Depending on the quantity of water-soluble aldehyde, a white precipitate or turbidity appears at once. When only small amounts of aldehyde are present, the turbidity becomes clearly visible only after several minutes and is best confirmed by comparison with a blank trial.

Reagent: 1 gram of dianilino-ethane is dissolved in 100 ml glacial acetic acid and the solution made up to 250 ml with water.

This procedure revealed:

0.2 γ	formaldehyde	23 γ	acetaldehyde
1 γ	hexamethylenetetramine	29 γ	butyraldehyde
15 γ	furfural		

(6) Other tests for aldehydes

(a) The formation of alkyl hydroxamic acids from benzene sulfohydroxamic acid, alkali, and aldehyde[100] can be used as the basis of a spot reaction for aldehyde.[101] One drop of the test solution is mixed with 1 or 2 drops of an alcohol solution of benzene sulfohydroxamic acid and 1 drop 1 N sodium hydroxide. After 5 minutes the mixture is acidified with 1 drop 0.5 N HCl. The addition of 1 drop 1 % ferric chloride solution produces a red color (*Idn. Limit:* 2 to 100 γ aliphatic or aromatic aldehyde).

(b) The test for sugars described on page 390, by reducing silver oxide, is a special application of a general aldehyde test.[102] This reaction may be used to differentiate aldehydes from ketones. Among the aliphatic aldehydes, the reactivity decreases as the number of carbon atoms increases.

Benzaldehyde and aromatic aldehydes react quite slowly.[103] Organic compounds that form silver sulfide interfere.

(c) One drop of the test solution is shaken with 1 ml ammoniacal fuchsin solution. If a violet color appears within 1 minute, aldehyde is present.[104] Aldehydes, such as vanillin and salicylaldehyde, which are insoluble in water, also react. (The fuchsin solution contains 0.05 g rosaniline base dissolved in 100 ml water, treated with 2 ml concentrated ammonia, boiled for 5 seconds, cooled, and made up to 200 ml with CO_2-free water.)

20. α,β-Unsaturated and Aromatic Aldehydes
(>C=C—CHO-group)

Test with hydrogen sulfide and sodium pentacyanoammine ferroate [105]

The light yellow aqueous solution of sodium pentacyanoammine ferroate $Na_3[Fe(CN)_5NH_3]$ gives a deep blue color with thioketones, and with aromatic, and α, β-unsaturated aldehydes in the presence of hydrogen sulfide. The reaction with these types of aldehydes probably involves the intermediate formation of thioaldehydes (which alone polymerize readily) with the ferroate. However, in the presence of pentacyanoammine ferroate, they react in the monomolecular form initially produced in (1), with replacement of ammonia as shown in (2):

$$RCHO + H_2S \rightarrow RCHS + H_2O \qquad (1)$$

$$Na_3[Fe(CN)_5NH_3] + RCHS \rightarrow Na_3[Fe(CN)_5(RCHS)] + NH_3 \qquad (2)$$

Procedure. A drop of 1 % solution of sodium pentacyanoammine ferroate and a drop of ammonium sulfide solution (free from polysulfides) are mixed in a microcrucible. A drop of the aqueous or alcoholic test solution is added, and the mixture is neutralized with dilute acetic acid. In the presence of reactive aldehydes, a blue to green color forms according to the amount of aldehyde present.

An excess of acetic acid is to be avoided, since a bluish turbidity can appear even in a blank test. The strength of the acetic acid should therefore correspond to the sulfide solution used.

The *limits of identification* obtained with this reagent are given in Table 16.

TABLE 16.   α, β-UNSATURATED AND AROMATIC ALDEHYDES

Name	Formula	Limit of Identification, γ
Benzaldehyde	C_6H_5CHO	1
Anisaldehyde	$C_6H_4(OCH_3)CHO$ (1, 4)	2
Salicylaldehyde		2
m-Hydroxybenzaldehyde	$C_6H_4(OH)CHO$	1
p-Hydroxybenzaldehyde		2
o-Benzaldehyde sulfonic acid	$C_6H_4(SO_3H)CHO$ (1, 2)	3
o-Nitrobenzaldehyde		4
m-Nitrobenzaldehyde	$C_6H_4(NO_2)CHO$	1
p-Nitrobenzaldehyde		2
Protocatechuic aldehyde	$C_6H_3(OH)_2CHO$ (3, 4, 1)	1
Vanillin	$C_6H_3(OH)(OCH_3)CHO$ (4, 3, 1)	1
Heliotropin	$H_2C\big\langle\!\!\begin{smallmatrix}O\\[2pt]O\end{smallmatrix}\!\!\big\rangle C_6H_3CHO$ (3, 4, 1)	1
o-Phthalaldehyde	$C_6H_4(CHO)_2$ (1, 2)	1
Cinnamaldehyde	$C_6H_5CH{:}CHCHO$	2
Furfural	HC——CH ‖ ‖ HC C·CHO O	1

21. o-Hydroxyaldehydes and Ketones $\left(\begin{smallmatrix}-OH\\ -CO\end{smallmatrix}\text{-group}\right)$

Test by formation of fluorescing aldazines [106] and ketazines [107]

In neutral or acetic acid solution, hydrazine condenses at both of its NH_2-groups with o-hydroxyaldehydes and o-hydroxyketones to produce crystal-line, light yellow insoluble Schiff bases:

$$2 \ \overset{\diagdown}{\underset{\diagup}{\mid}}\!\!\begin{matrix}-OH\\-CO\\|\end{matrix} \ + \ H_2N-NH_2 \ \longrightarrow \ \overset{OH\ \ \ \ HO}{\underset{C\!=\!N-N\!=\!C}{\diagup\diagdown}} \ + \ 2H_2O$$

Without exception, the solid but not the dissolved aldazines and ketazines of o-hydroxyaldehydes and o-hydroxyketones exhibit an intense yellow-orange fluorescence in ultraviolet light. The phenolic OH-group situated *ortho* to the aldehyde group is essential to the production of the fluorescence; the Schiff bases of the *meta-* and *para*-hydroxyaldehydes and ketones do not fluoresce. Furthermore, the symmetric structure with respect to the =N—N= group and this group itself appears to be essential, since the phenylhydrazone of salicylaldehyde which lacks these features does not fluoresce.

The condensation of o-hydroxyaldehydes with hydrazine to produce fluorescing aldazines occurs almost instantaneously even with small quantities of the aldehyde, and there seems to be no steric hindrance even when the aldehyde has a complicated structure. In contrast, all studies up to now seem to show that the condensations of o-hydroxyketones with hydrazine to produce the fluorescing ketazines proceed very slowly.* A fundamental advantage with respect to the analytical application of this fluorescence reaction, which is highly selective for o-hydroxyaldehydes and ketones is provided by the resistance of the aldazines and ketazines, once they have been formed, to dilute acids. Fluorescence reactions in neutral or alkaline solution are often impaired by the presence of even small amounts of fluorescing accompanying materials or impurities, and this deleterious effect is especially marked at high dilutions of the material to be detected. Such interferences are usually decreased or entirely averted by acidification. The acid-resistance of the fluorescent aldazines and ketazines is therefore of analytical importance.

Compare pages 185, 374, 377 regarding the use of the aldazine reaction for the detection of phenols, salicylaldehyde and saligenin (o-hydroxybenzyl alcohol). It should be noted that p-dimethylaminobenzaldehyde gives a fluorescent aldazine with hydrazine. Compare page 300.

Procedure. A drop of the solution of the test material in alcohol, acetone, dioxan, etc., is placed on filter paper and spotted with a drop of hydrazine solution. If preferred, filter paper impregnated with hydrazine solution may be used; the moist reagent paper is spotted with the test solution. According to the quantity of o-hydroxyaldehyde present, a more or less intense yellow-orange fluorescing fleck appears at once or within a minute or two. The fluorescing fleck persists even though the paper is bathed in acetic or dilute (1 N) mineral acid.

---

* No conclusive trials have been made as yet to learn whether this finding may be used as the basis for differentiating o-hydroxyaldehydes and ketones.

References pp. 314–319

If the highest sensitivity of the test is not needed, the solid test material may be spotted directly with hydrazine solution.

Reagent: 5 g hydrazine sulfate and 10 g sodium acetate dissolved in 100 ml water.

This procedure gave positive results with:

1 γ Salicylaldehyde

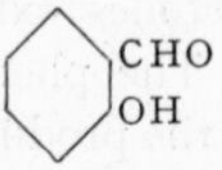

0.8 γ 6-Methyl-4, 5-dihydroxysalicylaldehyde

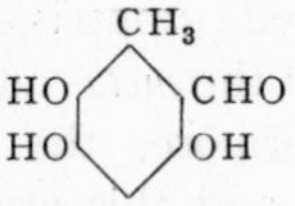

6.4 γ β-Orcinol aldehyde

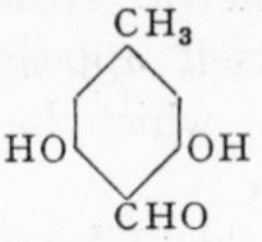

2.4 γ Thamnol

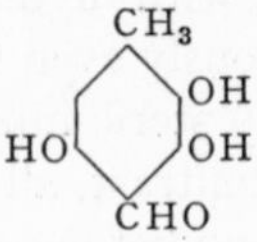

1.1 γ 4-Methylhaematommic acid

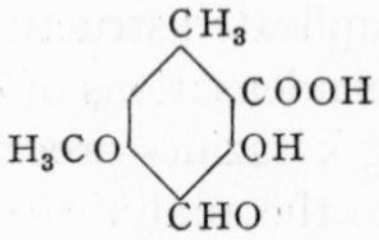

1.8 γ Haematommic acid methyl ester monomethylether

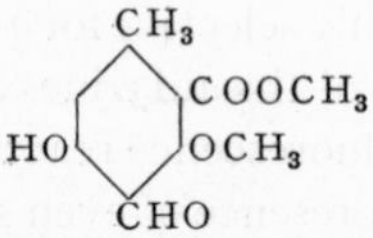

1.1 γ Haematommic acid methyl ester monobenzylether

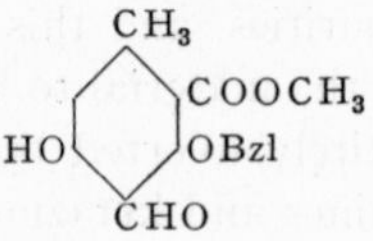

3.4 γ Psoromic acid

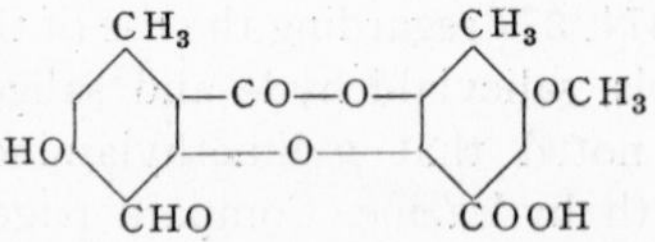

2.2 γ Protocetraric acid

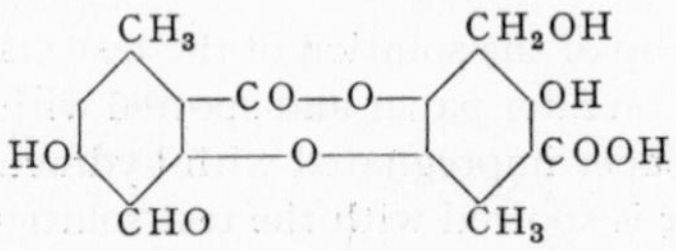

0.1 γ 2,4-Dihydroxyacetophenone (after evaporation with hydrazine solution)

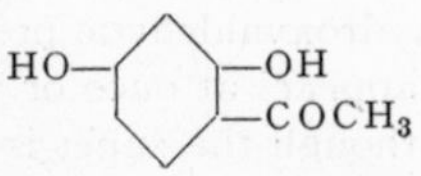

Besides these, a positive reaction was also given by norstictic acid and salazinic acid[108].

22. Methylene Ketones ($-CH_2CO$-group)

(1) Test with sodium nitroprusside [109]

Acetone gives an intense red-yellow color with sodium nitroprusside and alkali; this changes to pink-violet on acidifying with acetic acid. Under these conditions an alkaline solution of sodium nitroprusside is decolorized.

The basis of the color reaction is that the nitrogen oxide in sodium nitroprusside reacts with acetone to produce acid isonitrosoacetone, which remains in the complex anion. At the same time, the iron (III) is reduced to iron (II): [110]

$$Fe^{III} [(CN)_5NO]^{-2} + -CH_2COCH_3 + 2\ OH^- \rightarrow$$
$$[Fe^{II} (CN)_5ON=CHCOCH_3]^{-4} + 2\ H_2O$$

Other methyl ketones and compounds, which contain an enolizable CO-group:

$$-CH_2-CO- \rightleftharpoons -CH = C(OH)-$$

give analogous color reactions, while ketones which lack methyl or methylene groups bound to CO-groups are not active in this respect.

The nitroprusside reaction was long regarded as constituting a characteristic test for methyl ketones. However, this belief is unfounded since it occurs with all compounds which from the beginning contain an activated methylene group, or in which an active methylene group can arise through the shifting of a hydrogen atom. [111] This is shown by the finding that compounds which have no ketone character also yield colors with alkaline nitroprusside. Pertinent examples are: indene (I), pyrrole (II), indole (III), resorcinol (IV).

(I)   (II)   (III)

(IV)

The color reaction is therefore due to the isonitrosation of CH_2-groups. In harmony with this statement is the fact that in addition to (I)–(IV), the following also react with alkaline nitroprusside: cyclopentanone, cyclohexanone, orcinol, hexylresorcinol, phloroglucinol, malonic diethyl ester, phenylacetic ethyl ester, phenylisocrotonic ethyl ester, desoxybenzoin, hydantoin, cyanoacetic ethyl ester, vitamin C, digitoxin, strophanthin K, pyrrole-, indole-acetic acid.

It is remarkable that cinnamic aldehyde, $C_6H_5CH=CHCHO$, apparently is the only aldehyde which gives the same reaction with sodium nitroprusside as methylene ketones and hence can be characterized by the unique behavior.[112]

Procedure.[113] A drop of the aqueous or alcoholic test solution is mixed in a microcrucible with a drop of 5% sodium nitroprusside solution, and a drop of 30% sodium hydroxide solution. After a short time, when a slight color usually develops, 1 or 2 drops glacial acetic acid is added. A red or blue color indicates the presence of a methyl ketone.

The following were detected:

2 γ acetophenone (blue)	4 γ acetoacetic ester (orange)
10 γ acetone (pink)	10 γ diacetyl (pale pink)
10 γ methyl ethyl ketone (pink)	15 γ pyruvic acid (alkaline: red;
10 γ methylheptanone (brown-violet)	acid: dirty brown)
10 γ methyl stearyl ketone (red)	15 γ acetone dicarboxylic acid
2 γ acetylacetone (purple)	(violet)

(2) Test by conversion into indigo [114]

Indigo is formed by the action of o-nitrobenzaldehyde (I) on acetone in alkaline solution. o-Nitrophenyl-lactyl ketone (II) is first formed, which loses a molecule of acetic acid and probably forms o-nitrostyrene (III) as intermediate, which by intramolecular condensation is converted into indolone (IV), and this polymerizes to indigo (V):*

       (I)   (II)

     (III)   (IV)   (V)

* Another reaction path has been suggested by J. Tananescu and A. Baciu, *Bull. Soc. Chim. France*, [5], 4 (1937) 1673.

o-Nitrobenzaldehyde similarly forms indigo with all substances which contain the CH_3CO grouping, so that the formation of the dye may be applied as a test for this group joined to an hydrogen atom or to a carbon atom that does not carry groups which exert excessive hindrance. It should be noted that nitrobenzaldehyde in alkaline solution is used as reagent in the indigo test. Therefore, compounds in which the CH_3CO-group is set free by hydrolysis, can likewise give the indigo test.[115] Among these are: (a) halogen derivatives (such as ethylidene chloride), 2,2-dibromopropane, etc.; (b) acetals (such as acetaldehyde alcoholate acetal); (c) oximes (such as acetoxime, acetophenoneoxime, etc.); (d) bisulfite addition products (such as acetaldehyde sodium bisulfite, acetone sodium bisulfite, etc.).

Procedure. [116] A drop of the test solution which, if possible, should not be alcoholic, is treated in a micro test tube with a drop of an alkaline solution of o-nitrobenzaldehyde, and gently warmed in a water bath. The cooled mixture is extracted with chloroform. A blue color in the chloroform layer indicates the presence of a methyl ketone. Alcoholic solutions sometimes produce a red instead of a blue color in the chloroform layer.

Reagent: Saturated solution of o-nitrobenzaldehyde in 2 N sodium hydroxide.

The following amounts were detected:

100 γ acetone	200 γ acetylacetone
150 γ methyl ethyl ketone	40 γ diacetyl
150 γ methylheptanone	300 γ acetoacetic ester
50 γ acetophenone	100 γ acetaldehyde

23. Oximes and Hydroxamic Acids (=NOH and —NHOH groups)

(1) Test by splitting off hydroxylamine and oxidation to nitrous acid [117]

If aldoximes and ketoximes, or hydroxamic acids derived from carboxylic and sulfonic acids, are warmed with concentrated hydrochloric acid, the NOH-group is split off to give hydroxylamine hydrochloride (1, 1a, 1b). The hydroxylamine can be oxidized to nitrous acid by iodine in acetic acid solution (2).[118] If the oxidation is carried out in the presence of sulfanilic acid, the latter is diazotized by the nitrous acid (3). After the excess iodine is removed by means of thiosulfate (4), the p-diazoniumbenzene sulfonic acid (I) can be coupled with α-naphthylamine (II) to produce the red azo dye: p-benzenesulfonic acid-azo-α-naphthylamine (III) (5). The reactions are:

$$>C=NOH + H_2O + HCl \rightarrow >C=O + NH_2OH \cdot HCl \qquad (1)$$

$$RCO(NHOH) + H_2O + HCl \rightarrow RCOOH + NH_2OH \cdot HCl \qquad (1a)$$

$$RSO_2(NHOH) + H_2O + HCl \rightarrow RSO_3H + NH_2OH \cdot HCl \qquad (1b)$$

$$NH_2OH + 2 I_2 + H_2O \rightarrow HNO_2 + 4 HI \tag{2}$$

$$HO_3S \underset{}{\bigcirc} NH_2 + HNO_2 + H^+ \rightarrow HO_3S \underset{}{\bigcirc} \overset{+}{N} \equiv N + 2 H_2O \tag{3}$$

$$I_2 + 2 Na_2S_2O_3 \rightarrow 2 NaI + Na_2S_4O_6 \tag{4}$$

$$HO_3S \underset{}{\bigcirc} \overset{+}{N} \equiv N + \underset{}{\bigcirc}\!\!\bigcirc NH_2 \rightarrow HO_3S \underset{}{\bigcirc} N = N \underset{}{\bigcirc}\!\!\bigcirc \overset{+}{N}H_3 \tag{5}$$

    (I)   (II)   (III)

The reactions (1)–(5), of which (3) and (5) constitute the basis of the familiar and sensitive Griess test for nitrite, proceed so rapidly and completely that they can serve as the basis of a specific test for small amounts of aldoximes, ketoximes, and hydroxamic acids.

Procedure. The sample substance (solutions should be evaporated to dryness) is heated in a microcrucible with 3 drops concentrated hydrochloric acid until the volume is reduced to one-fifth of the original. A few mg solid sodium acetate, 1 or 2 drops of a solution of sulfanilic acid, and a drop of iodine in glacial acetic acid are added in succession. The mixture is left for 2 or 3 minutes. Any excess free iodine is removed by 0.1 N sodium thiosulfate, and then a drop of α-naphthylamine solution is added. A more or less intense red color appears, according to the amount of oxime or hydroxamic acid present.

Reagents: 1)   0.1 N iodine in acetic acid: 1.3 g iodine in 100 ml glacial acetic acid.
            2)   Sulfanilic acid solution: 10 g sulfanilic acid in 750 ml water plus 250 ml glacial acetic acid.
            3)   α-Naphthylamine solution: 3 g base in 700 ml water plus 300 ml glacial acetic acid.

The *limits of identification* for different oximes and hydroxamic acids, are given in Table 17.

(2) Detection of hydroxamic acids with fused benzoyl peroxide [119]

If aliphatic or aromatic hydroxamic acids are heated to 120–130° with benzoyl peroxide (m.p. 103°), nitrous acid is split out within several minutes:

$$RCONHOH + 2 (C_6H_5CO)_2O_2 \rightarrow RCOOH + 2 (C_6H_5CO)_2O + HNO_2$$

The resulting nitrous acid can be detected in the gas phase by means of the Griess reagent (compare Test 1).

TABLE 17. OXIMES AND HYDROXAMIC ACIDS

Name	Formula	Limit of identification, γ
Acetone oxime	$H_3C—C(NOH)—CH_3$	0.08
Diacetyl dioxime	$H_3C—C(NOH)—C(NOH)—CH_3$	0.03
Isonitrosoacetophenone	$C_6H_5—CO—CH(NOH)$	7
Cyclohexanedione dioxime		0.1
Isonitrosocamphor		0.5
Benzil dioxime	$C_6H_5—C(NOH)—C(NOH)—C_6H_5$	0.05
Oxobenzalbutanone oxime	$C_6H_5—CH=C(CH_3)—C(NOH)—CH_3$	0.2
Desoxybenzoin oxime	$C_6H_5—C(NOH)—CH_2—C_6H_5$	0.4
Benzoin oxime	$C_6H_5—C(NOH)—CH(OH)—C_6H_5$	0.1
Isonitrosomethyl ethyl ketone	$H_3C—CO—C(NOH)—CH_3$	8
Methyl ether of salicylal-doxime	$C_6H_4(OCH_3)CH(NOH)$	6
Benzhydroxamic acid	$C_6H_5—CONHOH$	0.2
Benzenesulfhydroxamic acid	$C_6H_5—SO_2(NHOH)$	0.9
Benzylbenzoin oxime	$C_6H_5—C(NOH)—\underset{\underset{CH_2C_6H_5}{\vert}}{C(OH)}—C_6H_5$	0.6
1-Nitroso-2-naphthol (as well as the isomeric 2-nitroso-1-naphthol)		0.5

References pp. 314–319

Procedure. A micro test tube is used. A little of the solid or the evaporation residue of a drop of its solution, or a drop of a solution in ether or benzene is treated with a drop of benzoyl peroxide solution and taken to dryness. The mouth of the test tube is covered with filter paper moistened with nitrite reagent solution and the tube is immersed in a glycerol bath previously heated to 120–130°. If aliphatic or aromatic hydroxamic acids were present, a pink or red stain appears within 3–10 minutes.

Reagents: *1)*   10% solution of benzoyl peroxide in benzene.
              2)   Freshly prepared mixture of equal volumes of 1% solution of sulfanilic acid in 30% acetic acid and 0.1% solution of α-naphthylamine in 30% acetic acid.

The procedure revealed: 30–40 γ benzhydroxamic acid, salicylohydroxamic acid, phenylacetohydroxamic acid, *p*-methoxybenzhydroxamic acid.

(3) Differentiation of aliphatic and aromatic oximes [119]

When oximes are heated to 120–130° with benzoyl peroxide, nitrous acid is produced only with aliphatic oximes, whereas aromatic oximes yield no more than traces of this product. Consequently, the fusion reaction may be utilised to distinguish aliphatic from aromatic oximes. The reaction leading to the production of nitrous acid may be:

$$\text{>C=NOH} + 2\ (C_6H_5CO)_2O_2 \rightarrow \text{>C=O} + 2\ (C_6H_5CO)_2O + HNO_2$$

The procedure and reagents are those described in (2).

The following were revealed:

       10 γ dimethylglyoxime
       20 γ cycloheptanedionedioxime
       40 γ camphoroxime

A positive response was obtained with: phenylglyoxaldoxime, 2-furaldioxime, 2,3-butanedionedioxime, 1,2-cyclohexanedionedioxime. No reaction was given by: diphenylglyoxime, salicylaldoxime, α-benzilmonoxime, α-benzildioxime, benzoinoxime.

24. Thioketones and Mercaptans (Thiols)
(>C=S and >C—SH (Na, K, etc.) groups)

(1) Test by catalytic acceleration of the iodine-azide reaction [120]

The reaction:

$$2\ NaN_3 + I_2 = 2\ NaI + 3\ N_2$$

which alone proceeds extremely slowly, is catalyzed not only by all inorganic sulfides, thiosulfates and thiocyanates (see Volume I, Chapter 4) but also by solid or dissolved organic compounds containing the group >C=S or >C—SH.

Other organic sulfur derivatives such as thioethers (R—S—R), disulfides (R—S—S—R) [with the exception of diacyldisulfides (R—CO—S—S—CO—R)], sulfones (R—SO$_2$—R), sulfinic acids (R—SO$_2$H) and sulfonic acids (R—SO$_3$H) or the salts of these acids, all exert no, or at the most very slight, effect on the reaction. The catalytic hastening of the iodine–azide reaction is therefore specific for thioketones and mercaptans (thiols). It permits the detection of very small quantities of these compounds of bivalent sulfur.

The mechanism of the catalytic effect of mercaptans and thioketones on the iodine–azide reaction has not been completely elucidated. In all likelihood the same explanation will not be valid for all compounds. The action of mercaptans is probably analogous to the catalytic activity of hydrogen sulfide, thiocyanates, and soluble metal sulfides. It possibly involves the formation of a reactive labile intermediate compound, RSI (1), which reacts with sodium azide, as shown in (2). The summation of (1) and (2) gives the equation of the uncatalyzed reaction, in which the regenerated catalyst no longer appears:

$$RS\,Na + I_2 \rightarrow R\text{—S—I} + NaI \;.\;.\;.\;.\;.\;.\;.\;. \text{rapid } (1)$$

$$R\text{—S—I} + 2\,NaN_3 \rightarrow RSNa + NaI + 3\,N_2 \;.\;.\;.\; \text{rapid } (2)$$

$$2\,Na\,N_3 + I_2 \rightarrow 2\,NaI + 3N_2 \;.\;.\;.\;.\;.\;.\;.\; \text{rapid } (1 + 2)$$

Thioketones probably also form an analogous labile intermediate product containing iodine, $>\!\!C\!<^{SI}_I$, which can react with sodium azide with regeneration of the catalytically active thioketones:

$$>\!\!C\!<^{SI}_I + 2\,NaN_3 \rightarrow \;>\!\!C\!=\!S + 2\,NaI + 3\,N_2$$

It is also possible that another type of intermediate compound is formed, as discussed in more detail (see page 411) in the test for carbon disulfide. Hence the evolution of nitrogen in a sodium azide–iodine solution can be used equally well for the detection of the $>\!\!C\!=\!S$ and $>\!\!C\text{—SH}$ groups as for inorganic sulfides. Under certain conditions (see later), it may also be used to differentiate between these two groups.

When drawing conclusions from the results of the iodine-azide reaction regarding the type of binding of bivalent sulfur in organic compounds, it is necessary to keep the following points in mind. An immediate distinct production of nitrogen (spontaneous reaction) can be taken as certain proof of the presence of $>\!\!CS\text{—}$ or $>\!\!CSH\text{—}$ groups, provided not too small samples are being tested. Likewise, complete lack of reaction is a sure indication of the absence of such groups. However, between these extremes, are instances in which a reaction begins only after several minutes or sometimes hours and furthermore usually continues quite slowly.[121] Such cases may involve slow hydrolytic cleavages being undergone by the test substance, or by its parts that are in water solution, with formation of SH- or SNa-containing products which, of course, react promptly with iodine-azide solution. It should also be noted in this connection, that the reagent solution is slightly alkaline because of its content of sodium azide, and this basicity favors hydrolytic splitting. This hydrolysis may be responsible for the fact that disulfides,[122] particularly those which are but slightly soluble in water (e.g. cystine), and likewise thioethers and sulfur-bearing ring compounds sometimes give a distinct iodine–azide reaction after they have been in contact with the reagent solution for several minutes.

Procedure. A drop of a solution of the test substance in water or an organic solvent * is mixed on a watch glass with a drop of iodine–azide solution, and observed for any evolution of little bubbles of nitrogen. Either a solid or liquid compound (after removal of the solvent) may be tested directly with the reagent. A positive reaction is then especially easy to see, even with very small amounts of substance.

Reagent: Solution of 3 g sodium azide in 100 ml 0.1 N iodine.

Compounds containing $>$C$=$S and $>$C—SH groups, i.e., thioketones and mercaptans may be differentiated by the fact that the latter are easily converted (oxidized) by iodine to the corresponding disulfides:

$$2R\text{—}SH + I_2 \rightarrow R\text{—}S\text{—}S\text{—}R + 2\ HI$$

which do not react with iodine-azide solution. Thioketones are not altered by iodine. Consequently, when a sample gives a positive reaction with iodine-azide solution, a fresh sample should be warmed briefly with an excess of alcoholic iodine solution containing sodium acetate and, after cooling, again tested with sodium azide–iodine solution. A positive reaction then indicates the presence of thioketones.

The *limits of identification* of thioketones and mercaptans through catalysis of the iodine–azide reaction are given in Table 18. As the drop size for the organic solutions is not constant, the number of drops per ml have been determined in each instance, in order to obtain the volume requisite for the calculation of the dilution limit.

---

* Carbon disulfide should not be used as a solvent, since as a thio compound it reacts with the iodine–azide solution (see page 411).

TABLE 18. THIOKETONES AND MERCAPTANS

Name and formula	Limit of identification and dilution limit	Solvent	No. of drops per ml
Thioacetic acid CH_3COSH	0.0003 γ 1 : 100,000,000	Acetone + water	30
Methylxanthic methyl ester $CH_3OCSSCH_3$	0.03 γ 1 : 1,000,000	Acetone + water	30
Potassium ethyl xanthate C_2H_5OCSSK	0.04 γ 1 : 1,000,000	Water	25
Rhodanine 	0.003 γ 1 : 10,000,000	Acetone + water	35
3-Amino-4-phenyl-5-thiotriazole 	0.03 γ 1 : 1,000,000	Acetone + water	30
Allyl isothiocyanate (allyl mustard oil) $CH_2=CHCH_2N=C=S$	15 γ 1 : 2,000	Acetone + water	35
Phenyl isothiocyanate (phenyl mustard oil) $C_6H_5-N=C=S$	0.25 γ 1 : 100,000	Acetone + water	40
p, p'-Dimethoxythiobenzophenone 	0.1 γ 1 : 200,000	Acetone + water	50
4-Thio-α-naphthoflavone 	0.02 γ 1 : 1,000,000	Acetone + water	55

(continued)

TABLE 18. THIOKETONES AND MERCAPTANS (CONTINUED)

Name and formula	Limit of identification and dilution limit	Solvent	No. of drops per ml
Diphenyl thiocarbonate C_6H_5O—CS—OC_6H_5	1 γ 1 : 20,000	Acetone + water	50
Di-p-tolyl trithiocarbonate $H_3CC_6H_4$—S—CS—S—$C_6H_4CH_3$	0.1 γ 1 : 200,000	Acetone + water	50
Methyl α-napthylcarbodithionate $C_{10}H_7CSSCH_3$	0.12 γ 1 : 100,000	Methyl alcohol	80
Thiourea H_2N—CS—NH_2	0.005 γ 1 : 10,000,000	Water	20
sym. Diphenylthiourea C_6H_5NH—CS—NHC_6H_5	0.6 γ 1 : 200,000	Alcohol + water	80
Diphenylthiocarbazone (Dithizone) C_6H_5N=N—CS—NH—NH—C_6H_5	2.5 γ 1 : 10,000	Acetone + water	40
Dithiooxamide (Rubeanic acid) H_2N—CS—CS—NH_2	0.03 γ 1 : 1,000,000	Acetone + water	30
Thioglycolic acid $CH_2(SH)COOH$	0.05 γ 1 : 1,000,000	Water	20

(2) Test for SH-groups by precipitation of cuprous salts [123]

Organic compounds containing SH groups may react with cupric ions in various ways. Sometimes water-insoluble, mostly dark colored, cupric salts are produced. This is the case with dithiocarbamates (see page 234) and also with compounds which contain two adjacent SH-groups, e.g., rubeanic acid. Another mode of reaction, which may occur in strong ammoniacal solution, leads to the production of black copper sulfide (e.g. cysteine). Along with this reaction, and predominating in the case of some mercapto compounds,[124] there is an initial redox reaction which yields cuprous ions and disulfide:

$$2 \text{ R—S}^{-1} + 2 \text{ Cu}^{+2} \rightarrow \text{Cu}_2^{+2} + \text{R—S—S—R} \tag{1}$$

Subsequently, the cuprous ions may react with unused mercaptan:

$$\text{Cu}_2^{+2} + 2 \text{ R—S}^{-1} \rightarrow \text{Cu}_2(RS)_2 \tag{2}$$

The cuprous salts of mercaptans are yellow, orange-yellow or yellow-brown; they are insoluble in water, dilute acids or ammonia. Accordingly, if an acetic acid or ammoniacal cuprous salt solution is used, the redox reaction (1), through which the mercaptan is consumed in the production of disulfide, may be by-passed and immediate precipitation of the cuprous mercaptan may occur.* It is advisable to use acetic acid-cuprous salt solutions as reagents for mercaptans, because interfering side reactions (particularly the formation of copper sulfide) are ordinarily thus repressed. Since this is not invariably the case, the following procedure provides an absolutely reliable test for mercaptans only when a yellow or brown precipitate or turbidity appears.

Procedure. A drop of the acetic acid or ammoniacal test solution is treated with one drop of copper solution on a spot plate. If mercaptans are present, a yellow or brown precipitate results, or a similar coloration if small quantities are involved.

Reagents: 1) 1.5 g cupric chloride and 3 g ammonium chloride are dissolved in a little water. The solution is treated with 3 ml concentrated ammonia and made up to 50 ml with water.
2) 20 % hydroxylamine hydrochloride solution in water.
Equal volumes of 1) and 2) are mixed just before the test.

The procedure gave positive results with:

2.5 γ Thioglycolic acid anilide C_6H_5—NH—CO—CH$_2$—SH (yellow precipitate)

5   γ Mercaptobenzothiazole   (yellow precipitate)

1   γ Potassium ethyl   S C$\begin{smallmatrix}\diagup OC_2H_5\\ \diagdown SK\end{smallmatrix}$ (yellow-brown
       xanthate   precipitate)

0.5 γ Rubeanic acid H_2N—CS—CS—NH$_2$ ⇌   (yellow-brown
                                 HN=C(SH)—C(SH)=NH   precipitate)

2.5 γ Potassium mercapto-   (yellow precipitate)
       phenylthiothiadiazolone

---

* There are however exceptions: Thioglycolic acid added to an acid solution of copper salts gives a yellow precipitate whereas, when added to a blue ammoniacal solution, only decolorization occurs.

25. **Dithiocarbamates** $\left(S = C{\Large<}_{\substack{S- \\ N<}}\text{-group} \right)$

Test by conversion into cupric salts soluble in organic solvents [125]

The dithiocarbamide group is present in the stable water-soluble and water-insoluble salts of the unstable dithiocarbamic acid (I) and its N-substituted derivatives (II) and (III).

$$S C{\Large<}_{\substack{SH \\ NH_2}} \qquad\qquad S C{\Large<}_{\substack{SH \\ NHR}} \qquad\qquad S C{\Large<}_{\substack{SH \\ NR_1R_2}}$$
$$\text{(I)} \qquad\qquad\qquad \text{(II)} \qquad\qquad\qquad \text{(III)}$$

In (II), R denotes an alkyl or aryl group; in (III) R_1 and R_2 are alkyl groups only, and R_1 may be the same as R_2.

Water-soluble salts of (II) and (III) with primary or secondary aliphatic amines are produced by addition reactions of carbon disulfide:

$$C S_2 + 2 NH_2R \longrightarrow S C{\Large<}_{\substack{SH \cdot NH_2R \\ NHR}} \tag{1}$$

$$C S_2 + 2 NHR_1R_2 \longrightarrow S C{\Large<}_{\substack{SH \cdot NHR_1R_2 \\ NR_1R_2}} \tag{2}$$

If alkali hydroxide or ammonia is present, the corresponding water-soluble alkali or ammonium salts of (II) and (III) result. With primary aromatic amines, carbon disulfide does not undergo a reaction analogous to (1); instead, symmetrical diaryl thioureas and hydrogen sulfide are formed (compare page 258). If, however, a mixture of ammonia and primary aromatic amines is allowed to react on carbon disulfide, ammonium salts of monoarylated dithiocarbamic acid result: [126]

$$C S_2 + NH_2R + NH_3 \longrightarrow S C{\Large<}_{\substack{SH \cdot NH_3 \\ NHR}} \tag{3}$$

By virtue of their CS- or CSH-groups, the salts formed in (1)–(3) catalytically accelerate the iodine–azide reaction (compare page 228) and furthermore they also form water-insoluble cuprous salts, which are yellow in most instances (compare page 232). However, a characteristic feature of water-soluble dithiocarbamates and their N-substituted derivatives is the ability to precipitate as brown cupric salts, which dissolve in water-immiscible organic liquids to produce red-brown solutions.* This property, which has been utilized for the colorimetric determination of small quantities of

---

* A notable exception is presented by the copper salt of diethanolamine-dithiocarbamic acid, which is soluble only in oxygen-containing organic liquids, but not in chloroform, benzene, etc.[127]

copper,[123] can also be employed in the detection of water-soluble dithio-carbamates and their N-substituted derivatives.

Procedure. A drop of the neutral test solution is treated in a micro test tube with a drop of an acetic acid copper chloride solution and then shaken out with two or three drops of chloroform. The presence of dithiocarbamates is shown by the fact that the chloroform layer assumes a reddish-brown color. Comparison with a blank is advisable when small quantities of dithiocarbamate are suspected.

Reagent: 1% solution of cupric chloride, mixed with an equal volume of 1 : 1 acetic acid.

A positive response was given by:

1.2 γ Ammonium dithiocarbamate $S C\!\!\begin{array}{l} \diagup S NH_4 \\ \diagdown NH_2 \end{array}$

2.5 γ Sodium diethyldithiocarbamate $S C\!\!\begin{array}{l} \diagup S Na \\ \diagdown N(C_2H_5)_2 \end{array}$

2 γ Ammonium phenyldithiocarbamate $S C\!\!\begin{array}{l} \diagup S NH_4 \\ \diagdown NHC_6H_5 \end{array}$

2 γ Ammonium *p*-aminophenyldithiocarbamate $S C\!\!\begin{array}{l} \diagup S NH_4 \\ \diagdown NHC_6H_4NH_2 \end{array}$

1.8 γ Piperidinium piperidyldithiocarbamate $S C\!\!\begin{array}{l} \diagup S H \cdot NHC_5H_{10} \\ \diagdown NC_5H_{10} \end{array}$

26. Xanthates $\left(S\!=\!C\!\!\begin{array}{l} \diagup S^- \\ \diagdown OR \end{array}\!\!\text{-group} \right)$

Test with molybdic acid [129]

The xanthate group is found in the relatively stable water-soluble alkali salts and in the water-insoluble heavy metal salts of the monoalkylester acid (I), which is derived from dithiocarbonic acid (II)

$$S C\!\!\begin{array}{l} \diagup S H \\ \diagdown OR \end{array} \qquad S C\!\!\begin{array}{l} \diagup S H \\ \diagdown OH \end{array} \qquad R = CH_3, \ C_2H_5, \ C_6H_5CH_2, \ \text{cellulose etc.}$$
(I)   (II)

Neither (I) or (II) can be isolated because the water-soluble salts are decomposed by dilute acids with production of carbon disulfide. For instance:

$$C_2H_5O\!-\!\underset{\underset{S}{\|}}{C}\!-\!S^- \ + H^+ \ \rightarrow \ C_2H_5O\!-\!\underset{\underset{S}{\|}}{C}\!-\!S H \ \rightarrow \ C S_2 + C_2H_5OH$$

By virtue of their $\diagup CS\!-$ and $\diagup C\!-\!SNa$ group, the water-soluble and water-insoluble xanthates catalytically accelerate the sodium azide-iodine

References pp. 314–319

reaction (compare page 228). The soluble xanthates react with either cuprous or cupric salts to yield yellow cuprous xanthates, which are insoluble in water and dilute acids. When cupric salts are used, the initial step produces cupric ions and the disulfide of the particular monoalkylester acid. Neither the iodine-azide reaction nor the formation of cuprous salt is characteristic for xanthates. On the other hand, the behavior of xanthates toward acid solutions of alkali molybdate is unequivocal. The resulting plum-blue precipitate dissolves in ether, chloroform, etc. to give a violet color. The composition of the precipitate corresponds to an addition compound of 1 MoO_3 and 2 ester acid. For instance, sodium ethyl xanthate gives

$$MoO_3.2 \left(C S \begin{matrix} ^{SH} \\ _{OC_2H_5} \end{matrix} \right).$$

The insoluble xanthates of zinc, cadmium and univalent copper react in this manner. It is notable that the monoesters, which are ordinarily unstable, are stabilized by coordinative binding to MoO_3.

Procedure. A micro test tube is used. A little of the solid, or a drop of solution of its alkali salt, is treated in succession with one drop each of 2% ammonium molybdate solution and 0.5 N hydrochloric acid and then shaken with several drops of chloroform. Depending on the quantity of xanthate present, the chloroform acquires a more or less intense violet color.

The *limit of identification* is 1 γ sodium xanthate.

27. Carboxylic Acids and Their Derivatives

Test by conversion into the iron^{III} salts of hydroxamic acids

Carboxylic acids, esters, amides and anhydrides can be readily converted into hydroxamic acids, RCO(NHOH). The procedure is different and characteristic for each type of compound.

All hydroxamic acids give a red or violet color with ferric chloride in weak acid solution. This color reaction is due to the acid CONHOH group, which is present in all hydroxamic acids. It reacts with the ferric ion to form water-soluble inner complex salts:

$$R-C \begin{matrix} ^{NHOH} \\ _{O} \end{matrix} + {}^1/_3 \, Fe^{+3} \rightarrow R-C \begin{matrix} ^{N-O} \\ _{O---Fe/3} \end{matrix} \overset{H}{|} + H^+$$

The conversion into hydroxamic acid and the formation of iron^{III} hydroxamate is used as a test for carboxylic acids and their derivatives.

References pp. 314–319

(1) Test for carboxylic acids (—COOH group) [130]

Carboxylic acids cannot be converted into hydroxamic acids by direct action with hydroxylamine. The acid chloride must be formed first and it then readily gives the alkali salt of hydroxamic acid on treatment with hydroxylamine and alkali. The underlying reactions of the test are:

$$RCOOH + SOCl_2 \rightarrow RCOCl + SO_2 + HCl$$

$$RCOCl + NH_2OH + 2\ NaOH \rightarrow RCO(NHONa) + NaCl + 2\ H_2O$$

$$RCO(NHONa) + HCl \rightarrow RCO(NHOH) + NaCl$$

$$3\ RCO(NHOH) + FeCl_3 \rightarrow 3\ HCl + Fe[RCO(NHO)]_3$$

Procedure. A drop of the test solution is evaporated to dryness in a micro-crucible, or a minute portion of the solid is taken for treatment there with 2 drops of thionyl chloride. The mixture is evaporated, almost to dryness, to convert the carboxylic acid into its chloride. Two drops of a saturated alcoholic solution of hydroxylamine hydrochloride are then added and drops of alcoholic caustic soda until the liquid is alkaline to litmus paper. Reaction takes place on re-heating. The mixture is acidified with a few drops of 0.5 N hydrochloric acid, and treated with a 1% solution of ferric chloride. The color change ranges from brown-red to dark violet (the acidity of the solution should again be tested with litmus).

The *limits of identification* obtained with several carboxylic acids are given in Table 19.

(2) Test for esters of carboxylic acids (—COOR group) [131]

Esters of carboxylic acids can be converted into alkali salts of hydroxamic acids on treatment with hydroxylamine hydrochloride in the presence of alkali hydroxide:

$$RCOOR_1 + NH_2OH + NaOH = RCO(NHONa) + R_1OH + H_2O$$

The free hydroxamic acid formed by acidification can be identified by the color reaction with ferric chloride (see above). Lactones, which may be regarded as inner esters, react similarly to esters.

Procedure. A drop of the ether solution of the ester is treated in a porcelain microcrucible with a drop of saturated alcoholic hydroxylamine hydrochloride solution and a drop of saturated alcoholic caustic potash. The mixture is heated over a microflame until the reaction begins, as indicated by a slight bubbling. After cooling, the mixture is acidified with 0.5 N hydrochloric acid, and a drop of 1% ferric chloride solution is added. A more or less intense violet color appears according to the amount of ester present.

The *limits of identification* for different esters are given in Table 20.

TABLE 19. CARBOXYLIC ACIDS

Name	Formula	Limit of identifi- cation	Color
Sodium acetate	CH_3COONa	100 γ	Violet-red
Monochloroacetic acid	$ClCH_2COOH$	12 γ	Violet
Dichloroacetic acid	$CHCl_2COOH$	11 γ	Red-violet
Glycine	NH_2CH_2COOH	15 γ	Lilac
Palmitic acid	$CH_3(CH_2)_{14}COOH$	16 γ	Brown-violet
Stearic acid	$CH_3(CH_2)_{16}COOH$	20 γ	Brown-violet
Crotonic acid	$CH_3—CH=CH—COOH$	33 γ	Violet
Oleic acid	$CH_3(CH_2)_7CH=CH(CH_2)_7COOH$	11 γ	Red-violet
Ricinoleic acid	$CH_3(CH_2)_5CH(OH)CH_2—CH=CH$ $\qquad\qquad\qquad\qquad\quad \mid$ $\qquad\qquad\qquad HOOC(CH_2)_7$	15 γ	Violet
Succinic acid	$HOOCCH_2—CH_2COOH$	11 γ	Violet
Tricarballylic acid	$CH_2\text{——}CH\text{——}CH_2$ $\;\mid\qquad\quad\mid\qquad\quad\mid$ $COOH\;\;COOH\;\;COOH$	11 γ	Violet
Citric acid	$CH_2\text{——}C(OH)\text{——}CH_2$ $\;\mid\qquad\qquad\mid\qquad\quad\mid$ $COOH\;\;\;COOH\;\;\;\;COOH$	—	Violet-red
Phenylacetic acid	$C_6H_5—CH_2COOH$	11 γ	Red-violet
Cinnamic acid	$C_6H_5—CH=CHCOOH$	33 γ	Violet
Anthranilic acid	$C_6H_4(NH_2)COOH\ (1,\ 2)$	12 γ	Dark violet
Thioacetic acid	CH_3COSH	—	Violet-red

References pp. 314–319

TABLE 20. ESTERS OF CARBOXYLIC ACIDS

Name	Formula	Limit of identification		Color
Ethyl formate	$HCOOC_2H_5$	11	γ	Violet-brown lilac
Ethyl ortho-formate	$HC(OC_2H_5)_3$	10	γ	Violet-red
Ethylurethan	$CO(NH_2)OC_2H_5$	10	γ	Gray-violet
Ethyl acetate	$CH_3COOC_2H_5$	2	γ	Violet
Vinyl acetate	$CH_3 \cdot COO \cdot CH=CH_2$	11	γ	Violet
Phenyl acetate	$CH_3COOC_6H_5$	2.5	γ	Violet-red-brown-red
Glycine ethyl ester hydro-chloride	$HCl \cdot H_2NCH_2COOC_2H_5$	13	γ	Violet-light brown
Ethyl stearate	$CH_3(CH_2)_{16}COOC_2H_5$	12	γ	Violet-red
Cetyl palmitate	$CH_3(CH_2)_{14}COOC_{16}H_{33}$	11	γ	Violet
Glyceryl oleate	$[CH_3(CH_2)_7CH=CH(CH_2)_7COO]_3Glyc.$	10	γ	Violet
Diethyl oxalate	$H_5C_2OOC—COOC_2H_5$	3	γ	Red-violet-violet-gray
Diethyl malonate	$H_5C_2OOC—CH_2—COOC_2H_5$	2.6	γ	Violet-red
Propyl benzoate	$C_6H_5COOC_3H_7$	3	γ	Violet
Methyl salicylate	$C_6H_4(OH)COOCH_3$	2.5	γ	Dark violet-green-violet
Phenyl salicylate	$C_6H_4(OH)COOC_6H_5$	6	γ	Dark blue-violet
Potassium xanthate	$SC{\overset{\diagup OC_2H_5}{\diagdown SK}}$	11	γ	Dark red to violet-red
α-Naphthyldithio-carboxylic acid methyl ester	$C_{10}H_7CSSCH_3$	11	γ	Deep violet-brown to dark brown
Coumarin		6	γ	Violet-red

References pp. 314–319

(3) *Test for carboxylic acid anhydrides* $\left(\begin{array}{c} -C{=}O \\ {>}O \text{ group} \\ -C{=}O \end{array} \right)^{131}$

Anhydrides of mono- and dicarboxylic acids react directly with hydroxylamine to give hydroxamic acids and the respective carboxylic acid:

$$\begin{array}{c} RC{<}^O_{} \\ {>}O + NH_2OH = RCO(NHOH) + RCOOH \\ RC{<}_O^{} \end{array}$$

In the presence of ferric ions, the colored inner complex iron[III] hydroxamate is formed.

Procedure. A drop of the ether solution of the anhydride is mixed in a porcelain microcrucible with 1 or 2 drops of the reagent solution and evaporated to dryness over a microburner. A few drops of water are added. A violet or pink color is formed according to the amount of anhydride present.

Reagent: A 0.5 % alcoholic solution of ferric chloride is acidified with a few drops concentrated hydrochloric acid and saturated (warm) with hydroxylamine hydrochloride. The reagent solution must be freshly prepared.

The *limits of identification* for different anhydrides are given in Table 21.

TABLE 21. CARBOXYLIC ACID ANHYDRIDES

Name	Formula	Limit of identification	Color
Acetic anhydride	$H_3C{-}C{<}^O$ $\phantom{H_3C{-}C}{>}O$ $H_3C{-}C{<}_O$	5 γ	Violet
Succinic anhydride	$CH_2{-}C{<}^O$ $\phantom{CH_2{-}C}{>}O$ $CH_2{-}C{<}_O$	5 γ	Red-brown
Thapsic anhydride	$OC{-}(CH_2)_{14}{-}CO$ $\phantom{OC{-}(CH_2)_1}O$	10 γ	Pink
Camphoric anhydride	$C{=}O$ $C_8H_{14}{<}{>}O$ $C{=}O$	10 γ	Lilac

(continued)

TABLE 21.   CARBOXYLIC ACID ANHYDRIDES (CONTINUED)

Name	Formula	Limit of identification	Color
Benzoic anhydride	(ring)—C O—O—O C—(ring)	6 γ	Pink
Phthalic anhydride	(formula)	5 γ	Violet
m-Nitrophthalic anhydride	(formula)	10 γ	Pink
Hemipinic anhydride	(formula)	5 γ	Lilac

28. Aliphatic Esters of Fatty Acids

Detection by reaction with sodium and 1,2-dinitrobenzene [132]

Aliphatic α-hydroxyketones (acyloins) may be prepared from aliphatic fatty acids by prolonged heating of ether or benzene solutions of their esters with metallic sodium.[133] There is intermediate formation of α-diketones and the light yellow benzene-insoluble sodium salts of endiols (*1*) which, after removal of any excess sodium, can be saponified to acyloins (*2*):

$$2\ R{-}COOR' + 4Na° \rightarrow \begin{matrix} R{-}C{-}ONa \\ \| \\ R{-}C{-}ONa \end{matrix} + 2\ R'ONa \qquad (1)$$

$$\begin{matrix} R{-}C{-}ONa \\ \| \\ R{-}C{-}ONa \end{matrix} + 2\ H_2O \rightarrow \begin{matrix} R{-}CHOH \\ | \\ R{-}CO \end{matrix} + 2\ NaOH \qquad (2)$$

Acyloins may be readily detected through the fact that they reduce, in alcoholic alkaline solution, 1,2-dinitrobenzene to yield the violet water-soluble alkali salts of an *o*-quinoid nitrol-nitroic acid and the corresponding α-diketones. (Compare page 205, where the detection of organic compounds which function as hydrogen donors is discussed.) Consequently, it is fundamentally possible by means of the synthesis of acyloins to arrive at a method of detecting the aliphatic fatty acid esters participating in the synthesis. This objective is reached in surprisingly simple and rapid fashion through the realization of (1) in the presence of 1,2-dinitrobenzene. If the reaction mixture is treated with water, without removing the excess sodium, the violet color, that is characteristic of acyloins, appears at once.

It is noteworthy, and in itself characteristic, that when metallic sodium comes into contact with a benzene or ether solution of an ester, which also contains some 1,2-dinitrobenzene, a red product appears almost immediately. Possibly, there is direct production here of the anhydrous salt of the *aci*-form of nitroso-nitrobenzene as shown in (3):

$$
2\ \begin{matrix} R-C-ONa \\ \| \\ R-C-ONa \end{matrix} + \left(\bigcirc\right)\!\!\begin{matrix} NO_2 \\ NO_2 \end{matrix} \longrightarrow \left(\bigcirc\right)\!\!\begin{matrix} =NONa \\ =NO_2Na \end{matrix} + 2\ \begin{matrix} R-CO \\ | \\ R-CO \end{matrix} + Na_2O \qquad (3)
$$

On the addition of water, the salt dissolves to give a violet solution. There is the possibility that the red product is a benzene-insoluble addition compound of the sodium salt of endiol and 1,2-dinitrobenzene, which forms acyloin when it is saponified, and that the latter reacts with the nitro compound more quickly than the hydrogen produced by the reaction of metallic sodium and water.

The procedure given here for the detection of aliphatic esters may not be applied in the presence of α-diketones, since they too give rise to sodium salts of endiols, which then yield a violet color on reaction with 1,2-dinitrobenzene.

A much greater restriction of the test is imposed by the fact that only benzene, toluene, or chloroform can serve as solvent for the ester. Alcohol and ether react with sodium to give hydrogen and sodium ethylate, with consequent reduction of the 1,2-dinitrobenzene to a colored quinoid compound.

Procedure. The test is conducted in a depression of a spot plate. A piece of metallic sodium the size of small seed is pressed into a disk by means of a glass rod. A drop of the benzene solution of the ester is added and then a drop of a 2.5% benzene solution of 1,2-dinitrobenzene. The system is stirred with a fine glass rod and after 1–2 minutes a drop of water is introduced. If esters are present, a deep to pale violet appears, the depth of the color depending on the quantity involved. A comparison blank is advisable when small amounts of ester are suspected.

The procedure revealed: 5 γ ethyl acetate; 10 γ butyl acetate; 5 γ ethylbenzoate.

A positive response was obtained with the following esters * : propyl acetate,

* According to results obtained by Angelita Barcelón in the laboratories of the Department of Chemistry, University of Cincinnati.

References pp. 314–319

ethyl malonate, ethyl benzoate, *n*-butyl formate, diethyl malonate, diethyl allylmalonate, diethyl oxalate, ethyl phenylacetate, ethyl phthalate, ethyl cinnamate.

29. 1,2-Dicarboxylic Acids $\left(\begin{array}{c} C\text{—COOH} \\ | \\ C\text{—COOH} \end{array} \text{group}\right)$

Test by melting with resorcinol [134]

Dicarboxylic acids with the carboxyl group in the 1,2 position * (one COOH group may be substituted by a SO_3H group) or their derivatives, such as esters, anhydrides, or imides, form dyes of the fluorescein type (saccharins) when melted with resorcinol, or heated with resorcinol and concentrated sulfuric acid. The condensation products which result give a vivid green-yellow fluorescence in alkaline solution. The reaction proceeds:

The 1,2-carboxylic acids with a free hydroxyl adjacent to the carboxyl group:

$$\begin{array}{c} >C\text{—COOH} \\ | \\ -C(OH)\text{—COOH} \end{array}$$

react with resorcinol in a different manner. They lose formic acid, i.e. carbon monoxide and water, through the action of hot concentrated sulfuric acid to form semialdehydes of malonic acid or its homologs (*1*), and these in their isomeric tautomeric enolic form then condense with resorcinol to produce umbelliferone or its homologs (*2*):

* Carboxyl groups in the *peri* position behave like those in the *ortho* position.

$$
\begin{array}{c}
\text{COOH} \\
| \\
\text{CH}_2 \\
| \\
\text{CHOH} \\
| \\
\text{COOH}
\end{array}
\quad
\xrightarrow[-\text{HCOOH}]{\text{H}_2\text{SO}_4}
\quad
\begin{array}{c}
\text{CHO} \\
| \\
\text{CH}_2 \\
| \\
\text{COOH}
\end{array}
\quad \rightleftharpoons \quad
\begin{array}{c}
\text{CHOH} \\
\| \\
\text{CH} \\
| \\
\text{COOH}
\end{array}
\qquad (1)
$$

$$
\text{HO}\!-\!\bigcirc\!-\!\text{OH} \; + \;
\begin{array}{c}
\text{HOCH} \\
\| \\
\text{CH} \\
| \\
\text{HOCO}
\end{array}
\quad \rightarrow \quad
\text{HO}\!-\!\bigcirc\!\! \begin{array}{c}\text{H}\\ \text{C}\\ \\ \text{CH}\\ |\\ \text{CO}\\ \diagdown \text{O}\diagup\end{array} \; + \; 2\,\text{H}_2\text{O}
\qquad (2)
$$

The resulting umbelliferones are almost colorless, but they give an appreciable fluorescence even in daylight. Under the mercury vapor lamp, the fluorescence is a brilliant blue in alkaline solution. (Compare page 419 concerning tests for coumarins.)

Procedure. A few milligrams of the test substance is placed in a microcrucible, or a drop of a solution is evaporated there to dryness. A little freshly sublimed resorcinol and a few drops of pure concentrated sulfuric acid are added and the mixture kept at 130° C. for 5 minutes, either on an asbestos plate or, better still, on an aluminum block provided with wells to hold 2 crucibles and a thermometer. When the reaction is complete, the crucible plus contents is dropped into water (50 ml beaker) to dissolve out the products. The solution is made alkaline with sodium hydroxide. In the presence of substances containing one of the pertinent groups, a fluorescence occurs, which is especially bright in ultraviolet light.

A blank test should always be carried out, because when the temperature has exceeded 130° C, even a blank shows a fluorescence, which is green by daylight, and green-blue in ultraviolet light. Apparently the resorcinol partially decomposes at the higher temperature, and gives rise to dicarboxylic acids.

The *limits of identification* and the colors of the fluorescence are given in Table 22.

30. Acylides, Arylurethanes, and Monoarylureas (Ar—NH—COR-group)

Detection through nitrosation and coupling with α-naphthol [135]

Compounds, which contain this group, where R may denote hydrogen, alkyl or aryl, methoxy or ethoxy, and also NH$_2$, can be nitrosated by means of nitrous acid (*1*). The resulting N-nitroso compounds are saponified in alkaline solution, a fact first established in the case of nitrosoacetanilide.[136] Diazotates are formed (*2*) and they can couple with α-naphthol to give red-violet water-soluble azo dyes (*3*). The following reactions:

TABLE 22. DICARBOXYLIC ACIDS

Name	Formula	Color of fluorescence		Limit of identification, γ	
		In daylight	In ultraviolet light	In daylight	In ultraviolet light
Tricarbal-lylic acid	CH$_2$——CH——CH$_2$ | | | COOH COOH COOH	Yellow-rose	Grass green	5	5
Citric acid	CH$_2$——C(OH)——CH$_2$ | | | COOH COOH COOH	Yellow	Sky blue	15	1
Tartaric acid	CHOHCOOH | CHOHCOOH	Brown-red	Dark blue-green		25
Phthalic acid	C$_6$H$_4$(COOH)$_2$ (1, 2)	Yellow-brown	Light green	5	5
3-Nitro-phthalic acid	C$_6$H$_3$(NO$_2$)(COOH)$_2$	Red	Pale violet		
Hemipinic acid	C$_6$H$_2$(OCH$_3$)$_2$(COOH)$_2$ (1,2,3,4)	Dark red	Green		
Trimellitic acid tri-methyl ester	C$_6$H$_3$(CO$_2$CH$_3$)$_3$ (1, 2, 4)	Yellow	Light green	2.5	2.5
Dihydroxy-maleic acid	C(OH)COOH $\|$ C(OH)COOH	Red	Blue-gray	40	15
Succinic acid or potassium succinate	CH$_2$COOH | CH$_2$COOH	Yellow	Emerald green	5	5
Succinic anhydride	O CH$_2$C \ O CH$_2$C / O	Yellow	Emerald green	5	5

(Continued)

TABLE 22. DICARBOXYLIC ACIDS (CONTINUED)

Name	Formula	Color of fluorescence		Limit of identification, γ	
		In daylight	In ultraviolet light	In daylight	In ultraviolet light
Succinimide	CH$_2$CO\ | >NH CH$_2$CO/	Yellow	Emerald green	5	5
Malic acid	CH$_2$COOH | CHOHCOOH	Yellow	Light blue		1
Saccharin	SO$_2$ NH CO	Yellow	Greenish yellow	10	5
Asparagine	H$_2$N—CH—COOH | CH$_2$—CONH$_2$	Dark wine-red	Dark green	5	10
Naphthalic acid	—COOH —COOH	Yellow-brown	Dark green	5	5

$$Ar—NH—COR + HNO_2 \rightarrow Ar—N(NO)—COR + H_2O \qquad (1)$$

$$Ar—N(NO)—COR + 2\ KOH \rightarrow Ar—N=N—OK + RCOOK + H_2O \qquad (2)$$

$$Ar—N=N—OK + \underset{}{\text{—OH}} \rightarrow Ar—N=N—\underset{}{\text{—OK}} + H_2O \qquad (3)$$

can be realized within the technique of spot test analysis if the starting materials are taken in very small amounts. The occurrence of this series of reactions can be established readily through the production of the dye.

Procedure. The test is made in a micro test tube. One drop of the test solution is mixed with a drop of 10% sodium nitrite solution and 1 : 1 hydrochloric acid and after a minute a drop of 10 N sodium or potassium hydroxide solution is

References pp. 314–319

added. A pinch (tip of knife blade) of urea is added,* the liquid is shaken, and a drop of 0.1 % alcoholic solution of *a* naphthol is introduced and the mixture then warmed. Depending on the quantity of acylide, etc. present, the liquid turns red or orange. A spot plate may also be used. A blank test is advisable only when very small quantities are being sought.

The following were revealed by this procedure:

0.5 γ	acetanilide	1	γ	acetylsulfothiazole
0.5 γ	acetylphenetidine	0.1 γ		monophenylurea
1 γ	*p*-acetylaminophenol	5	γ	phenylurethane
5 γ	3-ureido isonicotinic acid	1	γ	acetylarsanilic acid

A positive response was obtained with acetylnaphthalide, stovarsol, and monotoluylurea.

31. Alkyl- and Aryl-Acetates (—O—COCH₃ group)

Test by saponification to acetic acid [137]

Alkyl- and aryl esters of acetic acid, when warmed with alkali hydroxides or mineral acids, are split:

$$CH_3CO—OR + H_2O \rightarrow CH_3COOH + ROH$$

If the hydrolysis is conducted with concentrated sulfuric acid or syrupy phosphoric acid in the presence of not much water, anhydrous acetic acid results. The latter volatilizes to some extent even at room temperature and very considerably when warmed. Acetic acid vapors can be detected by their action on potassium iodide–iodate solution. The iodine released by the reaction:

$$5 \text{ KI} + \text{KIO}_3 + 6 \text{ CH}_3\text{COOH} \rightarrow 6 \text{ CH}_3\text{COOK} + 3 \text{ H}_2\text{O} + 3 \text{ I}_2$$

is readily revealed by the development of a yellow color, or by the starch–iodine test when small quantities are involved. If considerable amounts of the acetic ester are present, and if high sensitivity is not essential, vapors of acetic acid can also be detected by acid-base indicators. It is better to use

---

* A solution of alkali nitrite that has been acidified with hydrochloric acid and then made basic gives a yellow color on the addition of a solution of α-naphthol. This color reaction is due to the production of significant amounts of nitrosyl chloride or chlorine when nitrite solution is made acid with hydrochloric acid, with consequent production of alkali hypochlorite when alkali is added. The hypochlorite oxidizes α-naphthol to a colored quinone. This interference is completely avoided by adding urea, which has no effect at all on alkaline solutions of N-nitroso compounds.

phosphoric acid for the saponification because strong sulfuric acid has an oxidizing action on many organic materials and the resulting sulfurous acid likewise liberates iodine from iodide–iodate solution.

A requirement for the application of the test is the absence of acids which are volatile with water vapor, and also of compounds which react with phosphoric acid to split off acids of this kind. These include: formic, acetic, propionic, lactic, benzoic, salicylic acids, hydrogen halides and their salts, nitrites and isonitroso compounds. It should be noted that the vapors of volatile esters of acetic acid (e.g., alkyl- and aryl-acetates) liberate iodine on contact with aqueous iodide–iodate solution. The reason for this effect is that traces of acetic acid in the hydrolysis equilibrium of the ester are consumed by the iodide–iodate reaction and are constantly replenished through reestablishment of the equilibrium.

Esters of those carboxylic acids that are markedly volatile with steam (see above), and which are saponifiable with phosphoric acid, probably act analogously to alkyl- and aryl acetates. No studies along this line have been reported. Methyl salicylate does not saponify under the conditions of the test.

In the case of N-acetyl compounds, the speed and extent of the hydrolysis, with production of acetic acid, seem to depend on whether the nitrogen atom is bound to an aliphatic or aromatic radical. Acetamide and acetylglycine (the latter in quantities above 500 γ) are saponified by brief warming with concentrated phosporic acid, whereas acetanilide, acetnaphthalide, acetyltoluidine and phenacetin are not affected. The saponification is easy and complete when acetylglycine or acetanilide are warmed for a short time with alkali hydroxide, and the volatilization of the acetic acid from the resulting alkali acetate can thereupon be readily accomplished by warming with concentrated phosphoric acid. This type of saponification, and a test based on it, fails however with the other anilides just named.

Procedure. A drop of the test solution and a drop of syrupy phosphoric acid (sp.gr. 1.8) are placed in the apparatus shown in Fig. 23 (page 49). A drop of freshly prepared potassium iodide–iodate solution is placed on the knob of the stopper, the apparatus is closed, and the lower third of the bulb is held in boiling water for 60 seconds. After cooling, the apparatus is opened and the drop is placed in a depression of a spot plate along with a drop of starch solution. A blue color indicates the presence of alkyl- or aryl esters of acetic acid. With considerable quantities of the ester, a reliable indication is furnished by the yellow color of the exposed hanging drop.

  Reagents: 1) Potassium iodide–iodate solution: Equal volumes of 2% potassium iodide and 0.4% potassium iodate solutions are mixed just prior to use.
  2) Water-soluble starch, 0.1% solution.

References pp. 314–319

This procedure revealed the acetyl group in:

10 γ amyl acetate	5 γ linalyl acetate
15 γ ethyl acetate	5 γ acetyl phenol
15 γ butyl acetate	40 γ acetyl salicylic acid, methyl ester

Acetyl cellulose, which is a solid in contrast to the esters of acetic acid, which are liquids for the most part, also gives a distinct reaction.

32. Sulfonic Acids, Sulfinic acids, Sulfonamides, Sulfones
($-SO_3H$, $-SO_2H$, $-SO_2NH_2$ and $>SO_2$-groups)

(1) Detection through fusion with sodium formate [138]

It has long been known that if the alkali salts of benzene- and naphthalene-1-sulfonic acid are melted along with sodium formate they are converted to the corresponding carboxylic acids.[139] This exchange appears to be characteristic of all aromatic and aliphatic sulfonic acids. If the starting material is the free acid, the addition of alkali hydroxide permits the occurrence of the following reaction on sintering:

$$R\text{---}SO_3H + HCOONa + 2\ NaOH \rightarrow R\text{---}COONa + Na_2SO_3 + 2\ H_2O$$

However, because of unavoidable partial thermal decomposition, this reaction has no practical significance for the preparation of alkali salts and carboxylic acids from the particular sulfonic acids. On the other hand, it permits a rapid test for sulfonic acids, since the resulting alkali sulfite, which is stable under the conditions of the test,* or the gaseous sulfurous acid released from the sulfite by acidification, can be detected even in small amounts. The reaction on ferri-ferricyanide to produce Prussian blue is recommended.[140]

Sulfinic acids and sulfonamides react in the same manner as sulfonic acids when fused with sodium formate. Although no trials have been made as yet with sulfones, it is extremely likely that they too will produce alkali sulfite.

Procedure. The apparatus shown in Fig. 23, page 49 is used. A little of the solid or a drop of its aqueous solution is placed in the bulb and taken to dryness with a drop of an alkaline solution of sodium formate. The residue is heated over a bare flame for about 30 seconds, i.e., until a grey tinge indicates that incipient charring has occurred. The cold mass is acidified with 1 : 1 sulfuric acid, and the apparatus is closed after a drop of the ferri-ferricyanide reagent solution has been placed on the knob of the stopper. The suspended drop turns blue if sulfonic acids, etc. were

---

* A contributing factor may be the fact that when alkali salts of sulfonic acids are fused with an excess of sodium formate, the oxidation of the resulting sulfite to sulfate is prevented by the thermal decompositions:

$$2\ HCOONa \rightarrow 2\ H° + (COONa)_2 \text{ and } (COONa)_2 \rightarrow Na_2CO_3 + CO$$

present. Even slight color changes become quite visible if the drop is wiped onto a spot plate.

Reagents: *1*)   Alkaline sodium formate solution: 5 g sodium formate and 6 g sodium hydroxide dissolved in 100 ml water.

         2)   Ferri-ferricyanide solution: 0.08 g anhydrous ferric chloride and 0.1 g potassium ferricyanide in 100 ml water.

The procedure revealed:

   2.5 γ naphthalenesulfonic acid (1,4; 1,5; 2,6)
   2.5 γ naphtholdisulfonic acid (2,6,8)
   1   γ dihydroxynaphtholdisulfonic acid (1,8,3,6)
   5   γ dihydroxynaphtholsulfonic acid (2,3,6)
   2,5 γ naphthylaminesulfonic acid (1,3; 2,6)
   1   γ naphthylaminedisulfonic acid (2,3,6)
   1   γ sulfanilic acid
   0.25 γ taurine

Positive responses were given by H-acid, sulfosalicylic acid, Congo red, sulfopyridine, sulfometazine, sufonal, trional.

(2) *Test through formation of sulfite by alkali fusion* [141]

In the classical method of producing phenols by alkali fusion of aromatic sulfonic acids, alkali sulfite is formed when the SO_3H-group is exchanged for an OH-group, and its detection thereby provides the basis for a test for aromatic sulfonic acids. However, the production of alkali sulfite by alkali fusion is not limited to aromatic sulfonic acids; it also is formed from aliphatic sulfonic acids (with production of alcohols or alkali alcoholates) and likewise from amides of aromatic and aliphatic sulfonic acids. The reactions in the various alkali fusion processes are:

$$R—SO_3H + 3\,NaOH \rightarrow RONa + Na_2SO_3 + 2\,H_2O \qquad (1)$$

$$R—SO_3Na + 2\,NaOH \rightarrow RONa + Na_2SO_3 + H_2O \qquad (1a)$$

$$R—SO_2NH_2 + 3\,NaOH \rightarrow RONa + Na_2SO_3 + H_2O + NH_3 \qquad (2)$$

(N-substituted sulfonamides will evolve amines instead of ammonia)

$$R—SO_2H + 3\,NaOH + O \rightarrow RONa + Na_2SO_3 + 2\,H_2O \qquad (3)$$

$$R—SO_2Na + 2\,NaOH + O \rightarrow RONa + Na_2SO_3 + H_2O \qquad (3a)$$

$$\genfrac{}{}{0pt}{}{R}{R}{>}SO_2 + 4\,NaOH + O \rightarrow 2\,RONa + Na_2SO_3 + 2\,H_2O \qquad (1)$$

As shown by these equations, a production of sulfite on alkali fusion is characteristic of compounds containing oxidized, i.e., 4- and 6-valent sulfur. It is possible to differentiate such compounds, in combination with the alkali fusion, if solubility differences are taken into consideration. For instance, sulfonic acids and their alkali salts are soluble in water (the former with acid reaction), whereas sulfonamides and sulfones do not dissolve in water or acids. According to (2) and (3), sulfonamides and sulfones differ in that only sulfonamides yield ammonia (or amine) when fused with alkali. (It should be noted that amides of carboxylic acids behave analogously to sulfonamides when fused with alkali.) Water-soluble sulfinic acids (or their alkali salts) can be recognized by their precipitability from mineral acid solutions by ferric chloride. Though the test is admittedly not very sensitive, the reaction can serve to separate sulfinic from sulfonic acids.[142]

All the tests given in Volume I for the detection of sulfur dioxide liberated by acids from alkali sulfites can be used to reveal the production of sulfite resulting from the alkali fusion or organic compounds containing 4- and 6-valent sulfur. Especially good is the test which involves the formation of black Ni^{IV} oxyhydrate from green Ni^{II} hydroxide on contact with sulfur dioxide.[143] The reaction involves autoxidation of sulfur dioxide, which in turn causes the transformation of $Ni(OH)_2$ into $NiO(OH)_2$[144] which normally occurs only through oxidants. It is probable that when sulfur dioxide comes in contact with $Ni(OH)_2$, the initial product is basic sulfite, whose cationic and anionic components are then oxidized by atmospheric oxygen:

$$2\ Ni(OH)_2 + SO_2 \longrightarrow (NiOH)_2SO_3 + H_2O$$

$$\begin{matrix} Ni\diagup^{OH} \\ \diagdown \\ \quad\quad SO_3 \\ \diagup \\ Ni \\ \quad\diagdown_{OH} \end{matrix} + O_2 \longrightarrow NiO(OH)_2 + NiSO_4$$

The production of $NiO(OH)_2$ is easily discerned through a blackening or graying of the green $Ni(OH)_2$. Traces of $NiO(OH)_2$ can be detected by spotting with benzidine; a blue color (benzidine blue) develops.

It should be noted that alkali sulfide is produced in the alkali fusion of organic compounds which contain bivalent sulfur (thiophenols, thioalcohols, thioethers, disulfides, thioketones). On acidification, this sulfide yields hydrogen sulfide, which transforms the green nickel hydroxide to black nickel sulfide. The latter may be mistaken for black $NiO(OH)_2$. Therefore, it is well to make a preliminary alkali fusion; allow the mass to cool, add acid, and test the gas for hydrogen sulfide with lead acetate paper. If the test paper shows no darkening or browning, the procedure outlined below provides an indisputable test for oxidized sulfur in organic compounds. If the lead sulfide test was positive, the sample may be desulfurized (thiophenols, thioalcohols, thioketones) by warming the aqueous solution or suspension with lead carbonate. The filtrate or centrifugate from the PbS–PbCO$_3$ mixture is evaporated and the test for oxidized sulfur is then made with the dry evaporation residue.

Procedure. A very little of the solid sample, or the evaporation residue from one drop of test solution, is heated with a grain of sodium hydroxide over a small flame until the mixture just melts. A hard glass tube, whose bulb has a capacity of about 3 ml, is used. After cooling, the melt is dissolved in 2 drops water, 1 or 2 drops of concentrated hydrochloric acid are added (the acid reaction should be tested with litmus paper), and the walls of the tube washed with water. The rim of the tube is carefully wiped dry, and a strip of filter paper carrying Ni(OH)$_2$ is laid over the mouth. The bulb is then immersed in hot water for a few minutes to hasten the evolution of the sulfur dioxide. Sulfite is evidenced by the change of color of the nickel hydroxide from green to black or gray. When very small amounts are to be detected, it is best to spot the nickel hydroxide with an acetic acid solution of benzidine; a blue color is formed in the presence of a trace of NiO(OH)$_2$.

> *Reagents:* 1) Nickel hydroxide, washed alkali-free, prepared by precipitation of NiCl$_2$ with NaOH.
>
> 2) Benzidine: 0.05 g benzidine (free base or hydrochloride) dissolved in 10 ml 2 N acetic acid, diluted to 100 ml with water, and filtered.

The *limits of identification* attained by this test for sulfonic and sulfinic acids are given in Table 23.

(3) *Test by conversion into the iron^{III} salt of acethydroxamic acid* [145]

Sulfonic acids can be converted into sulfohydroxamic acids, which react with acetaldehyde in the presence of alkali:

$$RSO_2NHOH + CH_3CHO \rightarrow CH_3CONHOH + RSO_2H$$

giving acethydroxamic acid and sulfinic acids. Both of these products react with ferric chloride in weak acid solution to give a red soluble iron^{III} salt of hydroxamic acid (see page 236), and an orange-red insoluble iron^{III} salt of the sulfinic acid, respectively.[146]

The necessary conversion of the sulfonic acid to the sulfohydroxamic acid requires a preliminary preparation of the sulfone chloride, which then can be converted to the sulfohydroxamic acid with hydroxylamine. Thionyl chloride is used to prepare the sulfone chloride. The sulfohydroxamic acid reacts with acetaldehyde to give acethydroxamic acid and sulfinic acid, both of which, as stated, react with ferric chloride.

TABLE 23.   SULFONIC AND SULFINIC ACIDS AND SULFONES

Name	Formula	Limit of identification, γ
Potassium hydrogen benzene disulfonate	$C_6H_4(SO_3H)SO_3K$ (1, 4)	5
Sodium hydrogen β-naphthalene disulfonate	$C_{10}H_6(SO_3H)SO_3Na$ (2, 7)	3
Sodium hydrogen hydroxyquinoline disulfonic acid	$C_9H_4N(OH)(SO_3H)SO_3Na$ (8, 7, 5)	20
Sulfanilic acid	$C_6H_4(NH_2)SO_3H$ (1, 4)	12
o-Benzaldehyde sulfonic acid	$C_6H_4(CHO)SO_3H$ (1, 2)	12
Tartrazine	$\begin{array}{l} HOOC-C=N \\ \qquad\qquad\quad \searrow N-C_6H_4-SO_3H \\ HO_3S-C_6H_4-NH-N=C-CO \end{array}$	12
Potassium methionate	$CH_2(SO_3K)_2$	6
Camphorsulfonic acid	$C_{10}H_{15}OSO_3H$	5
α-Bromocamphorsulfonic acid	$C_{10}H_{14}OBrSO_3H$	14
Benzenesulfinic acid	$C_6H_5SO_2H$	6
α-Naphthalenesulfinic acid	$C_{10}H_7SO_2H$	12
Sulfonal	$\begin{array}{l} H_3C\diagdown \quad\diagup SO_2-C_2H_5 \\ \qquad\quad C \\ H_3C\diagup \quad\diagdown SO_2-C_2H_5 \end{array}$	6
Trional	$\begin{array}{l} H_3C\diagdown \quad\diagup SO_2-C_2H_5 \\ \qquad\quad C \\ H_5C_2\diagup \quad\diagdown SO_2-C_2H_5 \end{array}$	10

References pp. 314–319

The equations showing the formation of the characteristic colored ferric salts, starting from the free sulfonic acid, are:

$$RSO_3H + SOCl_2 \rightarrow RSO_2Cl + SO_2 + HCl$$

$$RSO_2Cl + NH_2OH \rightarrow RSO_2(NHOH) + HCl$$

$$RSO_2(NHOH) + CH_3CHO \rightarrow CH_3CO(NHOH) + RSO_2H$$

$$3\ CH_3CO(NHOH) + FeCl_3 \rightarrow Fe[CH_3CO(NHO)]_3 + 3\ HCl$$

$$3\ RSO_2H + FeCl_3 \rightarrow Fe(RSO_2)_3 + 3\ HCl$$

In spite of the complicated series of reactions, the procedure for carrying out the test is relatively simple.

Procedure. A little of the solid test substance (if necessary the evaporation residue from a drop of solution) is fumed in a microcrucible with a few drops of thionyl chloride. The product is treated with 2 drops of a saturated alcoholic solution of hydroxylamine hydrochloride and a drop of acetaldehyde, then made alkaline with a little 5 % sodium carbonate solution. After a short time, the mixture is acidified with 0.5 N hydrochloric acid. A drop of a dilute aqueous solution of ferric chloride is added and a brown to violet color or precipitate appears. A blank test remains light yellow.

When the salt of a sulfonic acid is being tested, it should be evaporated with hydrochloric acid before the treatment with thionyl chloride. Dyestuffs, whose color interferes with the recognition of the color change, can easily be decomposed with a few drops of bromine water.

The following were detected:

12 γ benzene sulfone chloride, $C_6H_5SO_2Cl$
20 γ naphthalene-β-sulfonic acid, $C_{10}H_7SO_3H$
25 γ sulfanilic acid, $C_6H_4(NH_2)SO_3H$
10 γ potassium hydrogen p-benzene sulfonate, $C_6H_4(SO_3K)SO_3H$
30 γ helianthin, $(CH_3)_2NC_6H_4N = NC_6H_4SO_3Na$
15 γ H-acid, $C_{10}H_4(OH)(NH_2)(SO_3H)_2$

(4) Test by reaction with methylenedisalicylic acid [147]

When methylenedisalicylic acid (I), which is colorless and not soluble in water, is heated to 120–150° with concentrated sulfuric acid, red quinoidal formaurindicarboxylic acid (II) * results:

---

* The acid was prepared [148] by oxidizing methylenedisalicylic acid with nitrosylsulfuric acid.

$$HO\!-\!\langle\ \rangle\!-\!CH_2\!-\!\langle\ \rangle\!-\!OH \quad + H_2SO_4 \;\rightarrow$$

$$\underset{HOOC}{\qquad}\qquad\qquad\underset{COOH}{\qquad}$$

(I)

$$HO\!-\!\langle\ \rangle\!-\!CH\!=\!\langle\ \rangle\!=\!O \quad + 2\,H_2O + SO_2$$

$$\underset{HOOC}{\qquad}\qquad\qquad\underset{COOH}{\qquad}$$

(II)

The reaction occurs because the concentrated sulfuric acid functions both as oxidant and dehydrant. Small quantities of free (unbound) sulfuric acid (up to 2.5 γ in drops) can be detected [148] by the formation of (II).

Numerous aromatic sulfonic acids, which are solid at room temperature, behave in the same way as concentrated sulfuric acid. The reason presumably is that sulfonic acids lose sulfur trioxide when their mixtures with methylene-disalicylic acid are heated, and this product behaves like concentrated sulfuric acid as regards oxidation and dehydration effects. It is known that sulfo-salicylic acid heated above its melting point decomposes in such manner that loss of sulfur trioxide must be assumed (see page 368). It is notable that the formation of formaurindicarboxylic acid on heating sulfosalicylic acid with methylenedisalicylic acid (m.p. 238°) occurs even at the melting point of the former (120°), i.e. below its decomposition temperature. Conse-quently, it seems that the tendency to decompose

$$RSO_3H \rightarrow RH + SO_3$$

is sufficient at relatively low temperatures to bring about the oxidation to formaurindicarboxylic acid on contact with methylenedisalicylic acid. Therefore, this behavior justifies the belief that the SO_3H group is acti-vated when sulfonic acids are heated.

Alkali and alkaline earth salts of sulfonic acids do not react with methylene-disalicylic acid. Accordingly, if such salts are presented for examination, it is necessary to liberate the sulfonic acid by taking the sample to dryness with concentrated hydrochloric acid, before the mixing and heating with methylenedisalicylic acid.

The procedure given here for the detection of sulfonic acids cannot be applied to colored compounds, e.g., dyestuffs containing the SO_3H group, because in such cases it is not possible to discern the production of small quantities of formaurindicarboxylic acid.

The cases studied thus far have not been adequate to prove that the SO_3H groups in all sulfonic acids are sufficiently activated on heating to react with methylenedisalicylic acid. The possibility must be kept in mind that an activation can be prevented by other groups in the sulfonic acids. This is hinted at by the finding that sulfanilic acid (which may be viewed as an inner ammonium salt) and likewise several other sulfonic acids (see below) do not react.

Procedure. A drop of the test solution is taken to dryness in a porcelain microcrucible with several milligrams of methylenedisalicylic acid. The crucible and its contents are then kept at 150° for three minutes in an oven. According to the quantity of sulfonic acid present, the residue turns red or pink. A comparison test is advisable when small amounts are involved.

Reagent: Methylenedisalicylic acid (solid)

This procedure revealed:

10 γ toluenesulfonic acid
10 γ 2,4-dinitro-1-naphthol-6-sulfonic acid
10 γ 2,4-dinitro-benzenesulfonic acid
25 γ benzenesulfonic acid (sodium salt)
50 γ d-camphorsulfonic acid
25 γ anthraquinone-6-sulfonic acid

The following compounds gave no response: sulfanilic acid, pyrocatechin-disulfonic acid, m-benzenedisulfonic acid, 8-hydroxyquinoline-5-sulfonic acid.

33. Sulfones ($>SO_2$-group)

Detection through pyrolytic splitting-off of sulfur dioxide [149]

When sulfones are heated dry, sulfur dioxide is given off. Sulfur dioxide obtained by such thermal decomposition may not be detected by reactions based on reduction reactions since the pyrolysis of organic compounds frequently yields reducing gaseous cleavage products (see Chapter 3). The sensitive test for sulfur dioxide, based on the fact that its autoxidation induces the oxidation of green nickel(II) hydroxide to black nickel(III) hydroxide, may be employed (see page 251).

The procedure given here for the detection of sulfones through the sulfur dioxide evolved cannot be applied in the presence of thioketones, mercapto and thiol compounds, sulfides and disulfides, because they give off hydrogen sulfide when heated and the latter forms black nickel sulfide on contact with nickel (II) hydroxide. The presence of such compounds can be revealed beforehand by heating a little of the sample in a micro test tube whose mouth is covered with moist lead acetate paper. If there is little or no blackening due to lead sulfide, a positive response to the test for sulfur dioxide with nickel(II) hydroxide may be taken as positive proof of the presence of sulfones.

References pp. 314–319

Procedure. A slight amount of the solid or a drop of the test solution is placed in a micro test tube. The mouth of the tube is covered with a disk of nickel hydroxide paper. The tube is heated over a micro burner. A black or grey circular stain on the green paper appears if the response is positive.

If much sulfur dioxide is formed, the initial black stain disappears and only a grey ring remains at its edge. In such cases it is well to repeat the procedure with less of the sample.

Reagent: Nickel hydroxide paper: Strips of filter paper are bathed in a 30% solution of $NiSO_4 \cdot 6\,H_2O$ in concentrated ammonium hydroxide. The dried strips are then bathed for several minutes in 1 N sodium hydroxide to obtain a homogeneous precipitation of $Ni(OH)_2$ in the pores of the paper. The paper, which should be washed with water, may not be allowed to dry. If stored over moist cotton wool, it will keep for months.

The procedure revealed:

5 γ   sulfonal

$$O_2S \begin{smallmatrix} \diagup C_2H_5 \\ \diagdown \\ C(CH_3)_2 \\ \diagup \\ O_2S \diagdown C_2H_5 \end{smallmatrix}$$

10 γ   4,4′-diaminodiphenyl sulfone $O_2S \begin{smallmatrix} \diagup C_6H_4NH_2 \\ \diagdown C_6H_4NH_2 \end{smallmatrix}$

20 γ   di-*n*-cetyl sulfone $O_2S(C_{16}H_{33})_2$

5 γ   benzylethyl sulfone $O_2S \begin{smallmatrix} \diagup CH_2C_6H_5 \\ \diagdown C_2H_5 \end{smallmatrix}$

Positive response was also obtained with di-*n*-butyl sulfone, di-*p*-nitrobenzy sulfone, di-*p*-methoxyphenyl sulfone, di-2-phenylethyl sulfone.

34. Aliphatic and Aromatic Amines

(1) Test for primary and secondary aliphatic amines by conversion to dithio-carbamate [150]

The dithiocarbamates of the corresponding bases are formed almost instantly at room temperature by the action of carbon disulfide on free primary and secondary aliphatic amines [151] (dissolved in inactive solvents, if necessary):

$$CS_2 + 2\,NH_2R \longrightarrow SC\begin{smallmatrix}\diagup SH \cdot NH_2R \\ \diagdown NHR\end{smallmatrix} \quad \text{and} \quad CS_2 + 2\,NHR_1R_2 \longrightarrow SC\begin{smallmatrix}\diagup SH \cdot NHR_1R_2 \\ \diagdown NR_1R_2\end{smallmatrix}$$

Tertiary aliphatic amines do not react.

The dithiocarbamates formed by these addition reactions may be detected after removing the excess carbon disulfide (b.p. 46°). The iodine–azide test (see page 228) may be applied because the dithiocarbamate contains the SH- and CS-groups necessary for the catalysis of the sodium azide–iodine reaction. Alternatively, the dithiocarbamate may be revealed by the formation of silver sulfide when silver nitrate solution is added to the dry evaporation residue.

When salts of the bases (the hydrochlorides, for example) are present, use may be made of the fact that triethylamine, which as a tertiary amine does not react with carbon disulfide, is so strong a base that it is able to liberate primary and secondary amines from solutions of their salts. It is merely necessary to add carbon disulfide and an excess of triethylamine, or a prepared mixture of these reagents, to the sample and proceed as prescribed.*

Tertiary aliphatic bases do not react. Aromatic amines, which likewise may react with carbon disulfide with production of thiourea derivatives[152], e.g.,

$$2\ C_6H_5NH_2 + CS_2 \longrightarrow C_6H_5{-}NH{-}CS{-}NH{-}C_6H_5 + H_2S$$

do not do so under the mild conditions employed here. Accordingly, primary and secondary aliphatic amines may be detected in the presence of aromatic amines.

It is obvious that the test with sodium azide-iodine here described cannot be used in the presence of mercaptans, thioketones and thiol compounds, which catalyze the sodium azide-iodine reaction.

Procedure. A drop of the alcoholic test solution, or of the free base, is mixed with a few drops of a 1 : 1 alcohol-carbon disulfide mixture in a microcrucible. After about 5 minutes, the excess carbon disulfide is volatilized. The apparatus described on page 44 (Fig. 17) may be used to advantage. A few drops of an iodine-azide solution, or of a 1% solution of silver nitrate in dilute nitric acid, is added. The mixture is observed for evolution of nitrogen or for a blackening due to silver sulfide.

The detection of dithiocarbamates may also be conducted on filter paper. The base and carbon disulfide (if necessary along with triethylamine) are mixed on filter paper and then spotted with acidified silver nitrate solution. The same limits of identification are obtained.

Reagent: Solution of 3 g sodium azide in 100 ml 0.1 N iodine.

The limits of identification for a number of primary and secondary amines are given in Table 24.

* In the presence of excess $N(C_2H_5)_3$ and CS_2, dithiocarbamates of triethylamine are formed *e.g.*, $RHN{-}CS{-}SH{\cdot}N(C_2H_5)_3$, or $R_1R_2N{-}CS{-}SH{\cdot}N(C_2H_5)_3$ in the case of a primary or secondary aliphatic amine.

TABLE 24. PRIMARY AND SECONDARY ALIPHATIC AMINES

Name	Formula	Detection of dithio-carbamate	
		With iodine–azide	With silver nitrate
Ethylamine	$CH_3-CH_2-NH_2$	6.5 γ	3 γ
Propylamine	$CH_3-CH_2-CH_2-NH_2$	13 γ	10 γ
Dipropyl-amine	$CH_3-CH_2-CH_2-NH-CH_2-CH_2-CH_3$	140 γ	125 γ
isoButyl-amine	$\begin{array}{c} H_3C \\ \\ H_3C \end{array}\!\!\!>\!CH-CH_2-NH_2$	10 γ	8 γ
Di-isoamyl-amine	$\left(\begin{array}{c} H_3C \\ \\ H_3C \end{array}\!\!\!>\!CH-CH_2-CH_2\right)_2\!\!NH$	102 γ	114 γ
Heptylamine	$CH_3-(CH_2)_6-NH_2$	12 γ	7 γ
Diethanol-amine	$(CH_2OH-CH_2)_2NH$	1 γ	0.6 γ
Benzylamine	$C_6H_5-CH_2-NH_2$	15 γ	8.5 γ
Piperidine	$H_2C\!\!<\!\!\begin{array}{c} CH_2-CH_2 \\ \\ CH_2-CH_2 \end{array}\!\!\!>\!NH$	4.5 γ	—
Phenylhy-drazine	$C_6H_5-NH-NH_2$	250 γ	200 γ
Glycine ester hydro-chloride	$C_2H_5OOC-CH_2-NH_2 \cdot HCl$	100 γ	70 γ
Leucylgly-cine	$HOOC-CH_2-NH-CO-CH-NH_2$ $\vert$ $(CH_3)_2CH-CH_2$	35 γ	35 γ
Leucylgly-cylglycine	$HOOC-CH_2-NH-CO-CH_2-NH-CO-CH-NH_2$ $\vert$ $(CH_3)_2CH-CH_2$	30 γ	35 γ
Arginylgly-cine	$H_2N-CH-CO-NH-CH_2-COOH$ $\vert$ $CH_2-(CH_2)_2-NH-C\!\!<\!\!\begin{array}{c}NH \\ NH_2\end{array}$	25 γ	30 γ

The formation of dithiocarbamate as a test for aliphatic amines may also be used to detect aliphatic and aromatic α- or o-diketones (compare page 203). They readily condense with ethylenediamine to form the dihydropyrazines. For example, with benzil:

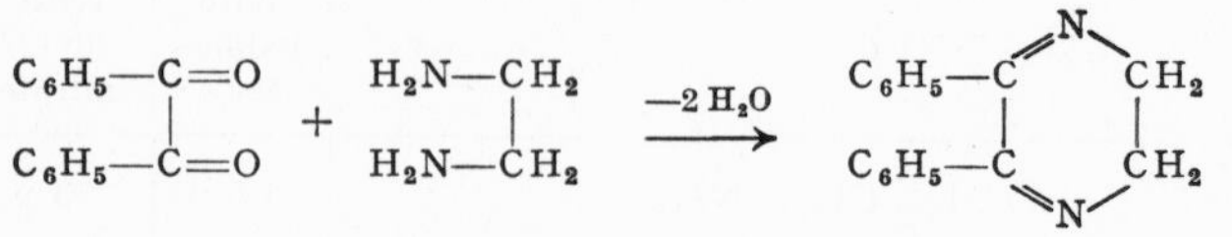

$$
\begin{array}{c}
C_6H_5-C=O \\
| \\
C_6H_5-C=O
\end{array}
+
\begin{array}{c}
H_2N-CH_2 \\
| \\
H_2N-CH_2
\end{array}
\xrightarrow{-2\,H_2O}
\begin{array}{c}
C_6H_5-C \overset{N}{\diagup}\diagdown CH_2 \\
| \qquad | \\
C_6H_5-C \underset{N}{\diagdown}\diagup CH_2
\end{array}
\qquad
\begin{array}{l}
\text{(2,3-diphenyl-5,6-} \\
\text{dihydropyrazine)}
\end{array}
$$

Ethylenediamine is consumed by the reaction, and consequently the presence of aliphatic or aromatic α- or o-diketones may be detected by the negative or weakened response to the dithiocarbamate test for ethylenediamine. Other materials, such as aldehydes and carboxylic acids, which react with ethylenediamine in other ways and thus consume it, must necessarily be absent.

Procedure. A drop of an approximately 0.02 % solution of ethylenediamine in alcohol is mixed with one drop of an alcohol or ether solution of a 1,2-diketone. After 10 minutes at room temperature, an alcohol solution of carbon disulfide is added and the mixture is evaporated on the water bath. A negative or very slight positive dithiocarbamate reaction, compared with the strong blank test on the pure ethylenediamine solution employed, indicates the presence of α- or o-diketones.

The following were revealed by this procedure:

6 γ diacetyl, $CH_3COCOCH_3$
55 γ benzil, $C_6H_5COCOC_6H_5$
6 γ phenanthraquinone, $C_6H_4COCOC_6H_4$

(2) Test for secondary aliphatic amines with sodium nitroprusside and acetaldehyde [153]

Secondary aliphatic amines form blue-violet soluble compounds (of unknown constitution) when they react with sodium nitroprusside and certain aldehydes (the most suitable is acetaldehyde) in solutions rendered alkaline with sodium carbonate. The reaction is analogous to that described (page 387) in the test for glycerol, which depends on the blue-violet color formed from a sodium nitroprusside-piperidine mixture and acrolein developed from the glycerol. Primary and tertiary amines do not interfere with the test, but the activity of the NH group appears to be affected by other groups in the molecule (see Table 25).

TABLE 25. SECONDARY ALIPHATIC AMINES

Name	Formula	Color	Limit of identification
Diethylamine	$(C_2H_5)_2NH$	Blue-violet	4 γ
Diethanol-amine	$(C_2H_4OH)_2NH$	Blue	100 γ
Di-*iso*amyl-amine	$[(CH_3)_2CHCH_2CH_2]_2NH$	Blue-violet	2 γ
Adrenalone (also adrenaline)	HO— / HO— ⬡ —CO—CH₂NHCH₃	Blue	10 γ
Spermidine	$H_2N(CH_2)_3—NH—(CH_2)_4NH_2$	Violet	70 γ
Spermine	$H_2N(CH_2)_3NHCH_2—CH_2$ | $H_2N(CH_2)_3NHCH_2—CH_2$	Violet	80 γ
Pyrrolidine	$H_2C—CH_2$ / $H_2C \quad CH_2$ / NH	Blue	0.5 γ
l-Proline	$H_2C—CH_2$ / $H_2C \quad CHCOOH$ / NH	Blue	1 γ
Piperidine	$H_2C \big\langle \begin{smallmatrix} CH_2—CH_2 \\ CH_2—CH_2 \end{smallmatrix} \big\rangle NH$	Blue-violet	5 γ
2,2'-Dimethyl-dicyclohexyl-amine	$\left(H_2C \big\langle \begin{smallmatrix} CH_2—CHCH_3 \\ CH_2—CH_2 \end{smallmatrix} \big\rangle CH \right)_2 NH$	Blue	100 γ
1-Phenyl-2-methylamino-propane	$C_6H_5—CH_2—CH—CH_3$ | $HN—CH_3$	Blue	10 γ

References pp. 314–319

Procedure. A drop of the test solution (neutral, acid, or alkaline) is mixed, on a spot plate or in a microcrucible, with a drop of the reagent solution, and a drop of a 2 % solution of sodium carbonate is added. If the test solution is acid, care must be taken to add sufficient carbonate to render the mixture alkaline. A blue to violet color is formed in the presence of secondary aliphatic amines. When small amounts are suspected, a blank test is advisable.

Reagent: 1% sodium nitroprusside solution to which 10% by volume of acetaldehyde is added. The reagent must be freshly prepared.

The *limits of identification* for a number of secondary amines are given in Table 25.

(3) *Detection of secondary aliphatic amines through formation of copper dithiocarbamates* [154]

Secondary aliphatic amines, and likewise cyclic secondary amines, react with carbon disulfide and ammoniacal copper sulfate solution to produce brown water-insoluble copper salts of the respective dithiocarbamic acids:

$$CS_2 + NHRR_1 + {}^1/_2 Cu^{+2} + NH_3 \longrightarrow SC \begin{smallmatrix} \diagup S-Cu/_2 \\ \diagdown NRR_1 \end{smallmatrix} + NH_4^+$$

These copper salts give brown solutions in benzene, chloroform, etc. and consequently the occurrence of the above reaction can be discerned even with very dilute solutions of the secondary bases, i.e., with solutions that are too dilute to yield a precipitate of the copper salts. The test described here is based on this finding.

Primary and tertiary aliphatic amines, aromatic amines, and also secondary aromatic-aliphatic amines do not react under the specific conditions. Organic compounds with basic NH-groups, which also contain hydrophilic groups, are not able to form benzene-soluble copper dithiocarbamates. Pertinent examples are: proline, diethanolamine, adrenaline, spermine, spermidine, and piperazine. This divergent behavior is of value when basic NH-groups are to be differentiated.

Procedure. A micro test tube is used. One drop of the acid test solution is treated with a drop of 5% copper sulfate solution and the mixture is made basic with ammonium hydroxide. The blue solution, which may be turbid because of the precipitation of insoluble bases, is shaken with two drops of a mixture of 1 volume of carbon disulfide and 3 volumes of benzene. If the reaction is positive, the benzene layer turns brown or yellow.

The test revealed:

2 γ Ephedrine   ⬡—CH—CH—NHCH₃
                     | |
                     OH   CH₃

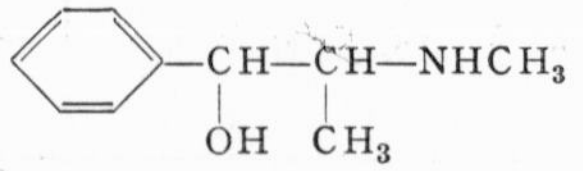

5 γ Pervitine   ⟨ ⟩—CH_2—$\underset{\underset{CH_3}{|}}{C}H$—$NHCH_3$

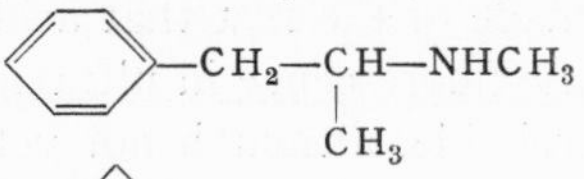

0,2 γ Piperidine $\underset{\underset{H}{N}}{\bigcirc}$

10 γ Coniine $\underset{\underset{H}{N}}{\bigcirc}$—$CH_2CH_2CH_3$

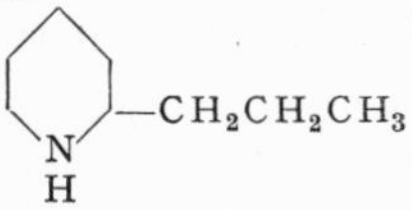

Benzedrine, $C_6H_5CH_2\underset{\underset{CH_3}{|}}{C}HNH_2$, whose physiological action is like that of Pervitine (q.v.), shows no copper dithiocarbamate reaction. This divergent behavior can be applied to differentiate these two compounds.

A positive response was given by small amounts of morpholine, emetine and piperine. (Comp. Chap. 5.)

(4) Test for primary, secondary and tertiary aliphatic and aromatic amines by melting with fluorescein chloride [155]

All compounds containing the NH_2-, NH- or $N(CH_3)$-groups give rise to rhodamine dyestuffs when melted with fluorescein chloride and anhydrous zinc chloride [156]. The properties of the dyestuffs vary characteristically according to the different types of amine used. The formation of the rhodamines starting from the colorless fluorescein chloride is shown in the general equation *:

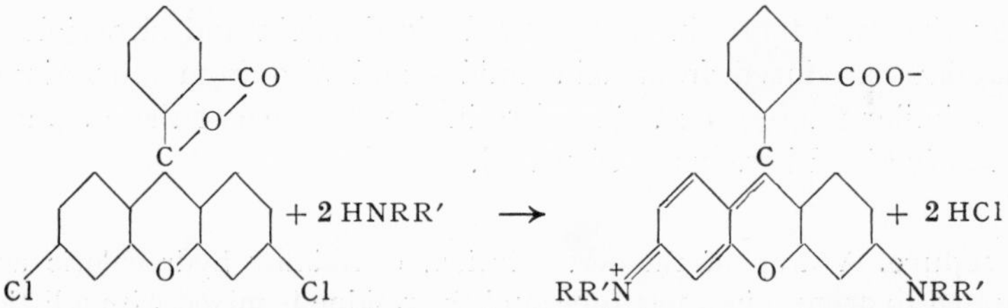

* In addition to the para quinonoid ammonium salt formulation given in this text, the rhodamine dyes can also be written as ortho quinonoid oxonium salts or as carbonium salts with the respective zwitter ions I and II.

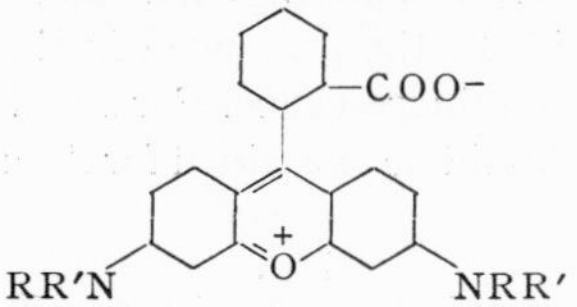

I 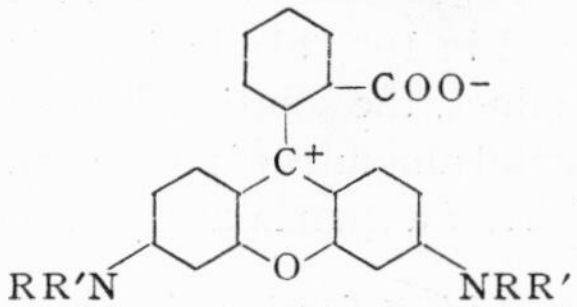   II

Compare in this respect [157], [158] and [159].

References pp. 314–319

In the following tests use is made of the fact that acid solutions of rhodamine dyes show a characteristic fluorescence in ultraviolet light, in some cases even in daylight. It is probable, although not yet proved, that the precipitation of violet thallic compounds from acid solutions of rhodamine dyes may also be used for the identification of rhodamine dyes synthesized through the interaction between the lactone fluorescein chlorid and primary or secondary aliphatic or aromatic amines. (Compare the test for rhodamine dyes described on page 465.)

Detection of primary aliphatic amines

On melting primary aliphatic amines or their salts with fluorescein chloride, the resulting light red dyestuffs exhibit *yellow-green* fluorescence. The general formula of these products, which are symmetrical dialkyl rhodamines, is:

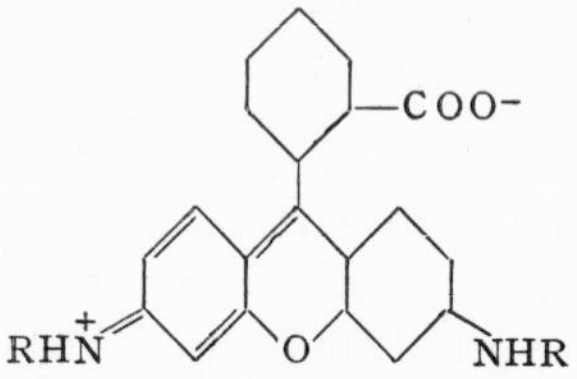

They give an intense fluorescence both in daylight and ultraviolet light. Rhodamines produced from acid amides and also from ammonium salts show a similar fluorescence. Therefore in the presence of these compounds the test described here cannot be used.

Procedure. A drop of the test solution, containing hydrochloric acid, is evaporated to dryness in a test tube, and the residue is mixed with a little fluorescein chloride (from the tip of a spatula) and twice the bulk of anhydrous zinc chloride. The mixture is then heated in an air bath (iron crucible or aluminum block) to 250 to 260° until all the zinc chloride has melted. When cool, the melt is dissolved in 10% alcoholic hydrochloric acid. In the presence of primary aliphatic amines, the solution shows a yellow-green fluorescence. For the detection of very small amounts of amines, the solution should be examined for fluorescence in the light of a quartz analytical lamp.

Limits of identification obtained by means of this test are given in Table 26.

TABLE 26. PRIMARY ALIPHATIC AMINES

Name	Formula	Color	Fluorescence	Ultra-violet fluorescence	Limit of identification
Ammonium chloride	NH_4Cl	Pink	Green	Yellow-green	30 γ
Hydroxylamine hydrochloride	$NH_2OH \cdot HCl$	Pink	Green	Yellow	20 γ
Hydrazine sulfate	$NH_2NH_2 \cdot H_2SO_4$	Orange	Green	Yellow	20 γ
Methylamine hydrochloride	$CH_3NH_2 \cdot HCl$	Red	Green	Yellow	10 γ
Glycine ester	$CH_2(NH_2)COOC_2H_5$	Pink	Green	Yellow	20 γ
Benzylamine	$C_6H_5CH_2NH_2$	Red	Green	Yellow-green	10 γ

Detection of secondary aliphatic amines [160]

Tetra-alkyl rhodamines (I) are formed on melting secondary aliphatic amines with fluorescein chloride (II):

(I)   (II)

Their acid solutions are red and exhibit an *orange-red* fluorescence. The difference in the fluorescence color from that of primary amines, which is yellow-green, gives a basis for the differentiation of these two classes of compounds.

The test is carried out as described for primary amines.

Limits of identification for some secondary amines are given in Table 27.

TABLE 27. SECONDARY ALIPHATIC AMINES

Name	Formula	Color	Fluores-cence	Ultra-violet fluores-cence	Limit of iden-tifica-tion
Diethylamine	$HN\begin{smallmatrix}C_2H_5\\C_2H_5\end{smallmatrix}$	Red	Orange-red	Orange-red	$4\,\gamma$
Piperidine	$HN\begin{smallmatrix}CH_2-CH_2\\CH_2-CH_2\end{smallmatrix}CH_2$	Red	Red	Orange-red	$4\,\gamma$
Aceturic ethyl ester	$CH_2COOC_2H_5$ $\mid$ $NHCOCH_3$	Orange	Orange	Orange-yellow	$20\,\gamma$

Another test for secondary aliphatic amines, which is more selective and easier to perform is given on page 262.

Detection of aromatic amines

Primary, secondary, and tertiary aromatic amines containing a methyl group, give rise to dyestuffs of the following types when melted with fluorescein chloride:

The alcoholic hydrochloric acid solutions of these dyestuffs are deep red-violet, but unlike the rhodamines formed from the aliphatic amines, they do not fluoresce. Hence the presence or absence of fluorescence affords a means of differentiation between aromatic and aliphatic amines. Benzal derivatives of amines behave similarly to the parent compounds.

The test is carried out as already described for the aliphatic amines (page 264).

Limits of identification for a number of aromatic amines are given in Table 28.

TABLE 28.	AROMATIC AMINES

Name	Formula	Color	Limit of identification
Aniline	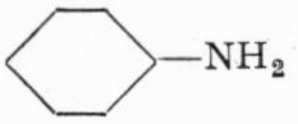	Red-violet	5 γ
α-Naphthylamine	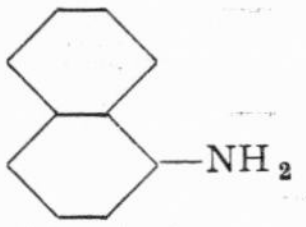	Dark violet	5 γ
β-Naphthylamine	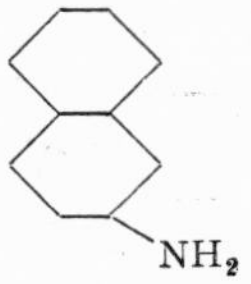	Red-violet	2 γ
β-Aminoanthra-quinone	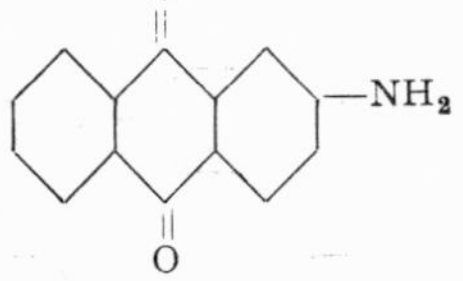	Red	4 γ
Benzidine		Red-violet	4 γ
o-Aminobenzalde-hyde	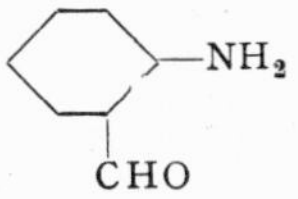	Red	2 γ

(continued)

References pp. 314–319

TABLE 28. AROMATIC AMINES (CONTINUED)

Name	Formula	Color	Limit of identification
p-Nitraniline	$H_2N-\langle\ \rangle-NO_2$	Red-violet	5 γ
p-Phenylenediamine	$H_2N-\langle\ \rangle-NH_2$	Purple	1 γ
p-Chloraniline	$H_2N-\langle\ \rangle-Cl$	Purple	4 γ
H-acid	$C_{10}H_4(NH_2)(OH)(SO_3H)_2$ (1, 8, 3, 6)	Red-violet	10 γ
Diphenylamine	$\langle\ \rangle-NH-\langle\ \rangle$	Purple	8 γ
Hydrazobenzene	$\langle\ \rangle-NH-NH-\langle\ \rangle$	Purple	4 γ
Acetanilide	$\langle\ \rangle-NHCOCH_3$	Scarlet	4 γ
Benzenesulfo-p-nitranilide	$\langle\ \rangle-SO_2-NH-\langle\ \rangle-NO_2$	Blue-violet	4 γ
p-Dimethylaminobenzaldehyde	$OHC-\langle\ \rangle-N(CH_3)_2$	Cherry red	4 γ
Michler's ketone	$(CH_3)_2N-\langle\ \rangle-CO-\langle\ \rangle-N(CH_3)_2$	Red	2 γ
Diethylaniline	$\langle\ \rangle-N(C_2H_5)_2$	Pink	400 γ
Benzylidene-p-nitraniline	$\langle\ \rangle-CH=N-\langle\ \rangle-NO_2$	Brown-violet	8 γ

References pp. 314–319

(5) *Test for primary, secondary and tertiary aliphatic and aromatic amines with fused potassium thiocyanate* [161]

When fused potassium thiocyanate (m.p. 173–179°) is brought in contact with solid ammonium salts, the following topochemical reaction takes place on the surface of the solid:

$$KCNS + NH_4X \rightarrow KX + NH_4CNS$$
$$(X = Cl, Br, I, \tfrac{1}{2}SO_4, \text{ etc.})$$

On further heating, the ammonium thiocyanate (m.p. 149°) undergoes a series of transformations depending on temperature, rate of heating, etc.[162] One transformation occurring in the fusion is the familiar rearrangement of ammonium thiocyanate into the isomeric thiourea which, in the imide form (isothiourea), decomposes on heating into hydrogen sulfide and cyanamide: [163]

$$NH_4CNS \rightleftharpoons S{=}C\begin{array}{l} {}^{\nearrow NH_2} \\ {}_{\searrow NH_2} \end{array} \rightleftharpoons H_2N{-}C\begin{array}{l} {}^{\nearrow SH} \\ {}_{\searrow NH} \end{array} \rightarrow H_2S + NH_2CN$$

Salts of aliphatic and aromatic amines, which are merely substituted ammonium salts, react in an analogous fashion. With primary and secondary amines the corresponding thiocyanates are formed first and remain in equilibrium with the respective substituted thioureas:

$$RNH_3CNS \rightleftharpoons S{=}C\begin{array}{l} {}^{\nearrow NH_2} \\ {}_{\searrow NHR} \end{array} \quad \text{and} \quad R_1R_2NH_2CNS \rightleftharpoons S{=}C\begin{array}{l} {}^{\nearrow NH_2} \\ {}_{\searrow NR_1R_2} \end{array}$$

Both of these substituted thioureas, probably in the isomeric imide forms, decompose at 200–250° with evolution of hydrogen sulfide to yield alkyl or aryl cyanamides. Salts of tertiary amines also split off hydrogen sulfide when heated with fused potassium thiocyanate, but the mechanism of the reaction is certainly different. It must be noted that cyclic nitrogen bases, in contrast to secondary and tertiary amines, react only faintly.

The facts that the reaction of salts of amines with fused potassium thiocyanate occurs almost instantaneously and that the hydrogen sulfide formed is easily detectible provide the possibility of a test for aliphatic and aromatic amines. Free bases must be converted into their hydrochlorides, before carrying out the test. This is readily accomplished by evaporation with an excess of dilute hydrochloric acid. The potassium thiocyanate used should be well dried since the moist salt itself yields hydrogen sulfide when heated.

When the test is used, attention must be given to the fact that organic compounds which split off water when heated interfere (compare page 286).

Procedure. One drop of a solution of the amine in alcohol, ether or other solvents, and one drop of 1 : 10 hydrochloric acid are evaporated to dryness in a micro test tube at a temperature of 110°. The dry residue * is mixed with an excess of well dried potassium thiocyanate and heated in an oil bath to about 200–250°. A piece of filter paper moistened with a drop of solution of 10% lead acetate is held over the mouth of the test tube. The presence of amines is detected by an almost immediate blackening of the paper.

Reagent: Potassium thiocyanate (pulverized and dried at 110°).

The test revealed:

15 γ ethylenediamine	25 γ benzylamine
50 γ aniline	15 γ benzidine
50 γ monomethylaniline	50 γ diphenylamine
50 γ dimethylaniline	50 γ histidine chloride
50 γ nitrosodiethylaniline	

The following cyclic nitrogen bases in amounts of 2000 γ react faintly: 8-hydroxyquinoline, 6-nitroquinoline, α-naphthoquinoline.

(6) Detection of tertiary amines with citric acid and acetic anhydride[164]

When aliphatic, alicyclic, aromatic-aliphatic and aromatic tertiary amines are heated briefly with a solution of citric acid in acetic anhydride, a red, violet, or blue color develops. Malonic or aconitic acid may be used instead of citric acid. The test seems very selective; its chemistry has not been elucidated as yet.

Procedure. A micro test tube is used. A little of the tertiary amine or a drop of its alcohol solution is united with a drop of a solution containing 2 grams of citric acid dissolved in 100 ml of acetic anhydride. The mixture is warmed in a water bath. A red to purple color appears when the response is positive.

The test may also be applied to the evaporation residue of the test solution taken to dryness with dilute hydrochloric acid.

The procedure revealed:

7 γ N-ethylpiperidine (red)
4 γ *p*-dimethylaminobenzaldehyde (red)
2 γ piperidine (dark violet)

A positive response was given by: trimethylamine hydrochloride, triethanol-amine, methylephedrine hydrochloride, tribenzylamine, hordenine sulfate, procaine hydrochloride, narceine, creatine, atropine sulfate, strychnine nitrate, brucine, codeine phosphate, scopolamine bromate, caffeine, histidine hydrochloride,

---

* In this respect it must be remembered that when organic bases are evaporated with hydrochloric acid and the excess of acid is expelled by heating to 110°, the chloride formed is not always stable but can be split into its components. A pertinent example is a mixture of the base α, α'-dipyridyl and hydrochloric acid, which when brought to a temperature of 110° is completely volatilized.

aminopyridine, antipyrine, quinine sulfate, cinchonine, pilocarpine hydrochloride, berberine hydrochloride, veratrine, dimethylaniline, α-picoline, nicotinic acid, 2,6-lutidine hydrochloride, pyridine-2,6-dicarboxylic acid, isonicotinic acid hydrazide, nicotinic acid hydrazide, 2-aminopyridine, 4-nitro-α-picoline N-oxide, quinoline, 3-hydroxyquinoline, 8-hydroxyquinoline, 2-amino-4,6-dihydroxypyrimidine, 2-aminothiazole hydrochloride, vitamin B_1 hydrochloride, acrinol.

(7) *Test for primary aromatic amines with glutaconic aldehyde* [165]

Acid solutions of primary aromatic amines give colored products with pyridine irradiated with ultraviolet light.[166] The reaction depends on the hydrolysis of pyridine in ultraviolet light to give the ammonium salt of glutaconic aldehyde enol, as shown in (1). This forms condensation products, of the type of Schiff base,[167] with primary aromatic amines (2):

$$(1)$$

$$(2)$$

Since the condensation (2) proceeds even with very slight amounts of primary amines, it may constitute the basis of a test for them. The colored products belong to the class of polymethine dyes.

Free glutaconic aldehyde is very unstable; it polymerizes readily, and even its yellow, water-soluble ammonium salt (formed by ultraviolet light on paper impregnated with pyridine) decomposes in a few days. It is therefore best to carry out the test with the aid of compounds that readily break up to yield glutaconic aldehyde. Among such materials are sodium glutaconic aldehyde enolate (I) and 4-pyridylpyridinium dichloride (II): [168]

NaOCH=CH—CH=CH—CHO   HCl·N⟨ ⟩—⟨ ⟩N·HCl

(I)   (II)

The latter breaks up with alkali to give the alkali enolate of glutaconic aldehyde (III) and 4-aminopyridine (IV), and liberates the reagent:

$$\underset{\underset{\text{N·HCl}}{\big|}}{\overset{\text{N—Cl}}{\big|}} + 3\ NaOH \longrightarrow \underset{O=\!CH\quad \overset{|}{C}HONa}{\overset{H}{\underset{HC}{\overset{C}{\diagup}}\diagdown CH}} + \underset{(IV)}{\overset{NH_2}{\bigcirc}} + 2\ NaCl + H_2O$$

(III)   (IV)

Procedure. A drop of the test solution and a drop of the reagent are placed in a microcrucible, made alkaline with 2 drops of 2 N sodium hydroxide, and at once 3 drops of 2 N hydrochloric acid are added. In the presence of a primary aromatic amine, a deep red to violet color or precipitate is formed.*

An alternative procedure is to impregnate spot paper with an alcoholic solution of sodium glutaconic aldehyde enolate (prepared by adding sodium hydroxide to an alcohol–water solution of 4-pyridylpyridinium dichloride). The warm test solution, slightly acidified with mineral acid, is spotted on the dry paper. The pale brown paper is stained red, violet, or dark brown. In the absence of amines, a white fleck is formed on the paper, owing to the destruction of the sodium glutaconic aldehyde enolate.

Reagent: 1% solution of 4-pyridylpyridinium dichloride in water.

The *limits of identification* for a number of amines are given in Table 29.

(8) Test for primary aromatic amines with sodium pentacyanoaquoferriate [169]

A green or blue color results on mixing primary aromatic amines with a light yellow sodium carbonate solution of sodium pentacyanoaquoferriate, $Na_2[Fe(CN)_5H_2O)]$. This color reaction also succeeds with solutions of sodium nitroprusside, that have been left for a long time in the light, or that have been treated with ultraviolet light for 15 minutes. Under these conditions the following changes occur:

$$Na_2[Fe(CN)_5NO] + H_2O \rightarrow Na_2[Fe(CN)_5H_2O] + NO \qquad (1)$$

The aquoferriate formed according to (1) reacts with the primary aromatic amines, with the liberation of one molecule of water. For instance with aniline:

$$Na_2[Fe(CN)_5H_2O] + C_6H_5NH_2 \rightarrow Na_2[Fe(CN)_5C_6H_5NH_2] + H_2O \qquad (2)$$

The compounds resulting from (2) are green or blue.

Procedure. A drop of the test solution is mixed with a drop of the reagent solution on a spot plate or in a microcrucible. If necessary, a little dilute sodium

* 4-Aminopyridine does not behave like an aromatic amine; therefore no colored Schiff base is formed when it breaks up.

carbonate solution is added. A more or less intense green or blue color appears at once or after a few minutes.

Reagent: Sodium pentacyanoaquoferriate solution. A 1 % solution of sodium pentacyanoaquoferroate is treated with bromine water until the color is violet, and then sufficient sodium nitroprusside is added to change the color to yellow. 2% Sodium carbonate solution is added. Instead, a solution of sodium nitroprusside (in 1 % sodium carbonate) which has been aged by long storing, or by 15 minutes irradiation in ultraviolet light,* may be used.

The *limits of identification* for a number of amines are given in Table 29.

(9) Other tests for primary aromatic amines

The fact that the hydrogen atoms of the NH_2 group are readily replaceable forms the basis of the following tests.[170] They may be carried out as spot reactions (in microcrucibles) with heating:

(*a*) Condensation with aromatic nitroso compounds to form azo dyes. *Reagent:* saturated solution of 5-nitroso-8-hydroxyquinoline or 10 % nitroso-dimethylaniline in glacial acetic acid (*Idn. Limit:* 1–100 γ).

(*b*) Condensation with furfural (or *p*-dimethylaminobenzaldehyde) to give Schiff bases, which are violet or orange colored.[171] *Reagent:* solution of 10 drops furfural in 10 ml glacial acetic acid, or a saturated solution of *p*-dimethylaminobenzaldehyde in glacial acetic acid (*Idn. Limit:* 0.1–200 γ). Secondary aromatic amines, also aliphatic amines and amino acids, react in the same way. Proteins react with *p*-dimethylaminobenzaldehyde, whereby red products are formed.

(*c*) Condensation with chloranil to form blue, red, or brown products. *Reagent:* saturated solution of chloranil in dioxan (*Idn. Limit:* 0.2–200 γ). Secondary amines react similarly; amino acids do not react. Phenols give red to violet colorations.

(*d*) Primary amines react with carbon disulfide to form symmetrical dialkylated thioureas and liberate hydrogen sulfide.[172] The latter can be detected with lead acetate paper in a suitable apparatus (*Idn. Limit:* 1 to 5 γ amine).

(*e*) The following procedure has been recommended.[173] One drop of the ether or acetone solution of the sample is placed on filter paper. The solvent is allowed to evaporate. The paper is then exposed, successively, for 5 minutes each, to the vapors of concentrated hydrochloric acid, and ethyl

* This is advisable when hydrazine or nitroso compounds are present, since they react with any excess of prussic salts (see p. 154).

TABLE 29. PRIMARY AROMATIC AMINES

Name	Formula	Test with Glutaconic aldehyde Limit of identifi- cation	Color	Test with $Na_2[Fe(CN)_5H_2O]$ Limit of identifi- cation	Color
Aniline	(structure) —NH$_2$	0.1 γ	Red-brown	0.5 γ	Green
o-Nitraniline		1 γ	Rose-red	Does not react	
m-Nitraniline	$C_6H_4(NO_2)NH_2$	1 γ	Bluish red	50 γ	Green
p-Nitraniline		0.3 γ	Rose-red	10 γ	Green
m-Bromo-aniline	Br (structure) —NH$_2$	1 γ	Red	5 γ	Green
p-Phenylene-diamine	NH$_2$—(structure)—NH$_2$	0.1 γ	Violet	0.1 γ	Blue
p-Amino-diphenyl	(structure)(structure)—NH$_2$	1 γ	Red	1 γ	Green
Benzidine	NH$_2$—(structure)(structure)—NH$_2$	0.1 γ	Red-brown	1 γ	Blue-green
α-Naphthyl-amine	$C_{10}H_7NH_2$	0.05 γ	Scarlet	2 γ	Blue-green
β-Naphthyl-amine		0.1 γ	Red	2 γ	Green
1,8-Naphthyl-enediamine	$C_{10}H_6(NH_2)_2$	1 γ	Red-brown	10 γ	Brown-green
K-Acid	$C_{10}H_4(OH)(NH_2)(SO_3H)_2$	2 γ	Orange	20 γ	Brown
α-Amino-pyridine	(structure) —NH$_2$ N	Does not react		10 γ	Green
Amino-tetrazole	N——N (structure) C—NH$_2$ NH	Does not react		100 γ	Violet-pink

nitrite (from alcohol, HCl and crystallized $NaNO_2$). Then the paper is spotted with an ether solution of resorcinol, held over ammonia, and finally steamed. An orange, red, or violet color indicates the presence of diazotizable NH_2 groups.

The condensations (a)–(b) of amines with p-nitrosodimethylaniline (formation of colored azo compounds) and with p-dimethylaminobenzaldehyde (formation of colored Schiff bases) can also be accomplished in melts of the respective reagents.[174] Particularly good is the condensation with p-dimethylaminobenzaldehyde (m.p. 73°), which can be carried out likewise with salts of amines; for example, the infusible sulfate, chloride and acetate of benzidine react in the same manner as the free base (m.p. 115°–120°).

(10) Test for diphenylamine and derivatives through oxidation to quinoneimides[175]

The well known and exceedingly sensitive color reaction for nitrite and nitrate with diphenylamine and concentrated sulfuric acid is based on the oxidation of diphenylamine to a blue quinoid derivative of benzidine (see page 168). It may be reversed to detect diphenylamine, and also its derivatives which have no substituent in the para position. The color reaction is quite selective if the solubility characteristics of diphenylamine and its derivatives are taken into consideration. Diphenylamine and benzidine are very weak bases which, in contrast to primary aromatic and mixed aliphatic-aromatic secondary amines, are not soluble in dilute mineral acids. Accordingly, they may be separated from other organic bases by digesting with dilute mineral acids. On the other hand, because of the weak basic character of the NH-group in the secondary aromatic amines, the introduction of sulfonic and carboxylic groups into one of the aromatic rings results in acidic compounds which are soluble in water and dilute alkalies. Such derivatives of aromatic secondary amines can therefore be separated from water-insoluble aromatic bases by digestion with dilute alkalies. Consequently, if the behavior toward acids and alkalies is given due consideration, oxidation by means of nitric acid can be used to differentiate certain secondary aromatic amines from their sulfonic and carboxylic acids.*

Procedure. A pinch of the test material is treated in a micro crucible with a drop of concentrated nitric acid (sp.gr. 1.4). If solutions in organic solvents or alkali hydroxides are being tested (see above), a drop of the liquid is brought to dryness in the crucible and a drop of concentrated nitric acid then added. Depending on the amount of secondary aromatic amine present, the color obtained is more or less blue or blue-green.

* Diphenylamine and its derivatives have considerable practical importance as redox indicators.[176]

The following were detected:

0.25 γ diphenylamine
0.30 γ phenyl α-naphthylamine
0.40 γ diphenylamine-2,2'-dicarboxylic acid
0.17 γ N,N'-diphenylbenzidine
0.3 γ diphenylamine-4-sulfonic acid

A direct bluing effect should not be expected with N-substituted derivatives of diphenylamine when treated with concentrated nitric acid. (4,4-Diphenylsemicarbazide is an exception. Its limit of identification is 5 γ.) It appears that these compounds are saponified when they are warmed with concentrated sulfuric acid to 150–160° with splitting out of diphenylamine:

$$OC \overset{N(C_6H_5)_2}{\underset{NH_2}{\Big\langle}} + H_2O \longrightarrow CO_2 + NH_3 + NH(C_6H_5)_2$$

If a little alkali nitrate is added to the cold reaction mass, a blue color results. This behavior was observed not only in the case of *as.* diphenylurea (10 γ) but also with N-methyldiphenylamine (2.5 γ) and N-acetyldiphenylamine (5γ). Only a yellow color results when ethyl-N,N-diphenyl carbamate and N,N-diphenylanthranilic acid are subjected to this treatment.

It is notable that the following give a blue color even at room temperature when treated with concentrated sulfuric acid with addition of alkali nitrite:

$$OC \overset{N(C_6H_5)_2}{\underset{NH_2}{\Big\langle}} \qquad HN{=}C \overset{N(C_6H_5)_2}{\underset{NH_2}{\Big\langle}} \qquad OC \overset{N(C_6H_5)_2}{\underset{OC_2H_5}{\Big\langle}}$$

as-Diphenylurea   as-Diphenylguanidine   Ethyl-N,N-diphenyl
(110 γ)   (100 γ)   (15 γ)   carbamate

$$OC \overset{N(C_6H_5)_2}{\underset{NHNH_2}{\Big\langle}} \qquad\qquad C_6H_4 \overset{N(C_6H_5)_2}{\underset{COOH}{\Big\langle}}$$

4,4-Diphenylsemicarbazide   N,N-Diphenylanthranilic acid
(2.5 γ)   (4 γ)

It is likely that in the cases just noted the —N(C$_6$H$_5$)$_2$-group is split off as N-nitrosodiphenylamine through the action of nitrous acid:

$$OC \overset{N(C_6H_5)_2}{\underset{NH_2}{\Big\langle}} + HNO_2 \longrightarrow CO_2 + ON{-}N(C_6H_5)_2 + NH_3$$

Saponification of the N-nitrosodiphenylamine thus yields diphenylamine and nitrous acid and hence the expected blue color.

According to the observations made up to the present, N-substituted diphenylamines can therefore be detected by warming with concentrated sulfuric acid to 150–160° and subsequent addition of alkali nitrate, as well as by their behavior toward concentrated sulfuric acid and alkali nitrite.

35. Cyclic Amines

(a) Carbazole and Derivatives

Detection with sulfuric acid and alkali nitrate [177]

Carbazole is closely related to diphenylamine from which it is obtained by heating in the vapor phase. Analogously to diphenylamine, carbazole and its derivatives react with concentrated nitric acid, or better with concentrated sulfuric acid plus alkali nitrate or nitrite, to yield colored products, which are never blue. Presumably the chemistry of this reaction is analogous to that of the diphenylamine-nitrate (nitrite) reaction. It is rather characteristic that carbazole and many carbazole derivatives give colored solutions in concentrated sulfuric acid (solvates); this is not true of diphenylamine and its derivatives and may therefore be used for differentiation.

Procedure. A drop of the test solution is evaporated on a spot plate and a drop of concentrated sulfuric acid and several milligrams of potassium nitrate are added.

The response was:

1 γ Carbazole (green)

10 γ 3-Nitro-carbazole (green)

0.5 γ N-Ethyl-carbazole (green)

2.5 γ N-Ethyl-4-amino carbazole (pale pink)

5 γ N-ethyl-3-diethylamino-carbazole (violet)

2.5 γ N-p-Toluene-sulfonylcarbazole (green)

As shown by the preceding, carbazole and its derivatives may be characterized by color reactions and differentiated from diphenylamine and its derivatives. However, a differentiation is not possible when these materials are presented in mixtures with each other.

(b) Pyrrole Bases

(1) Test by melting with fluorescein chloride [178]

Pyrrole and its derivatives containing the intact NH-group, and therefore functioning as secondary amines, form yellow-brown rhodamine dyes when melted with fluorescein chloride and anhydrous zinc chloride. Dissolved in dilute hydrochloric acid, these dyes display a blue fluorescence in ultraviolet light. This reaction can be applied as a test for pyrrole and pyrrole derivatives.

The procedure is the same as that given on page 263 *et seq.* for the detection of primary and secondary amines by means of the formation of yellow-green and orange-red fluorescing rhodamine dyes.

The limits of identification for pyrrole and some pyrrole derivatives are given in Table 30.

TABLE 30.   PYRROLE DERIVATIVES

Name	Formula	Color	Ultraviolet fluorescence	Limit of identification
Pyrrole		(Charred)	Blue	40 γ
Indole		Brown-red	Blue	12 γ
Carbazole		Yellow-green	Blue	30 γ
Acetindoxyl		Brown-red	Blue	20 γ

(2) Test with p-dimethylaminobenzaldehyde [179]

If a mixture of pyrrole (I) and a weakly acid alcoholic solution of *p*-dimethylaminobenzaldehyde (II) is warmed, a red-violet color develops. This color reaction is based on the fact that pyrrole can react in its tautomeric forms (Ia) and (Ib), which are known as pyrrolenine [180]:

References pp. 314–319

$$
\underset{(I)}{HN\underset{\alpha}{\overset{CH=CH}{\underset{CH=CH}{\Big|\beta}}}} \qquad \underset{(Ia)}{N\overset{CH_2-CH}{\underset{CH-CH}{\Big\|}}} \qquad \underset{(Ib)}{N\overset{CH-CH_2}{\underset{CH=CH}{\Big|}}}
$$

The CH_2-groups in (Ia) and (Ib) permit condensation with the aldehyde. For example, (Ib) reacts with loss of water:

$$
\underset{(II)}{N\overset{CH-CH_2}{\underset{CH=CH}{\Big|}}} + OCH-\!\!\bigcirc\!\!-N(CH_3)_2 \underset{}{\overset{H_2O}{\longrightarrow}} \underset{(III)}{N\overset{CH-C=CH-\bigcirc-N(CH_3)_2}{\underset{CH=CH}{\Big|}}} \quad (1)
$$

The compound (III) produced in (1) combines with H^+ ions and rearranges into the quinoidal red-violet compound (IV):

$$
\underset{(III)}{N\overset{CH-C=CH-\bigcirc-N(CH_3)_2}{\underset{CH=CH}{\Big|}}} + H^+ \rightarrow \underset{(IV)}{HN\overset{CH=C-CH=\bigcirc=\overset{+}{N}(CH_3)_2}{\underset{CH=CH}{\Big|}}} \quad (2)
$$

The procedure used here takes advantage of the fact that reactions (1) and (2) occur almost immediately and without warming if a concentrated solution of p-dimethylaminobenzaldehyde in concentrated hydrochloric acid is used as reagent.

The derivatives of pyrrole show the same ability to undergo this condensation provided they have an intact CH-group in the α- or β-position relative to the cyclic NH-group. Accordingly, indole (benzopyrrole), skatole (β-methylindole), and tryptophan (β-indolylalanine) react analogously to pyrrole, whereas carbazole (dibenzopyrrole) does not react with p-dimethylaminobenzaldehyde. In the color reactions of pyrrole derivatives with p-dimethylaminobenzaldehyde, it is of course also possible that, under the conditions of the test, there is first a fission into pyrrole or indole, and the condensation with the reagent then follows.

When p-dimethylaminobenzaldehyde is used as reagent for pyrrole bases, it should be noted that primary aromatic and aliphatic amines condense with this aldehyde to yield colored Schiff bases. The color of these products however is never violet, but yellow, orange-red, sometimes brown. Furthermore, the sensitivity of the color reaction based on the formation of Schiff bases, particularly in strong hydrochloric acid solution, is considerably lower [181] than that of the color reaction of pyrrole and pyrrole derivatives with p-dimethylaminobenzaldehyde, which rests on another kind of condensation.

Procedure. [182] One drop of the aqueous, ether, or alcoholic test solution is mixed with one or two drops of the reagent solution on a spot plate. If pyrrole or reaction-capable pyrrole derivatives are present, a violet color will appear at once or after a short time.

Reagent: *p*-Dimethylaminobenzaldehyde, 5% solution in concentrated hydrochloric acid.

This procedure revealed: 0.04 γ pyrrole; 0.06 γ indole; 0.1 γ tryptophan.

(c) Pyridine and Derivatives

Detection by conversion into polymethine dyes

Colored Schiff bases of glutaconic aldehyde (polymethine dyes) [183] are formed by the action of bromocyanogen and primary aromatic amines on pyridine. This color reaction requires the opening of the pyridine ring with formation of glutaconic aldehyde. This hydrolysis does not occur with pyridine alone but it occurs instantly and extensively after the addition of bromocyanogen to pyridine, i.e., when the valence of the cyclic nitrogen is raised from 3 to 5:

$$
\underset{NC \quad Br}{\boxed{}} + 2\,H_2O \longrightarrow \underset{O\dot{C}H \quad \dot{C}HOH}{HC \overset{CH}{\diagup} \diagdown CH} + NH_2CN + HBr \tag{1}
$$

If primary aromatic amines are present at this hydrolysis, they condense with the resulting glutaconic aldehyde to yield colored Schiff bases: [184]

$$
\underset{O\dot{C}H \quad \dot{C}HOH}{HC \overset{CH}{\diagup} \diagdown CH} + 2\,NH_2R \longrightarrow \underset{RN=\dot{C}H \quad \dot{C}HNHR}{HC \overset{CH}{\diagup} \diagdown CH} + 2\,H_2O \tag{2}
$$

Derivatives of pyridine with free α,α'-positions behave analogously to the parent compound; they give substituted glutaconic aldehydes and their colored Schiff bases. The formation of polymethine dyes constitutes the basis of numerous tests and colorimetric methods for determining pyridine and its derivatives.[185] The condensation with benzidine is quite serviceable.

Procedure.[186] A spot plate is used. One drop of the test solution is mixed with one drop of saturated bromine water and one drop of 2% potassium cyanide solution (production of bromocyanogen). A drop of a water suspension of benzidine is added. Depending on the amount of pyridine or reactive pyridine derivatives, a red to pink color appears at once or within a few minutes.

Reagent: 1 gram of hydrated sodium acetate is added to 100 ml of saturated water solution of benzidine dihydrochloride to precipitate the base in finely divided condition. A suitable suspension is obtained by shaking.

The procedure revealed:

0.2 γ pyridine

6 γ coramine   —CON(C₂H₅)₂

2 γ β-picoline   —CH₃

1 γ nicotinamide   —CONH₂

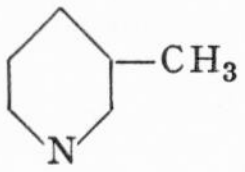

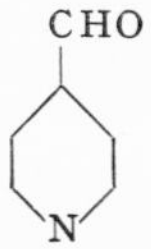

1 γ pyridine-4-aldehyde   CHO

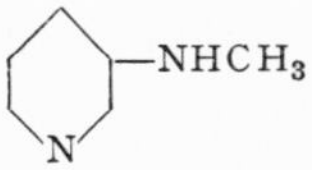

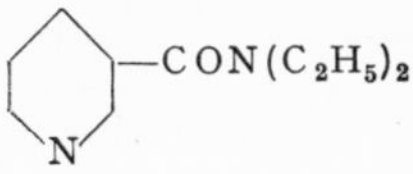

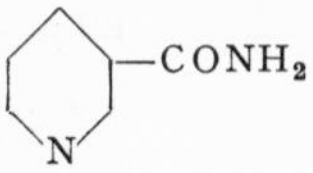

0.5 γ pyridinecarbinol   —CH₂OH
        tartrate
                      N.C₄H₆O₆

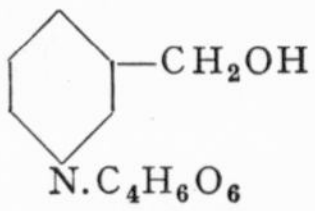

2 γ isonicotinic acid   CONHNH₂
      hydrazide

0.1 γ β-aminomethyl-   —NHCH₃
        pyridine

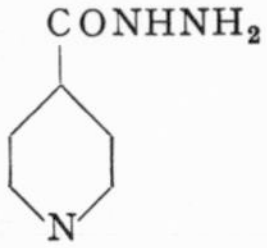

The pyridine contained in water-insoluble complex salts such as $[Znpy_2](CNS)_2$ is likewise detectable by the test just described.

36. α-Amino Carboxylic Acids (—CH(NH₂)—COOH group)

(1) Test by conversion to aldehyde [187]

α-Amino carboxylic acids are both deaminated and decarboxylated on treatment with alkali hypochlorite or hypobromite. There results an aldehyde with one carbon atom less than in the original amino acid. For example, glycocoll (glycine) is converted to formaldehyde:

$$CH_2(NH_2)COOH + NaOCl \rightarrow HCHO + NH_3 + CO_2 + NaCl$$

The ammonia produced in this reaction is oxidized by the excess hypochlorite:

$$2\,NH_3 + 3\,NaOCl \rightarrow N_2 + 3\,NaCl + 3\,H_2O$$

and consequently hexamethylenetetramine can no longer be produced by reaction of the ammonia and formaldehyde. The aldehyde may then be identified with fuchsin-sulfurous acid (see page 208) provided a great excess is used, since this reagent decomposes any unused hypochlorite. Fuchsin-sulfurous acid itself gives no red color with hypochlorite, but only a pale yellow decomposition product.

Procedure. A little of the test substance is treated with a few drops of hypochlorite solution in a microcrucible and warmed gently. When the reaction is complete, an excess of fuchsin-sulfurous acid is added drop by drop. A red color appears if amino acids are present.

Reagents: 1) Sodium hypochlorite (saturated solution).

2) Fuchsin-sulfurous acid (for preparation see page 209).

The following were detected by applying this test:

60 γ glycine,	$CH_2(NH_2)COOH$
100 γ alanine,	$CH_3CH(NH_2)COOH$
100 γ L-asparagine,	$CH(NH_2)COOH$ $\|$ CH_2CONH_2
100 γ L-aspartic acid,	CH_2COOH $\|$ $CH(NH_2)COOH$

100 γ tyrosine, $HO-\langle\rangle-CH_2CH(NH_2)COOH$

50 γ di-iodotyrosine, $HO-\langle\rangle-CH_2CH(NH_2)COOH$ (with I substituents)

60 γ D-arginine, $C\overset{NH_2}{\underset{NH(CH_2)_3CH(NH_2)COOH}{=\!NH}}$

2) Test with ninhydrin [188]

When solutions of amino acids, protein fission products, or primary or secondary amines are heated with ninhydrin (triketohydrindene hydrate), a deep blue color develops. The chemistry of this color reaction is complicated by the occurrence of various partial reactions. In the case of α-amino acids, the initial reaction is the cleavage of the amino acid accompanied by reduction of the ninhydrin (I):

$$\text{(I)} + RCH(NH_2)COOH \longrightarrow CO_2 + NH_3 + RCHO + \text{(II)}$$

The color was formerly believed to be due to the formation of (III), a substituted salt of diketo-hydrindylidene diketo-hydramine, as the result of

References pp. 314–319

a condensation between the ammonia produced, the excess ninhydrin (I), and reduced ninhydrin (II):

(I)   (II)   (III)

According to recent investigations,[189] the color observed is not due to a single substance, but to a number of colored materials. Some of these depend on the nature of the amino acid used, but the formation of the violet bis-1,3-diketoindenyl (IV)

(IV)

was observed in all cases.

Proline and hydroxyproline, from which ammonia is not produced by the reaction with ninhydrin, are exceptional in giving a reddish compound.[190] Contrary to an incorrect belief, ninhydrin reacts not only with α-amino acids, but also with β-amino acids, and primary and secondary aliphatic amines, with formation of similar colored compounds.[191] The exact constitution of these products is not known. Tertiary aliphatic amines, as well as all groups of aromatic amines, do not react with ninhydrin.

Ammonium salts in concentrations up to 10 % do not react with ninhydrin under the conditions of the spot test.

If ascorbic acid is present, a reddish brown fleck or ring appears (see page 370). Ascorbic acid can be differentiated from amino acids by their different stability toward sodium nitrite. Amino acids or primary amines are destroyed quantitatively by addition of 0.5 % sodium nitrite solution to the neutral or acid test solution, but ascorbic acid is not affected and can be detected by the spot test with ninhydrin. Concentrated solutions of glucose produce a color reaction similar to that given by ascorbic acid.

Procedure. [192] Two drops of ninhydrin solution are placed on filter paper and dried in an oven at 100–105°. Two drops of the test solution are put on the same place of the filter paper, and then the paper is redried for 5–10 minutes at the same temperature. In the presence of amino acids or amines, a blue, violet or reddish fleck or ring is formed. When only very small amounts of amino acids are present, a blank test with two drops of distilled water should be carried out.

Reagents: 1) 0.1 % solution of ninhydrin in citrate buffer.
         2) Citrate buffer, pH = 5. Dissolve 21.01 g of citric acid in 200 ml of N sodium hydroxide and dilute with water to one liter.

If highest sensibility of the test is not required, a solution of 0.1 % ninhydrin in water can be used instead of the solution in the citrate buffer.

The *limits of identification* attained for different α-amino acids and primary aliphatic amines are:

0.4 γ Glycine $H_2N—CH_2—COOH$

0.8 γ D-Alanine $CH_3—CH(NH_2)—COOH$

0.5 γ Serine $HOCH_2—CH(NH_2)—COOH$

0.6 γ Leucine $(CH_3)_2CH—CH_2—CH(NH_2)—COOH$

0.6 γ Isoleucine $C_2H_5—CH(CH_3)—CH(NH_2)—COOH$

1.0 γ Arginine $H_2N—\underset{\underset{NH}{\|}}{C}—NH—(CH_2)_3—CH(NH_2)—COOH$

1.2 γ Cystine $HOOC—CH(NH_2)—CH_2—S—S—CH_2—CH(NH_2)—COOH$

0.9 γ Tyrosine

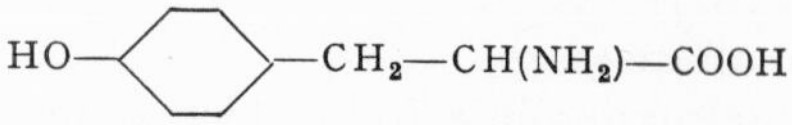

1.0 γ Tryptophan

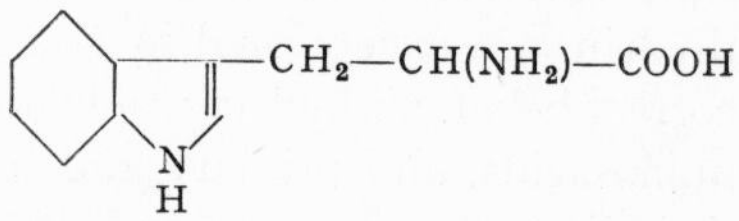

2.0 γ Histidine

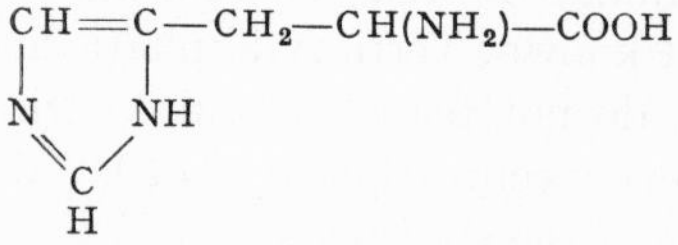

0.7 γ Valine $(CH_3)_2CH—CH(NH_2)—COOH$

10.0 γ Hydroxyproline

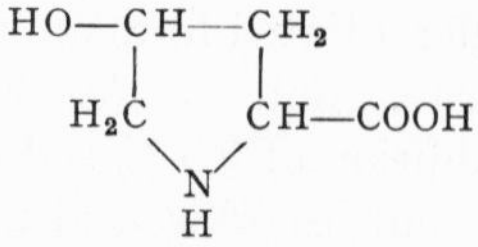

0.9 γ β-Alanine $H_2N—CH_2—CH_2—COOH$

0.4 γ Methylamine $CH_3—NH_2$

1.0 γ n-Butylamine $CH_3—CH_2—CH_2—CH_2—NH_2$

1.0 γ isoButylamine

0.5 γ Ethanolamine $HO—CH_2—CH_2—NH_2$

References pp. 314–319

37. Amino (Carboxylic, Sulfo, Imido) Acids

Test by reaction with fused potassium thiocyanate [193]

On page 269 a test was described for the detection of aliphatic and aromatic amines by means of fusions with potassium thiocyanate, whereby easily detectable hydrogen sulfide is formed. The test can only be carried out, however, if salts of the respective amines are present. These salts, which are substituted salts of ammonia, initially form ammonium salts of sulfocyanic acid and, when heated, yield substituted thioureas. The latter, in the iso-thiourea form, are decomposed into hydrogen sulfide and substituted cyan-amides. According to this scheme, free bases cannot enter the reaction. In contrast to the behavior of free bases, all aminocarboxylic acids (aliphatic and aromatic) as well as aromatic aminosulfo acids, react directly, *i.e.* without salification of the amino group, with potassium thiocyanate and evo-lution of hydrogen sulfide. The same behavior is shown by compounds in which an acidic hydrogen (NH-, OH-, COOH-, AsO_3H_2-group) is present and also in another position a basic nitrogen atom, so that the compounds may be regarded as amino acids, using the term in the widest sense.

The following explanation of the mechanism which leads to the production of hydrogen sulfide seems probable: In the fused mixture, the amino acids liberate thiocyanic acid, which in turn adds to the free amino group. This signifies that amino acids react as substituted ammonium salts and that substituted ammonium thiocyanates are formed which isomerize to substi-tuted thioureas and isothioureas, respectively. The following equations are constructed on this assumption; they refer to aminoacetic acid (glycine), o-aminobenzoic acid (anthranilic acid), and p-aminobenzenesulfonic acid (sulfanilic acid):

$$
\begin{array}{l}
CH_2COOH \\
\mid \qquad\qquad + KCNS \rightarrow \\
NH_2
\end{array}
\quad
\begin{array}{l}
CH_2COOK \\
\mid \qquad\qquad \rightarrow \\
NH_2 \cdot HCNS
\end{array}
\quad
\begin{array}{l}
\quad NHCH_2COOK \\
\mid \\
SC \qquad\qquad \rightarrow \\
\mid \\
NH_2
\end{array}
$$

$$
\rightarrow
\begin{array}{l}
NHCH_2COOK \\
\mid \\
C-SH \\
\parallel \\
NH
\end{array}
\quad \rightarrow
\begin{array}{l}
CH_2COOK \\
\mid \\
NHCN
\end{array}
\quad + H_2S
$$

$$\text{C}_6\text{H}_4(\text{COOH})\text{NH}_2 + \text{KCNS} \longrightarrow \text{C}_6\text{H}_4(\text{COOK})\text{NH}_2 \cdot \text{HCNS} \longrightarrow \overset{\displaystyle \text{NHC}_6\text{H}_4\text{COOK}}{\underset{\displaystyle \text{NH}_2}{\text{S}\overset{|}{\underset{|}{\text{C}}}}} \longrightarrow$$

$$\longrightarrow \overset{\displaystyle \text{NHC}_6\text{H}_4\text{COOK}}{\underset{\displaystyle \text{NH}}{\overset{|}{\text{C}}\underset{\|}{\text{—SH}}}} \qquad \longrightarrow \qquad \overset{\displaystyle \text{C}_6\text{H}_4\text{COOK}}{\underset{\displaystyle \text{NHCN}}{|}} + \text{H}_2\text{S}$$

$$\text{C}_6\text{H}_4(\text{SO}_3\text{H})\text{NH}_2 + \text{KCNS} \longrightarrow \text{C}_6\text{H}_4(\text{SO}_3\text{K})\text{NH}_2 \cdot \text{HCNS} \longrightarrow \overset{\displaystyle \text{NHC}_6\text{H}_4\text{SO}_3\text{K}}{\underset{\displaystyle \text{NH}_2}{\text{S}\overset{|}{\underset{|}{\text{C}}}}} \longrightarrow$$

$$\longrightarrow \overset{\displaystyle \text{NHC}_6\text{H}_4\text{SO}_3\text{K}}{\underset{\displaystyle \text{NH}}{\overset{|}{\text{C}}\underset{\|}{\text{—SH}}}} \qquad \longrightarrow \qquad \overset{\displaystyle \text{C}_6\text{H}_4\text{SO}_3\text{K}}{\underset{\displaystyle \text{NHCN}}{|}} + \text{H}_2\text{S}$$

The formation of derivatives of cyanamide as shown in the preceding equations has not yet been demonstrated experimentally, i.e., by the isolation of the respective compounds. It can be that guanidine derivatives may also be formed and there may be an interchange of COOH- and CN-groups in the amino acids.* In any event, there is no doubt that the reactions which lead to hydrogen sulfide do not occur in the wet way, but only in fusions where the activity of the reaction partners is greatly enhanced.

The following test for amino acids is selective and can be carried out in the presence of free amines. Salts of amines and ammonium salts, as well as solid carboxylic acids (see above) must be absent. The test is not applicable in the presence of organic compounds which split off water at the temperature of the fusion, since superheated water reacts with potassium thiocyanate with evolution of hydrogen sulfide. Consequently, the potassium thiocyanate used in the test must be pulverized and then thoroughly dried at 110°.

Procedure. A micro test tube is used. One drop of the test solution is evaporated to dryness and held for a short time at 110°. An excess of well dried potassium thiocyanate is added and the mixture heated in an oil bath to about 200–250°. A filter paper moistened with a 10% solution of lead acetate is placed at the open end of the test tube. In the presence of amino acids a black coloration can be observed on the paper. If alkaline solutions of amino acids are to be tested (in case of previous extraction of the bases with ether or chloroform) a drop of the solution is evaporated together with one drop of 1 : 1 hydrochloric acid, and the dried (110°) residue treated as described.

---

* The reaction $\text{RCOOH} + \text{HCNS} \rightarrow \text{RCN} + \text{CO}_2 + \text{H}_2\text{S}$, which occurs at temperatures above 190°, was proven by Lett [194] for several aliphatic and aromatic monocarboxylic acids.

The following were detected:

15 γ glycine (aminoacetic acid)
50 γ acetylglycine (aceturic acid)
25 γ anthranilic acid
50 γ sulfanilic acid

Furthermore, the following amino acids give a positive response (no limits of identification have so far been determined): phenylalanine (α-amino-β-phenylpropionic acid); tyrosine (β-(p-hydroxyphenyl)alanine); aspartic acid (aminosuccinic acid); methionine (2-amino-4-methylthiobutanoic acid); leucine (α-aminoisocaproic acid); tyramine (4-hydroxyphenethylamine), p-aminosalicylic acid, 1-amino-2-naphthol-4-sulfonic acid, and methyl red (p-dimethylaminoazobenzene-o-carboxylic acid), H-acid (1-amino-8-naphthol-3,6-disulfonic acid).

In accordance with their acidic nature, prontosil album (p-aminobenzenesulfonamide), sulfadiazine (2-sulfanilamidopyrimidine) and other "sulfa drugs" give a positive response. Barbituric acid and its derivatives, with the exception of 5-nitrobarbituric acid, also respond positively. Consequently, they behave as amino acids.

The behavior of alkali salts of ethylenediaminetetraacetic acid is interesting (see page 362). Whereas the acidic disodium salt yields hydrogen sulfide immediately with molten potassium thiocyanate, the tetra sodium salt is unreactive. Accordingly, these alkali salts can readily be distinguished through their divergent behavior toward this reagent.

38. Pyridine α-Carboxylic Acid and Derivatives $\left(\begin{array}{c} \end{array} \right)$—COO-group)

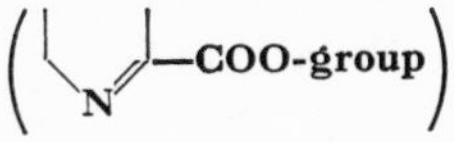

Detection through formation of colored iron (II) salts [195]

Of the three isomeric pyridine monocarboxylic acids, only the α-compound (picolinic acid, I) reacts in water or alcohol solution with ferrous sulfate to give a light yellow color, which is stable to acetic acid or dilute mineral acids.[196] The color reaction may be due to the production of the inner complex ferrous salt (II):

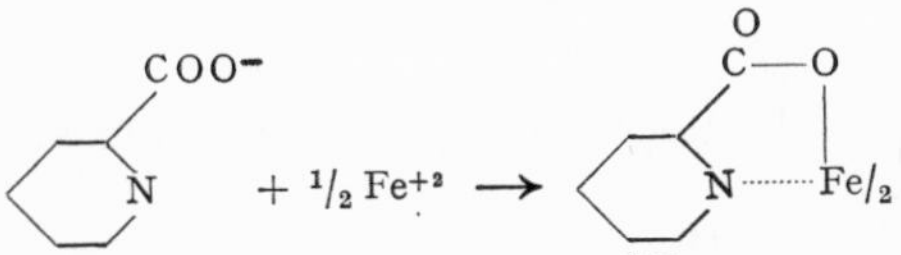

This assumption is supported by the color reaction with ferrous sulfate given by numerous derivatives of picolinic acid.[197] It is noteworthy that a deepening of the color of the complex salt follows the introduction of carboxyl groups into the molecule of the picolinic acid. Quinolinic acid (pyridine 2,3-dicarboxylic acid) gives an orange iron salt; pyridine tricarboxylic and tetra-

288 FUNCTIONAL GROUPS 4

carboxylic acids, with one COOH-group adjacent to the cyclic nitrogen atom, form red to violet ferrous salts. Similarly, the iron salt of pyridine pentacarboxylic acid is dark red. Accordingly, pyridine-α-carboxylic acid and derivatives can be detected by means of the color reaction with ferrous sulfate. In this connection it should be noted that compounds having a phenolic nature must not be present, since they give a red or violet color with the ferric ions that are practically always present in ferrous salts.

Procedure. A micro test tube is used. One drop of the test solution is treated with 1% acetic acid solution of ferrous sulfate. If the reaction is positive, a yellow-orange to red color appears. A comparison blank is advisable when dealing with slight amounts of the sample.

The test revealed:

5 γ picolinic acid; 10 γ quinolinic acid; 7 γ 6-carbinol-picolinic acid.

The following acids also give color reactions with ferrous sulfate:

Yellow-orange: 2-pyridine carboxylic acid, 4-methylpyridine carboxylic acid-(2), 4,6-dimethylpyridine carboxylic acid-(2), quinolinic carboxylic acid-(2), 4-methylquinolinic carboxylic acid-(2), pyridine dicarboxylic acid-(2,3), quinolinic acid-3-methyl ester, pyridine dicarboxylic acid-(2,4), pyridine dicarboxylic acid-(2,5), pyridine dicarboxylic acid-(2,6), pyridine carboxylic acid-(2)acetic acid-(5), 4-methylpyridine dicarboxylic acid-(2,3), 6-methylpyridine dicarboxylic acid-(2,4), 4-methylpyridine dicarboxylic acid-(2,3), 6-methylpyridine dicarboxylic acid-(2,4), 4-methyl-5-ethylpyridine dicarboxylic acid-(2,3), quinoline dicarboxylic acid (2,3).

Red-violet: 6-phenylpyridine carboxylic acid-(2), pyridine tricarboxylic acid (2,3,5) (2,3,6) (2,4,5) (2,4,6), 4-methylpyridinetricarboxylic acid-(2,3,5), 6-methylpyridine tricarboxylic acid-(2,3,4), pyridine tetracarboxylic acid-(2,3,5,6) (2,3,4,6), 4-methylpyridine tetracarboxylic acid-(2,3,5,6), pyridine pentacarboxylic acid

39. Acid Amides and Imides (-CONH₂, -CONHCO-, and -CONHR-groups)

Detection through acid saponification [198]

Most acid amides and imides are saponifiable by acids:

$$RCONH_2 + H_2O + H^+ \rightarrow RCOOH + NH_4^+ \qquad (1)$$

$$RCONHCOR + 2 H_2O + H^+ \rightarrow 2 RCOOH + NH_4^+ \qquad (2)$$

$$RCONHR_1 + H_2O + H^+ \rightarrow RCOOH + NH_3R_1^+ \qquad (3)$$

These hydrolyses proceed so far when even slight amounts of the test material are taken to dryness only once with concentrated hydrochloric acid that ammonium chloride and nonvolatile carboxylic acids can be detected in the evaporation residue. This constitutes the basis of selective tests, and even of a differentiation of the organic starting materials.

Nessler reagent is used to detect the ammonium chloride in the residue from the hydrochloric acid evaporation. This procedure is reliable in the case of water-insoluble amides and imides, since if need be any ammonium salts are easily removed by digestion with water. If the presence of water-soluble amides (urea, guanidine and its derivatives with free NH_2-groups, saccharin, etc.) needs to be considered, a separate sample should be tested directly with Nessler reagent. In this connection it should be noted that many amides of aliphatic carboxylic acids are saponified by caustic alkali and consequently show a reaction with Nessler reagent. If the Nessler test is positive when applied to the original sample, it is advisable to test the residue from the hydrochloric acid evaporation for carboxylic acid. This is readily done by means of potassium iodide and iodate (see page 116). The reaction with uranyl acetate and rhodamine B is recommended for benzene-soluble carboxylic acids (see page 120). Both of these tests can of course be applied only in the absence or previous removal of organic carboxylic and sulfonic acids or their salts.

Certain amides of aromatic acids are not saponifiable by evaporation with concentrated hydrochloric acid. An instance is the amide of triphenylacetic acid and likewise benzamide substituted in the 2,6-position. Such amides (and of course all other amides with $CONH_2$-groups) can be converted into the respective carboxylic acids by means of nitrous acid ($KNO_2 + HCl$): [199]

$$RCONH_2 + HNO_2 \rightarrow RCOOH + H_2O + N_2$$

Procedure. The test is conducted in a micro test tube. A little of the solid or one or two drops of the solution is taken to dryness along with a drop or two of concentrated hydrochloric acid. The excess acid is driven off by heating to 120°. To detect any resulting ammonium chloride, a drop of 1 N caustic alkali is added to the residue and the mouth of the tube is covered with a piece of filter paper moistened with Nessler reagent. Qualitative filter paper must be used because almost all quantitative papers contain ammonium salts which react with Nessler reagent. The development of a brown or yellow stain on gentle warming shows that hydrolyses (1) or (2) have taken place.

To detect acids in the evaporation residue, one drop each of 2% potassium iodide and 5% potassium iodate are added along with a little soluble starch or thyodene solution. A blue color indicates the presence of acids. The production of benzene-soluble carboxylic acids is revealed by means of a drop of 1% uranyl acetate solution and 4 drops of a saturated solution of rhodamine B in benzene. A red color in the benzene layer is obtained on shaking.

An evaporation with hydrochloric acid is not necessary when testing for benzene-soluble carboxylic acids produced by saponifying the amides with nitrous acid. In this case it is sufficient to add several centigrams of potassium nitrite and 1–3 drops of concentrated hydrochloric acid to the sample. The mixture is warmed after about 10 minutes and then shaken with several drops of benzene. The benzene solution is taken for the test for carboxylic acid.

The *Nessler reaction* revealed:

2	γ	benzamide	10	γ	glycolic acid amide
10	γ	benzilic acid amide	10	γ	saccharin
40	γ	Gallamine blue	25	γ	urea
5	γ	phthalimide	5	γ	salicylamide
0.5	γ	succinimide	5	γ	guanidine

The *iodide–iodate reaction* revealed:

2 γ benzamide, 2 γ benzilic acid amide

The color reaction with *rhodamine B* revealed:

10 γ benzamide, 1 γ benzilic acid amide

40. Anilides (—CONHC$_6$H$_5$-group)

Detection by splitting off aniline [200]

Anilides are N-phenylated amides of carboxylic acids or, what is the same thing, acyl derivatives of aniline. All anilides can be saponified by evaporation along with concentrated hydrochloric acid and thus yield aniline hydrochloride and the corresponding nonvolatile carboxylic acid. The saponification is rapid if the anilide is heated along with calcium hydroxide:

$$2 \text{ RCONHC}_6\text{H}_5 + \text{Ca(OH)}_2 \rightarrow (\text{RCOO})_2\text{Ca} + 2 \text{ C}_6\text{H}_5\text{NH}_2$$

The aniline volatilizes and can be detected in the vapor phase by means of the red color it gives with an acetic acid solution of furfural. (The chemistry of this color reaction is discussed on page 428.)

The test described here is specific for the —CONHC$_6$H$_5$-group, provided aniline and phenylhydrazine salts as well as derivatives of phenylhydrazine (comp. page 296) are absent. Acyl derivatives of α- and β-naphthylamine do not react. It is remarkable that the color reaction is also obtained with anilides, which contain a halogen atom, a CH$_3$-, NO$_2$-, or OH-group in the benzene ring.

Procedure. A drop of the alcohol solution of the sample is placed in a micro test tube along with several centigrams of calcium oxide. After the alcohol is driven off, the mouth of the tube is covered with a piece of filter paper, which has been moistened with a drop of freshly prepared mixture of 10 drops of furfural in 10 ml of glacial acetic acid. The reaction mixture is heated over a micro burner until charring begins. If anilides were present, a red stain appears on the reagent paper.

References pp. 314–319

A positive response was given by:

5 γ formanilide	50 γ p-nitroacetanilide
5 γ acetanilide	4 γ monophenylurea
5 γ benzanilide	2 γ carbanilide
3 γ salicylanilide	5 γ m-tolylurea
20 γ p-bromoacetanilide	7 γ phenylurethane
40 γ acetaminophenol	2 γ diphenylguanidine

41. Guanidine and its Derivatives $\left(HN{=}C \begin{smallmatrix} {-}NH_2 \\ \\ {\diagdown}NH \\ | \end{smallmatrix} \text{-group} \right)$

Detection by loss of ammonia [201]

Dry heating of guanidine results in diguanidine and ammonia:

$$2\ HN{=}C\begin{smallmatrix} \diagup NH_2 \\ \diagdown NH_2 \end{smallmatrix} \longrightarrow \underset{\underset{NH_2}{|}}{HN{=}C}{-}NH{-}\underset{\underset{NH_2}{|}}{C}{=}NH + NH_3 \qquad (1)$$

An analogous pyrolytic splitting out of ammonia also occurs when salts of guanidine or of its derivatives containing the group shown above are heated to about 250°. When diguanidine or cyclic derivatives of guanidine are heated no ammonia is split off. In analogy to *(1)*, the loss of ammonia by salts of guanidine with free NH_2-groups may involve the condensation:

$$2\ HN{=}C\begin{smallmatrix} \diagup \overset{+}{N}H_3 \\ \diagdown NH_2 \end{smallmatrix} \longrightarrow \underset{\underset{NH_2}{|}}{H_2\overset{+}{N}{=}C}{-}NH{-}\underset{\underset{NH_2}{|}}{C}{=}\overset{+}{N}H_2 + NH_3 \qquad (2)$$

The ammonia evolved as per *(2)* may be detected in the vapor phase by means of Nessler reagent.

The splitting off of ammonia from water-soluble hydrochlorides of these compounds is selective. No ammonia is given off when salts of primary, secondary, and tertiary amines are heated to 250°. This is also true of salts of amino acids, with the exception of salts of arginine, which is a derivative of guanidine. Guanidineacetic acid and methylguanidineacetic acid yield no ammonia when heated because they lose water and form the lactams: glyco-cyanidine and creatinine, which as cyclic derivatives of guanidine possess no free NH_2-groups available for condensation.

The test is not applicable in the presence of urea, thiourea, biuret and other urea derivatives with free NH_2-groups, since these compounds likewise yield ammonia when heated to 250°.

Procedure. A little of the solid is placed in a micro test tube. If preferred, a drop of the hydrochloric acid solution may be evaporated there. All of the moisture is removed by heating in a glycerol bath (180°) for about 10 minutes. The mouth of the test tube is covered with a disk of filter paper moistened with a drop of Nessler reagent. The tube is then brought to 250° in the glycerol bath. The evolution of ammonia is revealed by the development of a brown or yellow stain within several minutes.

This procedure revealed:

2 γ guanidine carbonate (chloride)	5 γ arginine chloride
5 γ nitroguanidine chloride	100 γ streptomycin sulfate
1 γ dicyandiamidine	0.3 γ dicyandiamide

A positive response was given by: streptomycin, streptidine, synthaline. It is notable that dry guanidine and some of its derivatives split off dicyanogen when heated.

42. Hydrazines

(a) Aliphatic and Aromatic Hydrazines ($>$N—NH$_2$-group)

(1) Test with sodium pentacyanoammineferroate [202]

Hydrazines containing a free NH$_2$-group react similarly to nitroso compounds (see page 154) and α, β-unsaturated and aromatic aldehydes (see page 219) on treatment with a solution of the light yellow sodium pentacyanoammineferroate Na$_3$[Fe(CN)$_5$NH$_3$]. Deeply colored soluble compounds are formed, probably by the replacement of the NH$_3$ molecule in the prussiate by a molecule of the hydrazine; for instance:

$$Na_3[Fe(CN)_5NH_3] + NH_2NHR \rightarrow NH_3 + Na_3[Fe(CN)_5NH_2NHR]$$

Procedure. Several drops of 1% sodium pentacyanoammineferroate solution are added to one drop of a neutral aqueous or alkaline solution of the test substance in a microcrucible. In a short while, the mixture turns deep red to violet. A few materials turn yellow when the solution is made alkaline with 2 N sodium hydroxide.

The *limits of identification* attained for various hydrazines are stated in Table 31.

(2) Test by formation of colored hydrazones with aldehydic azo dyestuffs [203]

Certain water-soluble azo dyes, formed by coupling diazotized p-aminobenzaldehyde with naphthol or aminonaphthol sulfonic acids,[204] by virtue of their free aldehyde group, can be condensed to hydrazones with acyl- and aryl hydrazines in weak acetic acid solution. The color is thus deepened or changed. For example, the dye (I), produced by coupling diazotized p-aminobenzaldehyde and crocein acid (2-hydroxynaphthalene-8-sulfonic acid), is yellow in aqueous solution. The addition of an acyl- or aryl-hydrazine to this solution produces a characteristic color change due to the formation

TABLE 31. HYDRAZINES

Name	Formula	Limit of identification in γ	Color (neutral)	Color (alkaline)
Phenylhydrazine	$C_6H_5NHNH_2$	0.5	Red	Red
1,1-Methylphenyl-hydrazine	$(C_6H_5)(CH_3)NNH_2$	3	Blood red	Dark blood red
1,1-Diphenyl-hydrazine	$(C_6H_5)_2NNH_2$	7	Violet	Brick-red
o-Nitrophenyl-hydrazine		1	Dark brown-red	Light yellow
m-Nitrophenyl-hydrazine	$C_6N_4(NO_2)NHNH_2$	0.4	Cherry-red	Brown-yellow
p-Nitrophenyl-hydrazine		0.5	Blue-violet	Brown-yellow
8-Hydroxy-naphthyl-hydrazine-3,6-disulfonic acid	$C_{10}H_4(OH)(SO_3H)_2NHNH_2$	3	Dark violet	Light red-yellow
Semicarbazide	$OC(NH_2)NHNH_2$	0.3	Cherry-red	Dark yellow
1,1-Diethyl hydrazine	$(C_2H_5)_2NNH_2$	0.6	Dark cherry	Golden
Benzoyl-hydrazide	$C_6H_5CONHNH_2$	0.12	Deep violet	Straw yellow

of the respective hydrazone. For example, with phenylhydrazine, the product is the violet hydrazone (II):

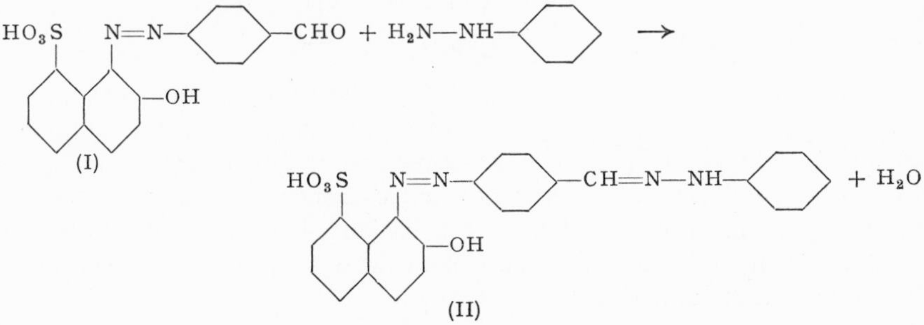

$$HO_3S \quad N{=}N{-}\bigcirc{-}CHO + H_2N{-}NH{-}\bigcirc \rightarrow$$

(I)

$$HO_3S \quad N{=}N{-}\bigcirc{-}CH{=}N{-}NH{-}\bigcirc + H_2O$$

(II)

References pp. 314–319

Procedure. A drop of a solution of the dyestuff in dilute acetic acid is mixed with a drop of 10 % sodium acetate solution and a drop of the aqueous or alcoholic test solution is added. When large amounts of a hydrazine are present, the color change is almost instantaneous; smaller amounts require up to 15 minutes. A blank is advisable.

Preparation of the reagent: p-Aminobenzaldehyde hydrochloride is suspended in dilute hydrochloric acid and diazotized with the calculated amount of sodium nitrite (1 mole $NaNO_2$ to 1 mole amine). The diazonium solution is poured into the equivalent amount of crocein acid dissolved in excess sodium carbonate, and the mixture finally acidified with acetic acid. The solution of the dyestuff will keep.

The various *limits of identification* for different hydrazines attained with this reagent are given in Table 32.

TABLE 32.   HYDRAZINES

Name	Formula	Limit of identification in γ	Color change
Phenylhydrazine	$C_6H_5NHNH_2$	1	Yellow-violet
1,1-Methylphenylhydrazine	$C_6H_5N(CH_3)NH_2$	2	Yellow-brown-red
1,1-Diphenylhydrazine	$(C_6H_5)_2NNH_2$	1	Yellow-red-brown
o-Nitrophenylhydrazine	$C_6H_4(NO_2)NHNH_2$	1	Yellow-brown-red
m-Nitrophenylhydrazine		1	Yellow-violet
Semicarbazide	$OC(NH_2)NHNH_2$	1	Yellow-brown-red
Benzoyl hydrazide	$C_6H_5CONHNH_2$	5	Yellow-orange

(b) Arylhydrazines (Ar—NH—NH$_2$-groups)

(1) Test with selenious acid and α-naphthylamine [205]

Arylhydrazines are oxidized by selenious acid to diazonium salts, which can be coupled with aromatic amines (α-naphthylamine is the most suitable) to form bright red to red-violet azo dyestuffs.[206] Small amounts of arylhydrazines (and also arylhydrazones and osazones) may be detected by applying this reaction. The following equations show the reactions in the test for phenylhydrazine in hydrochloric acid solution; the other arylhydrazines react similarly:

References pp. 314–319

$$\text{\textlangle}\bigcirc\text{\textrangle}-NH-\overset{+}{N}H_3 + SeO_2 \longrightarrow \text{\textlangle}\bigcirc\text{\textrangle}-\overset{+}{N}\equiv N + Se^0 + 2\,H_2O \qquad (1)$$

$$\text{\textlangle}\bigcirc\text{\textrangle}-\overset{+}{N}\equiv N + \text{\textlangle}\bigcirc\text{\textrangle}-NH_2 \longrightarrow \text{\textlangle}\bigcirc\text{\textrangle}-N=N-\text{\textlangle}\bigcirc\text{\textrangle}-\overset{+}{N}H_3 \qquad (2)$$

Procedure. A drop of the test solution is mixed with a drop of dilute hydrochloric acid, either in a microcrucible or on a spot plate, and a small amount of selenious acid is added. When large amounts of arylhydrazine are involved, the mixture is allowed to stand 1 or 2 minutes to permit the red selenium to separate. A drop of an acetic acid solution of α-napthylamine is added and a few crystals of sodium acetate. When primary arylhydrazines are present, red to violet dyes are formed. The color can be intensified by the addition of a drop of hydrochloric acid.

Reagent: α-Naphthylamine solution: 0.3 g α-naphthylamine is dissolved by boiling in 70 ml water and 30 ml glacial acetic acid. After cooling, the solution is filtered from any dark residue. The solution should be kept in the dark.

The *limits of identification* for some of the arylhydrazines are given in Table 33.

(2) Test for arylhydrazones and osazones

The foregoing test for arylhydrazines, by oxidation with selenious acid to the diazonium salt and coupling with α-naphthylamine, can also be applied to the detection of arylhydrazones and osazones. These compounds, saponified by boiling with concentrated hydrochloric acid, split off the arylhydrazine hydrochloride, which is stable against boiling. The test is then carried out as described for free arylhydrazines or their salts with mineral acids.

Procedure. A drop of the test solution or, better, a crystal of the solid, is evaporated nearly to dryness in a microcrucible with a few drops of concentrated hydrochloric acid. A small grain of selenious acid is added. After 1 or 2 minutes, a drop of the α-naphthylamine solution and a few crystals sodium acetate are added. When the color of the dye appears, it may be intensified by adding a few drops of hydrochloric acid. A red to violet azo dye indicates that arylhydrazones or osazones are present.

The *limits of identification* for some hydrazones and osazones are given in Table 33.

A rather characteristic test for phenylhydrazones of aldehydes and ketones

TABLE 33. HYDRAZINES, HYDRAZONES, OSAZONES

Name	Formula	Color	Limit of identification in γ
Phenylhydrazine	C_6H_5—NHNH$_2$	Red-violet	0.04
m- and p-Nitrophenylhydrazine	$C_6H_4(NO_2)$—NHNH$_2$	Red-violet	0.06
p-Bromophenylhydrazine	C_6H_4Br—NHNH$_2$	Violet	0.08
Tribromophenylhydrazine	$C_6H_2Br_3$—NHNH$_2$	Red	1 hot 10 cold
Naphthylhydrazine	$C_{10}H_7$—NHNH$_2$	Violet	0.03
Levulinic acid phenylhydrazone	$HOOC$—$(CH_2)_2$—$C(CH_3)$=$NNHC_6H_5$	Red-violet	0.1
Propionaldehyde phenylhydrazone	CH_3CH_2CH=$NNHC_6H_5$	Red-violet	0.09
Glucuronic acid phenylhydrazone	$HOOC$—$(CHOH)_4$—CH=$NNHC_6H_5$	Red-violet	0.7

Cinnamoylformic acid phenylhydrazone	C_6H_5—CH=CH—C=$NNHC_6H_5$
	             $\vert$
	             COOH
		Red-violet	2

α-Pyridylbenzoylphenylhydrazone	C_5H_4N—$C(C_6H_5)$=$NNHC_6H_5$	Red-violet	0.1
Glucosazone	OH HC=$NNHC_6H_5$ $\vert$ $\vert$ H_2C—$(CHOH)_4$—C=$NNHC_6H_5$	Red-violet	0.1
Dihydroxytartaric acid osazone	$HOOC$—C=$NNHC_6H_5$ $\vert$ $HOOC$—C=$NNHC_6H_5$	Red-violet	0.7

is provided by the splitting out of aniline by pyrolytic decomposition.* The aniline released can be detected readily by bringing the vapor into contact with filter paper, which has been moistened with an acetic acid solution of furfural. A red color ensues if aniline is present. (See furfural test, p. 428.)

* There probably occurs a hydrolysis due to thermally split-off water, whereby phenylhydrazine is formed, which according to

$$2C_6H_5NHNH_2 \rightarrow C_6H_5NH_2 + C_6H_6 + N_2 + NH_3$$

undergoes auto-reduction at high temperature.[206a]

43. Hydrazides of Carboxylic Acids (—CO—NH—NH₂-group)

(1) Test by hydrolytic cleavage and formation of salicylaldazine [207]

When the hydrazides of carboxylic acids are digested with warm concentrated hydrochloric acid, they are split with production of anions of the particular carboxylic acids and hydrazinium ions. However, the reaction is slow. In contrast, the cleavage is rapid and practically complete if these materials are warmed with dilute alkali hydroxide:

$$R—CO—NH—NH_2 + H_2O \rightarrow RCOO^- + NH_2—\overset{+}{N}H_3 \qquad (1)$$

In weak acid aqueous solution, hydrazine (or hydrazinium ion) condenses rapidly and quantitatively with salicylaldehyde to produce light yellow, insoluble salicylaldazine (compare page 220):

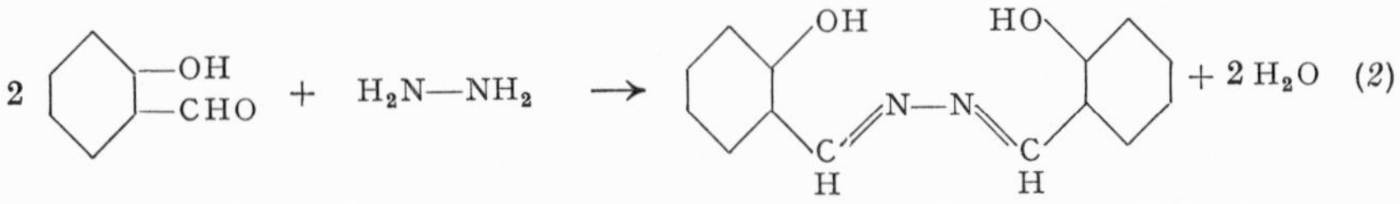

Solid salicylaldazine (disalicylhydrazine) fluoresces orange-yellow in ultraviolet light. Other *o*-hydroxyaldehydes also react with hydrazine to produce aldazines which, for the most part, fluoresce orange-yellow. Tests for salicylaldehyde (page 374) and *o*-hydroxy aldehydes (page 220) are based on the formation of fluorescing aldazines, and analogously, a specific and very sensitive test for hydrazine has been developed.[208]

The formation of salicylaldazine according to (1) and (2) is best achieved by warming the acid hydrazide with an alkaline solution of salicylaldehyde and then acidifying with acetic acid. In this way, it is possible to detect acid hydrazides which have a free terminal NH₂-group. The test is reliable provided the sample is free of hydrazine itself or of hydrazones of ketones and aldehydes which yield hydrazine or hydrazinium ions on warming with alkali hydroxide.

Procedure. A drop of the test solution or a little of the solid is mixed in a micro test tube with a drop of saturated aqueous salicylaldehyde solution and a drop of 1 N alkali hydroxide. The mixture is warmed in the water bath for 5–20 minutes, cooled, and then treated with a drop of 3 N acetic acid. The solution is poured on filter paper (S & S 589) and after 1–2 minutes the paper is examined under ultraviolet light. An orange-yellow to yellow-green fluorescence indicates the presence of an acid hydrazide. The fluorescent fleck persists when the paper is bathed in 6 N acetic acid. When small amounts of hydrazide are suspected, it is advisable to run a blank test.

The following were detected:

2.5 γ semicarbazide
1   γ benzoic acid hydrazide
1   γ p-nitrobenzoic acid hydrazide
5   γ salicylic acid hydrazide
0.5 γ o-pyridine carboxylic acid hydrazide (picolinic acid hydrazide)
0.5 γ m-pyridine carboxylic acid hydrazide (nicotinic acid hydrazide)
0.15 γ p-pyridine carboxylic acid hydrazide (isonicotinic acid hydrazide)
0.15 γ oxalyldihydrazide

(2) *Test through direct condensation with salicylaldehyde* [209]

Like hydrazine and its derivatives with a free NH_2-group, the hydrazides of carboxylic acids, since they possess the group —CO—NH—NH_2, can condense with aldehydes and ketones with loss of water. For example, with salicylaldehyde the general reaction is:

$$R—CO—NH—NH_2 + OC\underset{H}{\overset{OH}{\diagup}}\!\!\!\!\bigcirc \longrightarrow R—CO—NH—N\!\!=\!\!C\underset{H}{\overset{OH}{\diagup}}\!\!\!\!\bigcirc + H_2O \quad (1)$$

The resulting hydrazones, which structurally are similar to the orange-yellow fluorescing water-insoluble salicylaldazine (compare Test 1), likewise are not soluble in water and they fluoresce strongly (yellow-green to blue-green) in ultraviolet light. Because of the phenolic OH-group, the condensation products of (1) dissolve in ammonia, as do salicylaldehyde and salicylaldazine, and give yellow solutions. The behavior of the condensation products toward dilute acids (in which salicylaldazine is not soluble) seems to depend on the nature of the radical R. Some hydrazones dissolve in dilute acids to only a slight extent or not at all (e.g. the product formed by salicylhydrazide); others are dissolved by acids without decomposition (e.g. the products formed by the three isomeric pyridine carboxylic acid hydrazides), whereas, some are decomposed by acids (e.g. the condensation product of benzoic hydrazide with salicylaldehyde). The realization of (1) and the action of acids on the hydrazones formed in this reaction provide, of course, the possibility of a splitting-off of hydrazine, which condenses with salicylaldehyde to produce the acid-stable salicylaldazine, which fluoresces orange-yellow.

A neutral or weakly ammoniacal milieu is required to make the direct condensation with salicylaldehyde into a general test for acid hydrazides. Since, however, ammoniacal solutions of salicylaldehyde have a yellow-green fluorescence, it is impossible to detect directly the production of small quantities of ammonia-soluble condensation products which exhibit blue-green or yellow-green fluorescence. This impairment of the test is eliminated if a drop of the mixture of acid hydrazide and salicylaldehyde is treated with a little ammonia and then brought on filter paper. Under these conditions, the fluorescence due to the ammoniacal salicylaldehyde disappears within a few minutes, while the fluorescence of the condensation product of salicylaldehyde with the acid hydrazide persists. The intensity of this latter fluorescence gradually decreases and it completely disappears when small quantities are involved, but it is immediately restored if the fleck is held over ammonia. This is an instance of an effect sometimes encountered in spot testing, namely that a spot reaction on paper is particularly sensitive and reliable and hence the paper thus functions as if it were as an active participant in the reaction. In the present case, the course of events is, that ammoniacal solutions of salicylaldehyde are brought on paper, through loss of ammonia and hydrolytic cleavage of the ammonium phenolate they leave salicylaldehyde behind, which then either volatilizes from the surface of the paper or, because of the high state of division, is oxidized rapidly by the air to salicylic acid. This reasoning is supported by the fact that if a drop of a saturated aqueous solution of salicylaldehyde is placed on filter paper and treated with ammonia it immediately yields a yellow-green fluorescent fleck, which disappears rapidly. If 3–4 minutes elapse before the ammonia is brought into play, no fluorescence develops.

Procedure. One drop of the acid or neutral test solution is mixed with a drop of an acid aqueous solution of salicylaldehyde and transferred to a filter paper. After 3–5 minutes, the paper is held over ammonia water and the fleck is examined at once under ultraviolet light. A fleck which fluoresces blue-green or yellow-green indicates the presence of an acid hydrazide. The fluorescence disappears after several minutes, but it can be regenerated by a new exposure to ammonia. It is well to conduct a blank test in all cases.

Reagent: 9 ml of saturated aqueous solution of salicylaldehyde is acidified just before using with 1 ml glacial acetic acid.

The procedure gave a positive response with:

1   γ semicarbazide
1   γ benzoic acid hydrazide
0.5 γ salicylic acid hydrazide
2   γ o-pyridine carboxylic acid hydrazide (picolinic acid hydrazide)
1   γ m-pyridine carboxylic acid hydrazide (nicotinic acid hydrazide)
2   γ p-pyridine carboxylic acid hydrazide (isonicotinic acid hydrazide)
0.5 γ oxalyldihydrazide

The cyclic 3-aminonaphthalic acid hydrazide shows no reaction. p-Nitrobenzoic acid hydrazide gives no response; this is probably due to a quenching effect of the NO_2-group.

(3) Test with p-dimethylaminobenzaldehyde

When the hydrazide of a carboxylic acid is saponified with alkali hydroxide (compare Test 1), and the reaction mixture then acidified with acetic acid, the resulting hydrazine can be detected by adding an excess of p-dimethylaminobenzaldehyde. An orange to yellow color appears, according to the quantity of hydrazine present.[210] The same reaction also occurs if a neutral or weakly acid solution of the hydrazide is warmed directly with an acid solution of the aldehyde. Obviously, the hydrazide is partially saponified by acids, and the hydrazine is constantly removed from the rapidly established hydrolysis equilibrium by reaction with the aldehyde. The color reaction involves a condensation of aldehyde and hydrazine analogous to that in Test 1, but differs from the latter in that the aldazine (II) formed in (1) dissolves at once in acids with production of the quinoidal cation (III) as shown in (2):

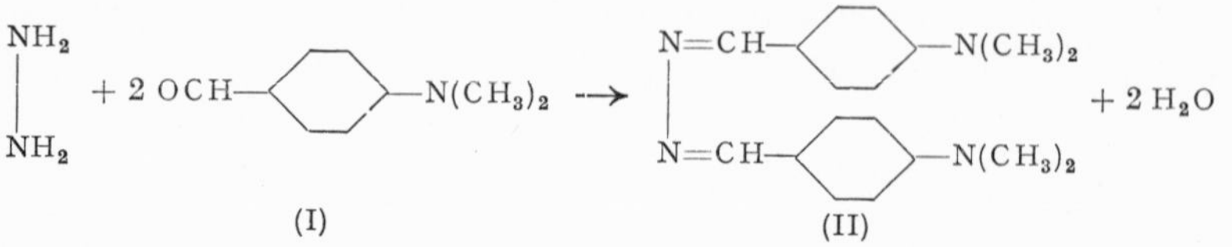

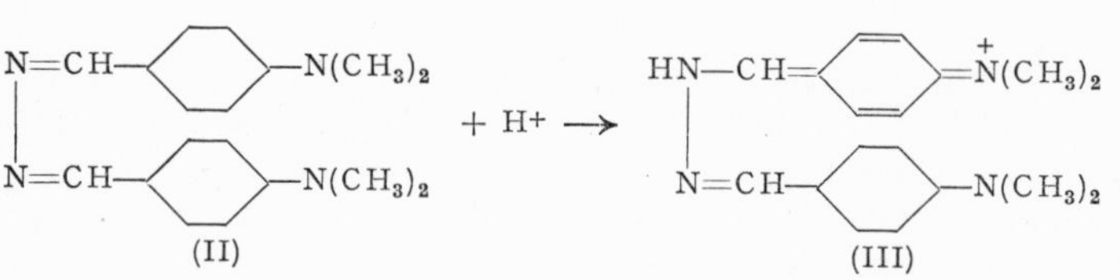

The formation of (III) can be detected with high sensitivity if a drop of the orange to yellow solution, which displays no fluorescence, is placed on filter paper. A red to pink fleck remains and it fluoresces with an intense red to salmon hue in ultraviolet light.[211] This effect, which can be observed in very dilute almost colorless solutions, probably involves the formation of a fluorescing adsorbate of (III) with the faintly acidic constituents of the paper whereby, in accord with the constitution of (III), consideration must be given to both an exchange- as well as an addition adsorption.[212] The red to salmon fluorescing fleck on the filter paper takes on a blue-green hue when treated with ammonia; the red fluorescence is restored by action of acids. These changes of the fluorescence color, which can be repeated at will, patently arise from a transition of adsorbed (III) into adsorbed aldazine (II) and vice versa.

Aromatic amines condense with p-dimethylaminobenzaldehyde to form

Schiff bases, which are yellow to orange in acid solution. Highly concentrated solutions of Schiff bases leave green fluorescent flecks on filter paper. These flecks disappear when bathed in ammoniacal alcohol and do not return on acidification. Since the blue-green fluorescing flecks of the Schiff base (II) remain on filter paper and the red fluorescence returns when spotted with acid, it is possible to detect acid hydrazides even in the presence of salts of aromatic amines.

It should be noted that the following test requires an excess of p-dimethylaminobenzaldehyde. The quantity of reagent prescribed provides sufficient excess for testing solutions containing not more than 1 per cent hydrazide. If greater concentrations are at hand, the aldehyde then condenses with the unsaponified acid hydrazide at its free NH_2-group analogous to the action in Test 2. This condensation yields a yellow fluorescing product.

Procedure.[211] A drop of the test solution is treated in a micro test tube with a drop of the acid solution of the aldehyde and the mixture is warmed in the water bath for 5–10 minutes. A drop of water is added to the cold solution and a drop of the latter is then placed on filter paper. The paper is bathed in 1 : 250 hydrochloric acid and viewed in ultraviolet light. A red to salmon fluorescence indicates the presence of an acid hydrazide. When bathed in 1 : 10 ammonia, the fleck turns blue-green. A blank test is advisable when very small quantities of hydrazide are involved.

Reagent: p-Dimethylaminobenzaldehyde solution: 0.4 g of the aldehyde is dissolved in 20 ml alcohol and the solution acidified by adding 2 ml concentrated hydrochloric acid.

The foregoing procedure revealed:

0.5 γ semicarbazide
0.05 γ benzoic acid hydrazide
0.1 γ p-nitrobenzoic acid hydrazide
0.25 γ o-pyridine carboxylic acid hydrazide (picolinic acid hydrazide)
0.1 γ m-pyridine carboxylic acid hydrazide (nicotinic acid hydrazide)
0.05 γ p-pyridine carboxylic acid hydrazide (isonicotinic acid hydrazide)

The cyclic 3-aminophthalic acid hydrazide ("luminol") shows no reaction.

44. Reactive $>CH_2$ and —NH₂ Groups

Test with sodium 1,2-naphthaquinone-4-sulfonate [213]

The yellow alkaline solution of the orthoquinoidal 1,2-naphthaquinone-4-sulfonic acid reacts with compounds which contain two removable hydrogen atoms attached to one carbon atom or nitrogen atom. Deeply colored paraquinoid imide condensation products result. In the case of primary aromatic amines, the reaction can be represented:

The colored products belong to the indophenol dyes. Sulfonamides behave like primary aromatic amines.[214] In alkaline solution, 1,2-naphthaquinone-4-sulfonic acid also reacts with α-aminocarboxylic acids,[215] and likewise with guanidine [216] to yield red p-quinoidal compounds.

Paraquinoid compounds of the general structure

are produced in the case of an active $H_2C\big\langle$ group.

The test may only be applied for orientation purposes, since the reactivity of the CH_2 and NH_2 groups is influenced by the other groups in the molecule. For example, in contrast to aniline, aniline derivatives with strongly negative groups, e.g., trinitroaniline and tribromoaniline, will not condense in this way. Negative groups in the ortho and para position particularly cause much interference with the reaction; negative groups in the meta position are less harmful.

Procedure. [217] A little of the solid or a drop of its solution is placed in a microcrucible along with two drops of the naphthaquinone sulfonate solution, and the mixture is made alkaline with two drops of 0.5 N sodium hydroxide. The color changes on acidifying with 2 N acetic acid; sometimes a precipitate appears.

Reagent: Saturated solution of sodium 1,2-naphthaquinone-4-sulfonate in 50% alcohol.

The *limits of identification* attained with various compounds are given in Table 34.

TABLE 34. REACTIVE CH$_2$ AND NH$_2$ GROUPS

Name	Formula	Limit of identification, γ	Color		Remarks
			In alkaline solution	In acetic acid solution	
Malonic ester	CH$_2$(COOC$_2$H$_5$)$_2$	1.2	Dark violet	Yellow precipitate	
Rhodanine	HN——CO | | SC CH$_2$ \ / S	0.6	Dark blue-violet	Red-yellow precipitate	
Ethyl acetoacetate	CH$_3$COCH$_2$COOC$_2$H$_5$	1.2	Blood red-violet	Yellow precipitate	Reaction very slow; enolic form
Thiocyanoacetic acid	(CNS)CH$_2$COOH	0.6	Red-brown	Orange	
Dibenzoylmethane	C$_6$H$_5$COCH$_2$COC$_6$H$_5$	12	Red-violet	White-yellow precipitate	Allow to stand some time
m-Nitroaniline	C$_6$H$_4$(NO$_2$)NH$_2$	6	Yellow-brown	Red precipitate	Allow to stand
Benzylamine	C$_6$H$_5$CH$_2$NH$_2$	0.6	Green	Brownish red	
Semicarbazide	OC(NH$_2$)NHNH$_2$	0.6	Orange-red	Light yellow	
Aniline	C$_6$H$_5$NH$_2$	0.12	Brick red	Bright orange-red	
β-Naphthoquinoline iodomethylate	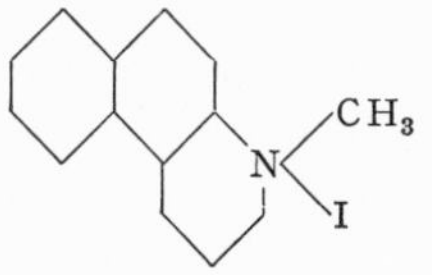 [structure with CH$_3$ and I on N]	1.2	Dark violet	Yellow-brown precipitate	

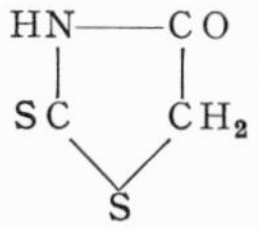

References pp. 314–319

(continued)

TABLE 34. REACTIVE CH_2 AND NH_2 GROUPS (CONTINUED)

Name	Formula	Limit of identification, γ	Color In alkaline solution	Color In acetic acid solution	Remarks
β-Naphthylamine	$C_{10}H_7NH_2$	0.6	Yellow-red to red-brown	Red precipitate	
Indole		0.6	Emerald green	Violet at first, then colorless to gray	
Piperidine		0.6	Scarlet	Light red precipitate	Reaction without addition of alkali
Pyrrole		0.6	Deep violet	Dark olive green	Very intense color

45. Tertiary Ring Bases

(1) Test with methyl iodide and sodium 1,2-naphthaquinone-4-sulfonate [217]

As stated on page 301, compounds which contain two removable hydrogen atoms bound to one nitrogen atom react with naphthaquinone sulfonic acid in alkaline solution to form water-soluble colored quinoid compounds. The methyl or ethyl groups, which when in CH_3I or C_2H_5I do not react with this reagent, may be activated by attaching the alkyl halide to a tertiary ring base or to an oxonium compound. The resulting quaternary compound reacts immediately with the reagent to give colored (red, red-violet, green) products. Since the color reaction is quite distinct, the formation of quaternary compounds and their reaction with naphthaquinone sulfonic acid can be used as a test for cyclic tertiary ring bases and for oxonium compounds. The compound being tested must not contain CH_2- or NH_2-groups since these groups react with the 1,2-naphthaquinone-4-sulfonate.

The underlying reactions of the test can be represented:*

$$(1)$$

$$(2)$$

Similar equations can be written for other alkylation agents, such as dimethyl sulfate, ethyl bromide, ethyl iodide, and p-bromotoluene sulfonic acid methyl ester. The formation of the quaternary compound proceeds best with methyl iodide or dimethyl sulfate.

Procedure. A little of the test substance (either the solid or a drop of solution) is mixed in a tall microcrucible with 5 or 6 drops of methyl iodide or dimethyl sulfate, and heated to gentle boiling on an asbestos plate. Substances hard to convert to quaternary compounds should be heated for some hours with methyl iodide in a closed capillary tube in a water bath at 100° C. The quaternary compound is treated with 2 or 3 drops of a saturated solution of sodium naphthaquinone sulfonate, and the mixture made alkaline with 0.5 N sodium hydroxide. The appearance of a color or a change of color indicates that the test is positive. On acidifying with 1 N acetic acid there is a change of color, as in the *Ehrlich-Herter* reaction (see page 301).

The *limits of identification* attainable by this method are given in Table 35.

(2) Detection by hydrogenation to secondary ring bases [218]

Tertiary six-membered ring bases are converted into secondary ring bases by treatment with zinc and hydrochloric acid:**

$$(1)$$

The hydrogenation (reduction) is so extensive within a few minutes in the case of many tertiary ring bases, that the resulting secondary bases can be detected. A suitable test involves their inclusion in benzene-soluble copper

---

* The course of the reaction as shown in (*1*) and (*2*) is very probable, but has not yet been verified experimentally. The assumptions rest on the results of F. Kröhnke's work on the condensation of iodomethylates of organic tertiary bases with aldehydes: *Ber.*, 66 (1933) 604, 1386.
** Compare the test for quinoline discussed on page 404.

TABLE 35. TERTIARY RING BASES

Name and formula	Methylating agent	Color		Limit of identification
		With NaOH	With CH$_3$COOH	
Pyridine C_5H_5N	CH_3I $(CH_3)_2SO_4$ C_2H_5Br	Red to red-violet	Orange-yellow	12 γ
α-Picoline $C_5H_4NCH_3$	CH_3I $(CH_3)_2SO_4$ C_2H_5Br	Dark blue-violet	Light yellow	12 γ
Quinoline C_9H_7N	CH_3I $(CH_3)_2SO_4$ C_2H_5Br	Dark brown-green to black-green	Pink	25 γ
Quinaldine $C_9H_6NCH_3$	CH_3I $(CH_3)_2SO_4$	Dark blue-violet to blue-green	Pale greenish yellow	12 γ
2,6-Dihydroxypyridine-4-carboxylic acid $C_5H_2N(OH)_2COOH$ (2, 6, 4)	CH_3I	Black-green	Pink striations then green precipitate	25 γ
Dimethylpyrone $C_5H_2O_2(CH_3)_2$ (2, 6)	CH_3I $(CH_3)_2SO_4$ C_2H_5Br	Brown-violet, after short standing green-black	Red color then dark red precipitate	25 γ
Chelidonic acid $C_5H_2O_2(COOH)_2$ (2, 6)	CH_3I	Dark olive green to green-black	Peach-red	25 γ
Cinchonine $C_{19}H_{22}ON_2$	CH_3I heated for some hours in a sealed tube	Cherry red	Yellow	100 γ

salts of dithiocarbamic acids (comp. pag. 262). This salt formation proceeds from the components:

$$C S_2 + HN\diagup \begin{smallmatrix} \\ H\ \ H \end{smallmatrix} + \tfrac{1}{2} Cu^{+2} + NH_3 \longrightarrow S C \diagdown \overset{S-Cu/_2}{\underset{N}{}} \diagup \begin{smallmatrix} \\ H\ \ H \end{smallmatrix} + NH_4^+ \qquad (2)$$

References pp. 314–319

Many tertiary ring bases can be detected in small amounts through (1) and (2) followed by extraction of the copper dithiocarbamate with benzene.

It is noteworthy that certain pyridine- and quinoline derivatives fail to give this reaction. Examples are pyridine dicarboxylic acids (2,3 and 3,4), pyridine-2-carbinol-6-carboxylic acid, acridine, sedulone, 6-nitroquinoline, and vitamin B_6 (pyridoxine). The reduced solutions of the first four of these exceptions show no change on the addition of carbon disulfide and ammoniacal copper salt solution. Reduced 6-nitroquinoline and vitamin B_6 yield brown precipitates, which are not extractable with benzene. Probably the hydrophilic groups in the molecules of these ring bases prevent the solubility of the copper dithiocarbamates in benzene. Besides this, OH- and COOH-groups in *para* position to the cyclic N-atom seem to impair reduction.

The procedure given here may not be applied in the presence of secondary aliphatic amines since they behave like secondary ring bases. Consequently, the test solution should first be made acidic with hydrochloric acid and treated with some carbon disulfide and strongly ammoniacal copper sulfate solution. The mixture is shaken with benzene. If the benzene layer does not become colored, the occurrence of the dithiocarbamate-copper reaction is then indicative of the presence of tertiary ring bases.

As shown by the schematic representation of the hydrogenation of tertiary ring bases, the hydrogen is taken up by the cyclic N-atom and a C-atom *ortho* to this nitrogen atom. These hydrogenated products are hydrogen donors in alkaline surroundings, and consequently they can be detected by the color reaction with *o*-dinitrobenzene (see page 131). Similarly, this procedure will also reveal tertiary ring bases which contain hydrophilic groups (for instance pyridine carboxylic acids), and therefore are not able to form benzene-soluble copper dithiocarbamates.

Procedure. One drop of the highly acid hydrochloric acid solution of the sample is treated in a micro test tube with several grains of zinc (10 mesh) and warmed for about 5 minutes in a water bath. After all the metal has dissolved, the solution is cooled and one drop of 5% copper sulfate solution is added and then ammonium hydroxide (drop by drop) until the blue color appears. The blue solution is shaken with two drops of a mixture of 1 volume of carbon disulfide and 3 volumes of benzene. A positive response is indicated by a yellow or brown color in the benzene layer.

The procedure revealed:

30 γ pyridine, 2 γ quinoline, 3 γ isoquinoline, 50 γ quinaldine, 5 a,a'-dipyridyl, 50 γ quinine hydrochloride, 20 γ cinchonine, 100 γ nicotinic acid, 40 γ β-pyridylcarbinol tartrate, 20 γ papaverine hydrochloride.

A positive response was obtained with: a (β,γ)-picoline, picolinic acid, coramine (N,N-diethylnicotinamide), β-naphthoquinoline, nicotine, a-nicotyrine, m-bromoquinoline nitrate.

46. Allyl Compounds ($>$C—CH=C$<$ group)

Test with phloroglucinol-hydrochloric acid [219]

Many vegetable ethereal oils (lavender, clove, orange blossom, etc.) give an intense red color when treated with an alcohol-hydrochloric acid solution of phloroglucinol (1,3,5-trihydroxybenzene). Since these oils contain allyl compounds, and since diallyl sulfide shows the same color reaction, it may be assumed that the presence of the allyl group, —CH$_2$—CH=CH$_2$, is required for this response. Interestingly, cinnamaldehyde (I) and also the unsaturated alcohol geraniol (II) give the color reaction, whereas, in contrast to safrole (III), the isomeric isosafrole (IIIa) with the propenyl group (—CH=CH—CH$_3$), and neurine (IV) with the vinyl group (—CH=CH$_2$) do not show this reaction.

The behavior of (I)–(IV) seems to indicate that the 3-membered carbon chain $>$C—CH=C$<$ contained in the allyl group is essential to the occurrence of the color reaction. The many allyl compounds which give a positive response to the phloroglucinol-hydrochloric acid reagent argue for this statement, but, as can be seen from the following report, there are notable exceptions. Therefore, a negative response to this test cannot be taken as positive proof of the absence of allyl compounds.

The chemistry of this color reaction is not known; perhaps a colored addition compound of phloroglucinol is produced by combination on the terminal unsaturated carbon atom.

Procedure. [220] A drop of the test solution is placed on filter paper and spotted with a drop of phloroglucinol-hydrochloric acid. A red or yellow color indicates the presence of allyl compounds.

Reagent: Phloroglucinol-hydrochloric acid solution: 1 ml of 10 % alcohol solution of phloroglucinol plus 9 ml of concentrated hydrochloric acid. The reagent should be stored in the dark.

The following *limits of identification* were obtained: [221]

1. Diallyl sulfide H_5C_3—S—C_3H_5 18 γ

2. Eugenol

             8 γ

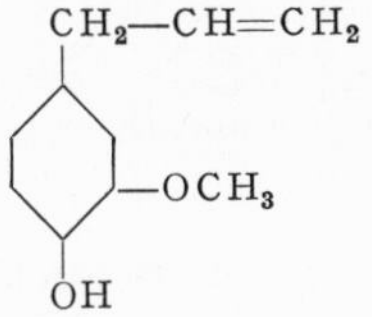

3. 2-Allylmercapto-6-(*iso*valeryl)-aminobenzothiazole   400 γ

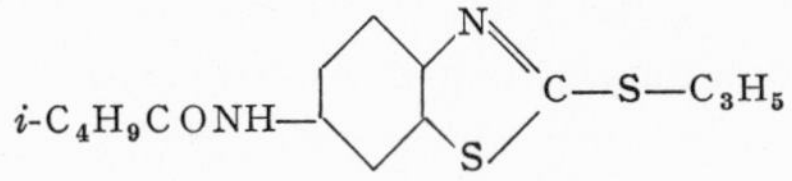

4. Succino-(2-allylmercaptobenzothiazolyl-6)-aminic acid   30 γ

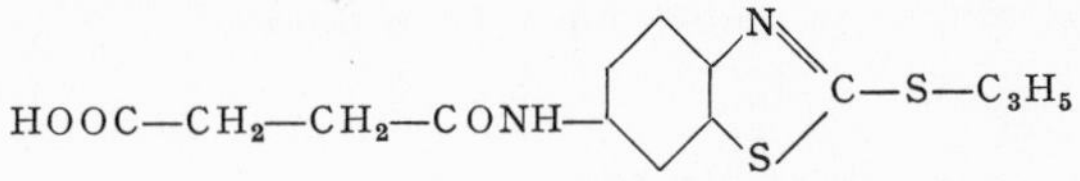

5. 2-Allylmercapto-6-(*o*-hydroxybenzal)-aminobenzothiazole   3 γ

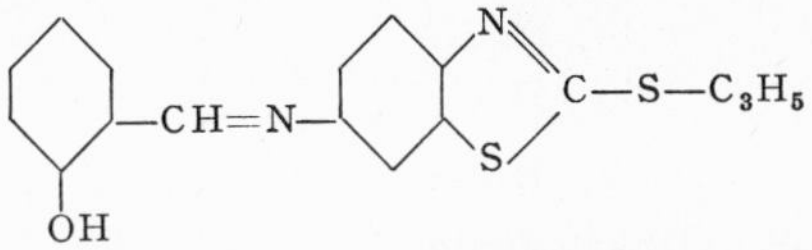

6. 2-Allylmercapto-6-(*o, p*-dihydroxybenzol)-aminobenzothiazole   1 γ

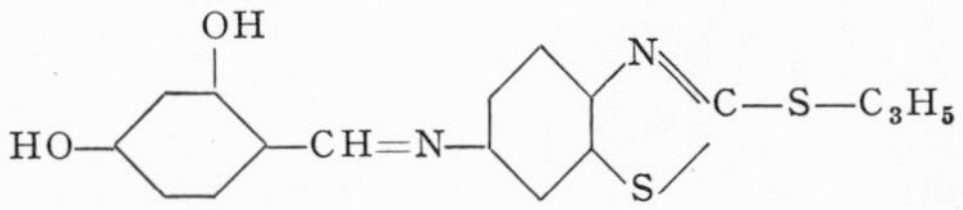

7. 2-Allylmercapto-6-(3', 4'-methylene-
dioxybenzal)-aminobenzothiazole   25 γ

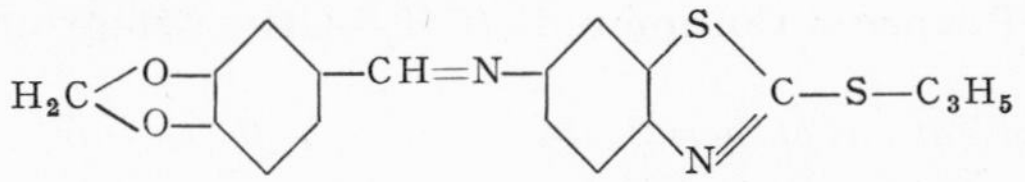

8. 2-Allylmercapto-6-(*p*-acetaminobenzal)-aminobenzothiazole   2 γ

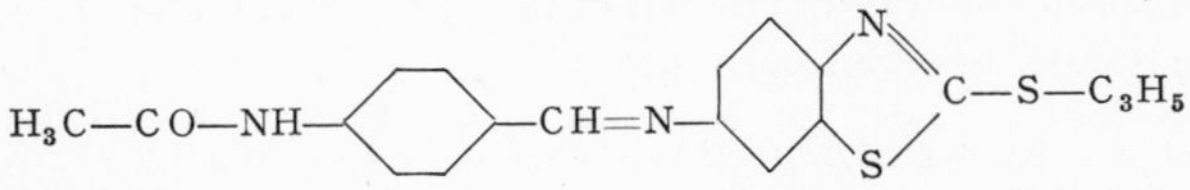

9. *p*-Hydroxybenzene-(1-azo-6)-2-allylmercaptobenzothiazole 0.1 γ

$$HO-\bigcirc-N=N-\bigcirc\begin{smallmatrix}N\\\\S\end{smallmatrix}C-S-C_3H_5$$

10. Allithiamine (addition compound of vitamin B_1 with alicin from garlic) 150 γ

The following compounds gave a positive response [219]: allylchloride, allylamine, diallylurea, 4-allyl-antipyrine, allyl alcohol, cinnamic alcohol.

The following compounds gave no reaction; the reason for their non-reactivity is unknown.

1. 2-Allylmercapto-6-(*n*-butyryl)-aminobenzothiazole

$$H_3C-CH_2-CH_2-CO-NH-\bigcirc\begin{smallmatrix}N\\\\S\end{smallmatrix}C-S-C_3H_5$$

2. 2-Allylmercapto-6-(*iso*caproyl)-aminobenzothiazole

$$i\text{-}C_5H_{11}-CO-NH-\bigcirc\begin{smallmatrix}N\\\\S\end{smallmatrix}C-S-C_3H_5$$

3. Dial (diallylbarbituric acid)

$$\begin{matrix}HN-CO\\OC\quad C\begin{smallmatrix}C_3H_5\\C_3H_5\end{smallmatrix}\\HN-CO\end{matrix}$$

4. Allyl methoxyphenylthiocyanate

$$\bigcirc\begin{smallmatrix}-OCH_2-CH=CH_2\\\\SCN\end{smallmatrix}$$

5. Allylacetoacetic ester

$$CH_3-CO-CH_2-COO-C_3H_5$$

47. Propenyl Compounds (CH₃—CH=CH-group)

Detection by formation of acetaldehyde through the action of benzoyl peroxide [222]

Compounds which contain the propenyl group, which is isomeric with the allyl group, produce acetaldehyde when they are oxidatively cleaved by even gentle heating with benzoyl peroxide:

$$CH_3-CH=CH-R + 2 (C_6H_5CO)_2O_2 \rightarrow CH_3CHO + RCHO + 2 (C_6H_5CO)_2O$$

The acetaldehyde may be detected in the vapor phase by means of the blue color it produces on coming into contact with a solution of sodium nitroprusside containing morpholine (compare page 334).

Obviously, the test given here may not be used if acetaldehyde or compounds which yield acetaldehyde under the prescribed conditions are present in the sample. Such materials include ethanol, O- and N-ethyl compounds, etc. (see page 180). A separation from ethylated nitrogen bases is readily secured by shaking the solution of the test substance in benzene, chloroform etc., with dilute hydrochloric acid; the bases then pass into the water solution as hydrochlorides.

Compounds which contain an allyl or vinyl group do not form acetaldehyde on treatment with benzoyl peroxide.

Procedure. A drop of the test solution is placed in a micro test tube and a drop of 5% solution of benzoyl peroxide in benzene is added. The mouth of the tube is covered with a disk of filter paper moistened with sodium nitroprusside-morpholine solution (for preparation see page 181). The test tube is plunged into boiling water. If propenyl compounds are present, the paper turns blue, the shade depending on the amount present.

Ethyl alcohol should not be used as solvent when very slight amounts of propenyl compounds are sought, because there is distinct oxidation of ethanol to acetaldehyde by benzoyl peroxide.

The following were detected:

100 γ Isosafrole

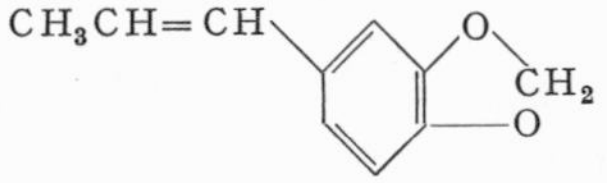

60 γ Anethole

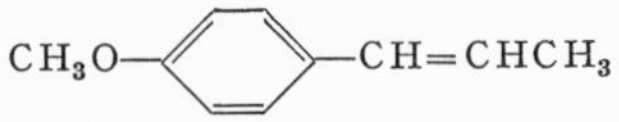

60 γ Isoeugenol

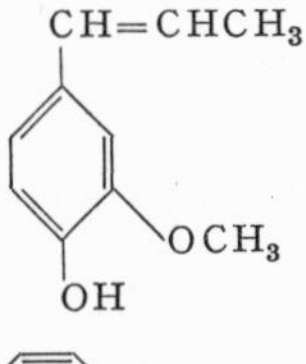

40 γ Anol

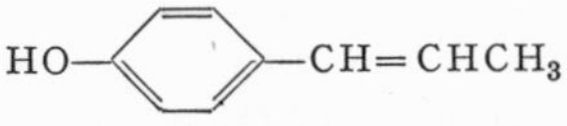

No acetaldehyde is produced from safrole or eugenol, namely the allyl compounds isomeric with isosafrole and isoeugenol.

It should be noted that the rather volatile propenyl compounds just mentioned give off vapors at water bath temperature (or even at room temperature) without addition of benzoyl peroxide and these volatilized portions color the paper blue. This effect is probably due to oxidation to acetaldehyde when the vapors come into contact with sodium nitroprusside. This behavior is characteristic for propenyl compounds and can be employed for their detection if the maximum sensitivity is not essential.

48. Sulfoxylate Compounds (—CH₂SO₂Na-group)

Detection through pyrolytic splitting-off of hydrogen sulfide [222]

Dry heating of formaldehyde sodium sulfoxylate (Rongalite) produces drogen sulfide and formaldehyde: [223]

$$2 \ H_2C \overset{\text{OH}}{\underset{\text{O—SONa}}{\diagup}} \longrightarrow 2 \ CH_2O + Na_2SO_4 + H_2S \qquad (1)$$

This effect is the basis of a specific test for Rongalite (Formopan, Discolite, Hydrosulfite A.W.) described in Vol. I, Chapter 4. Organic derivatives of Rongalite, which contain the —CH₂SO₂Na-group, and which are easily formed by condensing primary aromatic amines with Rongalite in alkali carbonate solution, likewise evolve hydrogen sulfide when they are heated to 250–280°. Possibly the following partial reactions occur:

$$R—NH—CH_2SO_2Na \rightarrow R—N=CH_2 + NaHSO_2 \qquad (2)$$

$$2 \ NaHSO_2 \rightarrow H_2S + Na_2SO_4 \qquad (3)$$

However, it should likewise be remembered that when organic compounds are pyrolyzed, the water produced acts locally as superheated steam, and effectuates first the hydrolysis:

$$R—NH—CH_2SO_2Na + H_2O \rightarrow R—NH_2 + CH_2(OH)SO_2Na \qquad (4)$$

which is then followed by the thermal decomposition represented in (1).

The detection of sulfoxylate compounds through the detection of pyrolytically evolved hydrogen sulfide is specific under the conditions prescribed here.

Procedure. The test is conducted in a micro test tube. A little of the solid is introduced and the mouth of the tube is then covered with a piece of moist lead acetate paper. The test tube is hung in a glycerol bath previously heated to 250° and the temperature is then raised to 270–280°. A positive response is signalled by the formation of a black or brown stain of lead sulfide on the white paper.

The limits of identification cannot be determined because when solutions of sulfoxylate compounds are taken to dryness there is oxidation of the —CH₂SO₂Na-group to the —CH₂SO₃Na-group. The latter does not yield hydrogen sulfide on pyrolysis. However, portions in the neighborhood of 0.3 mg of the following compounds gave a distinct response:

Rongalite $H_2C\begin{smallmatrix}\diagup OH\\ \diagdown OSONa\end{smallmatrix}$

Aldarsone

$$HO-\langle\ \rangle-AsO_3HNa$$

with NHCH$_2$SO$_2$Na substituent

Neosalvarsan $HO-\langle\ \rangle-As=As-\langle\ \rangle-OH$

with NH$_2$ and NHCH$_2$SO$_2$Na substituents

Sulfoxone sodium $NaO_2SH_2CHN-\langle\ \rangle-SO_2-\langle\ \rangle-NHCH_2SO_2Na$

49. Polyhalogen Compounds (—CHal$_3$- and CHHal$_2$-groups)

Detection with pyridine and alkali hydroxide

A red color is produced when chloroform, bromoform, iodoform, or chloral is warmed briefly with pyridine and alkali hydroxide solution.[224] Analogous color reactions were observed later with other polyhalogen compounds, including carbon tetrachloride, and employed for detection and in colorimetric determinations.[225] Only those halogen compounds are reactive which have at least two halogen atoms bound to one carbon atom. The constitution of the red water-soluble reaction products is unknown. Schiff bases of glutaconic aldehyde might be considered. They are formed by opening of the pyridine ring after addition of the polyhalogen compounds to the nitrogen (compare tests for pyridine and its derivatives, page 280). In the case of chloroform, the reaction scheme might be:

$$\text{(pyridinium)} \ \ \begin{smallmatrix}N-Cl\\|\\CHCl_2\end{smallmatrix} + 2\,NaOH \longrightarrow \begin{smallmatrix}N=CH \quad CHONa\\|\\CHCl_2\end{smallmatrix} + NaCl + H_2O$$

This scheme of reactions, which could apply to other polyhalogen compounds, is supported by the finding that addition of acetic acid to the red solution turns the color to yellow, and subsequent addition of primary aromatic amines, for instance benzidine, results in the precipitation of violet Schiff base of glutaconic aldehyde obtained by the pyridine test.

Not enough cases have been investigated as yet to permit any statement regarding the indisputability of the test. Basically it may be expected that not only polyhalogen compounds but also monohalogen compounds with mobile halogen atoms are capable of addition to pyridine, and thus susceptible to a subsequent cleavage to give colored compounds of glutaconic aldehyde.

Procedure.[226] A micro test tube is used. One drop of the test solution (acetone is recommended for water-insoluble compounds) is treated with two drops of pyridine and one drop of 5 N sodium hydroxide. The test tube is put into boiling water. Depending on the amount of reactive compound present, a red or pink color will appear within a few seconds or minutes in the pyridine layer. More prolonged heating causes the color to fade or to go over to brown or yellow. If a little benzidine hydrochloride is added and the mixture acidified with dilute acetic acid, a violet color or precipitate is obtained.

The following were detected:

1 γ chloroform	0.5 γ chloral hydrate
5 γ bromoform	0.5 γ trichloroacetic acid
50 γ iodoform	2.5 γ carbon tetrachloride

A strong response was given by: Chloromycetin (see page 499), trichloroethylene, tribromoethanol. No reaction was given by: hexachloroethane and D.D.T. (*p,p*-dichloro-diphenyl-trichloroethane).

REFERENCES

1. F. Feigl, *Anal. Chem.*, 27 (1955) 1315.
2. C. Liebermann, *Ber.*, 7 (1874) 247, 287, 806, 1098.
3. F. Feigl, V. Anger and O. Frehden, *Mikrochemie*, 15 (1934) 181, 183.
4. Compare O. Baudisch, *Ber.*, 54 (1921) 413.
5. H. W. Schwechten, *Ber.*, 65 (1932) 1734.
6. R. R. Fearon, *Analyst*, 71 (1946) 562.
7. E. F. C. Herington, *Analyst*, 78 (1953) 175.
8. F. Feigl and Cl. Costa Neto, *Anal. Chem.*, 28 (1956), in the press.
9. P. Baumgarten and J. Marggraff, *Ber.*, 63 (1930) 1019.
9a. F. Feigl and L. Hainberger, unpublished studies.
10. J. H. Yoe and L. G. Overholser, *J. Am. Chem. Soc.*, 61 (1939) 2058; 63 (1941) 3224.
11. F. Feigl, *Chemistry of Specific, Selective and Sensitive Reactions*, New York, 1949, p. 326.
12. F. Feigl and J. E. R. Marins, unpublished studies.
13. F. Feigl, *Anal. Chem.*, 27 (1955) 1316.
14. M. Illinsky and G. v. Knorre, *Ber.*, 18 (1885) 699.
15. Comp. F. J. Welcher, *Organic Analytical Reagents*, Vol. III, New York 1947, p. 299 ff.
16. I. M. Kolthoff and A. Langer, *J. Am. Chem. Soc.*, 62 (1940) 3172.
17. F. Feigl, Cl. Costa Neto and C. Stark, unpublished studies.
18. F. Feigl, V. Anger and O. Frehden, *Mikrochemie*, 15 (1934) 181, 183.
19. O. Dieffenbach, D.R.P., 192,519; *Chem. Abstr.*, 2 (1908) 1765.
20. S. Ohkuma, *J. Japan. Chem.*, 4 (1950) 622.
21. V. Anger, *Mikrochim. Acta*, 2 (1937) 6.
22. L. Pfaundler and A. Oppenheim, *Z. Chem.*, [2], 1 (1865) 470.
23. W. Borsche and E. Böcker, *Ber.*, 37 (1904) 1844.
24. P. K. Bose, *Analyst*, 56 (1931) 504.

25. P. Griess, *Ber.*, 12 (1879) 427; *Z. angew. Chem.*, (1899) 666.
26. F. Feigl and V. Gentil, unpublished studies.
27. F. Feigl and V. Gentil, *Anal. Chem.*, 27 (1955) 432.
28. F. Feigl, unpublished studies.
29. Regarding water-insoluble nitrates compare F. Feigl, Ref. 11, p. 305.
30. H. Wieland, *Ber.*, 46 (1913) 3296; 52 (1919) 886; G. W. Monier-Williams, *Analyst*, 56 (1931) 397.
31. Kiwi Grebler and J. V. Karabinos, *J. Res. Natl. Bur. Stand.*, 49 (1952) 463; *Chem. Abstr.*, 47 (1953) 2087.
32. P. H. Gore and G. K. Hughes, *Anal. Chim. Acta*, 5 (1951) 357.
33. O. Wallach and L. Belli, *Ber.*, 13 (1889) 525.
34. F. Buscarons, J. L. Marin & J. Claver, *Anal. Chim. Acta*, 3 (1949) 310, 417.
35. M. Borrel & R. Paris, *Anal. Chim. Acta*, 4 (1950) 267.
36. F. Feigl and C. Stark, *Mikrochim. Acta*, (1955) 996.
36a. A. J. Blair and D. A. Pantony, *Anal. Chim. Acta*, 13 (1955) 1.
37. G. Dragendorff, *Die gerichtliche chemische Ermittlung von Giften*, 1895, p. 111.
38. M. Siewert, *Z. anal. Chem.*, 60 (1927) 464; J. Koppel, *Chem. Ztg.*, 43 (1919) 777.
39. H. Apitzsch, *Ber.*, 38 (1905) 2895.
40. F. Feigl and R. Zappert, unpublished studies.
41. F. Feigl, C. Stark and L. Vokac, unpublished studies.
42. L. Malaprade, *Compt. rend.*, 185 (1927) 1132.
43. L. Malaprade, *Bull. Soc. Chim.*, [4], 43 (1928) 683.
44. F. Feigl and R. Zappert, unpublished studies.
45. O. Frehden and K. Fuerst, *Mikrochem. ver. Mikrochim. Acta*, 26 (1939) 36.
46. F. R. Duke and G. F. Smith, *Ind. Eng. Chem., Anal. Ed.*, 12 (1940) 201.
47. F. Feigl and E. Silva, unpublished studies.
48. C. Liebermann, *Ber.*, 7 (1874) 248, 806, 1098.
49. H. Decker and B. Solonina, *Ber.*, 35 (1902) 3217.
50. F. Feigl and R. Zappert, unpublished studies.
51. F. Feigl and T. Osterhud, unpublished studies.
52. E. Millon, *Compt. rend.*, 28 (1849) 40; A. Almén, *Z. anal. Chem.*, 17 (1878) 107; P. C. Plugge, *Arch. Pharm.*, 9 (1890) 9.
53. W. Vaubel, *Z. angew. Chem.*, 13 (1900) 1127.
54. F. Feigl and R. Zappert, unpublished studies.
55. F. Feigl and W. A. Mannheimer, unpublished studies.
56. K. Reimer and F. Tiemann, *Ber.*, 9 (1876) 824; 10 (1877) 213.
57. For details of the course of the reaction and comprehensive literature compare L. F. and M. Fieser, *Organic Chemistry*, 2nd ed., Boston, 1950, pp. 720–724.
58. F. Feigl, *Anal. Chem.*, 27 (1955) 1315.
59. F. Feigl, *Mikrochem. ver. Mikrochim. Acta*, 39 (1952) 404.
60. Compare R. Berg, *Die analytische Verwendung des Oxychinolins (Oxin) und seiner Derivate*, 2nd ed., Stuttgart 1938. See also F. J. Welcher, *Organic Analytical Reagents*, Vol. I, New York, 1947, Chapter XIII.
61. L. L. Merritt and I. K. Walker, *Ind. Eng. Chem., Anal. Ed.*, 16 (1944) 387.
62. F. Feigl and L. Hainberger, *Mikrochim. Acta*, (1955) 806; comp. also O. R. Hansen, *Acta Chem. Scand.*, 7 (1953) 1125.
63. W. B. Mors and B. Zaltman, *Bol. Inst. Quim. Agric.* (Rio), 34 (1954) 7.
64. F. Feigl., See Ref. 11, Chapter VI.
65. H. A. Liebhaffsky and E. H. Winslow, *J. Am. Chem. Soc.*, 69 (1947) 1130; 71 (1949) 3630.
66. F. Feigl, see Ref. 11, p. 547.
67. K. H. Meyer, *Ber.*, 47 (1918) 835.
68. F. Feigl and O. Frehden, unpublished studies.
69. C. Bertagnini, *Compt. rend.*, 35 (1852) 800; *Jahresber. Fortschr. Chem. verwandter Theile anderer Wissenschaften*, (1852) 615.
70. F. Raschig and L. Prahl, *Ann.*, 448 (1926) 265; see also G. Schroeter, *Ber.*, 59 (1926) 2341; 61 (1928) 1616.

71. A. Kurtenacker, *Z. anal. Chem.*, 64 (1924) 56.
72. F. Feigl and R. Zappert, unpublished studies.
73. F. Feigl, V. Gentil and D. Goldstein, unpublished studies.
74. J. Liebig, *Ann.*, 25 (1858) 27.
75. Comp. F. C. Whitmore, *Organic Chemistry*, New York, 1951, pp. 438, 563, 717.
76. M. Ishidate, *Mikrochim. Acta*, 3 (1938) 283.
77. See F. Feigl, Ref. 11, p. 270. See also F. J. Welcher, Ref. 60, Vol. 3, New York, 1947, Chapter VI.
78. W. N. Hirschel and J. A. Verhoeff, *Chem. Weekblad*, 20 (1923) 319; see also F. Feigl, *Rec. trav. chim.*, 58 (1939) 474.
79. M. Ishidate, *Mikrochim. Acta*, 3 (1938) 283.
80. H. L. Riley, J. F. Morley and N. A. C. Friend, *J. Chem. Soc.*, 135 (1932) 1875.
81. E. Schwenk and E. Borgwardt, *Ber.*, 65 (1932) 1609; G. Dupont, J. Allard and R. Dulon, *Bull. soc. chim.*, [4], 53 (1933) 599; W. Zacharewicz, *Chem. Abstr.*, 30 (1936) 8191.
82. M. Ishidate, *Mikrochim. Acta*, 3 (1938) 283.
83. F. Feigl and G. Franck, unpublished studies.
84. F. Feigl and D. Goldstein, unpublished studies.
85. V. Meyer, *Ber.*, 16 (1883) 2973; comp. also W. Steinkopf, *Die Chemie des Thiophens*, Dresden, 1941, p. 125–133.
86. W. Schlenk and O. Blum, *Ann.*, 433 (1923) 85.
87. N. Campbell, *Qualitative Organic Chemistry*, London, 1939, p. 44.
88. G. Denigès, *Compt. rend.*, 108 (1889) 350.
89. F. Feigl and Cl. Costa Neto, *Anal. Chem.*, 28 (1956) 397.
90. F. Weygand and H. Hofmann, *Ber.*, 83 (1950) 405.
91. H. Schiff, *Ann.*, 140 (1866) 93; B. v. Bitto, *Z. anal. Chem.*, 36 (1897) 373; E. Votocek, *Ber.*, 40 (1907) 414; L. Rosenthaler and G. Vegezzi, *Mitt. Lebensmittelunters. Hyg. (Eidg. Gesundheitsamt Bern)*, 45 (1954) 178.
92. H. Wieland and G. Scheuing, *Ber.*, 54 (1921) 2527.
93. F. Feigl and R. Zappert, unpublished studies.
94. O. Frehden and K. Fuerst, *Mikrochem. ver. Mikrochim. Acta*, 26 (1939) 39.
95. R. Wasicky and O. Frehden, *Mikrochim. Acta*, 1 (1927) 55.
96. F. Feigl and G. Frank, unpublished studies.
97. E. v. Bandrowski, *Ber.*, 27 (1894) 480; see also J. J. Ritter and G. H. Schmitz, *J. Am. Chem. Soc.*, 51 (1929) 1587.
98. G. Woker, *Ber.*, 47 (1914) 1024. See also G. Woker, *Die Katalyse* (Vols. 27/28 of *Die Chemische Analyse*), Stuttgart, 1931, p. 232
99. H. W. Wanzlick and W. Loechel, *Chem. Ber.*, 86 (1953) 1463.
100. A. Angeli, *Chem. Ztg.*, 20 (1896) 176; E. Rimini, *Gazz. chim. ital.*, 31 (1901) 84.
101. F. Feigl and R. Zappert, unpublished studies.
102. E. Tollens, *Ber.*, 15 (1882) 1635.
103. W. Ponndorf, *Ber.*, 64 (1931) 1913.
104. A. B. Wang, *Chem. Abstr.*, 26 (1932) 1920.
105. H. W. Schwechten, *Ber.*, 65 (1932) 1734. Compare also F. Feigl, V. Anger and R. Zappert, *Mikrochemie*, 15 (1934) 192.
106. F. Feigl and Y. Hashimoto (Kyoto), unpublished studies.
107. According to private communication by J. Mueller, Vienna, and observations of the author.
108. See Y. Asahina, *Acta Phytochim. (Japan)*, 8 (1934) 33 regarding the constitution of these depsides and depsidones; compare W. B. Mors, *Rev. Brasil. Biol.*, 12 (1952) 389.
109. E. Legal, *Jahresber. Fortschr. Chem. verwandter Theile anderer Wissenschaften*, (1883) 1648; B. v. Bitto, *Ann.*, 267 (1892) 372; G. Denigès, *Bull. Soc. Chim.*, [3], 15 (1896) 1058 and 17 (1897) 381.
110. L. Cambi, *Chem. Zbl.*, 1913, I, 1756; 1914, II, 1100.
111. Private information by S. Ohkuma, Tokyo.
112. Comp. M. Pesez and P. Poirier, *Méthodes et Réactions de l'Analyse Organique*, Paris, 1954, p. 40.
113. F. Feigl and R. Zappert, unpublished studies.

114. A. v. Baeyer and V. Drewsen, *Ber.*, 15 (1882) 2856; F. Penzoldt, *Arch. klin. Med.*, 48 (1883) 132. Compare also R. J. Le Fèvre and J. Pearson, *J. Chem. Soc.*, 135 (1932) 2807.
115. J. Kamlet, *Ind. Eng. Chem., Anal. Ed.*, 16 (1944) 362.
116. F. Feigl, R. Zappert and J. V. Sanchez, *Mikrochemie*, 17 (1935) 169.
117. F. Feigl. and V Demant, *Mikrochim. Acta*, 1 (1937) 132.
118. J. Blom, *Ber.*, 59 (1926) 121; compare also F. Raschig, *Schwefel- und Stickstoffstudien*, Leipzig, 1924, p. 183.
119. F. Feigl and Cl. Costa Neto, unpublished studies.
120. F. Feigl, *Mikrochemie*, 15 (1934) 1. Compare also E. Chargaff, *Dissertation*, Vienna 1928.
121. Comp. W. Awe, *Mikrochemie ver. Mikrochim. Acta*, 38 (1951) 574.
122. E. Friedmann, *J. prakt. Chem.*, [2], 146 (1936) 179.
123. F. Feigl and D. Goldstein, unpublished studies.
124. Compare F. Feigl, Ref. 11, p. 236.
125. F. Feigl and D. Goldstein, unpublished studies.
126. S. H. Losanitsch, *Ber.*, 24 (1891) 3021; 40 (1907) 2970.
127. E. Geiger and H. G. Mueller, *Helv. Chim. Acta*, 26 (1943) 996.
128. Compare F. J. Welcher, *Organic Analytical Reagents*, Vol. IV, New York, 1948, Chapt. 3.
129. E. J. Smith and E. Jones, *A Scheme of Qualitative Organic Analysis*, London, 1953, p. 200.
130. F. Feigl, V. Anger and O. Frehden, *Mikrochemie*, 15 (1934) 18. Compare D. Davidson, *J. Chem. Educ.*, 17 (1940) 81.
131. F. Feigl, V. Anger and O. Frehden, *Mikrochemie*, 15 (1934) 12.
132. F. Feigl and Cl. Costa Neto, unpublished studies.
133. S. M. McElvain in *Organic Reactions*, Vol. IV, New York, 1948, p. 256.
134. F. Feigl, V. Anger and O. Frehden, unpublished studies.
135. F. Feigl, *Anal. Chem.*, 27 (1955) 1315.
136. E. Bamberger, *Ber.*, 27 (1894) 915.
137. F. Feigl and V. Gentil, unpublished studies.
138. F. Feigl, *Anal. Chem.*, 27 (1955) 1315.
139. V. Meier, *Ber.*, 3 (1870) 112, 364.
140. G. B. Heisig and A. Lerner, *Ind. Eng. Chem., Anal. Ed.*, 13 (1941) 843.
141. F. Feigl and A. Lenzer, *Mikrochim. Acta*, 1 (1937) 129.
142. See F. Feigl, Ref. 11, p. 289.
143. F. Feigl and E. Fraenckel, *Ber.*, 65 (1932) 545.
144. F. Haber and F. Bran, *Z. physik. Chem.*, 35 (1900) 84; compare W. Böttger and E. Thoma, *J. prakt. Chem.*, [2], 147 (1936) 11.
145. F. Feigl and V. Anger, *Mikrochemie*, 15 (1934) 23.
146. Compare F. Feigl, Ref. 11, p. 289.
147. F. Feigl and Cl. Costa Neto, unpublished studies.
148. L. Kahl, *Ber.*, 31 (1898) 148.
149. F. Feigl and Cl. Costa Neto, unpublished studies.
150. F. Feigl and G. Frank, unpublished studies.
151. A. W. Hofmann, *Ber.*, 1 (1868) 25, 169.
152. A. W. Hofmann, *Ann.*, 57 (1846) 266; 70 (1849) 144.
153. F. Feigl and V. Anger, *Mikrochim. Acta*, 1 (1937) 138.
154. F. Feigl and L. Hainberger, unpublished studies.
155. F. Feigl, V. Anger and R. Zappert, *Mikrochemie*, 16 (1934) 67.
156. P. Friedlaender, *Fortschritte der Teerfarbenfabrikation*, Vol. II (1891), pages 79, 81; *ibid.*, III (1896), p. 174.
157. P. Karrer, *Organic Chemistry*, 4th ed., Amsterdam 1950, p. 634.
158. L. E. Fieser and M. Fieser, *Organic Chemistry*, 2nd ed., New York, 1950, p. 905.
159. R. Kuhn, *Naturwissenschaften*, 20 (1932) 622.
160. F. Feigl, V. Anger and R. Zappert, *Mikrochemie*, 16 (1934) 70.
161. F. Feigl and H. E. Feigl, *Mikrochim. Acta*, (1954) 85.
162. W. Gluud, K. Keller and W. Klempt, *Z. angew. Chem.*, 39 (1926) 1071.
163. H. Krall, *J. Chem. Soc.*, 103 (1913) 1383.
164. S. Ohkuma, *J. Pharm. Soc. Japan*, 75 (1955) 1124.

165. F. Feigl, V. Anger and R. Zappert, *Mikrochemie*, 16 (1934) 74.
166. H. Freytag and W. Neudert, *J. prakt. Chem.*, [2], 135 (1932) 15.
167. F. Feigl and V. Anger, *J. prakt. Chem.*, [2], 139 (1934) 180.
168. W. Koenig and H. Greiner, *Ber.*, 64 (1931) 1049.
169. V. Anger, *Mikrochim. Acta*, 2 (1937) 3.
170. O. Frehden and L. Goldschmidt, *Mikrochim. Acta*, 1 (1937) 338.
171. See also S. N. Chakravarti and M. B. Roy, *Analyst*, 62 (1937) 603.
172. O. Frehden and K. Fuerst, *Mikrochim. Acta*, 3 (1938) 197.
173. S. J. Burnistrov, *Chem. Abstr.*, 34 (1940) 2287.
174. F. Feigl, Cl. Costa Neto and C. Stark, unpublished studies.
175. F. Feigl, H. Blom and D. Goldstein, unpublished studies.
176. Comp. O. Tomicek, *Chemical Indicators*, London, 1951, p. 171.
177. D. Goldstein (Rio de Janeiro), unpublished studies.
178. F. Feigl, V. Anger and R. Zappert, *Mikrochemie*, 16 (1934) 71.
179. H. Fischer and F. Meyer-Betz, *Z. physiol. Chem.*, 75 (1911) 232; see also E. Salkowsky, *Biochem. Z.*, 103 (1920) 185.
180. H. Fischer and H. Orth, *Die Chemie des Pyrrols*, Vol. I, p. 66, Leipzig 1934; see also N.V. Sidgwick and R. W. J. Taylor, *Organic Chemistry of Nitrogen*, p. 484, Oxford, 1937.
181. Compare O. Frehden and L. Goldschmidt, *Mikrochim. Acta*, 1 (1937) 338.
182. F. Feigl and Cl. Costa Neto, unpublished studies.
183. W. Koenigs, *J. prakt. Chem.*, [2], 69 (1904) 105; compare also P. Karrer, *Organic Chemistry*, 4th engl. ed., New York, 1950, p. 807.
184. Comp. H. A. Waisman and C. A. Elvehjem, *Ind. Eng. Chem., Anal. Ed.*, 13 (1941) 221.
185. Comp. M. Pesez and P. Poirier, *Méthodes et Réactions de l'Analyse Organique*, Paris 1954, p. 126; see also J. W. Kulikow *et al.*, *Z. anal. Chem.*, 79 (1930) 454.
186. F. Feigl and D. Goldstein, unpublished studies.
187. O. Frehden and L. Goldschmidt, *Mikrochim. Acta*, 2 (1937) 186.
188. S. Ruhemann, *J. Chem. Soc.*, 97 (1910) 1438, 2025; 99 (1911) 792, 1486.
189. R. Moubacher and R. Ibrahim, *J. Chem. Soc.*, (1949) 702, and A. Schoenberg and R. Moubacher, *Chem. Reviews*, 50 (1952) 272.
190. W. Grassmann and K. Arnim, *Ann.*, 509 (1934) 288, explained the mechanism of this reaction.
191. Compare C. Neuberg, *Biochem. Z.*, 56 (1913) 500.
192. A. Bondi and J. Dobkin (Rehovoth), unpublished studies.
193. H. E. Feigl (Cambridge), unpublished studies.
194. E. A. Letts, *Ber.*, 5 (1872) 669.
195. F. Feigl and C. Stark, unpublished studies.
196. H. Weidel, *Ber.*, 12 (1879) 1994.
197. Comp. Beilstein, *Handb. org. Chem.*, Vol II, 4th ed., Berlin 1931.
198. F. Feigl and L. Hainberger, unpublished studies.
199. E. J. Smith and E. Jones, *A Scheme of Qualitative Organic Analysis*, London, 1953, p. 114.
200. F. Feigl and C. Stark, unpublished studies.
201. F. Feigl and Cl. Costa Neto, *Mikrochim. Acta*, (1955) 969.
202. F. Feigl, V. Anger and O. Frehden, *Mikrochemie*, 15 (1934) 184.
203. F. Feigl, V. Anger and R. Zappert, *Mikrochemie*, 15 (1934) 190.
204. P. Friedlaender, *Fortschritte der Teerfarbenfabrikation*, Vol. IV (1899) p. 705.
205. F. Feigl and V. Demant, *Mikrochim. Acta*, 1 (1937) 134.
206. J. J. Postowsky *et al.*, *Ber.*, 69 (1936) 1913.
206a. A. G. Green and S. Wolff, *Ber.*, 44 (1911) 2574.
207. F. Feigl and W. A. Mannheimer, unpublished studies.
208. F. Feigl and W. A. Mannheimer, *Mikrochemie ver. Mikrochim. Acta*, 40 (1953) 50.
209. F. Feigl, H. E. Feigl and W. A. Mannheimer, unpublished studies.
210. M. Pesez and A. Petit, *Bull. Soc. Chim. France*, 1947, 122.
211. F. Feigl and W. A. Mannheimer, *Mikrochemie ver. Mikrochim. Acta*, 40 (1953) 355.
212. F. Feigl, Ref. 11, p. 530.
213. P. Ehrlich and C. A. Herter, *Z. physiol. Chem.*, 41 (1904) 329.

214. E. G. Schmidt, *J. Biol. Chem.*, 122 (1938) 757; F. J. Bandelin, *Science*, 106 (1947) 426.
215. O. Folin, *J. Biol. Chem.*, 51 (1922) 377, 393.
216. M. X. Sullivan and W. C. Hess, *J. Am. Chem. Soc.*, 58 (1936) 47.
217. F. Feigl and O. Frehden, *Mikrochemie*, 16 (1934) 79.
218. F. Feigl and C. Stark, unpublished studies.
219. K. Kobert, *Z. anal. Chem.*, 46 (1907) 711.
220. Y. Hashimoto (Kyoto), unpublished studies.
221. Compounds 3–9 were synthesized by T. Takahashi and Z. Okada (Kyoto); compound 10 by T. Fujiwara (Kyoto).
222. F. Feigl and E. Silva, unpublished studies.
223. G. Panizzon, *Melliand's Textilber.*, 12 (1931) 119.
224. K. Fujiwara, *Chem. Abstr.*, 11 (1917) 3201.
225. Comp. M. Pesez and P. Poirier, *Méthodes et Réactions de l'Analyse Organique*, Paris, 1954, p. 111 and 130.
226. F. Feigl and V. Gentil, unpublished studies.

Chapter 5

Identification of Individual Organic Compounds

General Remarks

The detection of functional groups, the topic of the preceding chapter, was formerly known as the *structural-analytical* method of organic analysis, an exceedingly apt designation.[1] By its side was placed the *ultimate-analytical* method, i.e., the qualitative and quantitative determination of the elements composing the compound. In addition there is the final identification of individual organic compounds by *molecular-analytical* methods. The latter are based on the measurement of physical properties, which are related to the architecture and size of the molecule of organic compounds. Included are the determination of the melting- and boiling points and density of compounds, and also optical methods. The sample itself serves for the melting- and boiling point determinations, or it may be mixed with known materials to obtain characteristic points such as eutectic temperatures. This latter method has recently been used to characterize organic materials and mixtures in micro quantities, an important advance whose usefulness will doubtless become more apparent [2]. Solutions in various solvents or melts serve for determinations of the molecular weight through measurement of the elevation of the boiling point or lowering of the freezing point. The determination can be carried out on derivatives of the compound in question since in some cases they offer more favorable properties. The optical methods include the measurement of the refractive index, optical activity, ultraviolet absorption, Raman spectrum, form and optical characteristics of the crystals, etc.

Physical methods of identification are very reliable. Their employment, however, assumes, as a rule, the previous isolation of organic compounds in a state of high purity, an operation that may be costly with regard to time and material. Consequently, the importance of chemical identifications, which succeed rapidly and consume but little amounts of the mixtures to which they may often be applied directly, should not be underestimated. Rather they should be held in high esteem, and especially because they have the added advantage of not requiring special apparatus. Comparatively few cases have been known hitherto in which it is possible, through characteristic reactions, to make a direct specific test for particular or individual organic compounds. The chief reason is that the majority of all organic compounds with typical groups also have homologous relatives, and when a certain functional group can be identified by a suitable reaction, the same type of reaction yielding similar reaction products may be given by the homologous compounds. Numerous pertinent examples are given in Chapter 4. Consequently, at first sight, there seems to be little prospect of success for searches directed toward the discovery of specific or selective tests for individual organic compounds. This situation is responsible for the fact that hitherto the detection of functional groups often served particularly to disclose the possibility of arriving by preparative methods at derivatives which, after isolation and purification, can be characterized by physical methods and thus allow reliable conclusions to be drawn regarding the starting material. There is no doubt but that this course of action offers the greatest surety in identifying individual organic compounds. However, its application is necessarily limited by the preparative step, with its inescapable requirement of sufficient starting material and its inevitable loss of intermediate and final products, to say nothing about the necessary consumption of time. Therefore, efforts must be made to develop tests for individual compounds through appropriate modification and combination of well established group reactions which can be accomplished quickly. Such efforts as well as studies to discover new analytically useful reactions of organic compounds will be aided by experiences which, in part, are often overlooked and hence not used. Some of these findings are of recent date.

First of all, it should be noted that, in the great majority of cases where recourse is taken to qualitative organic analysis, the analyst is not faced with an inextricable artificial mixture of organic compounds. As a rule, the available information about the origin, method of preparation, action, and use of the material being examined can provide valuable clues as to the lines along which the tests should be made. In fact, the analytical goal is often well defined by the answer to the question as to whether particular compounds are present or absent. In such instances, tests for functional groups if need be in combination with preliminary tests (both conducted within the technique of spot test analysis), may be entirely adequate, and the intensity of the response to a characteristic reaction may even permit conclusions as to how much of a particular compound is present.

Another point, often given too little consideration, is that the reactivity of certain groups in organic compounds is sometimes strongly affected by the remainder of the molecule or by the groups it contains. This influence may show itself through widely differing reaction rates, through loss of reactivity, and through differences in the solubility and in the basic or acidic character, as well as in the color or fluorescence of the reaction products. It is obvious that such peculiarities in the response to tests for functional groups can sometimes serve for the detection of individual compounds. In the search for specific and selective organic reagents for inorganic analysis, special consideration has been given recently to the activity of particular salt-forming groups and to the influence exerted on this action by the remainder of the molecule, as well as by the reaction milieu. It is likely that the findings [3] obtained in this area of study will also be useful to the chemical methods of organic analysis dealing with the detection of functional groups and individual compounds. This point is discussed in Chapter I and is confirmed by numerous examples to be found throughout the text.

Of greatest importance for the sure detection of individual compounds is the possibility of removing homologs from a common reaction theater. This possibility always is provided when only the lowest member of an homologous series is volatile or sublimable at room temperature or on slight warming, or if cleavage through heat or chemical action yields a volatile or sublimable product which in turn can be identified in the vapor phase by a suitable test. In such cases, a group reaction, which is non-specific in solution, can become completely specific for an individual compound if the test is carried out on the vapor phase.

The most extensive use of a separation of reaction theaters occurs in chromatography. The solution components are collected in definite, separate zones through adsorption on a powdered adsorber (column chromatography) or on porous paper (paper chromatography). Specific tests for minute amounts of individual compounds can then be accomplished in these zones, either directly or after elution, by means of tests which must be sensitive but not necessarily specific or selective. Furthermore, the products of selective group reactions can be adsorptively separated from water solution or from solution in organic solvents, and in this way individual compounds can be detected in certain zones. It may be safely assumed that spot test analysis will play an important role in all varieties of chromatography and vice versa.

The following sections contain descriptions of spot tests which, in part, are characteristic for individual compounds and, in part, respond to those representatives of a particular class of compounds that have practical importance and are most likely to occur in the samples presented for study and analysis.

As in the preliminary tests and the test for functional groups, the tests for individual compounds will again stress the importance of noting the response of the sample to different tests if more than one identifying procedure is available. Greater certainty in judging the nature of the sample is secured by such multiplicity of findings and the truth of the verdict will also be assisted by conducting "pattern trials" in which the typical reaction picture is exhibited as shown by the pure compound in various dilutions.

It should be noted that there are no strict boundaries between tests for functional groups and tests for establishing the identity or presence of individual organic compounds. In every case, the essential feature is the occurrence of definite chemical reactions involving certain groups of radicals. Furthermore, tests for functional groups are often used for the detection of organic compounds, the procedure being modified to suit the occasion of course. Consequently, the distinction employed in this text is therefore justified in that the tests used for identifying individual compounds are often much more selective than the tests given in Chapter 4 for functional groups, which in their turn are more selective than the preliminary tests outlined in Chapter 3.

1. Acetylene

(1) Test by formation of cuprous acetylide [4]

Acetylene, either gaseous or dissolved in water or organic solvents, reacts with colorless ammoniacal solutions of cuprous salts to produce cuprous acetylide (carbide or more correctly cuproacetylenic carbide):

$$Cu_2^{+2} + C_2H_2 + 2 NH_3 \rightarrow C_2Cu_2 + 2 NH_4^+$$

The copper salt, a monohydrate,[5] appears as an amorphous precipitate, whose color is red-brown to red-violet, depending on the degree of dispersion. It is soluble in dilute mineral acids, with regeneration of acetylene, which forms colorless addition products with acid cuprous salt solutions.[6] An analogous behavior toward cuprous salts is shown by homologs of acetylene (acetylenic hydrocarbons), which in conformity with the general formula $C_nH_{2n+1}C\equiv CH$ contain a terminal triply bound carbon linked to an acidic hydrogen atom, or, more correctly, the H-atom becomes acidic through the triply bound C-atom.

The detection of acetylene through precipitation of copper acetylide from ammoniacal cuprous solutions is impaired by sulfide ions because of the formation of black cuprous sulfide. Mercapto compounds similarly precipitate yellow cuprous salts of the particular mercaptans (sometimes mixed with some copper sulfide). Larger quantities of alkali cyanide prevent the precipitation of cuprous acetylide. This masking is due to the formation of complex $[Cu_2(CN)_4]^{-2}$ anions, with consequent lowering of the concentration of Cu_2^{+2} ions to such extent that the solubility product of cuprous acetylide is not reached. No interference with the test is occasioned by hydrides of phosphorus and arsenic, which always are present in commercial acetylene, and which impart to it the unpleasant odor usually associated with this gas.

The sensitivity of the acetylene test was established by means of a saturated water solution prepared from previously purified gas. In the dilutions, the solubility (at 18°) was taken as 0.118 g acetylene per 100 ml water.[7]

Procedure. A drop of the ammoniacal cuprous solution is placed in a depression of a spot plate and a drop of the acetylene solution is added. According to the quantity of acetylene present, a red-brown precipitate or a brown-violet color appears in the practically colorless solution. When dealing with very small amounts of acetylene it is well to run a parallel blank test.

Identification Limit: 1 γ acetylene.

The test can also be made by allowing gaseous acetylene to react with a hanging drop of the reagent solution in a gas-evolution apparatus (Fig. 23, page 49). The identification limit then is about 5 γ acetylene.

Reagents: 1) Solution of 1.5 g cupric chloride and 3 g ammonium chloride in 20 ml concentrated ammonia, diluted to 50 ml with water

2) 5 g hydroxylamine hydrochloride in 50 ml water.

To prepare the ammoniacal cuprous solution, 1 ml of the blue solution *1)* is combined with 2 ml of solution *2)*; decolorization ensues.

(2) Test by protective layer effect on silver chromate[8]

When acetylene (gaseous, or dissolved in water, acetone, etc.) reacts with a nitric acid or ammoniacal solution of silver chromate, an orange or yellow flocculent precipitate is formed. The product * is an addition compound of silver acetylide and silver chromate:

$$4\,Ag^+ + CrO_4^{-2} + C_2H_2 \rightarrow Ag_2C_2 \cdot Ag_2CrO_4 + 2\,H^+$$

When conducted as a spot test, this reaction will reveal 2.5 γ acetylene in aqueous solution. A more sensitive and more reliable test is provided by the reaction on a suspension of red-brown silver chromate in water or dilute acetic acid. The yellow brown addition product is then formed through a topochemical reaction on, or very close to, the surface of the silver chromate or via its dissolved portions. A result of this envelopment of the acid-soluble silver chromate by the acid-insoluble $Ag_2C_2 \cdot Ag_2CrO_4$ is that the unused silver chromate is markedly protected against rapid and complete solution in

---

* A compound, $C_2H_2 \cdot Ag_2O \cdot Ag_2CrO_4$, which probably should be viewed as $Ag_2C_2 \cdot Ag_2CrO_4 \cdot H_2O$, has been prepared from silver chromate and acetylene.[9] F. Feigl and A. Caldas (unpublished studies) found that the precipitate produced from nitric acid solutions of silver chromate by acetylene shows the ratio Ag : CrO_4 = 4 : 1.

References pp. 440–444

dilute nitric or sulfuric acid. (A similar "protective layer effect"[10] exists also against ammonia.) Water suspensions of brown-red silver arsenate, brown-red mercury[(I)]and yellow mercury[(II)] chromate behave analogously toward acetylene, in that they too, after reaction with acetylene, are coated with a layer of acid-resistant acetylene compound and thus shielded from a subsequent action of dilute nitric acid. The "protective layer effect" on silver chromate is the basis of a test for acetylene, which is just as sensitive as the test *1*. No studies have been reported regarding the behavior of homologs of acetylene possessing a terminal ≡CH-group.

The detection of acetylene by means of the protection of silver chromate due to $Ag_2C_2 \cdot Ag_2CrO_4$, formed is, of course, applicable only in the absence of hydrogen sulfide and halogen hydracids. The test can be carried out as a spot reaction in a porcelain crucible (Procedure I) or in a larger volume of liquid (Procedure II), with employment of "analytical flotation". The latter operation makes use of the fact that slight amounts of precipitate, suspended in several milliliters of water, are often gathered into the interface and thus made more visible when the suspension is shaken with an organic liquid that is immiscible with water. (Obviously, the organic liquid must not be a solvent for the precipitate.)[11]

The sensitivity of the acetylene test by procedures I and II was determined on dilutions of a saturated water solution of the purified gas.

Procedure I. Single drops of the yellow ammoniacal solution of silver chromate are placed in two small porcelain crucibles, and the red-brown silver chromate is precipitated by adding one drop of 6 *N* acetic acid to each. One drop of the solution being tested for acetylene is added to one of the suspensions, and a drop of water to the other, which serves as a blank. The mixtures are stirred from time to time over a period of 1–10 minutes depending on the quantity of acetylene expected. The blank is then treated with drops of 1 : 10 nitric acid until the silver chromate is completely decomposed and a clear yellow solution is obtained. The same number of drops of dilute nitric acid is then added to the actual test; for the sake of certainty, a drop or two extra may be added. If acetylene is present, a residue of undissolved red-brown silver chromate will be seen; the amount will be in accord with the quantity of acetylene present.

Limit of Identification: 1 γ acetylene.

Reagent: Ammoniacal solution of silver chromate: well washed silver chromate, prepared by adding potassium chromate solution to silver nitrate solution, is added to (1 : 5) ammonia water, vigorously shaken, and filtered. The yellow solution is stored in a closed bottle and away from light. If a turbidity develops on standing, more ammonia should be added, or the suspension should be filtered.

Procedure II. Two test tubes (capacity about 3 ml) fitted with glass stoppers are used. One drop of ammoniacal silver chromate solution is placed in each tube and the red-brown silver chromate is precipitated by adding one drop of 6 N acetic acid. One drop of the aqueous test solution is added to one tube, and a drop of water to the other. Each mixture is then diluted with a drop or two of water, the tubes are stoppered and shaken for about one minute. Both suspensions are then covered with 1 ml of amyl alcohol. The blank is then treated with successive drops of 1 : 10 nitric acid (vigorous shaking) until the silver chromate is completely dissolved and no particles of precipitate remain in the water-amyl alcohol interface. The silver chromate suspension being tested for acetylene is then shaken with the same number of drops of nitric acid plus one extra for the sake of certainty. If acetylene was present, the water-amyl alcohol interface contains a considerable or a slight coating of red-brown silver chromate.

Limit of Identification: 1 γ acetylene.

Reagent: As in Procedure I.

2. Anthracene and Phenanthrene

(1) *Detection by conversion into anthraquinone and phenanthraquinone* [12]

In contrast to other aromatic hydrocarbons, anthracene is not nitrated by concentrated nitric acid but is converted to anthraquinone.[13] Its isomer, phenanthrene, is nitrated, but when only small amounts are involved phenanthraquinone is also formed. Even a single evaporation with concentrated nitric acid yields enough of the respective quinone to permit an indirect test for these hydrocarbons to be based on this result.

A sensitive test for anthraquinone and phenathraquinone depends on the catalytic action of these compounds on the color reaction between formaldehyde and 1,2-dinitrobenzene. The chemistry of this reaction is discussed on page 205.

Procedure. The test is conducted in a micro test tube. One drop of the test solution (benzene, ether) is evaporated to dryness and a drop or two of concentrated nitric acid (sp.gr. 1.4) is added to the residue. The evaporation is then repeated. One drop of 25% sodium carbonate solution is added, followed by one drop of 4% formaldehyde solution, and one drop of a 5% solution of 1,2-dinitrobenzene in benzene. The mixture is placed in boiling water and shaken occasionally. After 1–4 minutes, a violet color appears, the shade depending on the amount of anthracene or phenanthrene present. A blank test is advisable when small amounts are suspected.

This procedure will reveal anthracene even though large amounts of naphthalene are also present. The latter is only nitrated by concentrated nitric acid. It should be noted that benzene-soluble benzoins react directly with 1,2-dinitrobenzene without the addition of formaldehyde. A separate test should consequently be run with this fact in mind.

The *limits of identifications* are:

    2 γ anthracene;   3 γ phenanthrene.

(2) Differentiation of anthracene and phenanthrene[14]

Insoluble addition products, which differ markedly in color, are produced when concentrated benzene solutions of anthracene or phenanthrene are treated with benzene solutions of picric acid. The anthracene compound is brick-red, whereas the phenathrene addition product, like that of naphthalene, is yellow. When benzene or ether solutions of their components are evaporated, these colored addition compounds are left. They likewise result if the dry components are ground thus constituting the products of solid-solid reactions. The formation readily occurs on filter paper.

Procedure. Picric acid paper is prepared by soaking filter paper in a 10% solution of picric acid in benzene and drying in the air. A drop of the ether or benzene solution being tested for anthracene is placed on the dry paper. If anthracene is present, a red or pink stain appears on the yellow paper.

Limit of identification: 3 γ anthracene.

3. Carbon monoxide

Test with phosphomolybdic acid and palladium chloride[15]

When carbon monoxide is passed through a solution of phosphomolybdic acid, there is no noticeable effect. If, however, some palladium chloride is added, there is immediate formation of molybdenum blue:

$$2 MoO_3 + CO \rightarrow Mo_2O_5 + CO_2 \qquad (1)$$

The catalytic hastening of the redox reaction (*1*) is brought about by even very small concentrations of palladium ions, and this fact makes possible an extremely sensitive and specific test for palladium (comp. Vol. I, Chap. 3). The mechanism of the catalysis resides in the production of elementary palladium:

$$Pd^{+2} + CO + H_2O \rightarrow Pd^{\circ} + CO_2 + 2 H^+ \qquad (2)$$

which adsorbs carbon monoxide (likewise hydrogen). This adsorption activates the carbon monoxide (hydrogen) to enter into redox reactions, which proceed at an immeasurably slow rate when there is no adsorption.[16] According to the state of aggregation of the catalyst, the production of molybdenum blue with cooperation of palladium presents therefore an instance of heterogeneous catalysis, initiated by the invisible quantities of dispersed palladium formed by reaction (*2*).

Redox reaction (*2*) is the basis of an old test for carbon monoxide [17] carried out on filter paper impregnated with 1% palladium[II] chloride. When this yellow paper is exposed to carbon monoxide, as little as 0.01–0.03% CO in the gas produces a black to gray color. The test with $PdCl_2$ paper is not sensitive enough when carried out as a spot reaction. Likewise, the use of paper impregnated with relatively much palladous salt is not advantageous and furthermore such paper deteriorates because of reduction by the cellulose, particularly when illuminated. In contrast, if a solution of phosphomolybdic acid, containing as little as 0.02 % of palladium chloride, is employed as reagent, the occurrence of reaction (2) produces the catalyst for the reaction (1). Quantities of carbon monoxide which are too small to be revealed by the classic palladium chloride reaction can thus be detected through the production of molybdenum blue. The reaction may be conducted as a spot test.

A test for carbon monoxide employing the technique of spot test analysis is a useful tool in qualitative organic analysis, since many organic compounds yield carbon monoxide when they are disintegrated by concentrated sulfuric acid.[18] The most familiar example is the decomposition, by removal of water, of formic and oxalic acid:

$$HCO_2H \rightarrow H_2O + CO$$
$$H_2C_2O_4 \rightarrow H_2O + CO_2 + CO$$

α-Hydroxy- and α-ketocarboxylic acids are broken down in various ways by warming with concentrated sulfuric acid; carbon monoxide may be produced directly or via formic and oxalic acid:

$$RCH(OH)COOH \rightarrow RCHO + HCO_2H$$
$$R(CO)COOH \rightarrow RCOOH + CO$$
$$2\ R(CO)COOH \rightarrow R\text{—}R + H_2C_2O_4 + 2\ CO$$

At room temperature, tertiary carboxylic acids are broken down quantitatively with production of the respective carbinols (tertiary alcohols):

$$\begin{array}{c} R \\ R\text{—}C\text{—}COOH \\ R \end{array} \rightarrow \begin{array}{c} R \\ R\text{—}C\text{—}OH + CO \\ R \end{array} \qquad (R = \text{alkyl or aryl})$$

In general, the lower members of the α-hydroxy acids undergo considerable disintegration even at a temperature range of 80–100°, while the higher members require temperatures of 140–160°.

Syrupy phosphoric acid behaves like concentrated sulfuric acid with respect to splitting carbon monoxide out of organic compounds. This must be remembered if palladium-bearing phosphomolybdic acid is used as reagent for carbon monoxide. When warmed with concentrated sulfuric acid, almost all organic compounds produce sulfur dioxide, which likewise yields molybdenum blue with phosphomolybdic acid. Therefore, syrupy phosphoric acid must invariably be used for splitting carbon monoxide from organic compounds.

The following test is not applicable when the action of syrupy phosphoric acid on the sample yields volatile products which act on palladium-bearing phosphomolybdic acid. Such products are sulfur dioxide, hydrogen sulfide, and hydrocyanic acid.

Procedure. [19] A drop of the test solution is taken to dryness in the bulb of the apparatus described on page 49 (Fig. 23). Alternatively, a little of the solid sample may be placed in the apparatus. A drop of syrupy phosphoric acid is then introduced. The knob of the stopper is dipped into the reagent solution, and then put into place. The closed apparatus is heated with a micro burner until the mass solidifies. Care must be taken that the drop hanging on the knob does not go to dryness. After cooling, the drop is wiped onto filter paper and moistened with a drop of water. If carbon monoxide was produced, a blue to blue-green color appears. A blank test is advisable.

Reagents: *1*) Phosphoric acid, 85 %, kept at 250° until no more steam is given off.

2) Palladium chloride-bearing phosphomolybdic acid:

   (*a*) 0.02 g $PdCl_2$ is dissolved in 2 drops of concentrated hydrochloric acid and brought to 10 ml with water;

   (*b*) cold saturated solution of phosphomolybdic acid in water. The reagent consists of a mixture of 2 ml (*a*) and 8 ml (*b*).

Limits of Detection: 5 γ oxalic acid,   10 γ tartaric acid,
                         10 γ citric acid,   25 γ mandelic acid.

4. Dicyanogen

Detection with potassium cyanide and 8-hydroxyquinoline (oxine) [20]

The detection of gaseous dicyanogen is primarily of interest in studies of the thermal cleavage products of nitrogenous organic compounds since such pyrolyses may yield dicyanogen alone or along with prussic acid. These cannot be differentiated by the reaction with copper-benzidine acetate described on page 93. The former undergoes an irreversible hydrolysis:

$$(CN)_2 + H_2O \rightarrow HCN + HCNO$$

and consequently also responds to the test for hydrogen cyanide.

Dicyanogen can be specifically detected through its reaction on a concentrated solution of potassium cyanide which contains some oxine.

A red color appears.[21] The composition of this product is not known. However, certain statements can be made regarding the manner of its formation. The color reaction occurs only in the presence of much alkali cyanide, which leads to the supposition that—in analogy to polyhalides—polycyanide ions are formed from cyanide ions and dicyanogen:

$$CN^- + (CN)_2 \rightarrow [CN...(CN)_2]^-$$

The production of polycyanide ions prevents the saponification of the dicyanogen or at least it is lessened. It cannot be stated with certainty how the dicyanogen preserved in polycyanide ions acts on oxine. It is conceivable that the dicyanogen adds to the nitrogen atom of oxine (I) with formation of addition compounds of the type II or IIa:

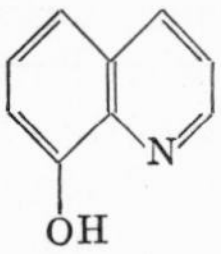

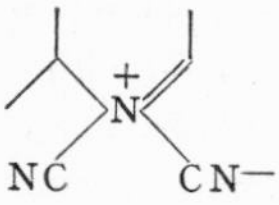

It is likewise possible that the dicyanogen oxidizes the oxine to a quinoid compound:

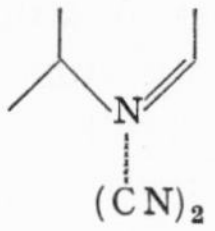

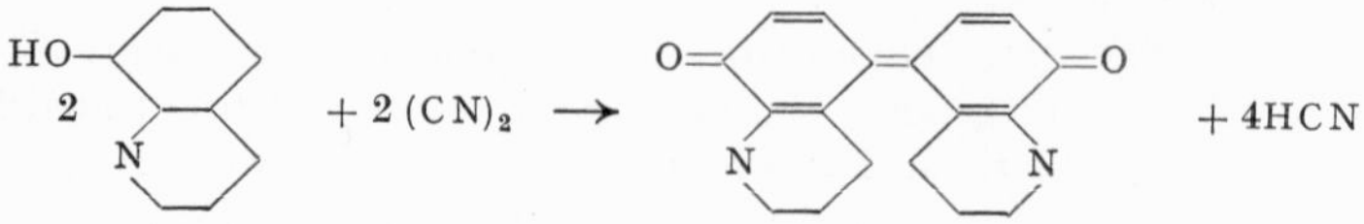

The identification limit of the test is 1 γ dicyanogen. This value was determined by heating a mixture of mercuric cyanide and mercuric chloride and assuming that the yield of dicyanogen is 50 %, which is usual when the reaction

$$Hg(CN)_2 + HgCl_2 \rightarrow Hg_2Cl_2 + (CN)_2$$

is used for the preparation of pure dicyanogen. [22]

Procedure. A tiny particle of the dry sample is placed in a micro test tube and the mouth of the tube is covered with a disk of oxine paper that has been moistened with a drop of 25% potassium cyanide solution. When the tube is heated over a micro burner, a more of less intense red circular stain appears on the paper.

Reagent: Oxine paper is prepared by bathing filter paper in a 10% solution of oxine in ether and drying in the air. The reagent paper keeps.

With the aid of this test it was possible to show that the pyrolysis of uric acid and purine derivatives, guanidine and cyclic guanidine derivatives, and likewise pterines, dimethylglyoxime, furildioxime, and (but not diphenyldioxime) yield dicyanogen. This is not true of the pyrolysis of oxamide and barbituric acid, which give only hydrogen cyanide when they are thermally decomposed as shown by the reaction (blue color) with benzidine–copper acetate (page 93). See also the detection of oxamide (page 394).

5. Formaldehyde

(1) Test with chromotropic acid [23]

When formaldehyde is warmed with chromotropic acid (1,8-dihydroxy-naphthalene-3,6-disulfonic acid) in strong sulfuric acid solution, a violet-pink color develops. The chemistry of this color reaction is not known with certainty. In view of the fact that aromatic hydroxy compounds condense with formaldehyde [24] to yield colorless hydroxydiphenylmethanes, it is probable that the initial step of the color reaction consists of a condensation of the phenolic chromotropic acid with formaldehyde as shown in (1) and this is followed by an oxidation to a p-quinoidal compound as shown in (2). (See the Le Rosen test described on page 133).

$$2 \ \text{(chromotropic acid)} + CH_2O \rightarrow \text{(methylene-bridged product)} + H_2O \qquad (1)$$

$$\text{(product)} + O \rightarrow \text{(}p\text{-quinoidal compound)} + H_2O \qquad (2)$$

Sulfuric acid participates in both (1) and (2). In the former it functions as a dehydrant to bring about the condensation, in (2) it serves as oxidant and is reduced to sulfurous acid.

Acet-, propion-, butyr-, *iso*butyr-, and *iso*valeraldehydes, oenanthal, crotonaldehyde, chloral hydrate, glyoxal, and aromatic aldehydes give no reaction with a sulfuric acid solution of chromotropic acid. Glyceraldehyde, furfural, arabinose, fructose, and sucrose give a yellow coloration. Other sugars, acetone, and carboxylic acids do not react. High concentrations of furfural give a reddish color. Aromatic carboxylic acids, such as benzoic and phenylacetic, give no reaction.

Procedure. A drop of the sample solution is mixed with 2 ml 12 N sulfuric acid in a test tube, a little solid chromotropic acid is added, and the tube heated for 10 minutes in a water bath at 60°. A bright violet color appears in the presence of formaldehyde. For small amounts a blank test is advisable.

Limit of Identification: 0.14 γ formaldehyde.
Reagent: 12 *N* sulfuric acid (100 ml water plus 150 ml conc. H_2SO_4).

A violet to pink color produced by this procedure revealed 0.5 γ formaldehyde in the presence of:

0.047	mg	fructose	i.e.	94 times the quantity
0.99	mg	cane sugar		100 times the quantity
0.19	mg	furfural		380 times the quantity
2.16	mg	arabinose		4326 times the quantity
3.48	mg	milk sugar		6956 times the quantity
5.05	mg	dextrose		10100 times the quantity

The detection of formaldehyde with chromotropic acid can be applied also to compounds which split off formaldehyde on treatment with acids. Instances are: hexamethylenetetramine, formaldoxime, trimethylene-α-mannite, cellulose formals, etc. [25]

In harmony with the reactions suggested above for the formaldehyde–chromotropic acid test is the fact that the greatest sensitivity is attained in concentrated sulfuric acid rather than in 12 *N* acid as prescribed in the Procedure. The maximum effectiveness as condensing agent and oxidant is shown by the concentrated acid.[26] Since the sulfuric acid is diluted when it comes into contact with aqueous formaldehyde, the detection of minimal amounts of the latter is best accomplished by taking the formaldehyde to dryness along with some ammonia water. Hexamethylenetetramine results and when the evaporation residue is gently warmed with concentrated sulfuric acid and chromotropic acid there is immediate reaction because the water in the concentrated sulfuric acid brings about the hydrolytic cleavage of the hexamethylenetetramine into formaldehyde and ammonia. It is also possible to sublime the hexamethylenetetramine by heating to around 300° and the vapor will then give a positive response if brought into contact with concentrated sulfuric acid and chromotropic acid. If conducted within the technique of spot test analysis, these procedures have identification limits of 0.025 and 0.0025 γ formaldehyde, respectively.

The fact that formaldehyde, released if need be by the action of concentrated sulfuric acid, gives the chromotropic acid tests in the vapor phase, makes possible a convenient method of detecting compounds which split out formaldehyde.

(2) Detection through demasking effects

Formaldehyde reacts with cyanide ions or with ethylenediamine to yield addition or condensation products that are water-soluble:

$$CH_2O + CN^- \longrightarrow CH_2 \begin{smallmatrix} \diagup O^- \\ \diagdown CN \end{smallmatrix} \tag{1}$$

$$2\ CH_2O + \begin{matrix} H_2C - NH_2 \\ | \\ H_2C - NH_2 \end{matrix} \longrightarrow \begin{matrix} H_2C - N = CH_2 \\ | \\ H_2C - H = CH_2 \end{matrix} + 2\ H_2O \tag{2}$$

These reactions also occur when formaldehyde acts on certain complex salts, whose anion or cation contain CN groups or ethylenediamine molecules. This is shown by the fact there is an immediate precipitation of the red nickel salt if formaldehyde is added to a solution of $Na_2[Ni(CN)_4]$ containing dimethylglyoxime, in which the concentration of nickel ions is too low to permit the normal reaction with dimethylglyoxime.[27] Similarly, the addition of formaldehyde to a solution of silver-ethylenediamine chromate yields a red-brown precipitate of silver chromate. Therefore, formaldehyde releases nickel or silver ions from the complex equilibria

$$[Ni(CN)_4]^{-2} \rightleftharpoons Ni^{+2} + 4\ CN^-$$

$$[Ag\ en]^+ \rightleftharpoons Ag^+ + en$$

and thus enables these ions to give their normal reactions with dimethyl-glyoxime and chromate ions, respectively. Even slight amounts of formaldehyde are sufficient to give these effects and the following tests take advantage of these findings.

The detection of formaldehyde through its demasking actions cannot be applied to acidic solutions since hydrogen ions likewise set the metals free by reacting with cyanide ions or with ethylenediamine. Acid solutions can be neutralized by means of calcium carbonate, or the formaldehyde can be driven out by heating the test solution and then detected in the vapor phase by means of the equilibrium solutions. However, the sensitivity is less when this procedure is employed.

When formaldehyde reacts with silver ethylenediamine chromate solution, the initial product is red-brown silver chromate. If considerable amounts of formaldehyde are present, the precipitate quickly turns black because of the secondary reactions:

$$Ag_2CrO_4 + CH_2O + 3\ OH^- \rightarrow 2\ Ag^0 + HCOO^- + CrO_4^{-2} + 2\ H_2O$$

$$Ag_2CrO_4 + 2\ OH^- \rightarrow Ag_2O + CrO_4^{-2} + H_2O$$

The hydroxyl ions participating in these reactions are provided by the alkaline equilibrium solution.

Procedure I (demasking of nickel).[28] A drop of the neutral test solution is placed on filter paper impregnated with the nickel cyanide-dimethylglyoxime equilibrium solution. Depending on the amount of formaldehyde present, the resulting stain is red or pink. When amounts below 2 γ are suspected, a blank should be run with a drop of water on a separate strip of reagent paper and with rapid drying of the fleck.

Limit of identification: 0.5 γ formaldehyde.

Among the aliphatic and aromatic aldehydes, besides formaldehyde, only acetaldehyde gives a positive reaction. Acidic solutions can be made basic before the test by adding ammonia water.

Reagent paper: About 0.5 g of freshly precipitated nickel dimethylglyoxime is suspended in 100 ml water, 0.1 g potassium cyanide added, shaken vigorously, and filtered after 24 hours. The equilibrium solution should be stored in borosilicate bottles. Whatman No. 1 filter paper is moistened with the solution and dried in an oven or under an infra red lamp. It should be stored in a closed container.

Procedure II (demasking of silver).[29] One drop of the neutral test solution is treated on a spot plate with a drop of the silver ethylenediamine chromate solution. Formaldehyde yields an immediate red precipitate, which turns black.

Limit of identification: 3.5 γ formaldehyde.

Reagent: 3 grams of freshly prepared silver chromate, washed with water, is suspended in 20 ml water and 1 gram of ethylenediamine is added. The suspension is boiled for 5 minutes and then filtered. The filtrate is made up to 100 ml with water, allowed to stand for one hour, and filtered.

If acidic solutions are presented for examination, the portion tested should be neutralized with calcium carbonate beforehand.

Procedure II is less sensitive than I, but it has the advantage of not giving a response with acetaldehyde.

6. Acetaldehyde

Detection with piperidine or morpholine and sodium nitroprusside [30]

When acetaldehyde is added to a solution of sodium nitroprusside containing piperidine, a blue color appears. This color reaction likewise occurs if instead of piperidine the reagent contains another secondary aliphatic amine. A test for such amines is based on this fact (see page 260). The chemistry of the color reaction is unknown. When testing for acetaldehyde, it is better to use the less expensive morpholine in place of the piperidine.

Even slight quantities of acrolein (see test for glycerol, page 387), croton-aldehyde, and tiglic aldehyde react analogously to acetaldehyde.[31] Propion-aldehyde reacts only at high concentrations.

References pp. 440–444

Procedure. One drop of the solution to be tested for acetaldehyde is placed on a spot plate or filter paper. One drop of the reagent solution is added. A more or less intense blue color appears, the shade depending on the quantity of acetaldehyde involved.

Limit of identification: 1 γ acetaldehyde.

Reagent: Freshly prepared mixture of equal volumes of 20% water solution of morpholine and 5% water solution of sodium nitroprusside.

The color reaction is obtained likewise if acetaldehyde vapor comes into contact with filter paper moistened with the reagent. This is the basis of indirect tests for compounds which yield acetaldehyde when oxidatively cleaved or by any other way.

7. Chloroform

Test by conversion to alkali cyanide

A number of reactions show that the three chlorine atoms of chloroform are reactive. For example, the action of ammonia, in the presence of caustic alkali, results in the production of cyanide:

$$CHCl_3 + 4\,NaOH + NH_3 \rightarrow 3\,NaCl + 4\,H_2O + NaCN$$

As pointed out (page 93) the hydrocyanic acid liberated from alkali cyanides by acidification with mineral acids can be detected with high sensitivity through the bluing, of a copper acetate-benzidine mixture. The color is due to a meriquinoid oxidation product of benzidine, which is produced as a result of the raised oxidation potential of the bivalent copper in the presence of cyanide ions. 2,7-Diaminofluorene (I) can be used in place of benzidine [32]; it is oxidized to the p-quinoid imine (II):

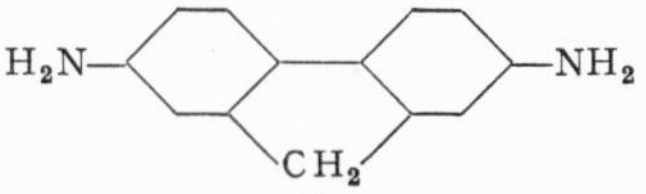

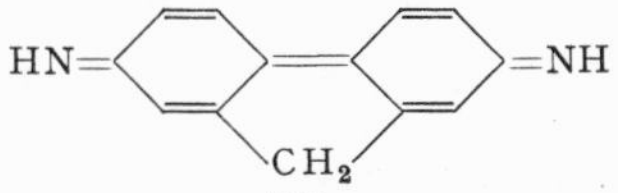

The action of hydrocyanic acid on Congo paper impregnated with mercuric chloride (see Volume I, Chap. 4) can also be used to detect the cyanide formed in the above reaction. Bromoform behaves similarly to chloroform.

Procedure. [33] One drop of the test solution, in a microcrucible, is allowed to stand for several minutes, at room temperature, with 2 drops of 20 % sodium hydroxide and 1 drop of concentrated ammonia. A particle of clay plate is then added, and the mixture heated to boiling. After cooling, it is acidified with 20 % sulfuric acid. The crucible is covered with a small watch glass carrying a strip of moist reagent paper. The prussic acid is expelled by cautious heating. A blue color indicates the presence of chloroform. The formation and liberation of the prussic acid can also be accomplished in the apparatus described on page 49 (Fig. 23).

Limit of Identification: 16 γ chloroform.

Reagent: Copper acetate-diaminofluorene solution: 0.3 % copper acetate solution is mixed with an equal volume of a saturated solution of 2,7-diaminofluorene in 50 % alcohol.

8. Bromoform

Detection through oxidative cleavage with benzoyl peroxide [33a]

If bromoform is warmed with benzoyl peroxide (m.p. 103°) bromine is released, probably by the reaction:

$$CHBr_3 + 2 (C_6H_5CO)_2O_2 \rightarrow CO_2 + HBr + 2 (C_6H_5CO)O + Br_2$$

This reaction occurs even at water bath temperature and more quickly at 110–120°. The liberated bromine can be detected in the vapor phase by its reaction on iodide-starch paper.

Chloroform (b.p. 61°) behaves analogously but it can be separated from bromoform (b.p. 151°) by warming the sample.

The following procedure is particularly suited for detecting bromoform in mixtures with other organic liquids such as benzene and high-boiling hydrocarbons.

Procedure. A drop of the test solution is treated in a micro test tube with a drop of 10% solution of benzoyl peroxide in benzene. The mouth of the test tube is covered with a piece of moistened starch-iodide paper. The test tube is placed in boiling water. If bromoform was present, a blue stain appears on the paper, the depth of the color depending on the amount of bromoform.

The *limit of identification* is 50 γ bromoform.

9. Chloral

(1) Test by conversion to isatin-β-imine [34]

Chloral (trichloroacetaldehyde), which usually occurs as its water-soluble stable hydrate (I), can be converted, through a number of intermediate steps, into isatin.[35] The yield is good. The most important steps of this interesting synthesis are: the production of chloraloxime (II), which reacts with aniline, in acid solution, to give isonitrosoacetanilide (III). The latter is dehydrated, with ring-closure, by means of concentrated sulfuric acid, and so forms isatin-β-imine (IV). The latter is saponified by water to give isatin (V). The corresponding equations are:

$$C Cl_3 CH(OH)_2 + NH_2OH \longrightarrow C Cl_3 CHNOH + 2 H_2O \qquad (1)$$
$$\text{(I)} \qquad\qquad\qquad\qquad\qquad \text{(II)}$$

$$CCl_3CHNOH + C_6H_5NH_2 + H_2O \longrightarrow C_6H_5NHCOCHNOH + 3HCl \qquad (2)$$
$$\text{(III)}$$

$$(3)$$

$$(4)$$

Many primary aromatic amines with a free ortho-position behave analogously to aniline; they yield the corresponding derivatives of isatin-β-imine or isatin.

The realization of reactions (1)–(3) suffices for the detection of chloral. The resulting isatin-β-imine gives a red solution in concentrated sulfuric acid. A partial saponification to isatin is of no fundamental importance, since isatin gives a yellow solution in concentrated sulfuric acid.

Reactions (1)–(4) can be carried out successfully with one drop of a dilute water solution of chloral hydrate (or alcoholate, ammoniate). This makes a specific test for chloral possible.

When applying this test it should be remembered that many organic compounds (especially carbohydrates) caramelize or char when warmed with concentrated sulfuric acid, and thus interfere with the recognition of isatin. It is best in such cases to extract the chloral from the sample with ether, and to carry out the conversion into isatin-β-imine with the evaporation residue from a drop or two of the ether solution.

Procedure. A drop of the test solution is placed in a microcrucible and evaporated to dryness along with a drop of the acid aniline-hydroxylamine solution. One micro drop of concentrated sulfuric acid is added to the residue and the crucible is heated for 30 seconds in an oven at 110°. Depending on the quantity of chloral present, a wine-red to yellow color develops. A blank is advisable for small amounts of chloral.

Limit of Identification: 2.5 γ chloral.

Dilution Limit: 1 : 20,000.

Reagent: Aniline-hydroxylamine solution: To 1 g aniline (pure or freshly distilled) add 1 ml concentrated hydrochloric acid and then dilute with 5 ml water. The aniline hydrochloride solution is united with a solution of 1 g hydroxylamine sulfate in 5 ml water. Any aniline sulfate precipitate is filtered off. The solution keeps for several days.

(2) *Detection through conversion into acetaldehyde*

A macro test [36] for chloral hydrate consists in subjecting it to the action of nascent hydrogen (zinc and dilute sulfuric acid) to yield acetaldehyde:

$$CCl_3CHO + 6 H^0 \rightarrow CH_3CHO + 3 HCl \qquad (1)$$

This product is then brought into contact, in the vapor phase, with a solution of sodium nitroprusside containing piperidine; a blue color results (compare page 334).

The conversion of chloral into acetaldehyde can likewise be accomplished by warming with formaldehyde-sodium sulfoxylate (Rongalite) [37], which here functions as hydrogen donor for the realization of (1):

$$H_2C\Big\langle{}^{OH}_{SO_2Na} + H_2O \rightarrow H_2C\Big\langle{}^{OH}_{SO_3Na} + 2H^0 \qquad (2)*$$

Both procedures for producing acetaldehyde can be translated into the technique of spot test analysis; they both lead to the same detection limits. If the test material is acidic or alkaline, the treatment with zinc and sulfuric acid is required.

The test cannot be applied in the presence of acetaldehyde or acetaldehyde-bisulfite, nor of compounds which give off hydrogen sulfide or sulfur dioxide when treated with zinc and dilute acid, since these products enter into color reactions with sodium nitroprusside (compare Volume I, Chapter 4).

Procedure. The test is carried out in a micro test tube. About 0.5–0.7 gram of Rongalite is treated with a drop of the test solution and the mouth of the test tube is covered with a disk of filter paper that has been moistened with a drop of the freshly prepared reagent solution. The same quantity of granulated zinc (40 mesh) and 1–2 drops of dilute sulfuric acid may be used in place of the Rongalite. The test tube is kept in boiling water for about three minutes. If chloral was present, a blue stain appears on the yellow reagent paper. The depth of the color depends on the amount of chloral present.

Limit of identification: 10 γ chloral.
Reagent: Freshly prepared mixture of equal volumes of 5% sodium nitroprusside solution and 20% piperidine or morpholine solution.

There is no doubt that bromal hydrate will react analogously with respect to its conversion into acetaldehyde and hence the procedure for the detection of chloral will also apply.

* This equation does not mean formation of hydrogen by pure hydrolysis; this kind of hydrolysis occurs only in the presence of an appropriate hydrogen acceptor.

References pp. 440–444

10. Methyl alcohol

Test by conversion to formaldehyde [38]

The specific test for formaldehyde with chromotropic acid described on page 331 can be used for the detection of methyl alcohol since in acid solution the latter is readily oxidized to formaldehyde by permanganate:

$$5 \, CH_3OH + 2 \, MnO_4^- + 6 \, H^+ \rightarrow 5 \, CH_2O + 2 \, Mn^{+2} + 8 \, H_2O$$

If the experimental conditions prescribed here are maintained, i.e., slight acidity and brief reaction time, ethyl alcohol is oxidized by permanganate solely to acetaldehyde without production of noticeable quantities of form-aldehyde, as is the case when less mild oxidizing conditions prevail. The excess permanganate and the manganese dioxide produced by the reaction:

$$3 \, Mn^{+2} + 2 \, MnO_4^- + 2 \, H_2O \rightarrow 5 \, MnO_2 + 4 \, H^+$$

can be removed, prior to the test with chromotropic acid, by means of sodium sulfite.

Procedure. A drop of the test solution is mixed with a drop of 5% phosphoric acid and a drop of 5% potassium permanganate solution in a test tube for 1 minute. A little solid sodium bisulfite is then added, with shaking, until the mixture is decolorized. If any brown precipitate of the higher oxides of manganese remains undissolved, a further drop of phosphoric acid should be added and a very little sodium bisulfite. When the solution is colorless, 4 ml of 12 N sulfuric acid and a little finely powdered chromotropic acid are added; the mixture is well shaken, and then heated to 60° for 10 minutes. A violet color, that deepens on cooling, indicates the presence of methyl alcohol.

Limit of Identification: 3.5 γ methyl alcohol.

No reaction was given by: ethyl alcohol, propyl alcohol, *iso*propyl alcohol, butyl alcohol, trimethylcarbinol, *n*-primary amyl alcohol, *iso*amyl alcohol, amyl-ene hydrate, ethylene glycol, propylene glycol, erythrite, adomite, mannite, dul-cite, acetaldehyde, butylaldehyde, *iso*butylaldehyde, *iso*valeraldehyde, methyl glyoxal, acetone, oxalic acid, lactic acid, tartaric acid, citric acid, dextrose. *Color reactions* were given by: glycerol (yellow color and green fluorescence); furfural brownish color); arabinose, fructose, milk sugar, cane sugar (yellow color).

11. Ethyl alcohol

Detection through oxidation to acetaldehyde

Ethyl alcohol is oxidized by permanganate in the presence of sulfuric acid to give acetaldehyde. The latter can be detected in the vapor phase through the blue color it produces when it comes in contact with a solution of sodium nitroprusside containing morpholine or piperidine. (Compare the detection of secondary aliphatic amines, page 260). The oxidation of ethanol always produces some acetic acid along with the acetaldehyde and consequently the sensitivity of the test based on the formation of acetaldehyde is low because of this side reaction.

Methyl alcohol is oxidized to formaldehyde, which does not react with nitroprusside. Accordingly, it is possible to thus distinguish between ethanol and methanol. Because of the difficulty of regulating the amount of oxidant required, the detection of slight quantities of ethyl alcohol in methyl alcohol is uncertain. The same holds for the detection of ethanol in the presence of other materials that are oxidizable by permanganate. Propyl alcohol is oxidized to propionaldehyde, which likewise responds to the nitroprusside test, though to a much less degree. Because of its alcohol content, ordinary ether gives an aldehyde reaction. Since this result is obtained even with the pure ether intended for anesthesia, it appears that the oxidation

$$C_2H_5\text{—}O\text{—}C_2H_5 + O \rightarrow C_2H_5OH + CH_3CHO$$

is possible. Therefore, the procedure given here is of limited applicability.

Procedure.[39] One drop of the test solution is treated in a micro test tube with a drop of acidified permanganate solution and the mixture is shaken. The mouth of the test tube is covered with a disk of filter paper moistened with a drop of sodium nitroprusside-morpholine solution (see page 335). If ethanol is present, a blue stain appears on the paper at once or within a few minutes. The depth of the color and the time required for it to develop depend on the quantity of ethanol involved.

Reagent: Acidified permanganate solution: Equal volumes of 0.1 N permanganate and 1 : 1 sulfuric acid.
Limit of identification: 150 γ ethanol.

12. Formic acid

(1) Test by conversion to formaldehyde [40]

Formic acid is readily reduced to formaldehyde by nascent hydrogen generated from magnesium powder and dilute hydrochloric acid:

$$HCO_2H + 2 H° \rightarrow CH_2O + H_2O$$

The formaldehyde can then be identified by the chromotropic acid test (see page 231).

Procedure. A drop of the test solution is mixed in a test tube with a drop of 2 N hydrochloric acid; magnesium powder is then added until no further gas is liberated. Three milliliters of 12 N sulfuric acid and a little chromotropic acid are then added; the tube is heated for 10 minutes at 60° in a water bath. A violet-pink appears if formic acid is present.

Limit of Identification: 1.4 γ formic acid.

Solutions of the following compounds were tested with chromotropic acid after treatment with magnesium and hydrochloric acid:

No reaction: glycolic-, glyoxylic-, oxalic-, malic-, citric-, malonic-, salicylic-, uric-, protocatechuic acids; alloxan, arabinose, galactose.
Yellow color: glyceric acid, pyruvic acid.
Yellow to orange color: levulose; saccharose, raffinose.
Yellow to green color: rhamnose.

Glucose interferes with the test because of partial breakdown to formic acid. Consequently, small amounts of formic acid cannot be detected in the presence of much grape sugar.

(2) Test by reaction with mercuric chloride [41, 42]

When formic acid or an alkali formate is warmed with mercuric chloride, in acetic acid-acetate buffered solution, white, crystalline mercurous chloride precipitates:

$$2 \, HgCl_2 + HCO_2^- \rightarrow Hg_2Cl_2 + CO_2 + 2 \, Cl^- + H^+$$

Small amounts of mercurous chloride can be detected by the reaction with ammonia (blackening due to formation of finely divided elementary mercury):

$$Hg_2Cl_2 + 2 \, NH_3 \rightarrow HgNH_2Cl + NH_4Cl + Hg°$$

If dilute solutions of mercuric chloride are used, and if the following conditions are maintained, no reaction is given by even large quantities of the following acids: acetic, glycolic, lactic, oxalic, tartaric, citric, malic. Therefore, the test is recommended for detecting formic acid (formate) in mixtures with carboxylic and sulfonic acids (or their alkali salts).

Procedure. A drop of the acid, neutral, or weakly basic test solution is placed in a microcrucible and one drop of 10% mercuric chloride solution and one drop of buffer solution are added. The mixture is taken to dryness in the oven at 100° (exclude light). The evaporation residue is taken up in a drop of water and a drop of 0.1 N ammonia is added. According to the formate content, a more or less intense black to grey color appears. The buffer solution contains 1 ml glacial acetic acid and 1 gram sodium acetate per 100 ml water.

Limit of Identification: 5 γ formic acid.

This method revealed 5 γ formate in one drop of saturated sodium oxalate solution. This corresponds to a ratio 1 : 370.

13. Acetic acid

(1) Test with lanthanum nitrate and iodine [43]

When lanthanum salts are mixed under suitable conditions with iodine and ammonia in the presence of acetic acid or alkali acetates, a dark blue precipitate or solution results.[44] This probably is due to the adsorption of iodine on basic lanthanum acetate; however, this effect occurs only on a suitable variety of this substrate.

Nitrates, chlorides, bromides, and iodides do not interfere with the detection of small amounts of acetate, even when present in 30 to 40 times excess, but they do weaken the intensity of the blue color. Sulfates, however, interfere in relatively small amounts, and similarly all anions that form insoluble salts with lanthanum (e.g., phosphates), and all cations that give precipitates with ammonia. Sulfates and phosphates may be removed by precipitation with barium nitrate and the test carried out on the filtrate. Propionates react similarly to acetates.

Procedure. A drop of the test solution is mixed on a spot plate with a drop of a 5% solution of lanthanum nitrate and a drop of 0.01 N iodine solution. A drop of 1 N ammonia is added, and in a few minutes (in the presence of acetates) a blue to blue-brown ring develops around the drop of ammonia.[45]

Limit of Identification: 50 γ acetic acid.

(2) Test by formation of indigo [46]

Acetone is formed by the dry distallation of calcium acetate:

$$\begin{matrix} H_3C-COO \\ H_3C-COO \end{matrix} \Big> Ca \rightarrow \begin{matrix} H_3C \\ H_3C \end{matrix} \Big> CO + CaCO_3$$

When acetone, in alkaline solution, is allowed to react with o-nitrobenzaldehyde, indigo is formed, with intermediate production of o-nitrophenyl lactic acid ketone (see test for methylene ketones, page 223). Starting with small amounts of calcium acetate, indigo can be formed by the action of acetone vapor on reagent paper impregnated with an alkaline solution of o-nitrobenzaldehyde. In this way, acetic acid can be decisively detected in the presence of formic acid and all the mineral acids. It is interesting to note that acetone vapor obtained by heating acetone or acetone-water mixtures reacts but slowly and incompletely. The rapid formation of indigo in this test is probably due to the fact that the acetone vapor formed in the distillation of calcium acetate reaches the nitrobenzaldehyde at a higher temperature and hence in a more reactive condition.

Acetates of other alkaline earth metals and likewise zinc, magnesium, lead and alkali metal acetates react in the same way as calcium acetate when subjected to dry distillation, i.e., they yield acetone.[47]

Propionic acid and other fatty acids cannot be detected by the indigo reaction; when their calcium salts are subjected to dry distillation, higher ketones (without the CH_3CO group) are formed, but no acetone. This test is less sensitive in the presence of other fatty acids because the acetone is mixed with higher ketones as well as mixed ketones, which are the chief products in the distillation of the calcium salts.

It must be noted that the acetic acid test is unsuccessful in the presence of large amounts of copper, silver, and mercury salts. Chromates and manganese dioxide are, however, without effect.

Procedure. The solid sample is mixed with calcium carbonate, or a drop of the acid solution is evaporated to dryness with calcium carbonate. The residue is transferred to the hard glass tube (Fig. 28) described on page 50. The conversion into calcium acetate may also be carried out in the ignition tube. The open end of the tube is covered with a strip of filter paper moistened with a freshly prepared alkaline solution of o-nitrobenzaldehyde. The glass cap is put in place. The strip of filter paper may alternatively be kept in position by running through it a thin thread of glass thickened to a knob at one end, which rests on the paper and keeps it weighted down. The tube is then hung through the asbestos plate and gradually heated. The acetone vaporizes and colors the yellow paper blue or blue-green, according to the amount evolved. When very small amounts of acetate are involved, it is advisable to remove the glass cap together with the filter paper after the distillation, and to spot the paper with a drop of 1 : 10 hydrochloric acid. The original yellow color of the paper is discharged by the acid so that the blue of the indigo shows up more clearly against the white paper.

Limit of Identification: 60 γ acetic acid.

Reagent: Saturated solution of o-nitrobenzaldehyde in 2 N sodium hydroxide.

(3) Other tests for acetic acid

(a) The acetaldehyde formed by the dry distillation of a mixture of acetate with $Ca(OH)_2$ and calcium formate may be identified by the reaction with 5 % sodium nitroprusside and 20 % piperidine (see page 334).[48] The procedure for this test is the same as for test 2 (*Idn. Limit:* 10 to 15 γ acetic acid).

(b) A drop of acetate solution, that is exactly neutralized, may be identified by the formation of the red-brown complex ferric acetate on addition of $FeCl_3$[49] (*Idn. Limit:* 10 γ acetic acid). It is best to neutralize acid solutions by heating with $CaCO_3$; alkaline solutions by heating with excess $Zn(NO_3)_2$ and then filtering.

14. Monochloracetic acid

Detection with concentrated sulfuric acid and chromotropic acid [50]

If monochloroacetic acid (b.p. 189°) is warmed with concentrated sulfuric acid to 150–180°, considerable amounts of formaldehyde result. This effect can be ascribed to two partial reactions in which concentrated sulfuric acid takes part without however appearing in the corresponding reaction equations. The first step is an hydrolysis of chloroacetic acid to glycolic acid:

$$CH_2ClCOOH + H_2O \rightarrow CH_2OHCOOH + HCl \qquad (1)$$

This hydrolysis is accomplished by the water contained in the concentrated sulfuric acid. Under the conditions of the test, the water is in a state comparable to superheated steam and accordingly is particularly reactive. The glycolic acid produced in (1) is—like other α-hydroxycarboxylic acids — cleaved by the concentrated sulfuric acid, functioning as a dehydrant,[51] with formation of formaldehyde:

$$CH_2OHCOOH \rightarrow H_2O + CO + CH_2O \qquad (2)$$

Formaldehyde reacts with chromotropic acid and concentrated sulfuric acid to give a red-violet quinoid compound (compare page 331), the concentrated sulfuric acid serving as condensing and oxidizing agent. Therefore, if chloroacetic acid is heated with concentrated sulfuric acid in the presence of chromotropic acid, the color characteristic of formaldehyde appears. In the test described here, the concentrated sulfuric acid accordingly acts as dehydrating agent, as oxidant, and as water donor.*

Procedure. The test is conducted in a micro test tube. A tiny crystal of monochloroacetic acid, or a drop of the aqueous solution of this acid (m.p. 65°) is kept at 105° for 30 minutes and then treated with 1–2 drops of concentrated sulfuric acid. One or two tiny particles of chromotropic acid are added and the mixture heated over a micro burner or in a glycerol bath at 170°. A more or less intense violet color appears, the depth depending on the amount of monochloroacetic acid present.

The heating may also be carried on in the gas absorption apparatus commonly used in spot test analysis (Fig. 23, page 49). The formaldehyde in the vapor phase is allowed to come into contact with a drop of concentrated sulfuric acid containing some chromotropic acid.

Limit of detection: 5 γ monochloroacetic acid.

It is characteristic of the test described here that the color reaction does not occur at temperatures below 150–170°. Free formaldehyde and the ma-

* This is supported by the finding that compounds which lose water when heated above 150° act in the same fashion as concentrated sulfuric acid. They include: cellulose, hydrated sulfates of zinc and manganese.

jority of formaldehyde-yielding compounds show this color reaction even at room temperature or after brief warming in the water bath. It is therefore advisable, if no color appears or only a pale coloration, to continue the heating either over an open flame or in a glycerol bath previously brought to 170°. If a violet color results or if the shade deepens, the presence of monochloroacetic acid is assured.

15. Phenoxyacetic acids

Detection with concentrated sulfuric acid and chromotropic acid [52]

Brief heating of phenoxyacetic acid (and its halogen-substituted derivatives) with concentrated sulfuric acid and chromotropic acid to 150° yields the violet color characteristic of formaldehyde. The chemistry of the color reaction is analogous to that of monochloroacetic acid discussed in 14. Because of its water content, the concentrated sulfuric acid brings about the hydrolysis of phenoxyacetic acid to phenol and glycolic acid:

$$C_6H_5OCH_2COOH + H_2O \rightarrow CH_2OHCOOH + C_6H_5OH$$

This is followed by the cleavage of the glycolic acid to yield formaldehyde, which reacts with the chromotropic acid present.

When the test is applied directly, there is interference by compounds which split out formaldehyde when heated with concentrated sulfuric acid, and which thus also give the chromotropic acid reaction. However, the test becomes quite selective for phenoxyacetic acid and halogenated phenoxyacetic acids if use is made of the solubility of these acids in benzene. The interfering compounds can thus be taken out of the reaction theatre, including those which caramelize when heated with concentrated sulfuric acid and so impair the recognition of the color reaction.

Procedure. A micro test tube is used. A drop of the test solution (benzene) is taken to dryness, 2 ml concentrated sulfuric acid added and several mg of solid chromotropic acid mixed in. The mixture is kept at 250° for 90 to 120 seconds. A more or less intense violet color indicates the presence of phenoxyacetic acid or halogen derivatives of this acid.

Limit of identification: 0.05 γ 2,4-dichlorophenoxyacetic acid.

The following acids react in analogous fashion: *p*-phenoxyacetic, *o*- and *p*-chlorophenoxyacetic, 2,4-dibromophenoxyacetic.

The detection of phenoxyacetic acids and their halogen derivatives can be conducted by the procedure given for the detection of monochloroacetic acid, in which the formaldehyde split out is detected in the vapor phase by contact with chromotropic acid and concentrated sulfuric acid. However, the sensitivity is then only about 1/10th as great.

16. Aminoacetic acid

Detection by conversion into glycolic acid [53]

In organic compounds NH_2-groups can be exchanged for OH groups by warming with nitrous acid. Accordingly, it is possible to produce hydroxyacetic acid (glycolic acid) from aminoacetic acid (glycine):

$$CH_2NH_2COOH + HNO_2 \rightarrow CH_2OHCOOH + H_2O + N_2 \qquad (1)$$

If glycolic acid is gently warmed with concentrated sulfuric acid, the former is split with production of formaldehyde:

$$CH_2OHCOOH \rightarrow CH_2O + CO + H_2O \qquad (2)$$

Since formaldehyde gives a violet color with concentrated sulfuric acid and chromotropic acid (see detection of formaldehyde page 331), this color reaction occurs if (2) is carried out in the presence of chromotropic acid. Therefore, if glycine is converted into glycolic acid as shown in (1), it can be detected by means of the formaldehyde-chromotropic acid reaction.

Other amino acids do not interfere with the test because only glycine is convertible into glycolic acid.

The test described here may not be applied in the presence of compounds which yield formaldehyde, such as hexamethylenetetramine and its salts, or sulfoxylate compounds.

Procedure. The test is conducted in a micro test tube. One drop of the test solution is mixed with one drop of a 1% solution of sodium nitrite and one drop of concentrated hydrochloric acid. The mixture is heated briefly to boiling over a free flame. After evaporation to dryness at 105–110° in an oven, the residue is cooled and treated with 2 or 3 drops of the freshly prepared reagent. The mixture is kept in a boiling water bath for 5–10 minutes. A violet color indicates the presence of glycine.

Reagent:　A suspension of chromotropic acid in concentrated sulfuric acid is centrifuged. The supernatant liquid is used as reagent.

Limit of identification: 10 γ aminoacetic acid.

17. Glycolic acid

(1) Test with 2,7-dihydroxynaphthalene and sulfuric acid [54]

When glycolic acid ($CH_2OHCOOH$) is heated with a solution of 2,7-dihydroxynaphthalene (I) in concentrated sulfuric acid, a violet to violet-red color gradually develops. This color reaction probably depends on the condensation of the formaldehyde (split off from the glycolic acid by the action of the concentrated sulfuric acid [55]) with the 2,7-dihydroxynaphthalene, in the position *ortho* to one of the OH groups:

$$HOCH_2COOH \longrightarrow CH_2O + CO + H_2O$$

(I)   (II)

The colorless product, 2,2′,7,7′-tetrahydroxy-1,1′-dinaphthylmethane (II), dissolved in sulfuric acid, is gradually oxidized to a deep red-violet dyestuff, whose constitution is not known.[56] It is probable that (II) is oxidized to a quinoidal compound by the concentrated sulfuric acid (compare page 133).

Neither formic acid, acetic acid, oxalic acid, succinic acid, citric acid, benzoic acid, nor salicylic acid interferes with the test. Both lactic acid * and malic acid give a yellow color and green fluorescence with the reagent, whereas tartaric acid gives an olive to dark green color. Aldehydes such as salicylaldehyde, anisaldehyde, or acetaldehyde react with 2,7-dihydroxy-naphthalene similarly to formaldehyde, with formation of oxidizable condensation products. Under the conditions of the test, certain glycols give yellow colors. [58]

Procedure. A drop of the test solution is mixed in a micro test tube with 2 ml of the reagent solution and heated for 10 to 15 minutes in a water bath. A red to violet-red appears, according to the amount of glycolic acid present.

Limit of Identification: 0.2 γ glycolic acid.

Reagent: 2,7-Dihydroxynaphthalene, 0.01 g dissolved in 100 ml concentrated sulfuric acid.

A freshly prepared reagent solution is yellow, with a green fluorescence, but both color and fluorescence disappear on heating for a short time, or after standing overnight in a stoppered bottle. The reagent is gradually colored violet by the action of a number of oxidizing agents (persulfates, hydrogen peroxide, chlorates, chromates). On standing for a few hours exposed to the air, a slight red to violet-red forms. The reagent remains colorless when heated for 30 minutes, but in the presence of formaldehyde liberated from glycolic acid, the characteristic color develops at once.

The test is also applicable in the presence of citric acid. The glycolic acid can be detected by the appearance of an orange to orange-red color and a green fluorescence. In this way, 1 γ glycolic acid may be detected in the presence of 20,000 times the quantity of citric acid.

* This reaction is also applicable as a test for lactic acid according to a communication from A. Bondi.[57]

(2) Detection with chromotropic acid and sulfuric acid [59]

As stated in Test *1* and also with respect to the detection of aminoacetic acid (page 346), glycolic acid yields formaldehyde when warmed with concentrated sulfuric acid. Since formaldehyde is readily detected by the violet color it produces with chromotropic acid, a mixture of chromotropic acid and sulfuric acid can serve as a reagent for glycolic acid. The absence of formaldehyde and compounds which split off formaldehyde is assumed.

Procedure. A drop of the test solution is taken to dryness at 105–110° in a micro test tube. The residue is treated with 2 or 3 drops of the reagent (preparation see page 346) and the mixture is kept for 3 minutes in a boiling water bath. A violet color develops if glycolic acid was present. A comparison blank is recommended when dilute solutions are being examined.

Limit of identification: 0.2 γ glycolic acid.

18. Lactic acid

(1) Test with p-hydroxydiphenyl and sulfuric acid [60]

When lactic acid is gently warmed with concentrated sulfuric acid, it decomposes initially into acetaldehyde and formic acid:

$$CH_3CH(OH)COOH \rightarrow CH_3CHO + HCOOH$$

The formic acid is dehydrated by the concentrated sulfuric acid:

$$HCOOH \rightarrow H_2O + CO$$

The acetaldehyde reacts with *p*-hydroxydiphenyl (I), probably by condensation at the position *ortho* to the OH-group, and forms di-*p*-hydroxydiphenylethane (II):

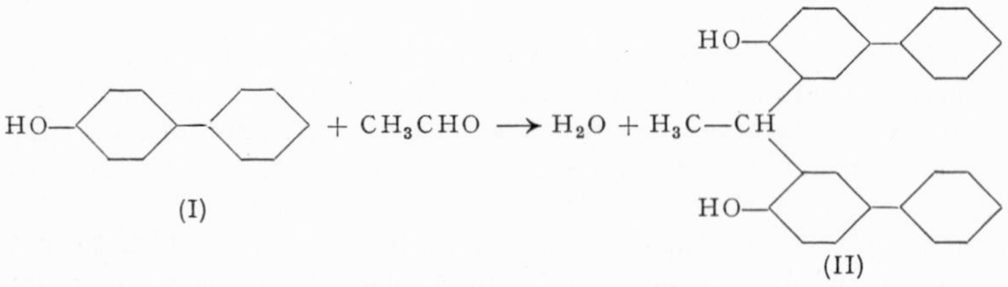

In sulfuric acid solution, (II) is slowly oxidized to a violet product of unknown constitution. Therefore, analogous to the detection of glycolic acid by means of 2,7-dihydroxynaphthalene, the present test involves an aldehyde-phenol reaction in which concentrated sulfuric acid functions as condensing and oxidizing agent. In fact, metaldehyde, paraldehyde, aldol, and propionaldehyde react similarly to acetaldehyde with *p*-hydroxydiphenyl and sulfuric acid to give deep violet products. With formaldehyde the color is blue-green, with butyraldehyde red, and with heptyl aldehyde orange. Accordingly, α-hydroxybutyric acid and pyruvic acid give the same color reaction as lactic acid.

Procedure. A drop of the test solution and 1 ml concentrated sulfuric acid are heated for 2 minutes in a dry test tube in a water bath at 85°. After cooling under the tap to 28°, a pinch of solid p-hydroxydiphenyl is added, the mixture is swirled several times, and left for 10 to 30 minutes. The violet color appears gradually and deepens after some time. A blank test for comparison is advisable when small quantities of lactic acid are suspected.

Limit of Identification: 1.5 γ lactic acid.

(2) Test with o-*hydroxydiphenyl and sulfuric acid (fluorescence test)* [60]

The acetaldehyde formed on heating lactic acid with concentrated sulfuric acid can also be detected by the blue fluorescence with o-hydroxydiphenyl. Formaldehyde, metaldehyde, paraldehyde, aldol, and the next higher homologs of the aldehyde series behave analogously to acetaldehyde. Pyruvic acid does not interfere. The chemical basis of the fluorescing reaction is not known.

Procedure. A drop of the test solution is mixed with a crystal of o-hydroxydiphenyl and 0.5 to 1 ml concentrated sulfuric acid in a dry test tube and heated for 2 minutes at 85° C. in a water bath. It is then examined for a blue fluorescence while holding the test tube against black paper.

Limit of Identification: 1 γ lactic acid.

19. Glyceric acid

Test with naphthoresorcinol and sulfuric acid [60]

When an aqueous solution of glyceric acid (I) is heated with concentrated sulfuric acid containing a little dissolved naphthoresorcinol (II), an intense blue appears.

$$
\begin{array}{l}
CH_2OH \\
| \\
CHOH \\
| \\
COOH
\end{array}
$$

(I)   (II)

The chemistry of this color reaction is unknown, but probably it can be regarded from the same standpoint as the aldehyde-phenol reactions for glycolic- and lactic acid. The mono- and diphosphoric esters of glyceric acid behave similarly to the free alcohol acid.[61]

Glycolic acid and glycocole (glycine) give a brown color; lactic, α- and β-hydroxybutyric, erythronic, gluconic, glyoxylic, pyruvic, levulinic, malic, saccharic, citric, mesoxalic, and dihydroxytartaric acid do not react under the conditions of the test. Tartronic and quinic acids give a greenish color, glucuronic acid a yellow color with a greenish fluorescence, tartaric acid a green to blue-green color, and malic acid a yellow color and a blue fluorescence.[62]

Procedure. A drop of the test solution is mixed with 0.75 ml of the reagent solution and heated for 30 to 50 minutes in a water bath at 90° C. In the presence of glyceric acid a blue color appears, which is light or dark according to the amount present.

Limit of Identification: 10 γ glyceric acid.

Reagent: Naphthoresorcinol, 0.01 g dissolved in 100 ml 96 % sulfuric acid.

20. Pyruvic acid

Test with o-*hydroxydiphenyl and sulfuric acid after reduction to lactic acid* [63]

Pyruvic acid can be reduced to lactic acid by the action of nascent hydrogen (magnesium plus acid):

$$CH_3COCOOH + 2 H^0 \rightarrow CH_3CH(OH)COOH$$

The lactic acid formed can be detected by conversion to acetaldehyde, and the subsequent color reaction with hydroxydiphenyl and sulfuric acid (page 348). The higher homologous α-ketonic acids behave similarly to pyruvic acid.

Procedure. A drop of the test solution is placed in a dry test tube. A little magnesium powder is added and a small drop of concentrated sulfuric acid is allowed to run down the wall of the tube. After the magnesium has dissolved, a crystal of o-hydroxydiphenyl and 0.5 to 1 ml concentrated sulfuric acid are added. The mixture is heated to 85° C. in a water bath for 2 minutes and observed for any color reaction.

Limit of Identification: 3 γ pyruvic acid.

21. Glyoxalic acid

(1) Test with pyrogallolcarboxylic acid and sulfuric acid [64]

When glyoxalic acid (I) and pyrogallolcarboxylic acid (II) are brought together in the presence of excess concentrated sulfuric acid, a blue color develops. The chemistry of this reaction, which is specific for glyoxalic acid, is not known. Probably, in analogy with the tests for glycolic, lactic, and

glyceric acid, an aldehyde-phenol condensation occurs through direct participation of the aldehyde group of the glyoxalic acid.

OCH—COOH·H$_2$O or (HO)$_2$CH—COOH

(I)

$$
\begin{array}{c}
\text{OH} \\
\text{(ring)} \quad
\begin{array}{l}
\text{—OH} \\
\text{—OH}
\end{array} \\
\text{COOH} \\
\text{(II)}
\end{array}
$$

Since the condensation of aldehydes and phenols always occurs *ortho* to
a phenolic OH-group, the case of glyoxalic acid may possibly also involve
the anhydrization of this OH-group with the COOH-group of the glyoxalic
acid with production of a phenol ester. The assumption that the formation
of a phenol ester plays a role in the intense color effect is supported by the
fact that propionaldehyde, butyraldehyde, *iso*butyraldehyde, isovalerian-
aldehyde, and aromatic aldehydes react to give only a yellow color. Formaldehyde and acrolein yield an orange coloration.

Mesoxalic acid [HO$_2$C—CO—CO$_2$H·H$_2$O or HO$_2$C—C(OH)$_2$—CO$_2$H] behaves similarly to glyoxalic acid, a finding that can be ascribed to the fact
that the former is decomposed by concentrated sulfuric acid into carbonic
acid and glyoxalic acid:

$$HO_2C—CO—CO_2H·H_2O \rightarrow H_2O + CO_2 + OCH—COOH$$

For the same reason, dihydroxytartaric acid also reacts under the conditions
of the test.

Procedure. A drop of the test material is treated in a micro test tube with a
little solid pyrogallolcarboxylic acid and a drop or two of concentrated sulfuric
acid. The mixture is cooled by plunging the test tube into water and 0.2–0.7 ml
additional sulfuric acid is added. The mixture is then kept at 40° for about 30
minutes in warm water. A dark to light blue color indicates the presence of
glyoxalic acid.

Limit of Identification: 1 γ glyoxalic acid.

Solutions of the following compounds gave:

No reaction: arabinose, dextrose, saccharose, urea, hippuric acid, alloxan,
alloxantin, allantoin, uracyl, uric acid, diphenylamine, glycolic
acid, lactic acid, α- and β-hydroxybutyric acid, *iso*butyric acid,
glyceric acid, gluconic acid, pyruvic acid, levulinic acid, oxalic
acid, malonic acid, tartronic acid, malic acid, tartaric acid,
citric acid, *o*, *m*, *p*-hydroxybenzoic acid, protocatechuic acid.
Yellow color: glucuronic acid.
Olive green: levulose.

References pp. 440–444

(2) Test by conversion into glycolic acid [65]

Nascent hydrogen, generated from magnesium powder and dilute sulfuric acid, reduces glyoxalic acid to glycolic acid:

$$OCHCOOH + 2 H° \rightarrow CH_2(OH)COOH$$

The resulting glycolic acid can be detected by the delicate test with 2,7-dihydroxynaphthalene described on page 346. Before the reduction essential to this test is carried out, it is necessary to be sure that no glycolic acid is present. Oxalic acid is likewise reduced to glycolic acid by nascent hydrogen (see page 354). In order to test for and, if necessary, to remove oxalic acid, the test solution should be treated with several drops of saturated calcium sulfate solution to precipitate calcium oxalate.* The reduction to glycolic acid is carried out in the filtrate or centrifugate.

Procedure. A drop of the test solution is treated in a semimicro test tube with a drop of 1 N sulfuric acid and a little magnesium powder. After the metal has dissolved, two milliliters of the reagent is added and the test tube kept in boiling water for 15–20 minutes. A red to violet color develops if glyoxalic acid was present.

Limit of Identification: 0.5 γ glyoxalic acid.

Reagent: 0.01 g 2,7-dihydroxynaphthalene, dissolved in 100 ml concentrated sulfuric acid (see remarks on p. 347).

(3) Test with phenylhydrazine and oxidizing agents [67]

If glyoxalic acid is warmed with phenylhydrazine in the presence of a mineral acid, and an oxidizing agent (potassium ferricyanide, alkali persulfate, hydrogen peroxide, etc.) then added to the cold reaction mixture, a red color appears. The mechanism of this reaction is unknown. It seems logical to assume that two reactions of phenylhydrazine play a role, namely: the formation of glyoxalic acid-phenylhydrazone (I) as shown in (1); and the conversion of phenylhydrazine into a diazonium salt (II) through the action of the particular oxidant as shown in (2):

$$CHOCOOH + NH_2NHC_6H_5 \rightarrow C_6H_5NHN=CHCOOH + H_2O \qquad (1)$$
$$\text{(I)}$$

$$C_6H_5NHNH_2 \cdot HX + 2 O \rightarrow C_6H_5-\overset{+}{N}\equiv N\overset{-}{X} + 2 H_2O \qquad (2)$$
$$\text{(II)}$$

It is possible that the red water-soluble compound is the product of a coupling of (I) and (II) and has the structure of an azo compound:

* Brief heating with acetic anhydride completely decomposes (dehydrates) oxalic and formic acid.[66] No study has been made of this behavior for the elimination of these acids in the course of analysis.

$$\langle \rangle -N=N-\langle \rangle -NH-N=CHCOOH$$

The color reaction with phenylhydrazine and oxidants appears to be specific for glyoxalic acid. Glyceric, oxalic, tartaric, citric, malonic, and mandelic acid produce no change in a mixture of phenylhydrazine and hydrogen peroxide (or other oxidants). On the contrary, it is very likely that, under the conditions of the test, glycolic acid reacts in the same manner since an oxidation to glyoxalic acid can occur:

$$CH_2OHCOOH + O \rightarrow CHOCOOH + H_2O$$

This assumption is strengthened by the fact that the glyoxalic acid test is positive when applied to a solution of oxalic acid which has been reduced with zinc and magnesium and which assuredly contains glycolic acid (see Tests 1 and 2 for oxalic acid).

Procedure.[68] A drop of the mineral acid test solution and a drop of freshly prepared 1% phenylhydrazine hydrochloride solution are placed in a depression of a spot plate. The plate is kept in an oven at 110° for five minutes. Then one drop of concentrated hydrochloric acid and one drop of 10 vol. % hydrogen peroxide are added to the cold reaction mixture. A red to pink tint appears at once, the color depending on the glyoxalic acid content of the sample. A blank test is advisable when slight quantities are involved.

Limit of Identification: 1 γ glyoxalic acid.

22. Oxalic acid

(1) Test by conversion into glycolic acid [69]

Oxalic acid is smoothly reduced to glycolic acid by nascent hydrogen:

$$(COOH)_2 + 4 H° \rightarrow CH_2OHCOOH + H_2O$$

The glycolic acid can then be identified by the delicate test with 2,7-dihydroxynaphthalene and concentrated sulfuric acid (see page 346). Glyoxalic acid is likewise reduced by nascent hydrogen to glycolic acid (compare page 352). However, glyoxalate ions are not precipitated by calcium sulfate solution from a neutral solution, and consequently oxalic acid may thus be separated beforehand from the interfering glyoxalic acid. Tartaric acid does not interfere with the test.

Procedure. The calcium salt of oxalic acid is precipitated from a neutral solution by the procedure employed for the detection of oxalic acid in the presence of tartaric acid and other anions [70]. The well-washed calcium oxalate is treated on the filter with warm 2 N sulfuric acid, and a drop of the filtrate is used for the test. The drop is placed in a dry test tube and a little magnesium powder is added. When the metal has dissolved, 2 ml of the reagent solution is added, and the tube is kept in boiling water for 15 to 20 minutes. A red to violet-red color appears if oxalic acid was present.

Limit of Identification: 1 γ oxalic acid.

Reagents: *1)* Calcium sulfate, hydrated (gypsum), saturated solution.

2) 2,7-Dihydroxynaphthalene, 0.01 g dissolved in 100 ml concentrated sulfuric acid (compare remark on page 347).

(2) Test by conversion into glyoxalic acid [71]

The reduction of oxalic acid by nascent hydrogen proceeds in two stages. Glyoxalic acid is the initial product, and then further reduction converts it to glycolic acid:

$$(COOH)_2 + 2 H° \rightarrow CHOCOOH + H_2O \qquad (1)$$

$$CHOCOOH + 2 H° \rightarrow CH_2OHCOOH \qquad (2)$$

A solution of oxalic acid, reduced by magnesium or zinc plus mineral acid, responds not only to the glycolic acid reaction described in Test (*1*), but also to the glyoxalic reaction with phenylhydrazine and hydrogen peroxide (see page 352). It is likely that we are dealing here not solely with the glyoxalic acid produced in (*1*), which on more exhaustive reduction, if even then, can be present only in minute quantity. Rather, the hydrogen peroxide required for the glyoxalic acid reaction may bring about a reoxidation of glycolic to glyoxalic acid:

$$CH_2OHCOOH + O \rightarrow CHOCOOH + H_2O$$

In other words, when the glyoxalic test is applied to a reduced oxalic acid solution, the response arises from the reduction products of both (*1*) and (*2*). A test for oxalic acid can be based on this fact; it is reliable in the absence of glyoxalic or glycolic acid.

The test can be applied to water-insoluble oxalates, a circumstance that can serve for the elimination of glyoxalic and glycolic ions, which are not precipitable by calcium acetate. Likewise, esters of oxalic acid can be detected by the following procedure, provided it is preceded by saponification to alkali oxalate by means of alcoholic alkali.

Procedure.[72] The test is conducted in a depression of a spot plate. A drop of 1 : 1 hydrochloric acid and a granule (about 0.4 g) of zinc are added to one drop of the test solution. After 5 minutes, any unused zinc is removed, a drop of freshly prepared 1% phenylhydrazine hydrochloride solution added, and the spot plate is then kept for 5 minutes in an oven at 110°. After cooling, a drop of concentrated hydrochloric acid and a drop of 3 per cent hydrogen peroxide solution are added. Depending on the quantity of oxalic acid that was present, a red color appears at once, or a pink one develops after 3–4 minutes. It is well to run a comparison blank test when small quantities are involved.

Limit of Identification: 1 γ oxalic acid.

(3) Test by formation of aniline blue [73]

When solid hydrated or anhydrous oxalic acid is heated to 240–250° with diphenylamine (m.p. 54°; b.p. 302°), diphenylamine blue (also known as aniline blue) results. This dyestuff is likewise formed when insoluble oxalates are heated with diphenylamine and syrupy phosphoric acid, the latter serving to liberate the oxalic acid. The synthesis of aniline blue can be represented by the condensation reactions (*1*) and (*2*) followed by oxidation (*3*):

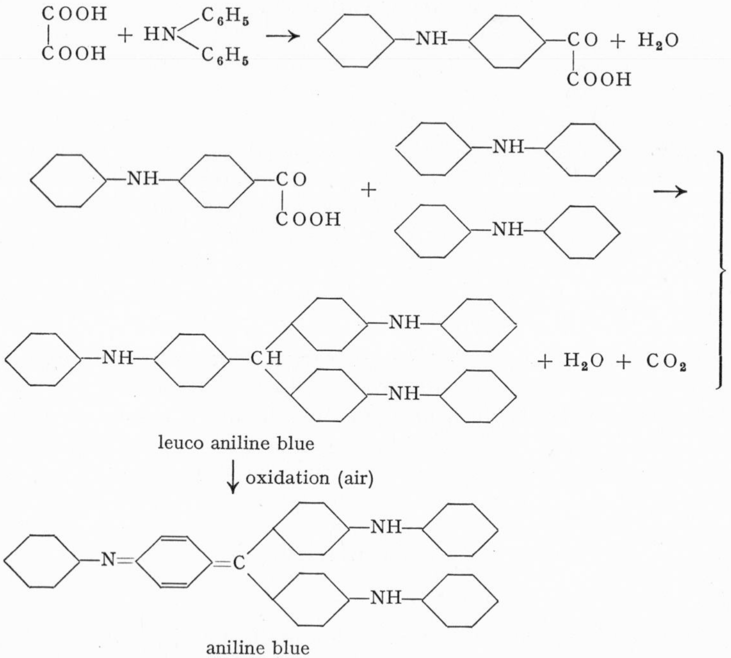

leuco aniline blue

↓ oxidation (air)

aniline blue

If it is assumed that oxalic acid breaks down during the fusion to yield carbon dioxide and formic acid, and that the latter is reactive, the formation of leuco aniline blue can be represented: [74]

$$3 \, C_6H_5NHC_6H_5 + HCOOH \rightarrow CH(C_6H_4NHC_6H_5)_3 + 2 \, H_2O$$

Formic, acetic, propionic, tartaric, citric, succinic, dihydroxymaleic, benzoic, phthalic, tricarballylic, glycolic, and glyoxylic acids do not react under the conditions of the experiment, so that the formation of aniline blue in the reaction with diphenylamine is very selective for oxalic acid.

Procedure. A tiny crystal of the sample (a solution must be evaporated to dryness) is melted with a little diphenylamine in a micro test tube over a free flame. After cooling, the melt is taken up in a drop of alcohol; a blue color indicates the presence of oxalic acid. Under the same conditions a blank test remains colorless.

Limit of Identification: 5 γ oxalic acid.

If oxalate ions are to be detected in a mixture containing other anions precipitated by Ca^{+2}-ions (sulfate, sulfite, fluoride, tartrate, or racemate ions) it is advisable to proceed as follows. The acetic acid solution is treated with $CaCl_2$ solution; the precipitate is then collected on a filter or in a centrifuge tube, and freed from water, either by drying or by washing with alcohol and ether. A little of the precipitate is mixed with diphenylamine in a dry test tube, then syrupy phosphoric acid is added, and the tube heated over a free flame. Calcium phosphate is formed and oxalic acid is liberated and can condense to aniline blue with the diphenylamine. The liquid turns blue, but the color fades on cooling. If the melt is taken up in alcohol, a brilliant blue solution is obtained. If taken up in water, the excess diphenylamine is precipitated and made light blue by absorption of the dye. A blank test that has been treated in the same way gives a pure white precipitate of diphenylamine. The dye can be extracted from the aqueous solution with ether, which increases the sensitivity of the reaction. After being left for a long time, the test that has been extracted with ether again separates into two layers. The blue-violet product then collects in the ether–water interface.

The oxalates of thorium and other rare earths, which can be precipitated from mineral acid solution, behave similarly to calcium oxalate.

When solid esters of oxalic acid are fused with diphenylamine (m.p. 53°), they too form aniline blue.

It must be remembered that oxidizing materials (both inorganic and organic) must be absent when the fusion test with diphenylamine is used.

23. Malic acid

Test with β-naphthol and sulfuric acid [75]

A bluish fluorescence is produced when malic acid (I) is heated with concentrated sulfuric acid containing a little β-naphthol (II). The chemistry of this reaction is not yet explained. Probably the malic acid is split by the concentrated sulfuric acid (phosphoric acid behaves analogously) to produce an aldehyde, which then condenses with the β-naphthol.

HO—CH—COOH
       |
       CH₂—COOH

(I)   (II)

The following acids do not interfere: oxalic, tartaric, citric, succinic, cinnamic, benzoic, salicylic, acetic, formic. A few hydroxy acids such as glycolic and tartaric cause a more or less intense green fluorescence.

Procedure. To detect malate ions in the mixed precipitate, which may contain the calcium salts of citric, tartaric, oxalic, succinic acid, etc., a little of the precipitate or a drop of the solution of the precipitate in dilute sulfuric acid is taken (after the calcium sulfate is removed by filtering or centrifuging). The test material is treated with one milliliter of the β-naphthol reagent and heated briefly on the water bath. A yellowish color with a blue fluorescence appears if malic acid was present.

When dilute solutions of malic acid or its salts are involved, it is best to add a little oxalate and then introduce calcium acetate. The precipitate of calcium oxalate functions as collector for the slight quantities of calcium malate. The fluorescence produced by the action of β-naphthol is visible, even in the presence of calcium sulfate, provided the quantity of malic acid is not exceedingly small.

Limit of Identification: 10 γ malic acid.

Reagent: Solution of 0.0025 g β-naphthol in 100 ml of 96 % sulfuric acid.

24. Tartaric acid

(1) Test with sulfuric acid and gallic acid [75]

On heating calcium tartrate with concentrated sulfuric acid, containing a little gallic acid, a blue color results, which is blue-green to yellow-green when only very small amounts of tartrate are present. This reaction depends on the fact that concentrated sulfuric acid splits tartaric acid (I) and produces glycol aldehyde (II):

$$
\begin{array}{cc}
\text{COOH} & \text{CHO} \\
| & | \\
[\text{CH(OH)}]_2 \longrightarrow \text{H}_2\text{O} + \text{CO}_2 + \text{CO} + \text{CH}_2\text{OH} \\
| & \\
\text{COOH} & \\
\text{(I)} & \text{(II)}
\end{array}
$$

The aldehyde then forms a colored condensation product with gallic acid, $C_6H_2(OH)_3COOH$. The concentrated sulfuric acid probably functions as dehydrant and oxidant. (Compare the Le Rosen test, page 133.)

Under these same conditions, colored products are produced also by glycolic, tartronic, glyceric, and glyoxylic acids, and also formaldehyde, and carbohydrates. No color is formed by oxalic, citric, succinic, lactic, malic, cinnamic, and salicylic acid and the fatty acids.

Procedure. A very small sample of the calcium precipitate is used for this test. It should be filtered, washed, and dried on a hardened filter paper (to avoid interference from fibers of cellulose which also react), transferred to a test tube, treated with 1 ml of the reagent solution, and heated to 120° to 150° over a free flame. When only an extremely small amount of the calcium precipitate is available, it is best to dissolve it on the filter in 2 N sulfuric acid and to use a drop of the filtrate for the test. The following colors are obtained with different amounts of tartaric acid:

100 γ blue
10 γ blue-green
5 γ bluish green
2 γ yellowish green

Reagent: Solution of 0.01 g gallic acid in 100 ml 96% sulfuric acid.

(2) Test with β, β'-dinaphthol and sulfuric acid [76]

A green fluorescence appears if tartaric acid is heated with concentrated sulfuric acid containing β, β'-dinaphthol:

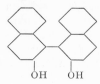

The following acids give no color reaction with this reagent: lactic, malic, α-hydroxybutyric, β-hydroxybutyric, erythronic, pyruvic, levulinic, oxalic, saccharic, citric, salicylic, *m*-hydroxybenzoic, *p*-hydroxybenzoic, protocatechuic, gallic, α-, β- and γ-resorcylic, pyrogallolcarboxylic, quinic, and cinnamic; formaldehyde and carbohydrates do not react.

Various colors are given by: glycolic and glyoxylic acids (red-brown to brown), glyceric and mesoxalic acids (gray), gluconic, glucuronic, dihydroxytartaric, tartronic, and malic acids (green).

Procedure. The sample or a drop of its solution is treated with a little solid β, β'-dinaphthol or a few ml of a 0.05% solution of dinaphthol in concentrated sulfuric acid, and heated for half an hour in a water bath at 85° C. When tartaric acid is present, a more or less strong luminous green fluorescence gradually appears during the heating, and deepens on cooling. At the same time, the violet fluorescence of the reagent itself disappears.

As little as 10 γ of tartaric acid can be detected, if a drop of the test solution is heated for 20 to 30 minutes with 1–2 ml of the reagent solution; 0.05 g tartaric acid can be detected in the presence of any amount of oxalic or succinic acids, and in the presence of 1000 times the amount of citric acid, or 150 times the amount of cinnamic acid, or 10 times the amount of malic acid.

Limit of Identification: 10 γ tartaric acid.

25. Citric acid

(1) Test by conversion into ammonium citrazinate [77]

The ammonium salt of 2,6-dihydroxypyridine-4-carboxylic acid (V) (citrazinic acid or 2,6-dihydroxyisonicotinic acid) exhibits an intense blue fluorescence in the solid state and in aqueous solutions. Citric acid can be converted without difficulty into this salt, starting with a drop of the acid test solution or with a small amount of the solid acid. The following test is based on the production of an ammoniacal solution of citrazinic acid.

The stages in the conversion of citric acid to the fluorescent ammonium salt of citrazinic acid are: the treatment of citric acid (I) with thionyl chloride to form aconitic acid chloride (II); this is converted into the triamide (III) by boiling with ammonia; this compound in its tautomeric form (IV) loses ammonia on heating with 80 % sulfuric acid, the ring closes, and the acid amide group in the middle is saponified. The product is citrazinic acid (V), and on the addition of ammonia, forms the fluorescent ammonium salt (VI): *

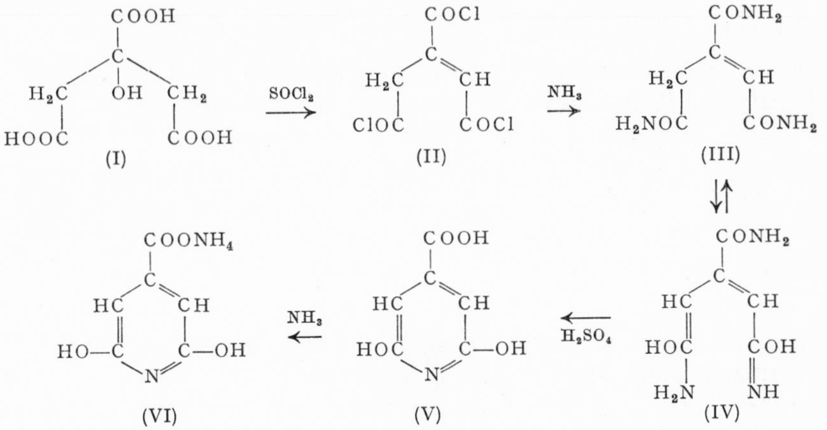

It can be assumed that the fluorescence is not due exclusively to the formation of the ammonium salt of citrazinic acid. The addition of excess ammonia may serve primarily to bind the sulfuric acid necessary to convert (IV) into (V). As a pyridinecarboxylic acid, citrazinic acid is amphoteric since it can form soluble salts not only with bases, by virtue of its carboxyl group, but also with acids, because of its basic cyclic nitrogen atom. Salification of the basic portion of citrazinic acid causes the fluorescence to disappear (compare Test 2).

The test based on the formation of fluorescent ammonium citrazinate is characteristic for citric and aconitic acid; malic and tartaric acid do not react. Intensely fluorescing materials can blanket the fluorescence of

---

* Apparently, part of the citric acid is transformed to citrazinate by other paths, possibly involving citryl chloride and citramide.[78]

ammonium citrazinate. In such cases, it is best to precipitate calcium citrate along with the calcium salts of other organic acids by adding calcium chloride and ammonia, and to dissolve the collected precipitate in dilute hydrochloric acid. This latter solution can then be tested for citric acid.

Procedure. A drop of the test solution is evaporated to dryness in a micro-crucible and the residue is treated with 4 drops of thionyl chloride and taken to fumes. About 8 drops of concentrated aqueous ammonia are then added and the mixture boiled over a microburner until about 2 drops of liquid remain in the crucible. After cooling, 6 drops of concentrated sulfuric acid are added and heating continued until sulfuric acid vapors are given off. The contents of the crucible are washed into a test tube and made ammoniacal. The solution is examined in ultraviolet light for an intense blue fluorescence.

Limit of Identification: 1 γ citric acid.

(2) Test by fusion with urea [79]

One of the classic methods of forming citrazinic acid is to heat the triamide of citric acid.[80] Ammonia is given off and ring closure ensues:

$$
\begin{array}{ccc}
\text{CONH}_2 & & \text{COOH} \\
| & & | \\
\text{C} & & \text{C} \\
\text{H}_2\text{C} \quad \text{OH} \quad \text{CH}_2 & \rightarrow & \text{HC} \quad\quad \text{CH} \\
| & & || \quad\quad || \\
\text{H}_2\text{NOC} \quad\quad \text{CONH}_2 & & \text{HO—C} \quad\quad \text{C—OH} \quad + 2\,\text{NH}_3 \\
& & \text{N}
\end{array}
$$

The triamide of citric acid appears to be readily formed and deamidated to citrazinic acid by simply heating a mixture of citric acid and urea to 180–200°.[79] This assumption is supported by the fact that the resulting product and its aqueous solution exhibit the same blue fluorescence as the ammoniacal solution of the ammonium citrazinate formed in Test *1*. An essential factor for the formation of the citric triamide may be the fact that when urea is heated from its melting point (132°) to temperatures up to 170°, it produces biuret and ammonia:

$$
2\,\text{OC} \begin{array}{c} \nearrow \text{NH}_2 \\ \searrow \text{NH}_2 \end{array} \rightarrow \begin{array}{cc} \text{NH}_2 & \text{NH}_2 \\ | & | \\ \text{OC—NH—CO} \end{array} + \text{NH}_3
$$

Accordingly, the gaseous ammonia acts on citric acid at a temperature which otherwise is reached by the superheated gas only in a closed vessel. Furthermore, the loss of water, which is essential to the amide formation, and its volatilization, can occur in the hot melt. In addition, the possibility is not excluded that the reaction path via the amide is not even necessary in the fusion reaction; at the temperature of the melt and with collaboration of the melt as solvent, there is distinct possibility of direct action of super-heated ammonia on molten citric acid (m.p. 153°) with loss of water and ring closure:

$$
\begin{array}{c}
\text{COOH} \\
|\\
\text{C}\\
\diagup\quad\diagdown\\
\text{H}_2\text{C}\quad\text{OH}\quad\text{CH}_2\\
|\qquad\qquad|\\
\text{HOOC}\qquad\text{COOH}
\end{array}
\;+\;\text{NH}_3\;\longrightarrow\;
\begin{array}{c}
\text{COOH}\\
|\\
\text{C}\\
\diagup\quad\diagdown\\
\text{HC}\qquad\text{CH}\\
||\qquad\qquad||\\
\text{HO}-\text{C}\qquad\text{C}-\text{OH}\\
\diagdown\quad\diagup\\
\text{N}
\end{array}
\;+\;3\,\text{H}_2\text{O}
$$

The reaction between citric acid and urea, which leads to fluorescent citrazinic acid, can be accomplished with small quantities; it occurs on heating to 150°, i.e., just below the melting point of citric acid. When this reaction is used analytically, it should be observed whether the sample has a self-fluorescence and note should be taken of its behavior when heated to 150° without addition of urea. Tartaric acid in quantities less than 500 γ shows no fluorescence. No studies have been reported regarding the behavior of other hydroxy acids. It may be expedient, when testing for citric acid, to make the simple and rapid fusion with urea first and, if the result is positive, confirm the finding by means of Test 1. A further check resides in the fact that the fluorescence of citrazinic acid is quenched on the addition of dilute mineral acid. The blue fluorescence is restored by adding ammonia to the acid solution.

Procedure. [81] The solution to be tested for citric acid is evaporated to dryness in a micro test tube. Alternatively, a slight quantity of the solid sample may be used. About 100–200 milligrams of urea are added, and the tube is kept for 2 minutes in an oil bath heated to 150°. After cooling, the solidified melt is taken up in 2 or 3 drops of water and examined in ultraviolet light for fluorescence. A blank without urea, and a test of the behavior of the fluorescing solution after addition of 1 : 5 hydrochloric acid, are advisable.

Limit of Identification: 2 γ citric acid.
Reagent: Urea (solid).

It is very remarkable that the solid, non-melting alkali- and alkaline earth citrates likewise yield blue fluorescent products when subjected to the procedure here described[82]. Probably alkali or alkaline salts of citrazinic acid are produced through solid body reactions. Consequently, the fusion reaction with urea can be employed also for the direct detection of salts of citric acid.

26. Ethylenediaminetetraacetic acid

(1) Test by masking the formation of nickel dimethylglyoxime *

The alkali salts of ethylenediaminetetraacetic acid (I) have great technical importance as water softeners, for cleaning iron surfaces, for preventing the precipitation of water-insoluble soaps, etc.[84] These actions are due to the fact that, in accord with its structure, the diamino acid is a powerful complex-former. Many metal ions react with the di- or tetra alkali salts ** of this acid to produce water-soluble alkali salts in which the respective metal atom is included in an inner complex anion. Anions of the coordination structure (II) are formed with bivalent metals:

$$
\begin{array}{cc}
\text{H}_2\text{C}\!\!-\!\!\text{CH}_2 & \text{H}_2\text{C}\!\!-\!\!\text{CH}_2 \\
\text{HOOCCH}_2\!\!-\!\!\text{N}\quad\text{N}\!\!-\!\!\text{CH}_2\text{COOH} & {}^-\text{OOCCH}_2\!\!-\!\!\text{N}\quad\text{N}\!\!-\!\!\text{CH}_2\text{COO}^- \\
\text{HOOCCH}_2 \qquad \text{CH}_2\text{COOH} & \text{H}_2\text{C}\quad\text{Me}\quad\text{CH}_2 \\
 & \text{OC}\!\!-\!\!\text{O}\qquad\text{O}\!\!-\!\!\text{CO} \\
\text{(I)} & \text{(II)}\quad\text{Me}=\text{bivalent metal}
\end{array}
$$

The concentration of free Me^{+2} ions is so slight in solutions of (II) that hydroxide, phosphate, etc. precipitations do not occur. The same is true in solutions of the salts of this diamino acid with tervalent and quadrivalent metals. Consequently, ethylenediaminetetraacetic acid or its anions act as masking agents in many analytical procedures.[85] Since the precipitation of the red nickel salt of dimethylglyoxime is prevented when ethylene-diaminetetraacetic acid or its alkali salts are present, a convenient test for this acid can be based on this effect. Although the anions of the diamino acid prevent the precipitation of nickel dimethylglyoxime, nevertheless if the nickel dimethylgloximate has once been formed, the precipitate is quite resistant to ammoniacal or acetic acid solutions of the alkali salts of ethylenediaminetetraacetic acid.

Procedure.[86] Single drops of 0.008% solution of hydrated nickel sulfate are placed in adjacent depressions of a spot plate, and a drop of the solution to be tested is added to one, and a drop of water to the other. Then one drop of dilute ammonia and one drop of 1% dimethylglyoxime alcoholic solution are added to each. A distinct precipitate of red nickel dimethylglyoxime will appear in the blank, whereas the other mixture will remain unaltered if ethylene-diaminetetraacetic acid is present.

Limit of Identification: 1.7 γ ethylenediaminetetraacetic acid.

* The test is based on a method for the quantitative determination of ethylenediaminetetra-acetic acid.[83]
** Compare page 287 regarding the differentiation of these alkali salts.

(2) Test by prevention of the formation of zinc–8-hydroxyquinoline [86]

As noted in Test *1*, ethylenediaminetetraacetate ions prevent precipitation and color reactions of numerous metal ions, because these metals are included in the anionic portion of water-soluble chelated compounds of this masking agent. A similar sequestering action also affects zinc ions with respect to their precipitability with 8-hydroxyquinoline (oxine), with which Zn^{+2} ions normally give a light yellow precipitate which fluoresces yellow in ultraviolet light. (Compare, detection of 8-hydroxyquinoline, page 378.) If zinc oxinate is dissolved in a dilute mineral acid, the non-fluorescing solution yields the yellow fluorescing salt on the addition of ammonia. However, if an excess of ethylenediaminetetraacetic acid is introduced prior to the alkalization, no precipitation occurs and consequently there also is no fluorescence. This behavior permits the detection of ethylenediaminetetraacetic acid if small quantities of zinc oxinate are used.

Procedure. A drop of the test solution is placed in a depression of a spot plate, and a drop of water in an adjoining depression. One drop of the solution of zinc oxinate in dilute hydrochloric acid is stirred into each. A drop of 1:1 ammonia is then introduced. A vigorous fluorescence, which is clearly visible in ultraviolet light, appears at once in the blank test.

Limit of Identification: 8 γ ethylenediaminetetraacetic acid.

Reagent: Solution of 0.025 g zinc oxinate* in 100 ml dilute hydrochloric acid.

27. Salicylic acid (and Salicylic esters)

Test by conversion into fluorescent alkali salicylates [87]

Both solid and dissolved alkali and alkaline earth salts of salicylic acid exhibit a strong blue-violet fluorescence in ultraviolet light. This effect can be observed even with minute quantities, provided the salicylate is present alone. The fluorescence test is not reliable if applied directly, say by alkalizing solutions of salicylic acid, since the alkali salts of many carboxylic acids and phenols, as well as numerous other organic compounds, also fluoresce. However, salicylic acid can be separated from accompanying materials by converting it into methyl- or ethyl salicylate. These esters are formed by heating solutions of salicylic acid in methyl- or ethyl alcohol with concentrated sulfuric acid, which acts to remove the water produced in the reaction:

$$C_6H_4(OH)COOH + ROH \rightarrow C_6H_4(OH)COOR + H_2O$$

---

* Preparation: The warm weakly ammoniacal solution of a zinc salt is treated with an alcohol solution of 8-hydroxyquinoline. The light yellow precipitate is thoroughly washed with water, then with alcohol, and dried.

References pp. 440–444

Although these esters boil at 223° and 232° respectively, their vapor pressures at room temperature, and even more when gently heated, are sufficient to permit their saponification, in the gas phase, on contact with alkali hydroxide or moist magnesium oxide:

$$C_6H_4(OH)COOR + KOH \rightarrow C_6H_4(OH)COOK + ROH$$

Salicylic acid can also be separated from organic admixed materials, to an extent adequate for qualitative detection, without going through the esterification step, by merely heating with concentrated sulfuric acid. In this case, the loss of water from one or two molecules leads to the salicyl anhydride (I) or (II):

(I)   (II)

The vapor pressure of this sublimable anhydride (b.p. 200°) is sufficient at 130° to produce fluorescent salicylates on contact with a caustic alkali solution or suspension of magnesia.

Starting with one drop of test solution, the esterification, saponification, and formation of the anhydride can be carried out in simple fashion in a closed space; salicylic acid can be detected with sensitivity and specificity in this way. Salicylaldehyde, or compounds which split off this aldehyde must be absent because the alkali or magnesium salts of this phenolic compound exhibit a blue-green fluorescence in ultraviolet light.

Procedure. The apparatus (Fig. 23, page 49) is used. A drop of the test solution is evaporated to dryness in the bulb (it is not essential to evaporate alcoholic solutions). A drop of concentrated sulfuric acid is then added. The knob of the stopper is dipped into 3% potassium hydroxide solution or a water suspension of magnesium oxide or hydroxide. The stopper with the hanging drop is put into position and the closed apparatus is placed in an oven at 130° for 5–10 minutes (or 15 minutes for very small amounts of salicylic acid). If salicylic acid was present, a violet fluorescence will be observed on the knob. A blank is imperative when small amounts of salicylic acid are involved.

Limit of Identification: 5 γ salicylic acid.

This esterification procedure will reveal acetylsalicylic acid (aspirin) $C_6H_4(OCOCH_3)COOH$, with an identification limit of 7 γ, following removal of the CH_3CO-group by evaporation with dilute caustic alkali. The procedure can also be applied to alkali salts of salicylic acid

Esters of salicylic acid with alcohols and phenols are liquids or solids which, without exception, have a pleasing odor, a fact which proves that they have a distinct vapor pressure even at room temperature. Their saponification can be accomplished by bringing the volatilized ester into contact with alkali hydroxide or magnesium oxide; the resulting alkali- or magnesium salicylate exhibits fluorescence. If several milligrams of a salicylic ester are placed in a microcrucible, which is then covered with a disk of filter paper impregnated with caustic alkali and weighted down with a watch glass, a circle, fluorescing blue-violet, will develop within 10–15 minutes at room temperature. A much more sensitive test for salicylic esters is to place a drop of the ether solution in the apparatus prescribed above (Figure 23) and then to volatilize the ether by brief immersion in boiling water. The knob, carrying a drop of caustic alkali or magnesium oxide suspension, is fitted into place, and the residual ester is kept at 130° for about 10 minutes. The resulting vapors are saponified by the base in the hanging drop, with production of fluorescent salicylate. This method revealed:

1 γ methyl salicylate (oil of wintergreen), $C_6H_4(OH)COOCH_3$
1.5 γ phenyl salicylate (salol), $C_6H_4(OH)COOC_6H_5$

28. Aniline sulfonic acids

Detection through release of sulfuric acid [88]

When aqueous solutions of sulfanilic acid (or its isometric metanilic and orthanilic acids) are treated with barium chloride there is no apparent change because the alkaline earth salts of alkylsulfonic acids are soluble in water. If an acidified water solution of the aniline sulfonic acids is treated with an excess of bromine water, light yellow tribromaniline precipitates and the solution then contains free sulfuric acid: [89]

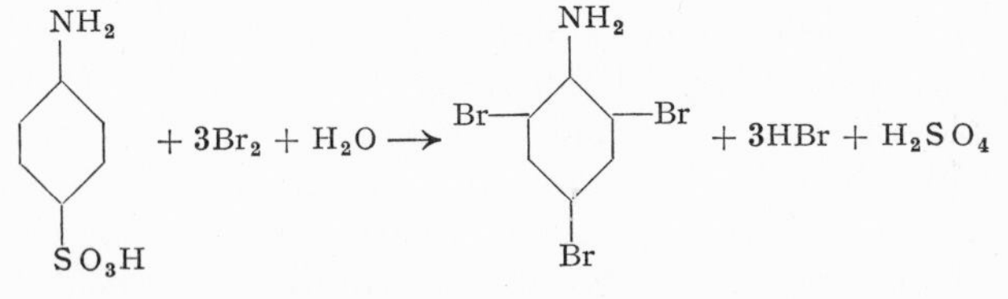

Since tribromaniline is readily soluble in ether, extraction of the suspension with this solvent (which also takes up the excess bromine) yields a clear solution in which the resulting SO_4^{-2} ions can be detected by precipitation of barium sulfate.

Sulfanilamide and sulfonamides react with bromine water to give insoluble brominated substitution products, which, for the most part, are soluble in ether, but in these cases there is no liberation of sulfuric acid. In contrast, phenol sulfonic acids behave similarly to the aniline sulfonic acids: 2,4,6-tribromophenol and free sulfuric acid result.

Procedure. A drop of the test solution is placed in a micro test tube and acidified with hydrochloric acid. Saturated bromine water (or a saturated solution of bromine in 5% potassium bromide) is added drop by drop; a precipitate or turbidity is produced. The suspension is shaken with a few drops of ether and one or two drops of 3% barium chloride solution are allowed to flow through the ether layer. An immediate precipitate or a turbidity which develops within a few minutes indicates the presence of sulfanilic acid.

Bromine water containing barium chloride may also be used. In this case a positive result is signalled by the presence of a precipitate or turbidity in the water layer after extraction with ether. A comparison blank with pure bromine water is advisable if this procedure is used.

Limit of Identification: 1 γ sulfanilic acid.

Since, as just stated, the phenolsulfonic acids likewise exchange the SO_3H-group for bromine on treatment with bromine water, the identification or detection of aniline sulfonic acids requires the supplementary detection of NH_2-groups. This can be accomplished by means of the formation of orange Schiff bases through the action of acetic acid solutions of p-dimethyl-aminobenzaldehyde (see page 273). If the test is conducted as a spot test on a porcelain plate, as little as 0.05 γ sulfanilic acid can be detected.

29. Rhodizonic acid

Detection by formation of barium rhodizonate [90]

The dark brown sodium salt of rhodizonic acid (I) is stable when dry. Its yellow water or orange solution is an excellent reagent for barium and lead ions. In neutral or acid solutions (buffered with acetate or tartrate), these ions give red and red-violet precipitates, respectively (see Volume I, Chap. 3). The formation of a crystalline red-violet precipitate with ethylene-diamine (propylenediamine) chloride is noted on page 396. These reactions may be employed for the detection of rhodizonic acid. The formation of the barium salt of this acid is the most sensitive. This salt (II) is obtained by the reaction of sodium rhodizonate with barium ions (likewise in alkaline solution) or by reaction of acidified solutions of rhodizonic acid with barium carbonate.

(I)　　　　　　　　(II)

Analogous reactions are given by tetrahydroxyquinone and croconic acid, whose structures are similar to that of rhodizonic acid (compare detection of inositol, page 393).

Procedure. If the sample is a neutral or alkaline solution of alkali salts of rhodizonic acid, a drop of the solution is treated with a drop of 2% barium chloride solution on a spot plate. Depending on the quantity of rhodizonic acid, a red precipitate or a pink coloration results. In case acid solutions are to be tested, a drop is treated on a spot plate with the least amount of barium carbonate until no more carbon dioxide is evolved. If rhodizonic acid is present, the unused barium carbonate will be coated with a red or pink layer.

Limit of Identification: 0.1 γ rhodizonic acid.

30. Anthraquinone sulfonic acids

(1) Detection by conversion into polyhydroxyanthraquinones [91]

The classic method for preparing alizarin is to fuse anthraquinone-2-sulfonic acid with caustic alkali in contact with air (Graebe, Liebermann, Perkin, 1869). Alizarin is formed more quickly if alkali nitrate or chlorate is present as oxygen donor:

$$+ \text{NaOH} + 2\text{O} \rightarrow \qquad + \text{Na}_2\text{SO}_4$$

The corresponding polyhydroxyanthraquinones are formed in an analogous manner from anthraquinone di- and trisulfonic acids. Sintering at temperatures below 200° is sufficient and if excess alkali hydroxide is used, violet alkali salts of the polyhydroxyanthraquinones result. Since anthraquinone sulfonic acids and their alkali salts are practically colorless in the solid state, the production of the colored phenolates in the sintering reaction is readily discerned.

Procedure. One drop of the test solution is placed in a depression of a spot plate. A tiny portion of the solid may also be taken for the test. A drop or two of sodium nitrate solution (1 gram in 10 ml of 20% sodium hydroxide) is added. The mixture is first taken to dryness and then kept at 160–180° for several minutes on a hot plate. Depending on the amount of anthraquinone sulfonic acid present, the residue turns more or less violet.

Limit of Identification: 2 γ anthraquinone-2-sulfonic acid.

(2) Detection through catalysis of the glucose-alkali hydroxide reaction [92]

An intense red-brown color appears if a strongly alkaline sugar solution is warmed. The chemistry of this reaction is not known. The reaction is slow with dilute caustic or carbonate solution, and with ammonium hydroxide or ammonium carbonate it does not occur at all. In these latter cases, the reaction is speeded up or initiated by adding anthraquinone sulfonic acid. This catalytic effect is so marked that it serves as the basis of a test for the anthraquinone sulfonic acids.

Procedure. The test is conducted in a micro test tube. One drop of the aqueous solution of the sulfonic acid or its alkali salt is treated with one drop of a 10% solution of glucose in 1 : 1 ammonium hydroxide. A yellow or red-brown color appears, the shade depending on the amount of anthraquinone sulfonic acid present. A blank test is advisable if slight amounts are suspected.

The *limits of identification* are: 0.4 γ anthraquinone-2-sulfonic acid; 30 γ anthraquinone disulfonic acid.

31. Sulfosalicylic acid

(1) Test with methylenedisalicylic acid [93]

When methylenedisalicylic acid (I) which is colorless and water-insoluble, is heated to 120–150° with concentrated sulfuric acid, red quinoidal formaurindicarboxylic acid (II) results:

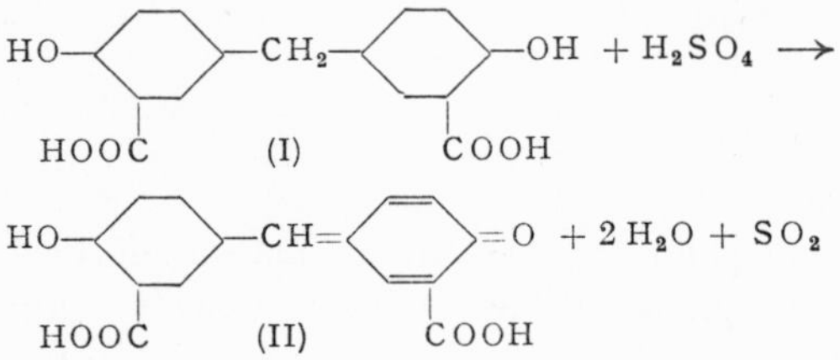

The reaction occurs because the concentrated sulfuric acid functions as both oxidant and dehydrant. The production of the red formaurindicarboxylic acid * makes possible the detection of slight quantities of free (unbound) sulfuric acid (as little as 2.5 γ per drop).[95]

5-Sulfosalicylic acid behaves toward methylenedisalicylic acid in the same manner as concentrated sulfuric acid, a fact which at first glance is not comprehensible. However, it has long been known that salicylic acid and phenol are produced when sulfosalicylic acid is heated above its melting point (120°).[96] Obviously, sulfur trioxide is produced when these two products are formed and it behaves like concentrated sulfuric acid with respect to dehydrating and oxidizing effects. It is noteworthy that the formation of the red formaurindicarboxylic acid occurs even when a colorless mixture

---

* Formaurindicarboxylic acid was prepared[94] by oxidation of methylenedisalicylic acid with nitrosylsulfuric acid (conc. H_2SO_4 plus crystals of KNO_2).

of powdered salicylic acid and methylenedisalicylic acid (m. p. 238°) is heated to 110° for a short time, or when a little solid methylenedisalicylic acid is added to fused salicylic acid. Consequently, it appears that formaurindicarboxylic acid can result from a reaction between two solids, or a solid and a melt, or a solid with a gas. The fusion reaction predominates under the conditions of the present test.

When applying the test with methylenedisalicylic acid, it should be noted that many aromatic sulfonic acids react in analogous fashion as concentrated sulfuric acid and sulfosalicylic acid do, i.e., they cause production of formaurindicarboxylic acid. The procedure given here is particularly useful as a convenient method of distinguishing between salicylic and sulfosalicylic acid. This is not possible with the ferric chloride color reaction because the latter, as a general phenol test, is not characteristic.

Procedure. A drop of the test solution is treated in a porcelain microcrucible with several milligrams of methylenedisalicylic acid. The mixture is taken to dryness and the residue kept in an oven at 150° for three minutes. According to the quantity of sulfosalicylic acid, the residue will be red or pink. A blank is advisable when small amounts are suspected.

Limit of Identification: 10 γ sulfosalicylic acid.

(2) Test by conversion to salicylic acid [97]

As stated in Test *1*, phenol as well as salicylic acid is formed when fused sulfosalicylic acid (m.p. 120°) is heated. The salicylic acid sublimes and can be detected through the action of the vapors on magnesium oxide. Magnesium salicylate is formed and it fluoresces blue in ultraviolet light (see page 363). It has been found that the melt of sulfosalicylic acid must be heated to at least 170° if detectable quantities of salicylic acid are to be produced rapidly enough. It is best to heat to higher temperatures and to employ freshly precipitated magnesium hydroxide to bind the sublimed salicylic acid.

Obviously this test for sulfosalicylic acid is not applicable in the presence of salicylic acid. The latter can be tested for as described on page 363 since sulfosalicylic acid does not interfere, because the temperature prescribed is below the decomposition temperature of sulfosalicylic acid.

If salts of sulfosalicylic acid are involved, the dry test material should be heated with syrupy phosphoric acid until vitreous phosphorus pentoxide remains.

Procedure. The apparatus (Fig. 23) described on p. 49 is used. A drop of the test solution is evaporated to dryness in the bulb, or a little of the solid is introduced. The knob of the stopper is charged with a drop of a suspension of magnesium hydroxide; the apparatus is closed, and a microflame is applied to the bottom.

After cooling, the suspended drop is wiped on a strip of filter paper and viewed in ultraviolet light. If sulfosalicylic acid is present, a blue fluorescing fleck will be seen on the paper. It is advisable to conduct a comparison test with a drop of the magnesium hydroxide suspension when very small quantities of sulfosalicylic acid are being sought.

Limit of Identification: 1.5 γ sulfosalicylic acid.

Reagent: Magnesium hydroxide suspension: 30 ml of 10 % solution of crystallized magnesium sulfate is treated with 2 ml of 5 N sodium hydroxide.

32. Ascorbic acid (Vitamin C)

Ascorbic acid (I), a lactone of an unsaturated sugar acid in which two enol groups produce the acidity, is converted, by even weak oxidizing agents, into dehydroascorbic acid (II), which actually is not an acid but a neutral lactone. It may be reconverted to ascorbic acid by reduction:

$$O=C-C(OH)=C(OH)-CH-CH(OH)-CH_2OH \quad (I)$$

oxidation $\downarrow\uparrow$ reduction

$$O=C-CO-CO-CH-CH(OH)-CH_2OH \quad (II)$$

Stronger oxidizing agents give rise to extensive decomposition of (I) or (II).

Ascorbic acid is therefore an active reductant, which can be detected by numerous color tests based on reducing actions. Insoluble reducible inorganic compounds which have been precipitated in the capillaries of filter paper, and which, due to their fine state of division, are exceptionally reactive, can be reduced by ascorbic acid. Two instances of this behavior, which are accompanied by striking color changes, are utilized here, and certain characteristic redox reactions in homogeneous systems are also described.

(1) Test by reduction of manganese dioxide [98]

Ascorbic acid reduces manganese dioxide to a manganous salt. Paper impregnated with highly dispersed MnO_2 is prepared easily by treating filter paper with potassium permanganate solution. Part of the cellulose is oxidized, and finely divided MnO_2 is precipitated in the capillaries of the paper. The color of the paper ranges from brown to almost white, according to the MnO_2 content. Larger quantities of ascorbic acid are revealed directly by the white fleck that results when a drop of the test solution is placed on the brown paper. Practically colorless reagent paper should be used for minute quantities of ascorbic acid. The removal of MnO_2, in this case, is made visible by bathing the spotted paper in benzidine solution which forms "benzidine blue" with traces of MnO_2 (comp. Vol. I, Chap. 3). Consequently, the whole surface will turn blue, except those spots that had been reduced by ascorbic acid.

Procedure. A drop of the weakly acidified (acetic acid), neutral, or alkaline test solution is placed on the reagent paper. After the liquid has been absorbed, the paper is bathed in benzidine solution. A white fleck on the blue paper indicates the presence of ascorbic acid.

Limit of Identification: 0.03 γ ascorbic acid (in 0.004 ml).

Reagents: 1) Manganese dioxide paper: 1 ml 0.2 N $KMnO_4$ is diluted to 1000 ml. The paper is soaked in this solution for 15 minutes. After draining, it is dried in a stream of heated air.

   2) Benzidine solution: saturated solution of benzidine hydrochloride diluted just before using with an equal volume of water.

Other reducing compounds in weakly acid solution exert the same effect on manganese dioxide, i.e., they reduce it to a manganous salt. Citric acid is an example. To detect ascorbic acid in the presence of the latter (in fruit juices, for instance) the test solution is shaken beforehand with an excess of calcium carbonate. A drop of the suspension is then applied to the reagent paper. This preliminary treatment produces insoluble calcium citrate and the reduction of MnO_2 paper by citric acid is thus prevented entirely while the action of ascorbic acid is practically not affected.

(2) Test by reduction of ammonium phosphomolybdate [98]

The complexly bound MoO_3 molecules, in water-soluble phosphomolybdic acid, $H_3PO_4 \cdot 12MoO_3 \cdot aq.$, are far more easily reduced than the hexavalent molybdenum of normal molybdate ions. In other words, certain reducing agents, which are without effect in acid solution toward MoO_4^{-2} ions, or which are only slightly active, reduce the latter immediately when PO_4^{-3} ions, which produce complex phosphomolybdate ions, are also present.[99] When phosphomolybdic acid is reduced, the solution turns from yellow to blue, an effect due to the resulting colloidally dispersed lower molybdenum oxides (the so-called molybdenum blue). Since even traces of the latter are discernible, phosphomolybdic acid is a good reagent for revealing reducing compounds (see p. 128). The enhanced reducibility of the complexly bound molybdenum is retained in the yellow ammonium phosphomolybdate, which is not soluble in water and mineral acids, but this is true only with respect to strong reductants. Accordingly, compounds with differing redox potentials can be differentiated by this means. Ascorbic acid acts on ammonium phosphomolybdate, and consequently can be detected by spotting paper impregnated with $(NH_4)_3PO_4 \cdot 12MoO_3$.*

Procedure. A drop of the acid, neutral, or alkaline test solution is placed on the reagent paper. According to the amount of ascorbic acid, a blue or green fleck appears on the yellow paper immediately, or after several minutes.

Limit of Identification: 0.1 γ ascorbic acid (in 0.01 ml).

Reagent: Ammonium phosphomolybdate paper. Filter paper is immersed in saturated alcohol solution of phosphomolybdic acid, allowed to drain, and dried in a current of cold air. It is then bathed in a concentrated ammonium nitrate solution that has been acidified with several drops of nitric acid. After washing with water, the paper is dried in a blast of heated air. It can be kept for several days in the dark.

On long standing and exposure to daylight, the yellow ammonium phosphomolybdate paper turns blue because of reduction by the cellulose.

Citric acid gives no reaction under the conditions just prescribed. It is possible to detect ascorbic acid in the presence of as much as 1000 parts of citric acid.

Uric acid and urates react readily with ammonium phosphomolybdate and may be detected through this reaction. However, mineral acids prevent this reduction. Consequently, ascorbic acid can be detected in urine, provided the sample is treated beforehand with several drops of concentrated hydrochloric acid.

(3) Test through precipitation of cuprous ferrocyanide [101]

Ascorbic acid reduces ammoniacal cupric solutions; the blue color is discharged. However, Cu_2^{+2} ions are detected with greater sensitivity through appropriate precipitation reactions from ammoniacal solutions. In contrast to the corresponding cupric salts, both cuprous ferrocyanide and cuprous ferricyanide are insoluble in ammonia. Accordingly, if ammoniacal cupric solutions, i.e., $[Cu(NH_3)_4]^{+2}$ ions, are reduced by ascorbic acid in the presence of alkali ferricyanide or alkali ferrocyanide, white $Cu_3[Fe(CN)_6]$ or $Cu_4[Fe(CN)_6]$ precipitates immediately. For stability reasons, it is better to use an ammoniacal $CuSO_4$—$K_3[Fe(CN)_6]$ solution as reagent.

Hydrazine and hydroxylamine and their salts must be absent because they show reducing actions similar to that of ascorbic acid.

Procedure. A watch glass on black paper, or a black spot plate is used. A drop of the ammoniacal, neutral, or weakly acid test solution is mixed

* Of course, ascorbic acid likewise reduces the water-soluble phosphomolybdic acid.[100]

with a drop of reagent solution. A white precipitate or turbidity appears, according to the amount of ascorbic acid present.

Limit of Identification: 0.5 γ ascorbic acid.

Reagent: A slight excess of freshly prepared 0.2 N potassium ferricyanide is added to 0.5 N copper sulfate and the resulting light brown precipitate is dissolved in ammonia. The emerald green solution keeps for several days.

(4) Test with chloranil [102]

Ascorbic acid is readily oxidized by chloranil (tetrachloro-p-quinone). In alcohol or water-alcohol solution, the redox reaction is discernible through the discharge of the yellow color of the chloranil solution, provided rather large quantities of the reactants are present. The redox reaction occurs also in dilute solutions, either of ascorbic acid or chloranil, and permits the detection of the ascorbic acid through the demonstrable consumption of chloranil. Since very dilute chloranil solutions are almost colorless, it is necessary to use the highly sensitive test for chloranil with tetrabase, (compare page 433). This test is based on the production of a blue diphenylmethane dyestuff through oxidation of the colorless tetrabase. Accordingly, if the acetic acid solution to be tested for ascorbic acid is treated with a little chloranil, warmed, and tetrabase then added, a negative response to the chloranil test shows that the latter has been consumed and consequently the presence of ascorbic acid is indicated.

As in the other tests for ascorbic acid based on redox reactions, the absence of other reducing agents is necessary. An advantage of the test with chloranil is that citric acid, tartaric acid, oxalic acid, formic acid, and formaldehyde do not react with chloranil.

Procedure. A drop of the aqueous neutral or acetic acid test solution is treated in a micro test tube with a drop of 0.001% alcoholic chloranil solution and the mixture is warmed for 5 minutes in the water bath. One drop of tetrabase solution is then added, and the heating continued for 2–3 minutes. A comparison test with a drop of water or dilute acetic acid should be made. The presence of ascorbic acid is indicated if, in contrast to the blank, no blue color appears or if a distinctly weaker blue results.

Limit of Identification: 0.5 γ ascorbic acid.

Reagent: 0.2 g tetrabase is dissolved in 1 : 1 acetic acid, and the volume made up to 10 ml with saturated sodium acetate solution.

(5) Other tests for ascorbic acid

a) The brown solution of ferric ferricyanide (equal parts of 1% $Fe_2(SO_4)_3$, 0.4% $K_3Fe(CN)_6$ and 8% CH_3COOH) gives a blue precipitate or color with ascorbic acid. (*Ind. Limit:* 3 γ ascorbic acid) [103]. Considerable quantities of cysteine, pyrogallol and glutathione react similarly to ascorbic acid.

Ascorbic acid is not stable if its alkaline solution stands in contact with air. However, this autoxidation proceeds gradually and so tests based on redox reactions with ammoniacal solutions of ascorbic acid are possible. This is the basis of the reactions *b–d* [104].

b) A red precipitate of cuprous-*p*-dimethylaminobenzylidenerhodanine appears when an ammoniacal solution of ascorbic acid is added to a solution consisting of 0.5 *N* copper sulfate plus an equal volume of 1 *N* sodium pyrophosphate plus several drops of saturated *p*-dimethylamino-benzylidenerhodanine. The reagent solution keeps for 1/2 day. One drop is placed on filter paper and spotted with one drop of the ammoniacal test solution. (*Idn. Limit:* 0.05 γ).

c) A drop of $Na_2CuP_2O_7$ solution (preparation, see *b*), to which has been added several crystals of KCNS, is mixed on a watch glass or black spot plate with a drop of the ammoniacal test solution. The production of cuprous thiocyanate results in a white precipitate or turbidity. (*Idn. Limit:* 2 γ).

d) A white fleck results when paper impregnated with a little PbO_2 or Tl_2O_3 is spotted with the ammoniacal test solution. The reduction of these higher oxides is made more evident by bathing the dried paper in a solution of benzidine hydrochloride (see page 371).

Hydrazine or hydroxylamine interfere with tests *a-c*.

e) The ninhydrin test for amino acids (page 282) can also serve for the detection of ascorbic acid [105]; a reddish-brown fleck or ring is obtained. (*Idn. Limit:* 10 γ). Large amounts of glucose interfere, but citric acid does not. Amino acids must be destroyed by adding a drop of 0.5 % $NaNO_2$.

f) The test for reducing sugars by means of triphenyltetrazolium chloride (page 389) can be employed for the detection of ascorbic acid. In view of the instability of alkaline solutions of ascorbic acid, the test solution must be added to a boiling mixture of two drops of triphenyltetrazolium chloride solution and one drop of 0.5 % NaOH. (*Idn. Limit:* 0.2 γ) [105].

g) Ascorbic acid seems to be the unique organic compound which reduces SeO_2 at room temperature to red elementary selenium.[105a] (*Idn. Limit:* 1 γ).

33. Salicylaldehyde

(*1*) *Test by conversion into yellow fluorescing alkali phenolate* [106]

Salicylaldehyde (I) is sparingly soluble in water, but it dissolves readily in organic liquids. It reacts with alkali hydroxides to produce water-soluble phenolates, whose yellow color in daylight, and blue-green fluorescence in ultraviolet light, may be related to the chelate nature of the salicylaldehyde (Ia) and its alkali salts (II).

(I)   (Ia)   (II)

The formation of water-soluble sodium or potassium salts of salicylaldehyde (o-hydroxybenzaldehyde) occurs instantly if a drop of its solution in water, alcohol, ether, etc., is placed on filter paper impregnated with caustic alkali. A yellow fleck results (*Idn. Limit:* 6 γ aldehyde); it displays a powerful blue-green fluorescence in ultraviolet light. If the test is carried out on an ether solution of the aldehyde which is so dilute that no visible yellow fleck remains, the blue-green fluorescence will still give a positive result down to a dilution of 1 : 1,000,000. Interestingly, the yellow ammoniacal solution of salicylaldehyde behaves differently. When a drop of the solution is put on filter paper, the fluorescence disappears after several minutes; spotting with ammonia or alkali hydroxide then produces no fluorescence.

The color of the yellow alkaline solutions of salicylaldehyde is discharged by the addition of mineral acids, and the fluorescence also disappears. When shaken with ether, the aldehyde quantitatively enters the ether layer. The *m*- and *p*-hydroxybenzaldehydes, which are isomeric with salicylaldehyde, are likewise soluble in alkali hydroxide (the *m*-compound with honey-yellow color) but the solutions show no fluorescence in ultraviolet light.

The test for salicylaldehyde through formation of the fluorescing alkali salt, takes advantages of the fact that this aldehyde (m.p. 2°) has a distinct vapor pressure even at room temperature, and this pressure increases distinctly when the material is moderately warmed. The boiling point is 197°. Accordingly, a fluorescing phenolate is formed immediately when the vaporizing aldehyde comes in contact with alkali hydroxide. This test for salicylaldehyde in the gas phase, though less sensitive than the test with dissolved aldehyde, is almost specific because it is not impaired by the presence of other compounds whose alkaline solutions are colored or fluorescent. Salicylic acid is an exception (see page 363).

Procedure. One drop of the solution in ether, or some other readily volatilized solvent, is placed in a microcrucible, which is then covered with a disk of filter paper impregnated with 1N potassium hydroxide. A small watch glass is placed on the filter paper, and the crucible is allowed to stand at 25–50° for 5–10 minutes. If salicylaldehyde is present, a circle, which fluoresces blue-green under the ultra-violet lamp, is formed. ›

Limit of Identification: 0.5 γ salicylaldehyde.

Test (*1*) and also Test (*2*) are given by compounds which split off salicyl-aldehyde when hydrolyzed by acids or when heated. Examples are: salicyl-aldoxime and its salts, salicyl alcohol, and salicin.

(*2*) *Test through conversion into fluorescing salicylaldazine* [106]

Salicylaldehyde, dissolved in acetic acid, alcohol, acetone, etc. quantitatively reacts with a solution of hydrazine or a hydrazine salt to yield the whitish-yellow water insoluble salicylaldazine:

$$H_2NNH_2 + 2 C_6H_4(OH)CHO \rightarrow C_6H_4(OH)CH{=}N{-}N{=}CH(OH)C_6H_4 + 2 H_2O$$

This product shows a strong orange fluorescence in ultraviolet light (compare page 220).

The precipitation occurs also from mineral acid solutions of hydrazine sulfate; it is complete after buffering with alkali acetate. The precipitating ability of salicylaldehyde stands in sharp contrast to the lack of reactivity observed under the same conditions with the isomeric *m*- and *p*-hydroxy-benzaldehydes. This divergence is probably due, as shown in the partial structural formulas (III)–(V), to the fact that only the condensation product of salicylaldehyde with hydrazine leads to a 6-membered ring (chelate ring) as a result of the coordination of the H-atom of the phenolic OH-group to the tervalent nitrogen atom ligated with the carbon atom.

      (III)   (IV)   (V)

A further indication of the singularity of the chelation is the fact that only the salicylaldazine exhibits a luminous greenish-yellow fluorescence, whereby traces of this compound may be detected in ultraviolet light.

It is interesting to note that only the solid salicylaldazine is fluorescent; its solutions in ether, chloroform, etc. show no fluorescence. If a drop of the non-fluorescing solution is placed on filter paper and the solvent allowed to evaporate, a yellow-green fluorescing spot is left.

The precipitation of salicylaldazine provides not merely a sensitive and specific test for hydrazine (Vol. I, Chap. 3), but also a means of detecting salicylaldehyde. If one drop of hydrazine solution containing alkali acetate is treated on paper with a drop of an ether solution of salicylaldehyde, a yellow fluorescent fleck results. (When slight amounts of salicylaldehyde are involved, the given order of addition must be observed.) The *identification limit* is 1 γ salicylaldehyde. It is better to take advantage of the vapor tension of salicylaldehyde, as in Test 1, and to accomplish the aldazine formation from the gas phase of this aldehyde.

Procedure. One drop of an ether solution of salicylaldehyde is placed in a microcrucible, which is then covered with a disk of filter paper that has been moistened with hydrazine sulfate solution containing alkali acetate. A watch glass is placed on the paper and the assembly allowed to stand for 5 minutes at 25–50°. If salicylaldehyde is present, a circle, which fluoresces yellow in ultraviolet light, forms on the paper.

Limit of Identification: 1 γ salicylaldehyde.

Reagent: Cold saturated solution of hydrazine sulfate or hydrochloride, to which several grams of sodium acetate has been added.

34. Saligenin (Salicyl alcohol)

(1) Test by conversion into salicylaldehyde [107]

When saligenin is warmed with a sulfuric acid solution of alkali chromate, the CH_2OH-group is oxidized to —CHO and salicylaldehyde is formed:

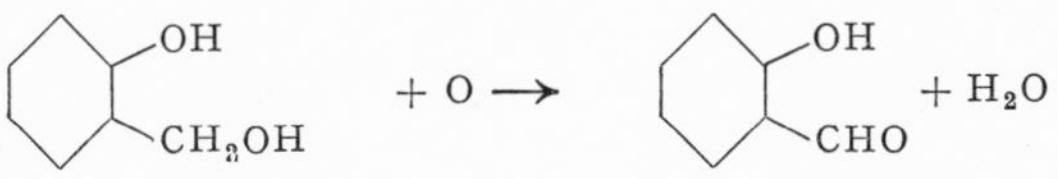

This volatile aldehyde may react in the vapor state with hydrazine acetate to give the fluorescing salicylaldazine (compare page 376).

The oxidation of salicyl alcohol to salicylaldehyde can be accomplished in simple fashion and without significant further oxidation to salicylic acid by heating the salicyl alcohol (m.p. 100°) with manganese dioxide to 240°. This probably is a topochemical redox reaction of the molten salicyl alcohol with solid manganese dioxide.

Procedure. A drop of the alcoholic solution is placed in a micro test tube along with several centigrams of manganese dioxide paste. The mouth of the test tube is covered with a disk of filter paper moistened with hydrazine solution. The test tube is heated for 5 minutes in an oil bath at 240–250°. If salicyl alcohol is present, a stain is formed on the paper and fluoresces yellow-green in ultraviolet light.

Limit of Identification: 2 γ salicyl alcohol.

References pp. 440–444

Reagents: 1) Manganese dioxide paste, prepared by warming a manganous solution with alkali hypobromite.

2) Hydrazine solution: 10 grams hydrazine sulfate and 10 grams sodium acetate per 100 ml water.

35. Carbolic acid

Test by conversion into salicylaldehyde [108]

When many phenols, including carbolic acid, are warmed with caustic alkali and chloroform, a CHO-group is introduced *ortho* to the OH- group (compare page 185). Accordingly, salicylaldehyde results from carbolic acid:

$$\text{C}_6\text{H}_5\text{—OK} + \text{CHCl}_3 + 3\,\text{KOH} \longrightarrow \text{C}_6\text{H}_4(\text{—OK})(\text{—CHO}) + 3\,\text{KCl} + 2\,\text{H}_2\text{O}$$

The salicylaldehyde can then be detected by taking advantage of its considerable vapor pressure at 100°, since reaction of the vapor with hydrazine yields the aldazine, which has a yellow-green fluorescence, or the vapor reacts with alkali and the yellow fluorescent alkali salt of the phenolic aldehyde is formed (see page 374). Methyl carbolic acids (cresols) behave similarly to carbolic acid because of the low vapor pressure of the resulting *o*-hydroxyaldehydes produced by the treatment with caustic alkali and chloroform.

Procedure. A drop of the alkaline test solution is placed in a microcrucible and evaporated at 110° in an oven. Ten or fifteen drops of chloroform are added to the dry residue; the chloroform is removed in a water bath (about 80°), and the treatment with chloroform is repeated. A drop of sulfuric acid is added to the residue, and the crucible is covered with a watch glass, whose lower side carries a disk of filter paper moistened with hydrazine solution or 1 N KOH. The covered crucible is kept in a drying oven at 110° for a minute or two, and the paper is then examined in ultraviolet light. A fleck which fluoresces yellow-green appears if hydrazine paper was used, whereas the fluorescence hue is blue-green if caustic alkali paper was employed. The fleck on the hydrazine paper is not affected by 6 N acetic acid; whereas the stain produced on the caustic alkali paper disappears when treated with dilute acetic acid.

Limit of Identification: 50 γ carbolic acid.

Reagent: Hydrazine solution: 10 g hydrazine sulfate and 10 g sodium acetate are boiled with 100 ml water.

36. 8-Hydroxyquinoline

Test by chemical adsorption from the vapor phase on alumina or magnesia [109]

8-Hydroxyquinoline (I), usually known as oxine, is widely used in analysis to precipitate metal ions from acetate-buffered or tartrated ammoniacal solutions.[110] The resulting crystalline metal oxinates are, for the most part, soluble in chloroform and other organic liquids that are immiscible with water. They are inner complex salts of the coordination formula (II):

$Me = \frac{1}{2} Mg, \frac{1}{2} Zn, \frac{1}{3} Al$, etc

(I)   (II)

Most metal oxinates of this structure are yellow to green-yellow. As solids, or dissolved in organic liquids, they have a strong yellow to blue-green fluorescence. It is highly probable that the fluorescence is related to the formation of salts of the amphoteric oxine. This idea is supported by the fact that not only metal oxinates but also practically all anhydrous salts of oxine with inorganic and organic acids fluoresce powerfully in the solid form (but not in aqueous solution) [111], whereas oxine itself exhibits no fluorescence either as solid or in solution. However, there is a salt-like binding of oxine to metal atom not only when formula-pure oxinates precipitate but also when slight quantities of oxine are chemically adsorbed on the surface of metal oxides. In other words, metal oxides (oxyhydrates and hydroxides) on contact with oxine dissolved in water or organic liquids, are brought to fluoresce with the same hue as is displayed by the corresponding metal oxinate.[112] The chemical adsorption of oxine (= HOx) on solid aluminum hydroxide (and analogously for Al_2O_3, MgO, ZnO, etc.) can be schematically represented as a surface reaction:

$$[Al(OH)_3]_x + HOx \rightarrow [Al(OH)_3]_{x-1} \cdot Al(OH)_2Ox + H_2O \qquad (1)$$
$$\text{yellow fluorescence}$$

If Al_2O_3, MgO, ZnO, etc. and solid oxine are placed under a watch glass, the oxide begins to fluoresce vigorously within a few minutes. The reason is that oxine, which melts at 79°, has sufficient vapor pressure even at room temperature to bring oxine vapor into contact with the oxide. The surface reaction just represented schematically occurs under these conditions and fluorescence ensues. This adsorption (on a metal oxide) of oxine derived from the vapor phase serves as the basis of the following test, which is strictly specific for oxine. Its derivatives, such as trichloro- and tribromo- as well as sulfonated 8-hydroxyquinoline, which have the same reactive group as the parent compound, do not exert enough vapor pressure, even when heated to 150°, to give the vapor phase test. However, these derivatives of oxine can be adsorbed on metal oxides from their solutions in water or organic liquids, and can be detected in this way by the formation of fluorescent products (see page 188).

Free oxine, which volatilizes to a noticeable degree even at room temperature, must be present if fluorescence is to be produced. It is easily soluble in alcohol, ether, chloroform, etc.; the solubility in water is around 0.06 g per 100 ml. In its water-soluble salts with alkalies or mineral acids, oxine does not have adequate vapor pressure to be adsorbed from the vapor phase. If, therefore, oxine is to be detected in water solutions of its salts, where perhaps it is accompanied by free alkali or free acid, the oxine must be set free and the water removed prior to making the fluorescence test. When a drop reaction is carried out, the water can be bound sufficiently by adding anhydrous sodium sulfate (conversion to $Na_2SO_4 \cdot 10H_2O$). Oxine can be liberated from acid solutions by adding ammonium carbonate. If alkaline solutions are presented for examination, they should be acidified first of all. The optimum conditions for the adsorption of oxine from the gas phase are observed in the following directions.

Procedure. The fluorescence test is conducted in the apparatus shown on page 49 (Fig. 23). The glass knob is coated with Al_2O_3 or MgO by dipping it into a thick paste of the oxide in water and then drying in an oven. A drop of an ether or chloroform solution to be tested for oxine is transferred to the bulb of the apparatus, and the main portion of the solvent is evaporated by plunging the bulb once into boiling water. This step is unnecessary when alcohol solutions are being tested. The apparatus is then closed with the stopper carrying the adsorbent and kept for five minutes in an oven at 110°. The stopper is then examined under a quartz lamp. When dealing with water solutions of oxine or its salts, a drop is placed in the apparatus and about 0.5 g anhydrous sodium sulfate added to bind the water. If it is necessary to liberate the oxine from its salts, solid ammonium carbonate should be added before the sodium sulfate. When Al_2O_3 or MgO serves as the adsorbent, the presence of oxine is indicated by a yellow-green fluorescence in ultraviolet light. Comparison with a blank test is advisable when the fluorescence is weak.

Limit of Identification: 0.25 γ 8-hydroxyquinoline.

37. Pyrocatechol

(1) Test with metaldehyde [113]

On treatment with metaldehyde in approximately $12 N$ sulfuric acid pyrocatechol gives a red-violet to pink color. The chemistry of this color reaction is not known. The action of the concentrated sulfuric acid may produce a phenol-aldehyde condensation which is followed by oxidation to a quinoid compound. Compare the Le Rosen test, page 133.

References pp. 440–444

The following information is available concerning the behavior (color reaction) of other aromatic hydroxy compounds toward metaldehyde and sulfuric acid: phenol, gradual greenish; orcinol, yellow to reddish; hydroquinone and hydroxyhydroquinone, yellow; guaiacol, red; veratrole, red; α- and β-naphthol, yellow; 1,3-dihydroxynaphthalene, yellow; 2,7-dihydroxynaphthalene, orange-red; 1,8-dihydroxynaphthalene, no reaction; 2,3-dihydroxynaphthalene (in water solution), no reaction; protocatechualdehyde, 2-hydroxy-3-methoxy-benzaldehyde, vanillin, veratraldehyde, piperonal, yellow; 2,3,4-trihydroxybenzaldehyde, yellow to reddish-yellow; salicylic acid, protocatechuic acid, gallic acid, pyrogallic acid, quinic acid, 3,4-dihydroxycinnamic acid, no reaction.

Procedure. A drop of the aqueous test solution is treated on a spot plate with a little solid metaldehyde and one milliliter of approximately 12 N sulfuric acid. The mixture is stirred with a glass rod. Depending on the quantity of pyrocatechol, a violet or red color appears immediately or after several minutes.

Limit of Identification: 4 γ pyrocatechol.

(2) Test with phloroglucinol [114]

If phloroglucinol and caustic alkali are added to a water solution of pyrocatechol, a green to blue-green color appears, which is stable for some time. The chemical basis of this color reaction is not known.

The behavior of other aromatic hydroxy compounds toward alkaline phloroglucinol has been reported as: phenol, resorcinol, orcinol, guaiacol, veratrole, α- and β-naphthol, 1,8-, 2,3-, and 2,7-dihydroxynaphthalene, vanillin, veratraldehyde, piperonal, salicylic acid, quinic acid, no reaction; hydroquinone, yellow-red to orange; pyrogallol, brownish to brown-red; naphthoresorcinol, reddish-yellow; 2,6-dihydroxynaphthalene, light orange-violet; 2-hydroxy-3-methoxybenzaldehyde, yellow; guaiacolaldehyde, yellow; protocatechualdehyde, yellow, gradually becoming olive-brown; 2,3,4-trihydroxybenzaldehyde, olive-green turning brown to red-brown; protocatechuic acid, yellow-green, later red-brown; 3,4-dihydroxycinnamaldehyde, green-yellow, later red-yellow; 3,4-dihydroxyphenylalanine, transient greenish-yellow, then yellow.

Procedure. One drop of the aqueous test solution, in a small test tube, is treated with a little solid phloroglucinol, washed down with several drops of water and the mixture is then rendered alkaline by shaking with a drop of 1 N sodium hydroxide solution. The total volume should be about 0.5 milliliter. Depending on the quantity of pyrocatechol present, a green or blue-green color appears immediately or within a minute or two.

Limit of Identification: 0.5 γ pyrocatechol.

References pp. 440–444

38. Resorcinol

Test with pyrocatechol and alkali hydroxide [115]

If a dilute aqueous solution of resorcinol is treated with solid pyrocatechol and dilute sodium hydroxide, a transient blue-green color appears and then gradually a pink to violet-red color develops on the surface of the solution, gradually progressing downward and increasing in intensity. The production of the red color is characteristic for the presence of resorcinol. The chemical basis of this color reaction is not known.

Orcinol gives a transient olive-green, going to brownish on standing; pyrogallol is colored olive-greenish briefly, then olive-yellow, and brownish on standing; phloroglucinol, permanently olive-green to blue-green; hydroxyhydroquinone orange-reddish, then orange-yellowish to light brownish on standing; phenol, *o,o'*- and *p,p'*-dihydroxydiphenyl, α- and β-naphthol, α,α'- and β,β'-dinaphthol, 1,8- and 2,7-dihydroxynaphthalene, no reaction; naphthoresorcinol, olive-greenish; 4-(*n*-hexyl)-resorcinol, transient blue-green, on the surface an olive-green ring, which is unchanged even after 5 minutes; 2,4-dihydroxybenzaldehyde, transient weak green, becoming weakly orange-yellowish on standing; 2,3,4-trihydroxybenzaldehyde, greenish-yellow, olive-yellow; 2,4,6-trihydroxybenzaldehyde, yellow, green, blue-green, olive green, and an olive-green ring; benzoic acid, salicylic acid, *m*- and *p*-hydroxybenzoic acid, protocatechuic acid, *o*-phthalic acid, 1-hydroxy-2-naphthoic acid, no reaction. The following additional color changes were observed: α-resorcylic acid gradually becomes green, on standing, a greenish-yellow ring; β-resorcylic acid, transient olive-greenish, then the upper half of the liquid slowly turns weak orange-pink; 2,4,6-trihydroxybenzoic acid, olive-greenish, green, blue-green, and a blue-green ring.

Procedure. One drop of the aqueous test solution is treated, in a small test tube, with some solid pyrocatechol and, with shaking, made up to 2 milliliters with water. One drop of 0.33 *N* sodium hydroxide is then added, the mixture is swirled once, and then allowed to stand quietly. The appearance of a pink to violet-red color in the upper half of the liquid indicates the presence of resorcinol. *Limit of Identification:* 1 γ resorcinol.

39. Hydroquinone

(1) Test with o-phthalaldehyde [116]

o-Phthalaldehyde, dissolved in concentrated sulfuric acid, gives with hydroquinone a blue to blue-violet color at once or within a few minutes, depending on the amount of hydroquinone present. Compounds such as quinic acid and the glucoside arbutin, which are split by concentrated sulfuric acid to yield hydroquinone, react in the same way. The chemical basis of this color reaction has not been clarified.

The results with other aromatic hydroxy compounds are: phloroglucinol, 2,5-dihydroxybenzaldehyde, p-hydroxybenzoic acid, protocatechuic acid, pyrogallolcarboxylic acid, no reaction; guaiacol, eugenol, m-hydroxybenzoic acid, o-resorcylic acid, hydroquinone carboxylic acid, o- and m-cresol, p,p'-dihydroxydiphenyl, yellow color; pyrocatechol, dark brown; resorcinol, yellow, reddish yellow; phenol, reddish, yellow-red, brown-red; orcinol, yellow, red-yellow; thymol, red; menthol, orange-reddish; hydroxyhydroquinone, red, violet-red; pinacol hydrate, yellowish; terpinol hydrate, brownish-red; pyrogallol, red-brown; resorcinol diacetic acid and gallic acid, intense yellow; salicylic acid, yellowish, orange-pink; a-resorcylic acid, greenish-yellowish; a-naphthol, brown-red; β-naphthol, yellow-red; 1-hydroxy-2-naphthoic acid, orange colors; 3-hydroxy-2-naphthoic acid, reddish brownish; o-hydroxydiphenyl, yellow with green fluorescence; m-hydroxydiphenyl, orange-red, brownish-red; o,o'-dihydroxydiphenyl, olive-greenish; p-cresol, brownish-yellow; β,β'-dinaphthol, reddish, brownish red; 1,3-dihydroxynaphthalene, brown-yellow; 1,4-dihydroxynaphthalene, red; 1,5-dihydroxynaphthalene, violet-red; 1,8-dihydroxynaphthalene, golden yellow; 2,6-dihydroxynaphthalene, brownish red; 2,7-dihydroxynaphthalene, red-brown to violet-brown; quinhydrone, violet; quinone, violet-brownish to violet.

Procedure. A drop of the aqueous solution to be tested is placed in a small test tube and some solid o-phthalaldehyde and 1.5 ml of concentrated sulfuric acid are added. A violet color, which appears at once or within a few minutes, indicates the presence of hydroquinone.

Limit of Identification: 7 γ hydroquinone.

(2) Test with phloroglucinol [117]

Small quantities of hydroquinone give an orange-pink color with phloroglucinol in alkaline solution. Larger quantities yield a more yellow-red to orange-red color. The chemistry of the color reaction is not known.

The following statements refer to the behavior of other aromatic hydroxy compounds toward phloroglucinol and alkali hydroxide: phenol, resorcinol, orcinol, no reaction; hydroxyhydroquinone, a brownish color; pyrogallol, light violet-orange to reddish-brown; pyrocatechol, green to blue-green; 2,5-dihydroxybenzaldehyde, yellow; 1,4-dihydroxynaphthalene, gradual orange-yellow; arbutin, no reaction; quinone and quinhydrone, same reaction as hydroquinone.

Procedure. One drop of the aqueous test solution is treated in a small test tube with a little solid phloroglucinol, rinsed down with several drops of water until the total volume is about 1 milliliter. Then a drop of 0.5 N sodium hydroxide solution is added with shaking. According to the quantity of hydroquinone, an orange-red to orange-pink color appears.

Limit of Identification: 0.5 γ hydroquinone.

40. Hydroxyhydroquinone

Test with p-*phthalaldehyde* [118]

A violet color forms if hydroxyhydroquinone is treated with *p*-phthalaldehyde (terephthalaldehyde) and concentrated sulfuric acid and, after dilution with water, the mixture is made weakly basic with alkali hydroxide. Probably a condensation product is formed; its composition and constitution are unknown.

The behavior of other phenols and phenolcarboxylic acids is: carbolic acid and orcinol, no reaction; thymol, faint yellow; pyrocatechol, olive-brownish; resorcinol, orange colors; hydroquinone, brownish; pyrogallol, brownish yellow; phloroglucinol, orange-yellowish turbidity; *p*-hydroxybenzoic acid, α- and β-resorcylic acid, no reaction; quinic acid, yellow; gallic acid, olive-green; tannic acid, brownish yellow; 3,4-dihydroxycinnamic acid, olive-brownish; protocatechuic acid and pyrogallolcarboxylic acid, intense yellow; 2,4,6-trihydroxybenzoic acid, orange turbidity.

Procedure. A drop of the aqueous solution to be tested is treated in a small test tube with some solid *p*-phthalaldehyde, and 0.5 ml concentrated sulfuric acid added. The mixture is gently warmed, cooled, diluted with water, and (with cooling) then made alkaline with 8 N sodium hydroxide. The total volume then should be about 7 milliliters. Depending on the quantity of hydroxyhydroquinone present, a violet to pink-violet color appears.

Limit of Identification: 5 γ hydroxyhydroquinone.

41. Phloroglucinol

Test with 2-*hydroxy-5-methoxybenzaldehyde* [118]

An orange-pink to orange-red color appears when phloroglucinol is treated with concentrated hydrochloric acid and 2-hydroxy-5-methoxybenzaldehyde. The chemistry of this quite sensitive color reaction has not been unravelled.

The following statements apply to the color reactions of other aromatic hydroxy compounds on treatment with concentrated hydrochloric acid and 2-hydroxy-5-methoxybenzaldehyde: resorcinol, phenol, pyrocatechol, hydroquinone, pyrogallol, hydroxyhydroquinone, α- and β-naphthol, 1,3-, 1,4-, 1,5-, 1,8-, 2,3-, 2,6-, 2,7-dihydroxynaphthalene, α-resorcylic acid, no reaction; orcinol, in small amounts, orange-yellow, in larger amounts, yellow-red; 2,4,6-trihydroxybenzaldehyde, no reaction at first, on standing light orange-yellow; 2,4,6-trihydroxybenzoic acid, no reaction at first, gradually increasing orange on standing.

Procedure. A drop of the aqueous test solution is placed in a depression of a spot plate and stirred with one drop of the aldehyde and one milliliter of concentrated hydrochloric acid. According to the quantity of phloroglucinol present, an orange- or orange-pink color appears immediately or after 5–8 minutes.

Limit of Identification: 1 γ phloroglucinol.

Reagent: 2-Hydroxy-5-methoxybenzaldehyde (m.p. = 4°).

42. Pyrogallol

Test with phloroglucinol [118]

As was pointed out in 40 and 41, a caustic alkaline solution of phloroglucinol reacts with pyrocatechol and hydroquinone to give characteristic blue-green or yellow-red colors. The same colors are produced in ammoniacal solutions. In addition, phloroglucinol reacts in ammoniacal solution with pyrogallol to give a violet-orange to violet-reddish color. The chemistry of the color reaction is not known.

The following information is available regarding the behavior of ammoniacal phloroglucinol solutions toward aromatic hydroxy compounds: phenol, 2,3- and 2,7-dihydroxynaphthalene, vanillin, veratraldehyde, salicylic acid, quinic acid, no reaction; pyrocatechol, blue-green; hydroquinone, yellow; resorcinol, yellow, olive-yellow; orcinol, light orange-yellowish; hydroxyhydroquinone, grey-brown, olive-brown; α-naphthol, bluish violet; β-naphthol, weak violet colors; 1,3-dihydroxynaphthalene, red-yellow; 1,8-dihydroxynaphthalene, grey; 2,6-dihydroxynaphthalene, yellow to orange-yellowish; protocatechuic acid, yellow, olive-green, green; 2,3,4-trihydroxybenzoic acid, olive-green, brown-olive. Gallic acid gives the same orange-reddish color as is produced by ammonia alone.

Procedure. A drop of the aqueous test solution is treated on a spot plate with a drop of aqueous phloroglucinol solution and a drop of concentrated ammonia. Depending on the quantity of pyrogallol present, a violet or a pink tending toward violet appears after about 30 seconds.

Limit of Identification: 1 γ pyrogallol.

Reagent: Solution of 0.05 g phloroglucinol in 25 ml water (freshly prepared).

43. Acetone

Test with guaiacoldialdehyde [118]

In strong alkaline solution, guaiacoldialdehyde $C_6H_2(CHO)_2(OH)(OCH_3)$

(1,3,4,5) reacts with acetone to give a difficultly soluble condensation product, whose constitution is unknown. Its color is orange to orange-red.

Other ketones react with alkaline guaiacoldialdehyde as follows: methyl ethyl ketone, yellow to brownish yellow color or precipitate; diethyl ketone, yellow color or precipitate; ethyl phenyl ketone, benzophenone, dibenzyl ketone, no reaction; acetophenone, methyl α-naphthyl ketone, yellow-red to brown-red products. No reaction is given by formaldehyde, acetaldehyde, chloral, methyl alcohol, ethyl alcohol.

Procedure. The test is conducted in a small test tube (1–2 ml). One drop of the aqueous test solution is treated with a little solid dialdehyde, rinsed down with a drop or two of water, and then granules of potassium hydroxide gradually added with constant shaking. The dialdehyde dissolves at first with a yellow color; with increasing amounts of base, the yellow-whitish potassium salt of the dialdehyde precipitates. If acetone is present, the condensation product precipitates and tints the sediment orange to orange-red.

Limit of Identification: 0.2 γ acetone.
Reagent: Guaiacoldialdehyde *.

44. *iso*Propyl alcohol

Test by conversion into acetone [119]

Suitable oxidants, such as alkali persulfate, readily convert *iso*propyl alcohol into acetone:

$$CH_3CH(OH)CH_3 + O \rightarrow CH_3COCH_3 + H_2O$$

The acetone can then be detected by the sensitive test with alkaline guaiacoldialdehyde just described.

Diphenylcarbinol, methylacetylcarbinol, furoin, benzoin, and propylene glycol give no reaction.

Procedure. The test is conducted in a small test tube. A drop of the test solution is diluted with one or two drops of water and then warmed briefly with a tiny crystal of ammonium persulfate over a low flame. A little of the liquid dialdehyde (m.p. 4°) and several granules of potassium hydroxide are then introduced. The remainder of the procedure is as described above. The quantity of persulfate must be kept as small as possible to avoid oxidation of the dialdehyde, whose reagent action is essential.

Limit of Identification: 3 γ *iso*propyl alcohol.

---

* The literature contains no precise directions for preparing guaiacoldialdehyde, which is also known as 4-hydroxy-5-methoxy*iso*phthalaldehyde.

45. Glycerol

(1) Test by conversion to acrolein [120]

When heated with a dehydrating agent, such as potassium bisulfate, glycerol produces acrolein, an unsaturated aldehyde: [121]

$$CH_2(OH)CH(OH)CH_2(OH) \rightarrow H_2C{=}CH - CHO + 2\,H_2O$$

When treated with an aqueous solution of sodium nitroprusside containing a little piperidine, acrolein gives a blue color, which turns violet-red [122] with alkali. The chemistry of this reaction is not known. It has not been possible to isolate a compound of definite formula from the components necessary for the color reaction, although the acrolein may be substituted by other aldehydes, and the piperidine by secondary aliphatic amines (page 260).

The acrolein formed by removal of two molecules of water from glycerol may alternatively be detected by reaction with dianisidine, in which case a colored Schiff base is formed, with elimination of a molecule of water.

The procedure given here makes use of the volatility of acrolein and the color reaction of the aldehyde vapor with dianisidine or with sodium nitroprusside solution containing piperidine. The procedure cannot be used in the presence of ethylene glycol or lactic acid since these compounds decompose under the conditions prescribed to yield acetaldehyde which reacts with the reagents in the same manner as acrolein.

Procedure. A small amount of the test substance or a drop of the test solution is placed in the hard glass tube described on page 50 (Fig. 28) and mixed with finely powdered potassium bisulfate. A piece of filter paper moistened with the reagent is placed over the open end of the tube and covered with the glass cap. The acrolein, produced by heating, colors the test paper a deep gentian blue. On treating the paper with $2\,N$ sodium hydroxide, the blue area changes to the color of a peach blossom.

When using the alternative solution of o-dianisidine in glacial acetic acid, a brown-red to yellow stain is formed on the paper.

Limit of Identification: 5 γ glycerol.

Reagents: 1) Freshly prepared mixture of 1 drop of 5 % solution of sodium nitroprusside and one drop of 20 % piperidine.

       2) Saturated solution of o-dianisidine in glacial acetic acid.

(2) Test by formation of 8-hydroxyquinoline [123]

When a mixture of aniline, glycerol, concentrated sulfuric acid and a weak oxidant (e.g., arsenic acid, nitraniline) is heated, quinoline is formed. If derivatives of aniline with a free *ortho*-position are employed in this Skraup[124] synthesis, numerous derivatives of quinoline can be produced. For example,

8-hydroxyquinoline results if o-aminophenol is used. In this synthesis,[125] the glycerol is dehydrated to acrolein by the concentrated sulfuric acid (1). The acrolein condenses, with ring-closure,[126] with o-aminophenol to produce 8-hydroxy-1,2-dihydroquinoline (2). The latter is then oxidized to 8-hydroxyquinoline (3):

$$CH_2OHCH(OH)CH_2OH \longrightarrow H_2C{=}CH{-}CHO + 2 H_2O \qquad (1)$$

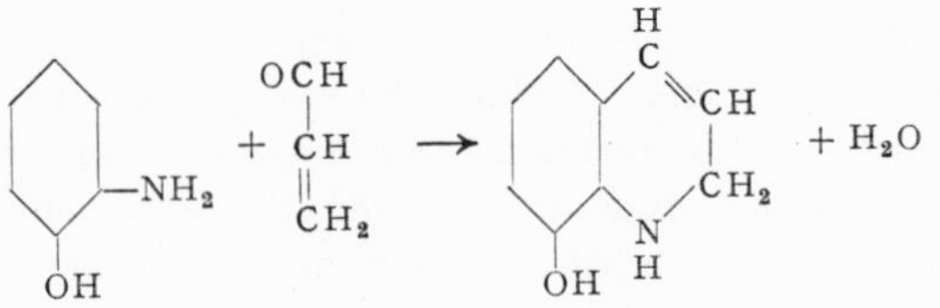

$$(2)$$

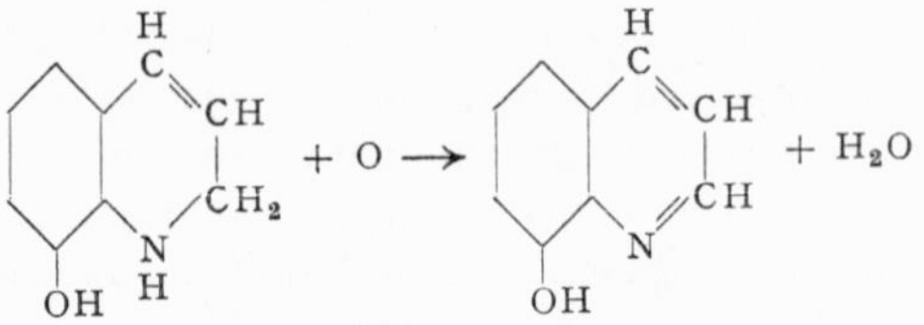

$$(3)$$

8-Hydroxyquinoline (oxine) reacts, under suitable conditions, with many metal ions to form water-insoluble inner complex salts.[127] The oxinates of colorless metal ions, either as solids or dissolved in organic liquids, exhibit an intense fluorescence, which is yellow-green in most instances (see page 378). Even at high dilutions, magnesium salts in ammoniacal solution precipitate magnesium oxinate:

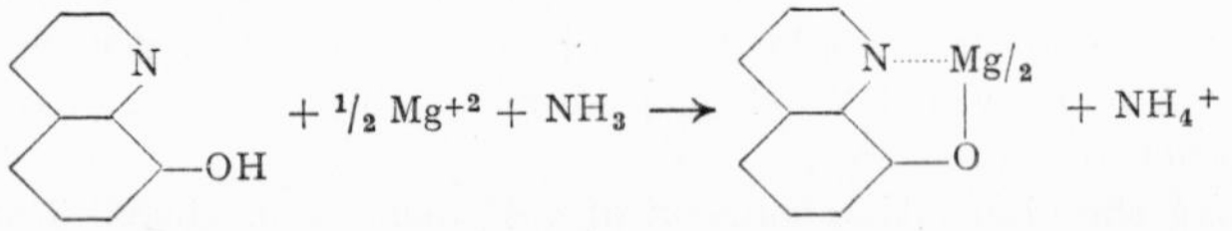

The Skraup synthesis, as represented in (1)–(3), can be accomplished with one drop of a very dilute aqueous or alcohol solution of glycerol, and the detection of the resulting oxine through its fluorescence reaction (4) thus provides a test for glycerol. Only crotonaldehyde interferes; under the given conditions it yields 2-methyl-8-hydroxyquinoline, whose inner complex magnesium salt likewise fluoresces yellow-green.

Procedure. Two drops of an alcohol solution of o-aminophenol are evaporated at 110° in a micro test tube. One drop of the test solution is added, followed by four drops of concentrated sulfuric acid containing arsenic acid. The tube is kept for 15 minutes in an oil bath at 140° and then cooled to room temperature. Five drops of conc. sodium hydroxide, one drop of 2 N magnesium sulfate solution, and

References pp. 440–444

three drops of concentrated ammonia are added, with agitation, and cooling by immersion in cold water. A bluish-green fluorescence in ultraviolet light indicates glycerol. If a turbidity develops, centrifuge. It is advisable to run a comparison blank test with a drop of water in place of the test solution.

Limit of Identification: 0.5 γ glycerol.

Reagents: *1)* 2 % solution of *o*-aminophenol in alcohol.

         2) 1 % solution of arsenic acid, in concentrated sulfuric acid.

(3) Other test for glycerol

The catalysis by glycerol of the decomposition of oxalic acid at 100° to 110° C., to form carbon dioxide and formic acid, may be applied as a test.[128] The carbon dioxide formed may be identified by the decolorization of paper impregnated with sodium carbonate-phenolphthalein solution (*Idn. Limit:* 5 γ glycerol). Alternatively, the monoformin (monoformic ester of glycerol) which is an intermediate compound, may be detected by the test for esters given on page 236 (*Idn. Limit:* 40 γ glycerol).

46. Carbohydrates

(1) Test for reducing sugars with triphenyltetrazolium chloride

If a colorless alkaline solution of triphenyltetrazolium chloride (I) is heated with a reducing sugar, red triphenylformazan (II) precipitates: [129]

$$\text{(I)} + H_2O + 2\,e \longrightarrow \text{(II)} + Cl^- + OH^-$$

    (I)   (II)

This reduction, which leads to the rupture of the tetrazolium ring, is brought about in neutral solution by hydrating enzymes exclusively[130], and in hot alkaline solution the formation of the formazan (II) is specific for reducing sugars.[131] An extremely sensitive test for sugars has been based on this reaction.[132] In contrast to most other tests for reducing sugars, aldehydes do not interfere with the triphenyltetrazolium chloride test. Furthermore, other reductants, such as hydrazine, hydroxylamine, sulfites, tartaric and citric acid, are completely inactive toward this reagent. Under the conditions of the test, only iron$^{(II)}$, metallic zinc, and zinc plus alkali react similarly with triphenyltetrazolium chloride. Ascorbic acid, which on the basis of its chemical constitution can be regarded as a reducing sugar (compare page 370), gives the same reaction.

Procedure. [132] A drop of the test solution is mixed, in a micro test tube or microcrucible, with two drops of 0,5% aqueous triphenyltetrazolium chloride solution and one drop of 0.5 N sodium hydroxide. The mixture is boiled for 1–2 minutes. A red color or precipitate appears according to the reducing sugar content.

Limit of Identification: 0.2 γ glucose, fructose, lactose, mannose, arabinose, ascorbic acid.

(2) Test for reducing sugars

Almost all the macrotests for reducing sugars may be applied as spot tests. As yet only one test is available, which is carried out merely by mixing drops of test solution and reagent on paper. Almost invariably it is essential to heat the reaction mixture (preferably in a microcrucible). Since all the tests depend on reducing properties, other reducing substances must not be present.

The *limits of identification* (drop size=0.04 ml) for a number of tests for reducing sugars are given in Table 36.[133]

TABLE 36. REDUCING SUGARS

Reagent	Color change	Identification limit
Nylander's solution (alkaline bismuth solution containing tartrate)	Blackening	10 γ
Ammoniacal AgNO$_3$ solution	Blackening	0.1 γ
Magnesium hypoiodite [Mg(OH)$_2$ and KI$_3$]	Decolorization	5 γ
Alkaline 0.001% methylene blue solution	Decolorization	1 γ
Alkaline dinitroacetanilide (1, 3, 4) solution	Violet	2 γ
m-Phenylenediamine hydrochloride (evaporated with 1 drop test solution)	Yellow-green Fluorescence	0.5 γ

The detection of reducing sugars through reduction of silver oxide may also be carried out as a highly sensitive spot reaction on paper.[134] Strips of filter paper are soaked in 0.2 N silver nitrate solution and dried. Single drops of the alkaline test solution and of a sodium hydroxide solution of approximately the same strength are placed next to each other on the paper. Two brown flecks of silver oxide develop. After about 1 minute, the paper is placed in ammonia water. The unchanged silver oxide dissolves completely within several minutes, while a black fleck of finely divided insoluble silver is left in the fleck produced by the sample containing reducing sugar.

Limit of Identification: 0.1 γ glucose.

The test cannot be applied in the presence of organic compounds containing CS- or SH-groups. Under the prescribed conditions, they form black Ag_2S, which likewise is not soluble in ammonia.

(3) Test for ketohexoses with stannous chloride, sulfuric acid, and urea [135]

A blue color is formed when ketohexoses are heated with a sulfuric acid solution of urea containing stannous chloride. Aldohexoses give a red color with this reagent, but only after prolonged heating. The chemistry of this reaction is not known.

Procedure.[136] A drop of the sugar solution is treated with 6 to 20 drops of the reagent solution in a microcrucible, heated for a minute over a microburner, and allowed to cool. When ketohexoses are present a blue color appears on cooling. The red color due to the aldohexoses only appears after longer boiling and is less intense.

Reagent solution: 4 g urea and 0.2 g $SnCl_2$ are dissolved by heating with 10 ml of 40 % sulfuric acid.

The following were detected:

8 γ levulose (blue)	20 γ dextrin (red)
15 γ saccharose (blue)	30 γ starch (red)
20 γ glucose (red)	

(4) Test for carbohydrates by hydrolysis to furfural [137]

Carbohydrates (di- and polysaccharides) are hydrolyzed by heating with strong mineral acids or with oxalic acid. Monosaccharides are formed:

$$(C_6H_{10}O_5)_x + x\ H_2O \rightarrow x\ C_6H_{12}O_6$$

On further heating, the monosaccharides (pentoses), by loss of water, are partly converted to furfural or similar aldehydes, such as hydroxymethylfurfural in the case of hexoses:

$$\begin{array}{cc} \text{CHOH} - \text{CHOH} \\ | \qquad\quad | \\ \text{HOCH}_2 - \text{CHOH} \quad \text{CHOH} - \text{CHO} \end{array} \rightarrow \begin{array}{c} \text{HC} \!-\!\!-\!\!-\! \text{CH} \\ \| \qquad \| \\ \text{HOCH}_2 - \text{C} \qquad \text{C} - \text{CHO} \\ \diagdown \!\! {}_O \!\! \diagup \end{array} + 3\ H_2O$$

These aldehydes are volatile in steam and react with *o*-dianisidine to form colored Schiff bases:

$$2 \ HOCH_2-C \overset{HC-\!-CH}{\underset{O}{\Large\diagdown\diagup}} C-CHO \ + \ H_2N-\!\!\!\left\langle\underset{H_3CO}{}\right\rangle-\!\!\!\left\langle\underset{OCH_3}{}\right\rangle-\!\!NH_2 \ \longrightarrow$$

$$HOCH_2-C \overset{HC-\!-CH}{\underset{O}{\Large\diagdown\diagup}} C-CH=N-\!\!\!\left\langle\underset{H_3CO}{}\right\rangle-\!\!\!\left\langle\underset{OCH_3}{}\right\rangle-\!\!N=HC-C \overset{HC-\!-CH}{\underset{O}{\Large\diagdown\diagup}} C-CH_2OH$$

It is probable that, following the formation of a Schiff base, the furan ring is cleaved "aminolytically". This has been established for the color reaction of furfural with aniline salts.[138] (Compare the test for furfural, page 428.)

Procedure. A little of the sample is mixed with about 8 mg oxalic acid in a tall microcrucible and a few drops of 1 : 3 sulfuric acid are added. The reaction is started by heating on an asbestos plate over a microburner. As soon as the contents of the crucible begin to brown, it is covered with a small watch glass, carrying on its underside a piece of filter paper impregnated with saturated solution of o-dianisidine in glacial acetic acid. The reagent paper gives a violet color with the furfural vapor when sugars or carbohydrates are present. After long exposure to the air, the violet gradually changes to blue.

The following were detected:

50 γ glucose	100 γ saccharose
50 γ levulose	100 γ lactose
10 γ sago starch	10 γ potato starch
10 γ arrowroot starch	10 γ corn starch
50 γ agar-agar	5 γ gum arabic
10 γ tragacanth	10 to 20 γ cellulose

The test for carbohydrates (di- and polysaccharides) based on their cleavage to furfural (or furfural derivatives) can be greatly simplified and improved as follows: The solid is heated for a short time with syrupy phosphoric acid and the resulting furfural (or its derivatives) in the gas phase is identified with aniline acetate paper through the production of a red dyestuff.

Procedure.[139] A pinch of the sample is placed in a microcrucible, or a drop of the test solution is taken to dryness there. One drop of syrupy phosphoric acid is added, and the crucible is covered with a disk of filter paper which has been moistened with aniline acetate solution. A small watch glass is used as a paper weight. The bottom of the crucible is cautiously heated for 30–60 seconds with a micro burner (spattering must be avoided). A pink to red color appears, the shade depending on the quantity of carbohydrate present.

References pp. 440-444

Reagent: 10 per cent solution of aniline in 10 per cent acetic acid.

The following were detected:

2.5 γ glucose	2.5 γ saccharose
2.5 γ levulose	2.5 γ arabinose
2.5 γ galactose	2.5 γ lactose
2.5 γ sorbose	5.0 γ agar-agar
2.5 γ maltose	3 γ starch (various origins)

Five micrograms of ethyl- and methyl cellulose gave a positive reaction, as did like quantities of acetyl cellulose and gum tragacanth.

47. Inositol

Detection through oxidation with nitric acid to alicyclic ketones

When inositol is warmed with concentrated nitric acid it is converted to leuconic acid. Omitting the intermediate stages, the reaction may be represented:[140]

$$
\begin{array}{c}
\text{HOH} \\
\text{C} \\
\text{HOHC} \quad \text{CHOH} \\
\text{HOHC} \quad \text{CHOH} \\
\text{C} \\
\text{HOH}
\end{array}
+ 7O \rightarrow
\begin{array}{c}
\text{OC} - \text{CO} \\
\text{OC} \quad \text{CO} \\
\text{C} \\
\text{O}
\end{array}
+ CO_2 + 6H_2O
$$

During this oxidation, the initial product is hexahydroxybenzene and subsequently salicyclic polyketones, tetrahydroxyquinone, rhodizonic acid, triquinoyl, and croconic acid appear. It is likely that, depending on the conditions, there results a mixture of leuconic acid with varying quantities of other ketonic compounds.

The keto compounds remaining after inositol has been fumed off with nitric acid have the following characteristic properties: (1) they or their hydrates, are acids which form red water-insoluble alkaline earth salts,[141] (2) they hasten the color reaction between formaldehyde and 1,2-dinitro-benzene (compare test for 1,2-diketones, page 205). The behaviors given in the following two procedures constitute the basis of the spot test described here.

Procedure I.[142] The test is conducted on a spot plate. A drop of the aqueous test solution is taken to dryness along with a drop of concentrated nitric acid. A drop of 5% calcium chloride solution and a drop of concentrated ammonium hydroxide are added to the residue. After evaporation, the spot plate is placed in an oven at 180°, or a hot plate may be used. According to the quantity of inositol present, a brown-red to light red residue is obtained almost at once or after 5–10 minutes at the most. A blank test is necessary only when the quantity of inositol is near the identification limit (2.5 γ).

This test is specific for inositol. However, considerable amounts of reducing sugars interfere because they undergo caramelization during heating and the resulting yellow makes it more difficult to discern the pink color due to inositol. Nevertheless, it is possible to detect 10 γ inositol in the presence of 1000 γ glucose.

Procedure II.[143] The evaporation with concentrated nitric acid is carried out in a micro test tube. The evaporation residue is treated with one drop of 4% formaldehyde solution and one drop of 25% sodium carbonate solution, and then with one drop of a 5% solution of 1,2-dinitrobenzene in benzene. The test tube is placed in boiling water and shaken. Depending on the amount of inositol, a more or less intense violet color develops within 1–4 minutes.

Limit of Identification: 5 γ inositol.

This procedure cannot be applied directly in the presence of reducing sugars, since they give a violet color with alkaline 1,2-dinitrobenzene (compare the detection of compounds which function as hydrogen donors, page 131). The interference by reducing sugars can be averted by oxidation with sodium hypobromite. The *procedure* is: a drop of the aqueous solution is treated with one drop of strong bromine water and one drop of 0.5 N sodium hydroxide. The mixture is warmed in the water bath for 1–2 minutes. The excess hypobromite is then decomposed by the addition of a drop of 10% hydrogen peroxide and the liquid is taken to dryness. The evaporation residue is carried through Procedure II. It is possible to detect 10 γ inositol in the presence of 1000 γ glucose in this manner.

48. Oxamide

Detection through dehydration to dicyanogen [144]

If oxamide is heated to 120–160° with phosphorus pentoxide, dehydration occurs with production of gaseous dicyanogen: [145]

$$\begin{array}{l} \text{CONH}_2 \\ | \qquad \rightarrow (\text{CN})_2 + 2\ \text{H}_2\text{O} \\ \text{CONH}_2 \end{array} \qquad (1)$$

Because of the binding, by the phosphorus pentoxide, of the water formed in (*1*), the dicyanogen remains unchanged and can be detected by contact with a concentrated solution of potassium cyanide containing oxine. A red color results (see page 329). Dry heating (pyrolysis) of oxamide cannot be substituted for the treatment with phosphorus pentoxide. Both procedures involve the primary cleavage shown in (*1*) but if water is present, there is irreversible hydrolysis of the dicyanogen in the vapor phase:

$$(\text{CN})_2 + \text{H}_2\text{O} \rightarrow \text{HCN} + \text{HCNO} \qquad (2)$$

References pp. 440–444

Consequently, when oxamide is pyrolyzed there is no dicyanogen in the vapor phase but only hydrogen cyanide can be detected there and this is not characteristic because many organic nitrogenous compounds likewise yield hydrogen cyanide when they are thermally decomposed.[146] The test described here, which is based on the dehydration by means of phosphorus pentoxide, is almost specific. Only glyoxime, which is isomeric with oxamide, likewise yields dicyanogen when it is gently heated with phosphorus pentoxide:

$$\begin{array}{l} HC = NOH \\ | \quad\quad \to (CN)_2 + 2\ H_2O \\ HC = NOH \end{array}$$

Since glyoxime is readily soluble in ether while oxamide is insoluble in this liquid, a separation of these isomers previous to the test is readily accomplished, if necessary.

Procedure. A little of the solid is mixed in a micro test tube with an excess of phosphorus pentoxide. The mouth of the test tube is covered with a disk of oxine paper (see page 330) that has been moistened with 25% potassium cyanide solution. The test tube is placed in a glycerol bath that has been heated to 160°. If dicyanogen is released, a circular pink or red stain develops on the yellow paper.

It is not possible to determine experimentally the limit of identification of this test because solutions of oxamide cannot be prepared. (Attempts to arrive at a figure by evaporating a water solution of ammonium oxalate and then heating the residue to 150°, which is the preparative method for producing oxamide, were not successful because hydrolysis prevents the quantitative dehydration to oxamide.) However, on the basis of the identification limits for the dicyanogen test, which were determined by heating a mixture of mercuric cyanide and mercuric chloride, it appears that about 0.35 γ oxamide can be revealed by the test, assuming that the yield of dicyanogen is only 50%.

In place of the direct test for dicyanogen, use can be made of its hydrolysis to hydrogen cyanide as shown in (2). This hydrolysis takes place when the gaseous dicyanogen released by phosphorus pentoxide comes into contact with a solution of copper-benzidine acetate. A blue color results (compare page 93). The procedure is the same as that just given except that instead of oxine paper, a disk is used that has been moistened with the hydrogen cyanide reagent solution.

49. Choline

Detection through pyrolytic splitting off of formaldehyde [147]

If choline is subjected to rapid dry heating, besides a carbonaceous residue there also result trimethylamine and formaldehyde. Accordingly, it is possible that one of the partial reactions in the pyrolytic decomposition is:

$$N(CH_3)_3 - CH_2CH_2OH \rightarrow N(CH_3)_3 + CH_3Cl + CH_2O$$
$$\text{Cl}$$

Both formaldehyde and trimethylamine are readily detectable in the vapor phase; the latter by its characteristic odor, by its effect on color indicators, and by reaction with manganese-silver nitrate solution (see page 91), and the former by the chromotropic acid test (see page 331).

When using the pyrolytic cleavage of choline salts it should be noted that certain other water-soluble compounds also yield basic vapors or formaldehyde when subjected to dry heating.

Among the compounds which split off ammonia are: urea and urea derivatives, guanidine and its salts, and ammonium salts of weak acids. Under the conditions prescribed for the present test, the color reaction with chromotropic acid is given by hexamethylenetetramine and its salts, by oxymethylene compounds (see page 191) and by sulfoxylate compounds (see page 312). Consequently, the detection of choline through the formaldehyde split off in the pyrolysis is not specific but only selective. However, the presence of choline is made quite probable if the formaldehyde reaction is supported by the detection of of basic vapors and particularly by the odor test of trimethylamine. Trimethylglycocoll and betaine yield trimethylamine when heated but no formaldehyde.

Procedure. A drop of the test solution is evaporated to dryness in the bulb of the gas absorption apparatus (Fig. 23). The residue is heated over a micro burner until definite charring is seen. The stopper is then put into place after its knob has been charged with a drop of the reagent solution (see page 191). If choline is present, the hanging drop turns deep to light violet after 1–2 minutes. If only small amounts of choline are involved in the test, the heating can be done in the closed apparatus and the result compared with that obtained in a blank.

Limit of Identification: 0.5 γ choline.

50. Ethylenediamine and Propylenediamine

Test by precipitation with sodium rhodizonate [148]

If the yellow-brown aqueous solution of sodium rhodizonate (I) is added to a neutral aqueous solution of an ethylenediamine salt (chloride, sulfate, etc.), a dark violet precipitate of ethylenediamine rhodizonate (II) is formed:

$$
\underset{(I)}{
\begin{array}{c}
\text{O} \\
\text{O}=\!\!\!\!\!<\!\!\!\!\!\begin{array}{c}\text{—ONa}\\\text{—ONa}\end{array} \\
\text{O}
\end{array}}
+ (NH_3\text{—}CH_2\text{—}CH_2\text{—}NH_3)\, Cl_2 \rightarrow
\underset{(II)}{
\begin{array}{c}
\text{O} \\
\text{O}=\!\!\!\!\!<\!\!\!\!\!\begin{array}{c}\text{—OH·}NH_2\text{—}CH_2\\\text{—OH·}NH_2\text{—}CH_2\end{array} \\
\text{O}
\end{array}}
+ 2NaCl
$$

It has not been established whether this salt is the sole product. There appears to be a side reaction in which a cyclic Schiff base is produced through a condensation of ethylenediamine with two adjacent CO-groups of the rhodizonic acid. Propylenediamine salts behave similarly to ethylenediamine. Ammonium-, di- and triethanolamine salts, hydrazine and hydroxylamine salts, and also the hydrochlorides of o-phenylenediamine and 1,8-naphthylenediamine do not react under the conditions prescribed here. The hydrochlorides of primary aromatic monoamines and of pyridine react only in very concentrated solution. On the other hand, a violet crystalline precipitate is given by benzidine hydrochloride even at high dilution. After the crystalline ethylenediamine rhodizonate has once been formed, it is rather stable against dilute acids but not against ammonia. The latter dissolves this violet salt as well as the similarly colored benzidine rhodizonate.

Pure benzidine sulfate reacts with sodium rhodizonate, but an excess of sulfate ions prevents the reaction. However, the ethylenediamine-rhodizonate reaction is not altered.

Salts of N-substituted derivatives of ethylenediamine seem to react similarly with sodium rhodizonate to yield colored salts. This has been found to be the case with N,N'-dibenzylethylenediamine, which gives a brick-red precipitate (compare Chap. 6).

Procedure. A drop of the neutral test solution and a drop of sodium rhodizonate solution are brought together on a spot plate. According to the quantity of ethylenediamine present, a violet precipitate appears at once or after brief standing. If the yellow-brown reagent solution is decolorized by adding one drop of the buffer solution, small amounts of the reaction product are easier to see. It is better to carry out the reaction on paper. One drop of the reagent solution is placed on the paper, then a drop of the test solution, and after three minutes the color of the reagent is discharged by adding a drop of the buffer solution.

Limit of Identification: 0.3 γ ethylenediamine.

Reagents: 1) Sodium rhodizonate 1 % aqueous solution (freshly prepared)

2) Buffer solution (pH = 2.79): 1.9 g sodium bitartrate and 1.5 g tartaric acid per 100 ml.

51. Phenylhydrazine

Test through conversion into dithizone [149]

Diphenylthiocarbazone (dithizone), which is widely used in inorganic analysis because of its ability to produce colored salts with metals,[150] can be prepared from phenylhydrazine.[151] The latter is condensed with carbon disulfide, as shown in (*1*), to produce the phenylhydrazine salt of β-phenyldithiocarbazic acid (I) which, when heated to about 100°, loses hydrogen sulfide and goes over into diphenylthiocarbazide (II) as shown in (*2*). When (II) reacts with alcoholic caustic alkali, the alkali salt of dithizone (III) is formed along with phenylthiosemicarbazide (IV) as shown in (*3*):

$$2\,C_6H_5-NH-NH_2 + CS_2 \rightarrow SC\Big\langle\begin{array}{l}SH\cdot NH_2NHC_6H_5\\NHNHC_6H_5\end{array} \qquad (1)$$
$$\text{(I)}$$

$$SC\Big\langle\begin{array}{l}SH\cdot NH_2NHC_6H_5\\NHNHC_6H_5\end{array} \rightarrow SC\Big\langle\begin{array}{l}NH\cdot NHC_6H_5\\NH\cdot NHC_6H_5\end{array} + H_2S \qquad (2)$$
$$\text{(II)}$$

$$2\,SC\Big\langle\begin{array}{l}NH\cdot NHC_6H_5\\NH\cdot NHC_6H_5\end{array} + C_2H_5ONa \rightarrow SC\Big\langle\begin{array}{l}NH-NNaC_6H_5\\N=N-C_6H_5\end{array} +$$
$$\text{(III)}$$

$$SC\Big\langle\begin{array}{l}NH-NHC_6H_5\\NH_2\end{array} + C_6H_5NH_2 + C_2H_5OH \qquad (3)$$
$$\text{(IV)}$$

Addition of acid to the red solution of (III) precipitates dithizone. The latter is not soluble in water, but gives green solutions in chloroform and carbon tetrachloride. On a preparative scale, this series of reactions gives a yield of about 53 per cent. However, it appears that small amounts of phenylhydrazine can be quantitatively converted into dithizone, if purification of the product, and isolation of the intermediate products of (*1*) and (*2*) are not attempted. This fact, together with the marked color quality of solutions of dithizone in chloroform, makes possible a test for phenylhydrazine, and probably for other alkylhydrazines.

Procedure. A drop of the ether or alcohol test solution is mixed with two drops of carbon disulfide in a micro test tube and evaporated to dryness on the water bath. Two or three drops of 1% sodium hydroxide in methyl or ethyl alcohol are then added and warmed on the water bath for two minutes. If much phenylhydrazine is present, a red color due to the alkali salt of dithizone appears.

References pp. 440–444

The solution is acidified with 1 : 1 hydrochloric acid and shaken with 1–3 drops of chloroform. Depending on the quantity of phenylhydrazine, the chloroform appears dark green to bluish green.

Limit of Identification: 5 γ phenylhydrazine.

52. α-Naphthylamine

Detection through condensation with nitrosoantipyrine [152]

α-Naphthylamine, as well as its hydrochloride or sulfate, condenses in acetic acid solution with nitrosoantipyrine to yield a violet azo dye:

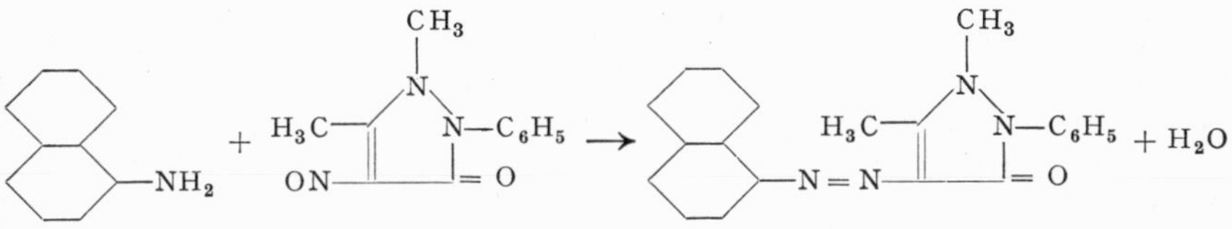

Aniline hydrochloride (sulfate) does not react with nitrosoantipyrine, but aniline acetate reacts similarly to give a violet color. β-Naphthylamine does not react in either acetic acid solution or in the form of its salts. Therefore, α-naphthylamine can be detected in the presence of any quantity of the β-isomer.

Procedure. One drop of the acetic acid test solution (base or hydrochloride) is treated in a micro test tube with a drop of the reagent solution. The mixture is heated in the water bath for 1–2 minutes. Depending on the quantity of α-naphthylamine, a more or less intense violet color appears. A blank comparison test is advisable when small amounts of α-naphthylamine are suspected.

Limit of Identification: 0.5 γ α-naphthylamine.

Reagent solution: 1 g of antipyrine is dissolved in 20 ml of 1 : 1 acetic acid and 0.6 g of sodium nitrite is added. After standing 10 minutes, with occasional shaking, 0.5 g sodium azide is added, and the volume is brought up to 150 ml with 1 : 1 acetic acid. The reagent solution will keep for several days.

α-Naphthylamine sulfonic acids likewise react with nitrosoantipyrine. However, the sensitivity is much lower than with α-naphthylamine and its salts. Brown condensation products result, as shown in the case of the 1,3- and 1,4-α-naphthylamine sulfonic acids. The limit of identification is 75 γ α-naphthylamine sulfonic acid. Brown-red condensation products are given by H-acid (8-amino-1-naphthol-3,6-disulfonic acid) and by 1,8-naphthylenediamine. Consequently, it appears that the violet color is characteristic for α-naphthylamine and a shift of the color toward brown occurs when acidic or basic groups are introduced into the aromatic ring.

References pp. 440–444

53. Tyrosine

Test with α-nitroso-β-naphthol [153]

Tyrosine (I) and proteins give a deep purple color on the addition of α-nitroso-β-naphthol (II) and nitric acid. The chemistry of the reaction is unknown. An essential step seems to be that the nitric acid apparently oxidizes the α-nitroso-β-naphthol to α-nitro-β-naphthol (III), as it can be replaced by manganese dioxide or lead dioxide.

The reaction is specific for tyrosine in the presence of other amino acids, 3,4-dihydroxyphenylalanine, adrenaline, thyroxine, aldehydes, sugars, or urea. Similar reactions are given by a number of p-substituted phenols, such as tyrosol, tyramine, p-cresol, p-ethylphenol, xylenol-1,2,4, p-chlorophenol, p-bromo-m-cresol, hydroquinone monomethyl ether, $β$-naphthol, and phenolphthalein.

Procedure. A drop of the test solution is mixed in a microcrucible with a drop of 0.2% alcoholic solution of α-nitroso-β-naphthol and heated. A drop of concentrated nitric acid is added to the hot solution. A purple color appears in the presence of tyrosine. The color fades within a few minutes.*

Limit of Identification: 0.05 γ tyrosine.

Proteins, which almost without exception contain tyrosine as an integral constituent can be readily detected by the color reaction with α-nitroso-β-naphthol and concentrated nitric acid. Preferably they should be hydrolyzed beforehand by heating with sodium hydroxide or sulfuric acid.

Tyrosine may be detected in pathological urine or serum as follows: [155] 0.5 ml of sample is diluted with 1 ml water and 1 ml 20 % trichloroacetic acid is added. The mixture is well stirred and either filtered or centrifuged to remove the precipitated albumin. As little as 0.05 γ tyrosine can be detected in a drop of the filtrate or clear centrifugate.

* Maciag and Schöntal[154] state that the color can be stabilized by adding ferric ammonium alum solution.

References pp. 440–444

54. Proteins

(1) *Test with tetrabromophenolphthalein ethyl ester* [156]

Tetrabromophenolphthalein ethyl ester

is yellow but its water-soluble alkali salts are blue. These salts are decomposed by dilute acetic acid with regeneration of the phenol. If the ester is brought into contact with proteins, which are generally in the colloid state, a blue color appears. Apparently this is due to the formation of a salt-like adsorption compound,[157] which, however, unlike the alkali salts, is not broken down by dilute acetic acid. The phenomenon known as "protein error" of indicators (displacement of the transformation range of pH indicators) appears to be involved. This effect is shown very strongly by tetrabromophenolphthalein ester. For practical purposes, the potassium salt is used, because the ester is usually not available. The blue alcoholic solution of this salt is changed to yellow (color of the free ester) by dilute acetic acid, but the color remains blue in the presence of protein. It then only changes to yellow on the addition of strong acetic acid or mineral acids.

The reaction seems to be specific for *native proteins*. Protein fission products, such as amino acids, di- and tripeptides, or peptones, do not react.

Alkaloids of high molecular weight, when present in large concentration, show a behavior similar to that of native proteins. Probably this is ascribable to the formation of adsorption compounds of colloidally dispersed alkaloid with tetrabromophenolphthalein ester, which are resistant to acetic acid.[158]

Procedure. A drop of the test solution is mixed on a spot plate or in a microcrucible with a drop of an alcoholic solution of the potassium salt of tetrabromophenolphthalein ethyl ester and then acidified with 1 to 2 drops of $0.2 N$ acetic acid. A blank test changes to yellow, while the color remains deep blue in the presence of proteins. When only small amounts of protein are present, the color is somewhat green.

Reagent: Potassium salt of tetrabromophenolphthalein ethyl ester, 0.1 % solution in alcohol.

The following were detected:

0.5 γ egg albumin	5 γ edestin
0.5 γ hemoglobin	0.5 γ clupein
0.35 γ serum albumin	0.5 γ salmin
0.5 γ casein	1 γ gliadin

A pathologically increased protein content in urine may be detected in a drop of urine by means of this reaction.

(2) Test after hydrolytic or thermal fission to amino and imino compounds

Proteins are hydrolyzed by strong mineral acids to yield simpler fission products such as polypeptides, amino acids, etc. Since tryptophan is an essential component of all proteins, it is broken down and produces indole and indole derivatives. All of these amino and imino products may be detected either by melting with fluorescein chloride (see page 263) or by condensation with *p*-dimethylaminobenzaldehyde. In the latter case, amino groups may give rise to colored Schiff bases. It seems, however, that the condensation of indole bases (see page 278) which have been formed by the acid splitting of proteins, plays the chief role in the following test with *p*-dimethylamino-benzaldehyde.

Procedure.[159] The sample to be tested for proteins (solid or in solution) is mixed in a microcrucible with several drops of a saturated glacial acetic acid solution of *p*-dimethylaminobenzaldehyde and one drop of fuming hydrochloric acid. A violet color indicates the presence of proteins.

After hydrolysis and production of violet condensation products, the following *identification limits* were obtained:

1 γ dried peptone	30 γ egg albumin
20 γ blood albumin	5 γ casein
100 γ hide powder	60 γ pancreatin
10 γ edestin	pepsin, very insensitive

Thyroglobin gives a positive albumin reaction, whereas the reaction with pure thyroxin results negatively. Hypophysis preparations give a positive response. As little as 1 % albumin (e.g. edestin) can be distinctly detected in mixtures with carbohydrates.

Dry heating also splits proteins. The resulting pyrrole and pyrrole derivatives volatilize with the combustion products. If the gaseous combustion products are brought into contact with filter paper that has been impregnated with a 5 % solution of *p*-dimethylaminobenzaldehyde in concentrated hydrochloric acid, a violet color appears on the paper.[160] The thermal decomposition can be conducted in a microcrucible or in a micro test tube. (Compare differentiation of animal and vegetable fibers, page 475.) The *identifi-cation limits* are around 100 γ protein.

If the fluorescence test is to be applied, the sample is evaporated to dryness with fuming hydrochloric acid and the residue is treated as described on page 263.

55. Pyridine and $\beta(\gamma)$-Picoline

Detection through formation of polymethine dyes from the vapor phase [161]

A test for pyridine and its derivatives with free α-positions is described in Chapter 4. It is based on the action of bromocyanogen and benzidine with solutions of the compounds in question to yield a red polymethine dye. Since pyridine and water form an azeotropic mixture, boiling at 95°, the color reaction may also be accomplished by bringing the vapor into contact with a solution of the necessary reagents. A selective test for pyridine results and also for the reactive pyridine bases (β- and γ-picoline) which likewise are volatile with steam. The corresponding volatility of β-pyridine carbinol is too slight to permit its analogous behavior.

Procedure. The apparatus shown in Fig. 23 (page 49) is used. A drop of the test solution is placed in the bulb; if the solution is acid it is necessary to add a drop or two of dilute alkali. The knob of the stopper is charged with a drop of the reagent and put in place. The closed apparatus is then kept in boiling water for 3–5 minutes. If pyridine is present, the hanging drop turns red or pink. Even slight colorations can be seen if the drop is wiped onto filter paper.

Reagent: A freshly prepared mixture of one drop each of 2% potassium cyanide, saturated bromine water, and suspension of benzidine base (comp. page 280).

Limit of Identification: 2.5 γ pyridine.

56. Quinoline (Differentiation from Isoquinoline)

Detection through hydrogenation and subsequent oxidation or bromination [162]

If quinoline (b.p. 239°) or its isomer, isoquinoline (b.p. 240°) is treated for several minutes with nascent hydrogen (zinc and hydrochloric acid) the reduction yields cyclic secondary ring bases. This is demonstrated easily through the reactions that are characteristic of secondary amines (compare also detection of tertiary ring bases, page 305. The reduction of quinoline produces dihydroquinoline [163]; dihydroisoquinoline is probably formed in the second case. The hydrogen is taken up by the cyclic N-atom and a C-atom *ortho* to this nitrogen atom.*

The reduced acid solutions of quinoline and isoquinoline behave in quite different manners toward alkali persulfate in the presence of copper salts. Only

---

* According to private information from Prof. P. Karrer, Zurich.

the solution containing dihydroquinoline yields a brown precipitate or color, depending on the quantity of the base present. A reliable test for distinguishing quinoline from isoquinoline can be made on the basis of this finding (Procedure I). Another differentiation is based on the behavior toward bromine water. Even very dilute solutions of reduced quinoline give a red color with bromine, whereas only higher concentrations of reduced isoquinoline respond analogously. If the bromine reaction is conducted as a test on filter paper, the isomeric bases are readily distinguished from each other (Procedure II).

The chemistry of the reactions underlying Procedures I and II has not yet been unravelled. When the copper ions activate persulfate toward reduced quinoline solutions, there is probably an oxidation that leads to a quinoidal product. Starting with quinoline, the following scheme may well be considered:

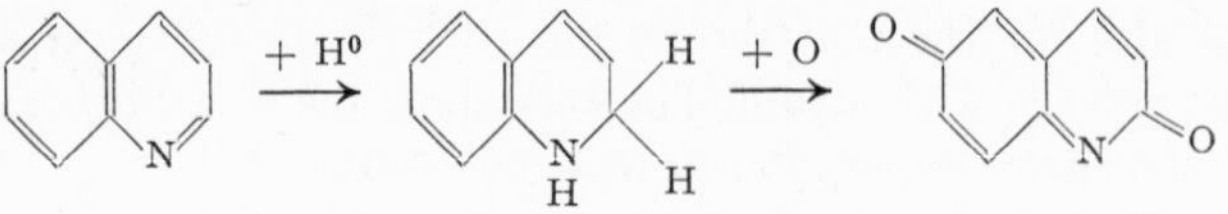

A red polybromide of dihydroquinoline is probably formed when bromine acts on the reduced solutions. This supposition is supported by the decomposition of the colored product by sulfosalicylic acid or sulfurous acid.

Since, as stated previously, isoquinoline is likewise reduced by zinc and hydrochloric acid, the differentiating reactions with persulfate and bromine, respectively, are obviously due to the greater reduction potential and ability to form the polybromide shown by dihydroquinoline as compared with its isomer dihydroisoquinoline.

Procedure I. A spot plate is used for the test. A drop of the test solution containing considerable hydrochloric acid is placed in a depression and 4 or 5 granules of 10 mesh zinc are added. The reduction is allowed to continue for 1–2 minutes and then any unused zinc is removed by means of a thin glass rod. One drop of 1% solution of copper sulfate is added and about 20 milligrams of solid potassium persulfate. The mixture is agitated by blowing onto its surface. Depending on the quantity of quinoline involved, a brown to yellow precipitate or color appears within 1–2 minutes. The color attains its maximum after 3–4 minutes.

Limit of Identification: 20 γ quinoline.

If isoquinoline solutions are carried through this procedure, no visible change occurs, no matter what their concentration.

Procedure II. The reduction (hydrogenation) is conducted as in Procedure I. The reduced solution is transferred to a filter paper by means of a pipette. The spot is held over strong bromine water for about 30 seconds. According to the quantity of quinoline present, the moist spot immediately turns pink or red. The color fades in an oven (110°) but does not disappear. The color is restored by renewed exposure to bromine vapor.

Limit of Identification: 2.5 γ quinoline.

Isoquinoline solutions, of all concentrations, leave only a pale yellow stain on the filter paper if carried through this procedure.

Procedures I and II are primarily suited for distinguishing between quinoline and isoquinoline, provided only one is present. The redox reaction with persulfate can be used to detect quinoline in the presence of isoquinoline. For example, Procedure I revealed 50 γ quinoline in the presence of 2000 γ isoquinoline when applied to one drop of the test solution.

The behavior of 10 % solutions of the following quinoline derivatives was studied: quinoline iodomethylate, 2-methylquinoline (quinaldine), β-naphthoquinoline, 6-nitroquinoline, *m*-bromoquinoline nitrate, cinchophen, 4-hydroxy-7-chloroquinoline, 4-hydroxy-7-chloroquinoline-3-carboxylic acid, 3-cyanoquinoline and acridine. Procedures I and II were applied. Only quinaldine and quinoline iodomethylate behave analogously to quinoline. However, the response to the reaction with persulfate or bromine was definitely weaker in the case of quinaldine. Accordingly, the tests for quinoline described here appear to be quite specific.

57. *p*-Phenylenediamine

Test by conversion into phenylene blue [164]

When *p*-phenylenediamine (I) is mixed with an oxidant, in the presence of aniline, in slightly acid solution, the indamine dye, phenylene blue (II), is formed immediately:

$$H_2N\!\!-\!\!\langle\ \rangle\!\!-\!\!NH_2 + \langle\ \rangle\!\!-\!\!NH_2 + O_2 \longrightarrow$$

(I)

$$HN\!\!=\!\!\langle\ \rangle\!\!=\!\!N\!\!-\!\!\langle\ \rangle\!\!-\!\!NH_2 + 2\,H_2O$$

(II)

No account is taken in this equation of the fact that in acid solution salts of the basic dye are formed of course.

As the equation indicates, essential features are the production of phenylquinonediimide and its oxidative condensation with an aromatic amine, which is not substituted in the position *para* to the nitrogen. Accordingly,

N-mono- or di-alkylated p-diamines with a free NH_2-group behave similarly to p-phenylenediamine; the aniline can be replaced by other aromatic monoamines with a free *para* position to the $-NH_2$. Bandrowski's base is an exception. Despite its p-phenylenediamine structure (see page 214) it does not react. However, it is easily split by reduction to yield p-phenylenediamine and can be detected in this manner (see page 464). Analogous oxidation and condensation reactions with phenols, which are not substituted in the *para* position, lead to indophenol dyes.

The formation of phenylene blue in accord with the preceding equation has been employed on the macro scale for the characterization of aniline (by means of p-phenylenediamine and persulfate).[165] It was shown in this connection that the dye base, after alkalization, can be extracted with carbon tetrachloride to yield a red solution.

Procedure. A drop of the acetic acid test solution is mixed with a drop of aniline water (one drop $C_6H_5NH_2$ in 50 ml H_2O) and several crystals of potassium persulfate are added. A dark to light blue color appears at once, according to the amount of p-phenylenediamine present.

Limit of Identification: 0.5 γ p-phenylenediamine.

58. Phosgene

Test by conversion to diphenylcarbohydrazide [166]

Due to its two mobile chlorine atoms, phosgene reacts quickly and quantitatively with an excess of alkyl- and arylhydrazines to form symmetric carbohydrazides.[167] For example, diphenylcarbohydrazide (diphenylcarbazide) is produced from phosgene and phenylhydrazine (in an inactive organic solvent):

$$\begin{matrix} C_6H_5-NH-NH_2 \\ + \\ C_6H_5-NH-NH_2 \end{matrix} \quad \begin{matrix} Cl \\ \\ Cl \end{matrix}CO \rightarrow \begin{matrix} C_6H_5-NH-NH \\ \\ C_6H_5-NH-NH \end{matrix}CO + 2\,HCl \qquad (1)$$

Diphenylcarbazide, in neutral, ammoniacal, or weakly acid solution, reacts with copper ions to form water-insoluble, deep violet inner complex copper-diphenylcarbazide.[168] This product can be extracted with water-immiscible organic liquids such as ether, chloroform, etc. The reaction is:

$$\tfrac{1}{2}\,Cu^{+2} + OC(NHNHC_6H_5)_2 \rightarrow OC\begin{matrix} NH-N-C_6H_5 \\ \\ Cu/2 \\ \\ NH-NH-C_6H_5 \end{matrix} + H^+ \qquad (2)$$

Reaction (2) permits the detection not only of small quantities of copper,[169] but also of small amounts of diphenylcarbazide. Consequently, the realization of (1) and (2) can serve for the detection of slight quantities of phosgene.

References pp. 440–444

Since free phenylhydrazine does not keep well, it is advisable to use its cinnamate for the reaction with phosgene.

Procedure. A drop of the test solution is mixed in a microcrucible with a granule of phenylhydrazine cinnamate, and after 5 minutes a drop of copper sulfate solution added. In the presence of phosgene, a red-violet to pink appears, according to the amount present.

Alternatively, spot paper (S & S 598g) is impregnated with the 1% copper sulfate solution and dried. Just before the test, a little solid phenylhydrazine cinnamate is rubbed on it. A drop of the test solution is added, followed, when the solvent has evaporated, by a drop of water. In the presence of phosgene, a red-violet stain forms.

Limit of Identification: 0.5 γ phosgene.

The test may be applied to the detection of phosgene in commercial chloroform and carbon tetrachloride. Chloroform for anesthesia, and pure carbon tetrachloride contain only traces of phosgene in comparison with the technical products.

59. Urea

(1) Test through deamination [170]

When urea , which melts at 131°, is heated slightly above its fusion point it loses ammonia. The loss is more rapid at 160–170°. The residue consists of biuret (II):

$$2\ O{=}C{<}^{NH_2}_{NH_2} \quad \rightarrow \quad \begin{matrix} O{=}C{<}^{NH_2}_{NH} \\ O{=}C{<}^{\ \ \ }_{NH_2} \end{matrix} + NH_3$$

(I)   (II)

In the absence of ammonium salts of carboxylic acids, this loss of ammonia at relatively low temperatures will reveal the presence of urea in solid, water-soluble test materials, since the ammonium salts of mineral acids decompose with evolution of ammonia only at temperatures above 300°. The same is true of salts of volatile organic bases (pyridine, ethylamine, ethanolamine, etc.). When small amounts of urea are to be detected through the evolution of ammonia, it should be remembered 1) that when molten urea is heated to temperatures exceeding the boiling point of water, and without the simultaneous release of water, hot dry ammonia is given off; 2) that the usual tests for ammonia are based on the OH^--reactions of hydrated ammonia. Therefore, provision must be made for cooling and hydrating the ammonia. A recommended test [171] for ammonia is provided by its reaction with a neutral solution containing Ag^+- and Mn^{+2}-ions, in which the essential reaction:

$$Mn^{+2} + 2\,Ag^+ + 4\,OH^- \rightarrow 2\,Ag° + MnO_2 + 2\,H_2O$$

produces a black mixture (or adsorption compound) of free silver and manganese dioxide.

The following test is applicable only in the absence of guanidine and its salts and also ammonium salts of weak carboxylic acids and phenols, since, when heated to about 160°, they decompose with release of ammonia.

Procedure. The test is conducted in a glass tube (10 cm × 8 mm) closed at one end. A drop of the aqueous neutral test solution is introduced, and evaporated in an oven at 120°. The tube is then immersed to a depth of 1.5 cm in a hot (about 160°) glycerol bath. The open end of the tube is closed with a disk of filter paper moistened with the reagent solution. According to the quantity of urea, a black to gray circle appears on the paper after a few (not more than 10) minutes.

Limit of Identification: 10 γ urea.

Reagent: Manganese nitrate – silver nitrate solution: 2.87 g $Mn(NO_3)_2$ is dissolved in 40 ml water and filtered if necessary. To this is added a solution of 3.35 g $AgNO_3$ in 40 ml water, and the mixture diluted to 100 ml. Dilute alkali is added drop by drop until a permanent black precipitate is formed. The filtrate is stored in a dark bottle.

(2) Test by conversion to diphenylcarbohydrazide [172]

When urea is heated to 150–200° with an excess of phenylhydrazine, diphenylcarbohydrazide (diphenylcarbazide) is formed.[173]

$$OC\begin{array}{l}NH_2\\NH_2\end{array} + 2\,NH_2NHC_6H_5 \longrightarrow OC\begin{array}{l}NH-NHC_6H_5\\NH-NHC_6H_5\end{array} + 2\,NH_3 \qquad (1)$$

Since the reaction temperature is above the melting point (131°) of urea, some biuret is doubtless produced (see page 407), but it too reacts with phenylhydrazine to form diphenylcarbazide:

$$H_2N-CO-NH-CO-NH_2 + 4\,NH_2NHC_6H_6 \longrightarrow 2\,OC\begin{array}{l}NH-NHC_6H_5\\NH-NHC_6H_5\end{array} + 3\,NH_3 \qquad (2)$$

Diphenylcarbazide reacts with many metal ions, and also with chromate and molybdate, to form colored inner complex salts; some of these are readily soluble in organic liquids.[174] In view of the fact, that excess phenylhydrazine always remains when reactions (1) and (2) are carried out, no metal salts which undergo redox reactions with phenylhydrazine may be used when testing for small amounts of diphenylcarbazide produced from urea. The reaction of diphenylcarbazide and an ammoniacal nickel solution is useful here; it leads to the precipitation of a violet inner complex nickel salt, which is soluble in chloroform.

Procedure. One drop of the aqueous test solution is evaporated to dryness in a micro test tube. A drop of phenylhydrazine is added and the mixture is kept for five minutes in an oil bath at 195°. After cooling, five drops of 1:1 ammonia and five drops of 10% nickel sulfate solution are added, and the mixture is then shaken with ten drops of chloroform. A red-violet color indicates the presence of urea. A blank test is essential when slight amounts are suspected.

Limit of Identification: 10 γ urea.

The mono- and disubstituted derivatives of urea, like the parent compound, form diphenylcarbazide when heated with phenylhydrazine. A reaction scheme analogous to (1) holds for these, the respective amines being liberated in place of or along with the ammonia. The following were tested; identification limits of 100–150 γ were obtained: methylurea, acetylmethylurea, *as*-diphenylurea, *m*-tolylurea, *sym*-di-*m*-tolylurea, allylurea, *tert.*-amylurea, *tert.*-butylurea.

Likewise, many urethans, *i.e.* ethyl esters of carbamic acid and its N-substituted derivatives, produce diphenylcarbazide when heated with phenylhydrazine. Again, a scheme analogous to (1) applies, in that ammonia or amine along with ethyl alcohol is split off. Identification limits of 100–300 γ were obtained with ethylurethan, phenylurethan, *n*-butylcarbamate.

It seems that N,N-dialkyl- and N,N-diaryl-carbamates, as well as cyclic derivatives of urea, are resistant toward phenylhydrazine. This lack of reactivity was observed in the case of N,N-diphenyl carbamate, N,N-di-*n*-butyl carbamate, and 6,8-dichlorobenzoylene urea.

When thiourea and its derivatives are heated with phenylhydrazine, the sulfur homolog of diphenylcarbazide is formed, namely diphenylthiocarbazide. It likewise reacts with nickel salts to produce a violet compound. However, the detection of the condensation of thiourea with phenylhydrazine is much less sensitive (*Identification limit* 800 γ). Thiourea and its derivatives can be detected by heating the solid sample to about 200°. Hydrogen sulfide is evolved and is easily detected by its action on lead acetate paper (*Identification limit:* 1 γ thiourea).[175]

(3) *Test by enzymatic hydrolysis to ammonia*

The hydrolysis of urea:

$$OC(NH_2)_2 + H_2O \rightarrow CO_2 + 2\,NH_3$$

by acids and alkalies is not hastened fundamentally even by warming. Probably, the hydrolysis occurs only *via* the isomer, ammonium cyanate, which is in equilibrium with urea

$$OC(NH_2)_2 \rightleftarrows NH_4CNO$$

and which is readily hydrolyzed according to:

$$NH_4CNO + H_2O \rightarrow CO_2 + 2 NH_3$$

From this point of view, the hydrolysis velocity of urea is determined by the rate at which the equilibrium is established between the isomers and by the quantity of ammonium cyanate in equilibrium.

In contrast to acids and bases, urease, the enzyme which occurs in soya beans, brings about complete hydrolysis of urea rapidly even at room temperature. A neutral or alkaline medium is required. The evolution of ammonia from urea by urease provides not only the basis of a quantitative micro determination of urea [176] but, with the aid of the Nessler reaction, it may also be used for the detection of urea.[177] The Nessler reaction involves the formation of a red-brown precipitate or a yellow color, due to $HgNH_2I \cdot HgI_2$,[178] which results when a basic solution of alkali mercuriiodide is added to solutions of ammonium salts:

$$[HgI_4]^{-2} \rightleftarrows HgI_2 + 2 I^-$$

$$HgI_2 + NH_3 + KOH \rightarrow KI + HgNH_2I + H_2O$$

$$HgNH_2I + HgI_2 \rightarrow HgNH_2I \cdot HgI_2$$

The following test for urea is reliable in the absence of ammonium salts and salts of volatile aliphatic amines, and guanidine, which give precipitates with Nessler solution. Urethans and ureides do not interfere.

Procedure. The test is conducted in a depression of a spot plate or in a porcelain microcrucible. A drop of the neutral or alkaline test solution is introduced, several milligrams of urease added, and stirred with a glass rod. After 2–5 minutes, a drop of Nessler solution is introduced. Depending on the amount of urea, a brown precipitate, turbidity, or yellow color appears. In case ammonium salts are present, a drop of the test solution should be taken to dryness along with a drop of dilute alkali. The ammonium salts are thus completely destroyed with release of ammonia, and without significant hydrolysis of urea. The evaporation residue is taken up in a drop of water, urease is added and the test continued as described. Stable solid urease products can be purchased.

Limit of Identification: 1 γ urea.

Reagent: Nessler reagent: 10 g mercuric iodide is made into a thin paste with a little water, 5 g potassium iodide is added and solution ensues. 20 g sodium hydroxide dissolved in 80 ml water is added and the whole made up to 100 ml. The rather turbid solution is allowed to stand several days, decanted, and stored in a brown bottle.

60. Carbon disulfide

(1) Test with sodium azide and iodine [179]

An aqueous solution containing sodium azide (NaN_3) and iodine (as KI_3) shows no change in the iodine content even on long standing. However, the addition of carbon disulfide brings about an immediate reaction, with vigorous evolution of nitrogen and consumption of iodine:

$$2\,NaN_3 + I_2 \rightarrow 2\,NaI + 3\,N_2$$

The carbon disulfide seemingly takes no part in this reaction but acts as a catalyst. This catalysis superficially is similar to that described in Volume I, Chapter 4, in the tests for inorganic sulfides, thiosulfates, thiocyanates, and in a test for organic compounds containing the $C=S$ and $C—SH$ groups (page 228).

The catalytic effect of carbon disulfide on the iodine-azide reaction is a typical intermediate reaction catalysis. Sodium azide and carbon disulfide form the sodium salt of azidodithiocarbonic acid, $CS(SH)N_3$ as shown in (1). This reaction is incomplete, but when concentrated solutions are employed, the azidodithiocarbonic acid can be detected by the formation of typical salts of such heavy metals as copper and bismuth.[180] The equilibrium reaction (1) is constantly disturbed in the presence of iodine since the dithiocarbonate formed is oxidized by iodine, as shown in (2), so that formation of the azidodithiocarbonate and its oxidation proceed until all the sodium azide is consumed. Summation of (1) and (2) gives (3), in which the catalytically active carbon disulfide no longer appears:

$$2\,NaN_3 + 2\,CS_2 \rightleftarrows 2\,CS(SNa)N_3 \qquad (1)$$

$$2\,CS(SNa)N_3 + I_2 \rightarrow 2\,CS_2 + 2\,NaI + 3\,N_2 \qquad (2)$$

$$2\,NaN_3 + I_2 \rightarrow 2\,NaI + 3\,N_2 \qquad (3)$$

Carbon disulfide can accordingly be detected by the evolution of nitrogen or through the disappearance of iodine from the sodium azide-iodine mixture. It must be remembered that mercaptans and thioketones likewise catalyze the iodine-azide reaction.

Procedure. The test for carbon disulfide in an organic liquid, e.g., alcohol, can be carried out by mixing one drop of the test solution with one drop of the reagent on a watch glass and noting the evolution of bubbles of nitrogen. When materials which consume iodine are present (hydrogen sulfide, etc.), the test solution should be treated beforehand with drops of iodine dissolved in potassium iodide or alcohol, until the iodine color is no longer discharged. The sodium azide – iodine mixture can then be added.

This test for carbon disulfide may alternatively be carried out similarly to the sulfide test (Vol. I, Chapter 4). In this, a drop of the test solution, which, if necessary, has previously been treated with iodine, is removed with a loop of platinum wire and touched to a drop of the iodine-azide solution hanging from a capillary tube. Any bubbles of nitrogen formed may be seen rising in the capillary tube.

Limit of Identification: 0.14 γ carbon disulfide.

Reagent: Sodium azide-iodine solution: 3 g NaN_3 dissolved in 100 ml 0.1 N iodine. The reagent solution is stable.

(2) Test with formaldehyde and plumbite solution [181]

Carbon disulfide is converted into trithiocarbonate on treatment with alkali hydroxide:

$$3 CS_2 + 6 KOH \rightarrow 2 K_2CS_3 + K_2CO_3 + 3 H_2O$$

The trithiocarbonate reacts with heavy metals to give insoluble salts, which are usually colored, and can, as in the case of the lead salt, be readily decomposed with formation of sulfide.

Appreciable amounts of carbon disulfide are rapidly converted into lead sulfide on treatment with concentrated caustic alkali and a plumbite solution. Small amounts of carbon disulfide are only very slowly converted to thiocarbonate, even in the presence of large amounts of alkali. However, the thiocarbonate formation, and consequently the production of lead sulfide, may be remarkably accelerated by formaldehyde (in a manner not yet understood). Acetaldehyde, benzaldehyde, arabinose, glucose, and lactose show the same effect.[182] This action affords a means of detecting small amounts of carbon disulfide.

Procedure. A drop of the test solution is placed on spot plate, 2 or 3 drops of 40% formaldehyde solution added and followed by a drop of a strongly alkaline plumbite solution. The mixture is stirred. A black precipitate, or a brown to black color is formed, depending on the amount of carbon disulfide originally present.

Limit of Identification: 3.5 γ carbon disulfide.

This test cannot be used without modification for the detection of carbon disulfide when hydrogen sulfide is present, because the formation of lead sulfide is then no longer a specific test for carbon disulfide. The hydrogen sulfide can be destroyed by adding bromine water:

$$H_2S + 4 Br_2 + 4 H_2O \rightarrow H_2SO_4 + 8 HBr$$

The excess bromine is removed by adding sulfosalicylic acid:

$$Br_2 + C_6H_3(OH)(COOH)(SO_3H) \rightarrow C_6H_2Br(OH)(COOH)(SO_3H) + HBr$$

Procedure. A drop of the test solution is treated on a spot plate with concentrated bromine water, added drop by drop, until the yellow color is permanent. The excess of bromine is removed by adding solid sulfosalicylic acid. Then 2 or 3 drops of a 40% solution of formaldehyde are added, followed by a drop of a strongly alkaline solution of plumbite, and the mixture stirred. A black precipitate, or a black to brown color, appears in the presence of carbon disulfide.

The following limit of identification is independent of the amount of hydrogen sulfide that may be present.

Limit of Identification: 10 γ carbon disulfide.

(3) Detection through formation of copper dimethyldithiocarbamate [183]

Carbon disulfide reacts with primary and secondary amines to yield water-soluble dithiocarbamates of the respective amines (compare page 262). These products give water insoluble yellow-brown copper salts soluble with the same color in benzene, chloroform, etc. These colored solutions can be obtained directly from the components and a sensitive test for carbon disulfide can be based on this fact. For example, if water saturated with carbon disulfide (0.2% CS_2) is added to an ammoniacal copper solution containing dimethylamine, extraction with benzene yields a yellow benzene layer at once. The same effect is secured if the blue copper solution is shaken with a solution of carbon disulfide in benzene, chloroform, ether, etc. The reaction is:

$$CS_2 + 2 NH(CH_3)_2 + 1/2\ Cu^{+2} \longrightarrow SC \underset{N(CH_3)_2}{\overset{S-Cu/2}{\big\langle}} + (CH_3)_2NH_2$$

The test based on this reaction is characteristic for carbon disulfide and compounds which split off carbon disulfide on treatment with acids (xanthates, trithiocarbonates).

Procedure. The test is conducted in a micro test tube. A drop of the liquid to be tested for carbon disulfide (benzene, chloroform, etc.) is treated with a drop or two of the blue reagent solution and shaken, if need be, with a drop or two of benzene. If carbon disulfide is present, a yellow-brown to light yellow color appears in the benzene layer. The depth of the color depends on the quantity of carbon disulfide involved.

Limit of Identification: 3 γ carbon disulfide.

Reagent: 9 ml of 0.2% copper sulfate solution is treated with 1 ml concentrated ammonium hydroxide and 0.5 g dimethylamine hydrochloride. The reagent solution keeps.

References pp. 440–444

61. Ephedrine

Detection through hydramine cleavage [184]

Hydrochlorides of compounds, which have an OH-group in the α-position to an aromatic ring and an amino-group in the β-position, undergo the so-called hydramine cleavage when they are subjected to dry heating.[185] This consists of the formation of the corresponding aromatic-aliphatic ketone through a change in the position of two hydrogen atoms, and the formation of the hydrochloride of the split-off amine:

$$\text{CH(OH)—CH—NHR.HCl} \longrightarrow \text{CO—CH}_2\text{— } + \text{NH}_2\text{R.HCl}$$

The hydramine cleavage also can be accomplished in the wet way by warming with caustic alkali. Accordingly, phenyl ethyl ketone and methylamine are formed from ephedrine:

$$C_6H_5 - CH(OH) - \underset{\underset{NHCH_3}{|}}{CH} - CH_3 \longrightarrow C_6H_5 - CO - CH_2 - CH_3 + H_2NCH_3$$

Since the hydramine cleavage occurs within a few minutes, and also with slight amounts, the detection of methylamine can serve as an indirect test for ephedrine.

A sensitive test for methylamine is based on its reaction with 2,4-dinitrochlorobenzene (I) [186] which leads to an orange-yellow water-insoluble condensation product (II):

$$O_2N-\langle\rangle-Cl + NH_2CH_3 \longrightarrow O_2N-\langle\rangle-NHCH_3 + HCl$$
$$\underset{(I)}{NO_2} \qquad\qquad \underset{(II)}{NO_2}$$

It is possible that the colored compound may possess the structure of an *o*- or *p*-quinoidal compound as shown in IIa or IIb:

$$O_2N-\langle\rangle=\overset{+}{N}HCH_3 \qquad\qquad {}^-O_2N=\langle\rangle=\overset{+}{N}HCH_3$$
$$\underset{(IIa)}{NO_2^-} \qquad\qquad \underset{(IIb)}{NO_2}$$

The ability of 2,4-dinitrochlorobenzene to condense is not restricted to methylamine; other primary and secondary aliphatic and aromatic amines react to give colored products.[187] It is noteworthy that if the condensation products are once formed they are then resistant to dilute acids and can be extracted by means of organic solvents that are immiscible with water.

The detection of the hydramine cleavage, and the related indirect detection of ephedrine, can be accomplished in two ways. Use can be made of the fact that the split-off methylamine is volatile and hence detectable in the vapor phase (Procedure I). The second method is to warm an ether solution of the alkaloid with caustic alkali and an alcohol solution of 2,4-dinitrochlorobenzene (Procedure II).

Procedure I. The gas adsorption apparatus shown in Fig. 23, page 49, is used. A little of the solid or a drop of its weakly acid solution is placed in the bulb and a drop 5 N alkali is added. A drop of a saturated solution of 2,4-dinitrochlorobenzene in alcohol is put on the knob of the stopper. The closed apparatus is kept in a warm water bath for 10 minutes. If ephedrine is present, the yellow condensation product forms in the hanging drop. It is advisable to rinse the drop into a micro test tube with as little chloroform as possible, and to shake the liquid after adding a drop or two of dilute acetic acid. The production of a yellow chloroform layer is characteristic for a positive response to the test.

Limit of Identification: 7 γ ephedrine.

The application of this procedure assumes the absence of compounds which yield methylamine when they undergo the hydramine cleavage. Adrenaline is a pertinent instance, and also the salts of volatile organic bases.

Procedure II. A micro test tube is used. One drop of the ether solution of the test material is treated with a drop of 5 N alkali and one drop of the 2,4-dinitrochlorobenzene solution. After 5 minutes in the heated water bath, the mixture will have acquired a yellow-brown color. The cooled solution is treated with a drop or two of chloroform and several drops of dilute acetic acid. The mixture is shaken. The color of the chloroform layer becomes honey yellow to pale yellow depending on the amount of ephedrine. A blank test will give a colorless chloroform layer.

Limit of Identification: 5 γ ephedrine.

Procedure II can be used to detect ephedrine in the presence of adrenaline, since the latter is not soluble in ether. On the other hand, care must be taken with respect to the absence of those amines which react similarly with 2,4-dinitrochlorobenzene.

In contrast to adrenaline, ephedrine gives the reaction for secondary amines with an ammoniacal solution of copper sulfate and carbon disulfide as described on page 262, 417, 418.

62. Adrenaline

Neither of the tests given here is decisive for adrenaline, but if both give a positive result there is a strong probability that adrenaline is present. The same is true of its salts and derivatives.

References pp. 440–444

(1) Detection through hydramine cleavage [188]

When warmed with caustic alkali, adrenaline, like ephedrine, undergoes the hydramine cleavage to yield 3,4-dihydroxyacetophenone and methylamine:

$$HO-\langle\ \rangle-CH(OH)-CH_2-NHCH_3 \rightarrow HO-\langle\ \rangle-CO-CH_3 + NH_2CH_3$$

$$\quad OH \qquad\qquad\qquad\qquad\qquad\qquad OH$$

The latter, and therefore adrenaline indirectly, can be detected by condensation with 2,4-dinitrochlorobenzene to give an orange-yellow compound that is soluble in organic liquids. The method, described as Procedure I for ephedrine (*q.v.*), should be employed; it involves the detection of methylamine in the vapor phase. The *limit of identification* is 5 γ adrenaline. It must be remembered that ephedrine and volatile aliphatic and aromatic amines react in the same manner.

The procedure II used for ephedrine cannot be employed because adrenaline is not soluble in ether. A direct test for adrenaline in aqueous alkaline solutions is uncertain because such solutions turn red on contact with the air and this interferes with the recognition of the condensation product of methylamine with 2,4-dinitrochlorobenzene.

(2) Detection by means of 1,2-dinitrobenzene [189]

By virtue of its being an *o*-diphenol and also because of the CH(OH)-group in the α-position, adrenaline is a powerful reducing agent. In alkaline solution it functions as hydrogen donor and thus can be detected by means of the color reaction with 1,2-dinitrobenzene which is characteristic for such compounds (see page 131).

Procedure. A micro test tube is used. A drop of the aqueous or alcoholic test solution or a grain of the solid is treated in turn with a drop of a saturated solution of 1,2-dinitrobenzene in alcohol and a drop of 0.5 N sodium hydroxide. The mixture is heated not longer than one minute at most over a free flame. Depending on the amount of reducing material present, the resulting color is more or less blue.

Limit of Identification: 5 γ adrenaline.

This test should not be used in the presence of compounds which act as reductants in alkaline solution.

63. Piperine

Detection through hydrolytic splitting-off of piperidine [190]

The alkaloid piperine (I) is found in the fruits of various kinds of pepper. It is the piperidide of the monobasic unsaturated piperic acid. The acid amide is rapidly split by acid and alkaline hydrolysis into its components, namely piperidine (II) and piperic acid (III):

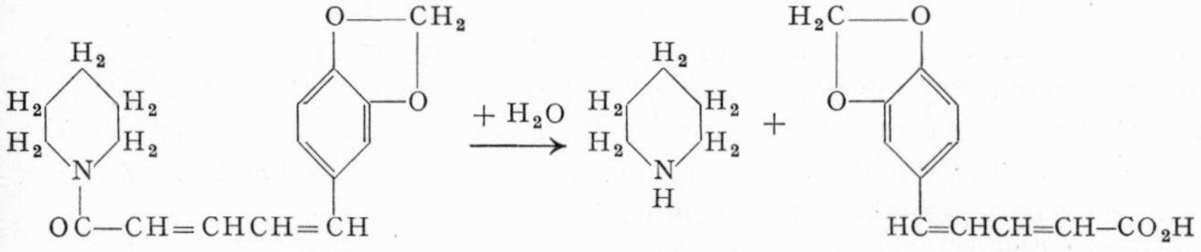

This hydrolysis can be proved through the detection of the liberated piperidine by means of the procedure given for secondary amines on page 262. Accordingly, the following test is an indirect means of establishing the presence of piperine.

Procedure. The test can be applied to a minimal quantity of the sample. (Pulverized pepper will also give satisfactory results.) The test portion is treated in a micro test tube with two drops of 1 : 1 hydrochloric acid and taken to dryness. The residue is then treated with a drop of 5% copper sulfate solution and a drop of concentrated ammonium hydroxide. Two or three drops of a mixture prepared from one volume carbon disulfide and three volumes benzene is added and the reaction mixture thoroughly shaken. If piperidine is present, the benzene layer will be brown to yellow.

Limit of Identification: **4** γ piperine.

The test is specific provided secondary amines are absent. They can be tested for, prior to hydrolysis of the sample.

64. Emetine and Cephaeline

Detection through formation of benzene-soluble copper dithiocarbamate [190]

Emetine and the structurally very similar cephaeline are the most important alkaloids in the rhizome of ipecacuanha. Inspection of the constitutional formula of emetine [191] shows that the alkaloid molecule contains a piperidine ring (cephaeline has OH in place of one of the OCH_3-groups):

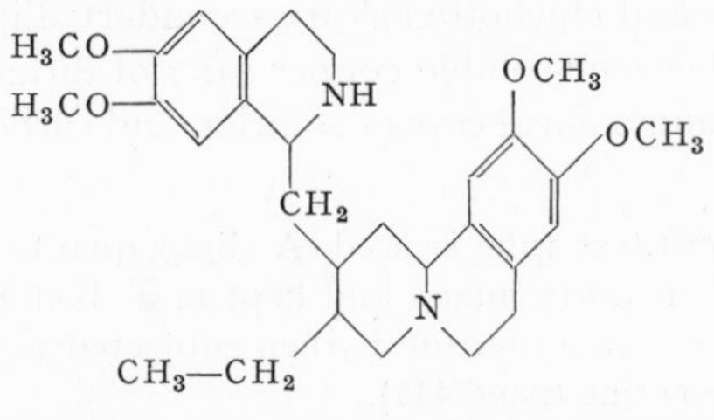

Because of the piperidine component, the alkaloid behaves analogously to piperidine toward ammoniacal copper salt solution and carbon disulfide. A brown copper salt of a dithiocarbamic acid results which is soluble in benzene.

Procedure. A drop of the acid test solution is treated in a micro test tube with a drop of a 5% solution of copper sulfate and two or three drops of concentrated ammonia and the mixture is then shaken with a few drops of a 1 : 3 mixture of carbon disulfide and benzene. A positive response has been obtained if the benzene layer is brown to yellow.

Limit of Identification: 2 γ emetine.

This procedure revealed emetine and cephaeline in the hydrochloric acid extract of dried ipecacuanha powder.

It may be expected that alkaloids which contain an NH-group also show the test for this group. In this category belong the anhalonium alkaloids (anhalonidine and anhalamine), as well as salsoline.

65. Cinchonine and Quinine

Detection through hydramine fission [190]

If cinchonine (I) is warmed with acetic acid, it undergoes hydramine fission (comp. detection of ephedrine, page 414). Cinchotoxine (II) results:

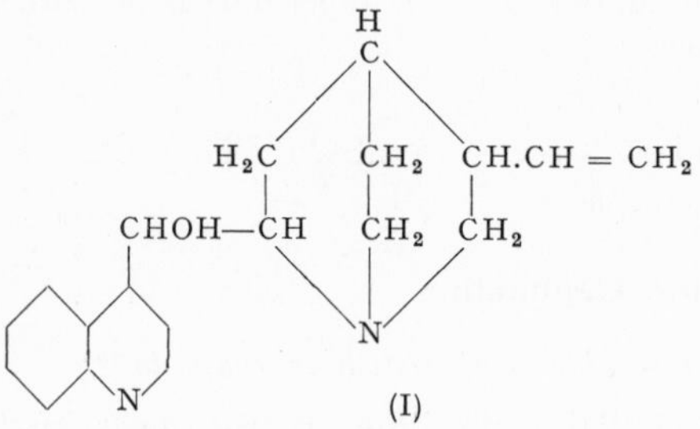

$$
\begin{array}{cc}
\text{(I)} & \text{(II)}
\end{array}
$$

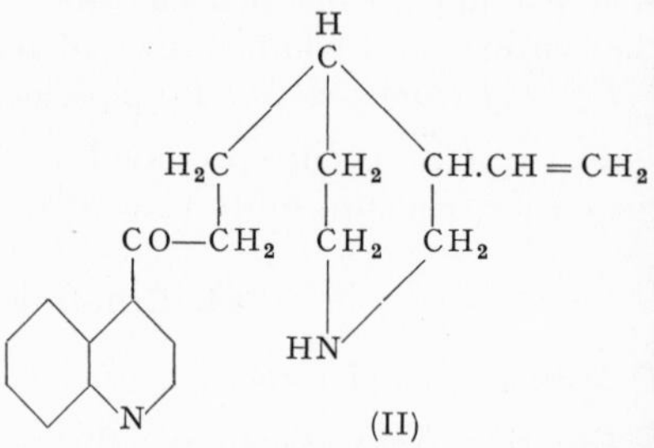

Quinine, which differs from cinchonine merely in a OCH_3-group in the 6'-position, yields the analogous keto compound, namely quinotoxine, when it undergoes the hydramine fission.

Both quinotoxine and cinchotoxine are secondary aliphatic bases, which give yellow-brown benzene-soluble copper salts of dithiocarbamic acids on treatment with an ammoniacal copper solution and carbon disulfide. (Comp. page 262.)

Procedure. A micro test tube is used. A slight quantity of the base and a drop of glacial acetic acid are mixed and kept in a boiling water bath for 20 minutes. The cooled reaction mixture is then subjected to the procedure given for the detection of emetine (page 417).

If salts of cinchonine or quinine are involved, it is necessary to isolate the

alkaloid prior to the test. This is accomplished easily by evaporating the sample
with ammonia before warming it with glacial acetic acid.

Limit of Identification: 20 γ cinchonine; 50 γ quinine hydrochloride.

Cinchonidine and hydrocinchonidine, which are isomeric with cinchonine
and hydrocinchonine, obviously give the reactions described here, since
these alkaloids likewise yield secondary bases when they undergo the
hydramine fission.

The test is not applicable in the presence of emetine and piperine (*q.v.*)
or of secondary aliphatic amines.

Quinine and cinchonine can easely be differentiated through the OCH_3-
group contained in quinine. This group is revealed by fusion with benzoyl
peroxide to produce formaldehyde (see page 179).

66. Coumarin

*Detection through conversion into fluorescing alkali salt of o-hydroxy cinnamic
acid* [192]

Coumarin (I) dissolves in dilute caustic alkali with cleavage of the pyrone
ring and formation of alkali salts of *o*-hydroxycinnamic acid or their anion
(II):

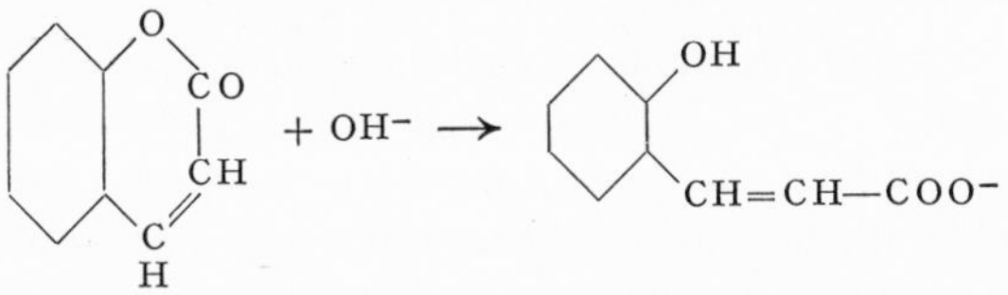

No fluorescence in ultraviolet light is exhibited by the freshly prepared
alkaline solution of (II) nor by solutions stored in the dark for months.
However, when irradiated with ultraviolet light, these solutions give a
yellow-green fluorescence within a few minutes, and the intensity increases
to a maximum. (Prolonged exposure of the alkaline solutions of coumarin
to daylight also produces the fluorescence.) This photo-effect can be demonstrated very effectively when a drop of a fresh alkaline solution of coumarin
is brought on filter paper. Half of the spot is covered with black paper and
the other half of the moist spot is left uncovered. The entire area is then
irradiated with ultraviolet light. The exposed portion of the spot begins
to fluoresce within a few minutes, and the intensity increases. If the rest
of the spot is uncovered after 6–8 minutes, the strongly fluorescing segment
stands out sharply from the other portion. If the irradiation is then resumed,
the portion of the spot originally shielded also begins to fluoresce, and after

sufficient exposure the entire area shows a uniform fluorescence. Therefore, in an alkaline solution of coumarin, the fluoresence is initiated by the irradiation, and the ultraviolet rays accelerate the innately sluggish conversion of a non-fluorescing compound into a fluorescing product.

It seems logical to assume that when coumarin is dissolved in caustic alkali, the initial product is the non-fluorescing *cis*-form (I) of *o*-hydroxycinnamic acid, which is converted by irradiation into an isomeric fluorescing *trans*-form (II):

(I)   (II)

Comparison of (I) and (II), i.e. of the anions of coumarinic and coumaric acids, shows that only in (II) is the H-atom of the phenol group so placed that its chelation (6-membered ring) to an unsaturated C-atom is not hindered by the COOH-group. It is possible that the chelated bonding is causally related to the fluorescence.

The tests described here have demonstrated that the photo-effect also appears in the alkaline solutions of such coumarin derivatives which have no free OH-groups in the benzene ring. Substituents seem to have an influence on the rate at which the fluorescence appears. For instance, if a drop of an alcohol-alkali solution of bergapten is placed on filter paper and exposed to ultraviolet rays, the start of the fluorescence can be discerned only after about 10 minutes exposure and the increase in the intensity of the fluorescence is much slower as compared with coumarin solutions of the same molarity.

Coumarin derivatives, which have free OH-groups in the benzene ring (umbelliferone, esculetin, daphnetin, etc.) are known to fluoresce deep blue in the solid state and in alkaline solution. No photo-effect could be found in alkaline solutions of these compounds.

The fluorescence following the ultraviolet irradiation of alkaline solutions of coumarin can be discerned with as little as 0.005 γ coumarin if a drop of the solution is exposed on filter paper. The corresponding dilution limit is 1 : 10,000,000. This type of test is not specific for coumarin since its derivatives containing no hydroxyl groups show the same behavior, and since hydroxycoumarins make it difficult to establish any fluorescence produced by irradiation because they possess a self-fluorescence. A capillary (adsorptive) separation on filter paper seems to provide a possibility of detecting compounds that fluoresce blue- and yellow-green, provided certain concentration ranges are observed.

A specific test for coumarin can be attained if use is made of the fact that this compound has a distinct vapor pressure at room temperature or when gently warmed. Therefore, the formation of (I) by contact of the coumarin vapor with caustic alkali and its conversion to the volatile product (II) on irradiation with ultraviolet light, can be accomplished.

Procedure. A drop of the ether solution is evaporated in a micro test tube or a tiny portion of the solid is taken. The mouth of the test tube is covered with a disk of filter paper moistened with 1 N-caustic alkali and the bottom of the tube is placed in hot water. After several minutes the paper is held under the quartz lamp. A yellow-green fluorescing circle appears in a short time.

Limit of Identification: 0.5 γ coumarin.

67. Morin and Hydroxyflavonols

Tests by formation of fluorescent metal compounds [193]

Derivatives of flavone (I) and flavonol (II) with OH- and OCH_3-groups in various positions of the two rings are (usually in the form of glucosides) important yellow plant pigments.

(I)   (II)

Among the flavone pigments, which in part are still used as mordant dyestuffs, are morin (5,7,2′,4′-tetrahydroxyflavonol) and its isomer quercetin (5,7,3′,4′-tetrahydroxy flavonol) whose structural formulas are (III) and (IV).

(III)   (IV)

The ability of hydroxy derivatives of flavone and flavonol to act as mordant dyes, i.e., to be fixed by alumina and other metal oxyhydrates, is related to the chelating position of OH-groups to CO-groups, as can be seen in (III) and (IV). Probably (and analogous to the case of the hydroxyanthraquinones, such as alizarin) the OH-group in the 5-position is particularly active. When the hydrogens of these hydroxyl groups are replaced by certain metal atoms, chelate bonding occurs with production of inner complex salts or adsorption compounds. Such compounds of morin display an intense yellow-green or blue-green fluorescence in ultraviolet light, and this is the basis of sensitive tests for these metals,[194] since solutions of morin in alcohol, alkali hydroxide, etc. do not fluoresce. Conversely, morin can be detected, with high sensitivity, through the formation of fluorescent metal compounds. The best procedure is to allow the test solution to react with an alkaline alkali beryllate solution or an acid solution of zirconium chloride. The former yields a yellow-green fluorescence, the latter a blue-green fluorescence (Procedures I and II). When morin reacts with alkali beryllate,[195] the resulting fluorescent product is a soluble compound, in which the beryllium is a constituent of an inner complex anion, as shown in (V) and (Va). The zirconium-morin reaction [196] in hydrochloric acid solution may involve a chemical adsorption of morin on the surface of the colloidally dispersed hydrolysis products of the zirconium chloride; (VI) presents a schematic picture of the hydrosol particles of the resulting adsorption compound. (Compare the statements relative to the zirconium-alizarin lake, Volume I, Chapter 3).

The partial structures (V), (Va), (VI) show the morin-beryllium (zirconium) chelate bondings, which are essential to the production of the fluorescence.

Quercetin behaves like morin. It is very likely (though not yet proven) that other hydroxyflavonols with an OH-group in the 5-position, will, like morin and quercetin, yield fluorescing compounds on treatment with alkaline beryllate and acid zirconium solutions. Whether the OH-group in the 3-position is likewise essential to the production of fluorescence, must be determined by a study of derivatives of flavone which have an OH-group in the 5-position.

Procedure I. Single drops of the acid 0.01% zirconium chloride solution are placed in adjacent depressions of a spot plate. One is treated with a drop of the test solution, the other with a drop of water. Both are then viewed in ultraviolet light. If morin is present, a yellow-green fluorescence is seen, whose hue depends on the quantity present. Very dilute solutions of morin give a blue-green fluorescence.

Limit of Identification: 0.01 γ morin.

Procedure II. Single drops of alkaline beryllate solution are placed in adjacent depressions of a spot plate. One is treated with a drop of the neutral or alkaline test solution, the other with a drop of water, or of the solvent used for the morin. A more or less intense yellow-green fluorescence appears, depending on the quantity of morin present.

Limit of Identification: 0.005 γ morin.

Reagent: Alkaline beryllate solution: 0.01 % beryllium sulfate solution is treated with drops of 0.5 N alkali until the initial precipitate has disappeared.

68. Cupferron (Neocupferron)

Test with gallium chloride and morin [197]

Cupferron (I) and neocupferron (II) are the common names for the water-soluble ammonium salts of nitrosophenylhydroxylamine and nitroso-α-naphthylhydroxylamine, respectively. Both compounds, particularly cupferron, have considerable importance as precipitants for metal ions from mineral acid solution. Their use enables the analyst to accomplish easily certain separations which otherwise are quite difficult.[198] The precipitates (metal cupferronates) are inner complex salts of the coordination structure (III) and are readily soluble in organic liquids, such as ether, chloroform, etc., which are not miscible with water. The analytical characteristics of neocupferron and the ammonium salts of other nitroso-arylhydroxylamines[199] are similar to those of cupferron.

A very sensitive and also specific test for gallium is based on the finding[200] that the colorless chloroform solution of gallium cupferronate when shaken with an acidic water-alcohol solution of morin displays an intense green-yellow fluorescence, which is especially visible in ultraviolet light. No other metal cupferronate (or its chloroform solution) behaves analogously. The hue of the fluorescence in the chloroform layer is completely identical with the yellow-green fluorescence displayed by a weakly acid dilute gallium salt solution after the addition of a morin solution. However, the gallium-morin fluorescence, produced in aqueous solution and in the absence of chloroform, cannot be extracted by chloroform. Since the fluorescence of metal compounds of morin is dependent on the presence of chelate bonds between metal atom and morin (compare page 421), it is probable that the fluorescence in chloroform solution involves the formation of an inner complex salt of morin as shown in (IV), whereas the chloroform–resistant fluorescence is related to the production of an adsorption compound (lake) of morin with

(IV)
fluorescent gallium morinate

(V)
fluorescent lake: morin chemically
adsorbed on gallium hydroxide

the colloidally dispersed hydrolysis products of gallium chloride. This latter adsorption complex is shown schematically in (V). Under these assumptions, it would be plausible to suppose then when a chloroform solution of gallium cupferronate is shaken with an aqueous solution of morin, the initial change:

$$\text{Ga(Cupf)}_3 + \text{HMor} \rightarrow \text{Ga(Mor)(Cupf)}_2 + \text{HCupf} \tag{1}$$

is followed by the disproportionation:

$$3\,\text{Ga(Mor)(Cupf)}_2 \rightarrow \text{Ga(Mor)}_3 + 2\,\text{Ga(Cupf)}_3 \tag{2}$$

But even the production of a mixed inner complex salt of gallium with the two chelate-formers, cupferron (HCupf) and morin (HMor) as shown in (1), would satisfactorily explain the solubility in chloroform and the fluorescence.

This behavior in the gallium–morin–cupferron–chloroform system is the only known instance in which a strictly specific test for gallium is attained by the collaboration of two organic reagents, cupferron and morin, which separately are entirely non-specific. If a weakly acid solution of gallium chloride is treated with an excess of morin and the resulting solution, which has a yellow-green fluorescence, is then shaken with chloroform, no fluorescence is seen in the chloroform layer. If, however, a drop of a solution of cupferron or neocupferron is introduced, and the system again shaken, the chloroform layer likewise displays a yellow-green fluorescence. This effect is given by quantities of cupferron or neocupferron which are too slight to be revealed by other means, such as the formation of colored ferric and vanadium compounds. The ammonium salts of other nitroso-arylhydroxyl-amines can be expected to show this same behavior.

Procedure. One drop of the gallium – morin solution (yellow-green fluorescence) is placed in a micro test tube and one drop of the solution to be tested is added along with three drops of water and a drop or two of chloroform. The mixture is well shaken. The resulting fluorescence in the chloroform layer can be seen without difficulty under ultraviolet light, provided the quantity of cupferron (neocupferron) is not too slight. It is advisable, after the extraction with chloroform, to pipette off the supernatant fluorescent water layer, replace it with water, and to repeat this washing process until the water no longer displays fluorescence. In this way, and by comparison with a blank test, even a slight fluorescence due to cupferron or neocupferron can be distinctly discerned in the chloroform layer.

Limit of Identification: 0.125 γ cupferron; 0.05 γ neocupferron.

Reagent: Gallium–morin solution. To 2 ml of 0.03 % gallium chloride solution add 3 ml of 0.02 % morin solution (in alcohol). The solution, which fluoresces light yellow in daylight and strongly yellow-green in ultraviolet light, is stable.

69. Thiophen

In Chapter 4 it was pointed out that 1,2-diketones in concentrated sulfuric acid solution condense with thiophen to yield colored quinoidal compounds that are known as indophenins. The tests for 1,2-diketones based on this type of reaction are, in part, the converse of the tests given here for thiophen. However, only the reaction with isatin-sulfuric acid has been used for this purpose. It has been found that a greater sensitivity in the thiophen test is given with the triketone ninhydrin, whereas with benzil the sensitivity is lower than with isatin.

(I) Detection by condensation with isatin [201]

Isatin (I), dissolved in concentrated sulfuric acid, condenses with thiophen (II), a reaction accompanied by a union of two thiophen molecules: [202]

The sulfuric acid does not function here solely as dehydrating agent. This fact is supported by the finding that no formation of indophenin occurs in syrupy phosphoric acid, which can be substituted for concentrated sulfuric acid in many condensations. The production of the dyestuff probably requires that the thiophen be sulfonated as well as oxidized [203] to α,α'-dithionyl (VI) by the concentrated sulfuric acid. The addition of a trace of nitric acid to the isatin-sulfuric acid is often recommended, but this device is not necessary, particularly if the reaction is conducted with gentle heating.

β-Methylthiophen (IV), β,β'-dimethylthiophen (V), α,α'-dithionyl (VI) and thiophthen (VII) analogously condense with isatin to yield blue dyestuffs. Since α-methyl- and α,α'-dimethylthiophen do not react, it is likely that the condensation with isatin occurs in the α-position of thiophen and thiophen homologs, as shown by the structural formula of indophenin (III).

| (IV) | (V) | (VI) | (VII) |

The indophenin reaction can be carried out as a drop reaction on a spot plate, in a porcelain microcrucible, or in a micro test tube. It should be noted that it is difficult to see a faint blue coloration in colored solutions, and that many colorless organic compounds give colored solutions in concentrated sulfuric acid. These interferences are avoided in the following procedure, which utilizes the facts that thiophen boils at 84° and that the indophenin reaction occurs very quickly when thiophen vapor comes in contact with a solution of isatin in concentrated sulfuric acid.

Procedure. [204] The apparatus shown in Figure 23, page 49 is used. A drop of the test solution (in thiophen-free benzene, etc.) is placed in the bulb, and the knob of the stopper is dipped into the yellow sulfuric acid solution of isatin. The apparatus is stoppered and placed in an oven at 80–90°. If thiophen is present, its vapors will color the suspended drop blue in 1–2 minutes; the intensity of the color depends on the quantity of thiophen. When traces are suspected, it is best to run a blank test.

Limit of Identification: 1.5 γ thiophen.
Reagent: 0.2 % solution of isatin in concentrated sulfuric acid.

(2) Detection through condensation with benzil [204]

The indophenin reaction employing benzil has been known for a long time.[205]

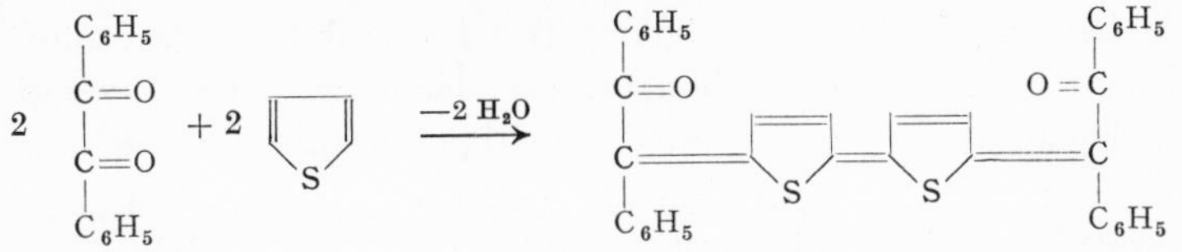

$$2 \begin{array}{c} C_6H_5 \\ | \\ C=O \\ | \\ C=O \\ | \\ C_6H_5 \end{array} + 2 \ \underset{S}{\langle \ \rangle} \ \xrightarrow{-2 \ H_2O} \begin{array}{c} C_6H_5 \\ | \\ C=O \\ | \\ C= \end{array} \underset{S}{=} \underset{S}{=} \begin{array}{c} C_6H_5 \\ | \\ O=C \\ | \\ C \\ | \\ C_6H_5 \end{array}$$

Solutions of benzil in concentrated sulfuric acid are not stable; the light yellow solution becomes brown to green after a short time. Therefore, it is better to use solid benzil or a solution of benzil in thiophen-free benzene as reagent.

Procedure. The test is made on a spot plate or in a micro test tube. A drop of the test solution is mixed with several milligrams of benzil, or with two drops of benzil solution, and a drop of concentrated sulfuric acid is then introduced. The mixture is shaken, or stirred with a thin glass rod. Depending on the quantity of thiophen present, a more or less intense violet color appears at once or within a few minutes.

Limit of Identification: 5 γ thiophen.

Reagents: 2 % solution of benzil in thiophen-free benzene.

(3) Test by condensation with ninhydrin [204]

The color reactions for thiophen given in Tests *1* and *2* involve condensation reactions with 1,2-diketones, dissolved in concentrated sulfuric acid, in which the latter functions both as dehydrant and oxidant. Polyketones which contain two adjacent CO-groups in open or closed carbon chains likewise appear capable of forming quinoidal dyestuffs with thiophen. The behavior of ninhydrin (triketohydrindene hydrate) strengthens this supposition. Even very dilute solutions of this triketone in concentrated sulfuric acid give a red color almost immediately following a slight addition of thiophen. It is probable that the red dyestuff, which is deep violet in greater concentrations, is formed by an analogous succession of reactions and probably has a constitution analogous to those of the dyestuffs formed by the reaction of thiophen with benzil or isatin. If this be true, the following reaction picture holds:

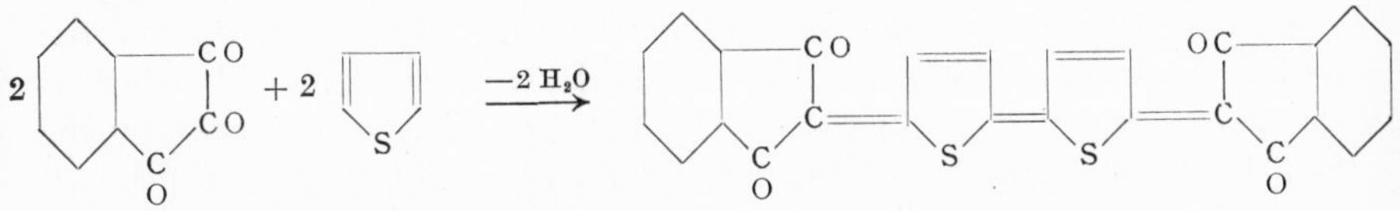

$$2 \ \underset{O}{\overset{CO}{\underset{\displaystyle C}{\bigcirc\!\!\!-}}}\!\!\overset{}{\underset{}{\big|}}CO + 2 \ \underset{S}{\langle \ \rangle} \ \xrightarrow{-2 \ H_2O} \ \cdots$$

The color reaction with ninhydrin is so sensitive that purified benzene, supposedly free of thiophen, often gives a pale but nevertheless easily discernible pink on the addition of ninhydrin dissolved in sulfuric acid.

If the hanging drop method given in Test 1 is used, ninhydrin solution will reveal 3 γ thiophen at room temperature. The reagent loses its activity at 80–90°. Good results are obtained according to the following directions.

Procedure. One drop of a freshly prepared 0.01% solution of ninhydrin in concentrated sulfuric acid is covered with a drop of the solution being tested. According to the amount of thiophen a deep violet to pink color appears.
Limit of Identification: 0.2 γ thiophen.

70. Furfural

Test through condensation with aniline [206]

Solutions of furfural (I) in organic liquids, or in water (in which it dissolves to the extent of 8 per cent), react with aniline (II) or aniline salt (the acetate is best) to produce a red precipitate or color. In this reaction, the first stage consists of the formation of a light yellow [207] Schiff base (III) through the condensation reaction (1). This then reacts with a second aniline molecule, with cleavage of the furfural ring and formation of a dianiline derivative of hydroxyglutaconic dialdehyde,[208] as shown in (2):

$$ \text{(1)} $$

$$ \text{(2)} $$

According to (IV), the condensation product belongs to the class of polymethine dyes discussed on pages 280 and 403 in connection with the tests for pyridine and its derivatives.

If the reactions (1) and (2) occur in acidic solution, salts of the dye with the acid employed will be formed. Consequently, this extremely sensitive color reaction requires the opening of the ring with production of the hydroxyglutaconic aldehyde; it is the dianilide of this aldehyde which is the colored reaction product (IV). This interpretation is supported by the fact that the normal condensation products (Schiff bases) of primary aromatic amines with aliphatic and aromatic aldehydes are not red but yellow to orange.[209]

Although furfural boils at 160°, its vapor pressure at room temperature is quite marked; this aldehyde is also readily volatilized with steam. Therefore, it can be sensitively detected in the gas phase by the production of the red compound (IV) when the vapors come into contact with aniline acetate. The test is not impaired by other volatile aldehydes, such as formaldehyde, acetaldehyde, benzaldehyde, etc. Other aromatic primary amines (or their acetates) react with furfural in the same manner as aniline does. The reaction product with benzidine is violet, but the test is less sensitive. However, furfural is detected with even greater sensitivity when xylidine is used in place of aniline.

Procedure. [210] One drop of the furfural solution (in water, alcohol, ether, etc.) is placed in a micro crucible, which is then covered with a disk of filter paper which has been moistened with a 10% solution of aniline in 10% acetic acid. A small watch glass is placed over the paper and the crucible is heated to 40°. A pink to red color appears on the filter paper, either at once or after 5–10 minutes, depending on the quantity of furfural present.

Limit of Identification: 0.05 γ furfural.

71. Enzymes

General [211]

A number of substances which can accelerate the velocity of a particular chemical reaction may often be detected in extremely small amounts by this catalytic action. The test is based either on the detection of a product of the catalysis or the disappearance of the participants in the reaction. Such tests for the catalyzing substances are specific or highly selective as proved by pertinent examples given in Volume I and also pages 228, 241 of this text. The following tests for certain enzyme groups are based on the same principle of catalytic action. All enzymes are organic substances which occur in plant and animal material and, as catalysts, play an important role in metabolic processes.[212] Such enzymes (biocatalysts) are distinguished by the deep-seated changes they effect in definite substrates, changes such as oxidation, reduction, alteration of hydrogen ion concentration, formation of characteristic compounds, etc. These changes may sometimes be detected by spot tests and with very small amounts of substrate, and hence the enzymes themselves detected by these sensitive tests.

Procedure. A drop of the substrate solution and a drop of the solution to be tested for a particular enzyme are mixed on a strip of filter paper or in a microcrucible. The sample and a blank (a drop of water and a drop of substrate) are kept for 40 to 60 minutes under a moist bell jar. The product of the reaction is then treated with suitable reagents.

The skeletal details concerning the detection of several enzymes are given in Table 37.

References pp. 440–444

TABLE 37.   ENZYMES

Enzyme	Substrate	Reagent	Color
Diastase	0.5 % Soluble starch	Fehling solution	Brick-red or orange
Inulase	0.5 % Inulin	Fehling solution	Brick-red or orange
Invertase	0.5 % Cane sugar	Fehling solution	Brick-red or orange
Emulsin	0.5 % Salicin	Fehling solution	Brick-red or orange
Emulsin	0.5 % Indican	Alkali with access to air	Blue
Lipase	0.2 % Emulsion of olive oil	Methyl red	Red
Butyrase	0.2 % Ethyl acetate-water emulsion	Methyl red	Red
Urease	1% Urea	Phenolphthalein	Pink
Phenolase	1 % Tincture of guaiac	Phenolphthalein	Blue
Tyrosinase	Tyrosine	Phenolphthalein	Brown

Other reactions, described elsewhere in this Volume, may also be applied as tests for enzymes. Examples are given in the following sections.[213]

Urease

(1) Test by the liberation of ammonia

Urease brings about the rapid and complete hydrolysis of urea into ammonia and carbon dioxide at room temperature. The enzyme may therefore be detected by mixing a drop of the test solution and a drop of a 10 per cent solution of urea in the apparatus shown in Figure 26, page 50. The funnel stopper is covered with a piece of filter paper impregnated with manganese-silver reagent solution (see page 91). If urease is present, the ammonia set free blackens the paper in ten minutes or less.

An alternative procedure is to place a drop of the solution being tested for urease in a depression of a spot plate and then add a drop of 10 per cent urea solution. After 5–10 minutes, the production of ammonia can be proved by adding a drop of Nessler solution (see page 120).

It should be noted that certain heavy metals ions (Hg^{+2}, Ag^+) and likewise Cu^{+2} in slight amounts inactivate relatively large quantities of urease, or greatly lengthen its required reaction period.[214]

(2) Test by splitting biuret and urea

A test for urease may be based on the fact that this enzyme accelerates the hydrolytic splitting of biuret as well as urea:

$$\underset{O=C-NH-C=O}{\overset{NH_2 \qquad NH_2}{|}} + 2\,H_2O \longrightarrow 2\,CO_2 + 3\,NH_3 \tag{1}$$

This hydrolysis can be shown by the procedure previously described if a biuret solution (saturated at room temperature) is used in place of a 10 % solution of urea. Another means of demonstrating this hydrolysis is the decomposition of a solution of the complex alkali-nickel biuret by means of urease (see following procedure).

When biuret reacts with nickel ions plus alkali hydroxide, the resulting yellow solution gives no red precipitate on the addition of dimethylglyoxime. This masking of the sensitive test for nickel is due to reaction (2) which produces the complex nickel-bearing anions of the *aci*-form of biuret: [215]

$$2 \; \underset{O=C-NH_2}{\overset{O=C-NH_2}{\underset{|}{\overset{|}{NH}}}} + Ni^{+2} + 4\,OH^- \rightleftharpoons \left[\underset{O-C=N \qquad N=C-O}{\overset{O=C-NH_2 \quad H_2N-C=O}{\underset{|}{\overset{|}{HN \qquad \diagdown Ni \diagup \qquad NH}}}} \right]^{-2} + 4\,H_2O \tag{2}$$

The equilibrium of this masking reaction lies so far to the right, that the concentration of nickel ions is insufficient to give a visible reaction with dimethylglyoxime. However, if urease is added to the solution containing the nickel biuret anions, and saponifies the *baso*-form of biuret as shown in (1), the restoration of equilibrium (2) releases nickel ions as well as the *baso*-form of biuret. The concentration of the nickel ions is brought to a level at which the dimethylglyoxime reaction can occur to a visible extent. The following test for urease is based on this demasking of nickel from solutions containing complex nickel biuret anions. This procedure has the advantage of being applicable in alkaline solutions and furthermore small amounts of ammonium salts do not interfere. Large quantities of ammonia cause precipitation of nickel dimethylglyoxime from the equilibrium solution. Proteins give the same effect and of course all acid substances which take up OH^- ions.

Procedure.[216] Drops of the clear alkali-nickel biuret reagent solution are placed in adjacent depressions of a spot plate. A drop of the neutral or alkaline test solution is added to one depression and a drop of water to the other. The mixtures are allowed to stand for 10–15 minutes at room temperaure and then both are treated with a drop of 1% dimethylglyoxime solution in 95% alcohol. If urease is present, there is an immediate precipitation of red nickel dimethylglyoxime. The yellow color of the blank remains as it was or it may show a slight change toward orange.

Reagent: Sodium-nickel biuret solution: 1 gram of nickel sulfate (hexahydrate) is dissolved in 50 ml of water and 1 gram of biuret is added. The solution is warmed and 15 ml of 1 N sodium hydroxide introduced. The precipitate of nickel hydroxide is filtered off. On long standing, particularly in open vessels, the solution becomes turbid because of the deposition of nickel hydroxide. Such solutions can be used after they are filtered.

Zymase

Zymase ferments sugar with the formation of alcohol and carbon dioxide. The carbon dioxide produced may be identified by the reaction described in Volume I (decolorization of sodium carbonate solution colored red with phenolphthalein). The test may be carried out in the apparatus described on page 49 (Fig. 23). A drop of the solution to be tested for zymase is mixed with a drop of a 5 % solution of glucose. In the presence of zymase, the drop is decolorized in about 10 minutes.

β-Glucosidases (Emulsin)

Emulsin causes the glucoside amygdalin to break down with liberation of prussic acid, which can easily be identified by the cyanide test described in Volume I, Chap. 4 (blue color with benzidine–copper acetate; see also p. 93).

A drop of the solution to be tested for emulsin is placed in the apparatus described on page 50 (Fig. 26). A little amygdalin is added and the funnel stopper is covered with a piece of filter paper impregnated with the benzidine–copper acetate reagent. A blue color after a few minutes indicates prussic acid, and hence emulsin.

Lipases

Lipases are ester-splitting enzymes. They can easily be identified by using the test for esters described on page 237. This test is based on the production of a red ferric salt of the hydroxamic acid of the underlying carboxylic acid.

A drop of a castor oil emulsion is placed in each of two microcrucibles. A drop of the solution to be tested for lipase is placed in one of the crucibles. After 1 to 2 hours, the contents of the crucibles are tested for esters. In the presence of lipase, the response is negative, or decidedly weaker, whereas the blank gives the characteristic violet color due to esters.

Catalase

Catalases catalyze the decomposition of hydrogen peroxide with liberation of molecular oxygen. These ferments can therefore be detected by the disappearance of hydrogen peroxide from the substrate. The titanium salt reaction based on the formation of yellow pertitanate compounds is used for the peroxide test. Another test with lead sulfide paper (conversion of black lead sulfide into white lead sulfate) also serves well.[217] Both tests are described in Volume I, Chapter 4.

A drop of the solution to be tested for catalase is mixed with a drop of a 3 % solution of hydrogen peroxide and left for one hour. In the presence of catalase, the addition of a titanium salt will give no color, or only a slight yellow, while the blank test develops an orange-yellow.

A drop of the solution treated with hydrogen peroxide may also be placed on lead sulfide paper. The positive or negative response to the hydrogen peroxide reaction can be noted; the latter indicates the presence of catalase.

Peroxidase (Blood) [218]

The hemoglobin of blood has the activity of a peroxidase and catalyzes the oxidation by hydrogen peroxide of benzidine to benzidine blue.

A drop of the solution to be tested for blood (*e.g.*, urine) is placed on spot paper (S & S 598g) and treated first with a drop of 3 % hydrogen peroxide and then with a drop of 0.05 % solution of benzidine in 10 % acetic acid. When blood is present, a blue stain appears after a time, varying from a few seconds to 1 minute according to the amount present. The color lasts for about one hour.

The sensitivity and rapidity of the test may be increased, but at the expense of the length of life of the color, by adding a drop of 2 N sodium hydroxide to the paper before applying the specimen, and then proceeding as just prescribed.

Other catalytic tests for blood are based on the development of a color or luminescence with leuco malachite green, phenolphthalein and luminol. A series of interferences must be taken into account when criminalistic investigations are being conducted.[219]

72. Tetrachloro-*p*-benzoquinone (Chloranil)

Test by oxidation of tetrabase [220]

Tetrachloro-*p*-benzoquinone (I), also known as chloranil, acts as an oxidant under suitable conditions. It is reduced to tetrachlorohydroquinone (II) or to the corresponding anion (IIa).

$$O=\underset{\underset{Cl\ Cl}{}}{\overset{\overset{Cl\ Cl}{}}{\bigcirc}}=O + 2\,\varepsilon \longrightarrow {}^-O-\underset{\underset{Cl\ Cl}{}}{\overset{\overset{Cl\ Cl}{}}{\bigcirc}}-O^-$$

(I)   (IIa)

For example, the addition of an alcohol solution of chloranil to an acidified alkali iodide or bromide solution liberates iodine or bromine, or, if introduced into an acetic acid solution of tetramethyl-p,p'-diaminodiphenylmethane (III) (tetrabase), there is immediate oxidation to a basic blue diphenyl-methane dyestuff which contains the quinoidal cation (IV). Consequently, tetrabase may be regarded as the air-stable leuco-form of the dye (IV).

When a dilute ether solution of chloranil is treated with a dilute ether solution of tetrabase, there is no noticeable change. If, however, a drop of the light yellow mixture is placed on filter paper or in a depression of a spot plate, evaporation of the ether leaves a deep blue residue which probably is identical with the blue oxidation product of the tetrabase, which can be produced by other means (electrolytic oxidation, lead dioxide, etc.).[221] The same effect may be observed if alcohol, chloroform, benzene, etc. is used as the mutual solvent. When the solution of (I) and (III) in a solvent which is not miscible with water is shaken with water, no change is apparent. Therefore, it seems that non-reactivity is produced as a consequence of the formation of stable solvates of chloranil and tetrabase, and a redox reaction, leading to a colored oxidation product of tetrabase, occurs only after the evaporation of the solvent. As a matter of fact, the blue product can also be formed by a solid-solid reaction, namely by grinding together dry chloranil and dry tetrabase. The reaction can be represented:

$$(CH_3)_2N-\bigcirc-CH_2-\bigcirc-N(CH_3)_2 + O=\underset{\underset{Cl\ Cl}{}}{\overset{\overset{Cl\ Cl}{}}{\bigcirc}}=O \longrightarrow$$

(III)

$$(CH_3)_2N-\bigcirc-CH=\bigcirc=\overset{+}{N}(CH_3)_2 + HO-\underset{\underset{Cl\ Cl}{}}{\overset{\overset{Cl\ Cl}{}}{\bigcirc}}-O^-$$

(IV)

The redox reaction between chloranil and tetrabase in the absence of solvents can be made the basis of a sensitive drop reaction for the detection of chloranil, even though bromanil and iodanil may be expected to react analogously.

Quinone, anthraquinone and phenanthraquinone do not react with tetra-base under the conditions prescribed here. Only benzoyl superoxide (and probably all organic peroxide compounds) oxidize tetrabase to the blue diphenylmethane dyestuff. Accordingly, the test is quite selective.

Procedure. A minimum quantity of the solid sample or a drop of its solution in ether, benzene, etc., is placed in a depression of a spot plate. One drop of an ether solution of tetrabase is added and stirred with a glass rod. A blue residue is left as the solvent evaporates. Alternatively, a drop of the ether test solution can be placed on filter paper, which has previously been spotted with a drop or two of the reagent solution. According to the quantity of chloranil present, the evaporation of the ether leaves a deep blue to light blue fleck.

Limit of Identification: 0.25 γ chloranil.

73. Pentachlorophenol

Test by conversion into chloranil

The colorless pentachlorophenol (I) is easily converted to chloranil (II) by brief warming with concentrated nitric acid: [222]

This reaction, whose occurrence is revealed by the yellow color due to the chloranil formed, is the basis of a test for nitric acid [223] and also of a colorimetric method for determining chloranil. [224] However, this procedure for the detection of any resulting chloranil is neither sensitive (*Idn. Limit:* 12 γ in one drop) nor unequivocal, because many phenols are easily converted to yellow nitro compounds by concentrated nitric acid. It is better, after oxidizing the pentachlorophenol by nitric acid, to detect the resulting chloranil by means of an acetic acid or citric acid solution of tetramethyl-*p,p'*-diaminodiphenylmethane (tetrabase) after buffering the free nitric acid with sodium acetate. A blue oxidation product of tetrabase is formed (compare the test for chloranil described on page 433). When small amounts of pentachlorophenol are suspected, the nitrous acid or nitrogen oxides, remaining after the reaction with the nitric acid, must be destroyed by adding urea $[CO(NH_2)_2 + 2HNO_2 \rightarrow CO_2 + 3H_2O + 2N_2]$. This precaution is necessary to prevent oxidation of the tetrabase by nitrogen oxides.

Procedure. [225] One drop of the test solution is evaporated in a micro test tube. The residue is treated with a drop of concentrated nitric acid and the mixture is briefly warmed over a flame or kept for 2 minutes in the boiling water bath. After cooling, several milligrams of urea are added, followed by a drop of a solution of tetrabase in citric acid [225a] and a pinch (tip of knife blade) of solid sodium acetate. The mixture is then reheated over the flame, or plunged into warm water. A blue color indicates the formation of chloranil and hence the presence of pentachlorophenol in the sample. When testing for small amounts, it is best to run a comparison blank.

Limit of Identification: 2.5 γ pentachlorophenol.

Reagent: Citric acid solution of tetrabase: 2.5 g tetramethyl-p,p'-diamino-diphenylmethane and 10 g citric acid are dissolved in 10 ml water and diluted to 500 ml.

74. Nitrosodiphenylamine

Detection with concentrated sulfuric acid [226]

Both the isomeric compounds: N-nitroso-diphenylamine (I) and p-nitroso-diphenylamine (II)

as well as their nuclear-substituted derivatives, give a blue color when they are treated with concentrated sulfuric acid in the cold or on gentle warming. These color reactions are the consequence of the saponification of (I) and (II), by the water contained in the concentrated sulfuric acid, to yield diphenylamine and nitrous acid. The latter oxidizes diphenylamine, as is well known, to blue quinoidal compounds (compare the nitrite and nitrate reactions, Volume I, Chapter 4).

The color reaction is specific for nitrosodiphenylamine. No other N- or C-nitroso compound reacts in an analogous manner.

Procedure. A micro crucible is used. A little of the solid is taken or a drop of the test solution is evaporated to dryness. A drop of concentrated sulfuric acid is added and the contents of the crucible then warmed gently, if necessary. A blue color shows the presence of nitrosodiphenylamine.

Limit of Identification: 0.5 γ N-nitrosodiphenylamine or p-nitrosodiphenyl-amine.

It is possible to differentiate between these two isomeric nitrosodiphenyl-amines by taking advantage of the fact that N-nitroso compounds, in contrast to C-nitroso compounds, are easily denitrosated by hydrazoic acid (see page 154). If sodium azide and dilute hydrochloric acid are added to diphenylnitrosamine, the reaction

$$(C_6H_5)_2N - NO + HN_3 \rightarrow (C_6H_5)_2NH + N_2 + N_2O$$

occurs almost immediately. Consequently, if the foregoing test has resulted positively, a new portion of the sample is taken to dryness with several centigrams of sodium azide and a drop of dilute hydrochloric acid. If the residue gives no reaction when treated with concentrated sulfuric acid, or if it yields a distinctly weaker blue color than the same amount of the untreated sample, it may be concluded that the nitrosamine (I) is present.

75. p-Nitrosodimethyl(ethyl)aniline

Detection through splitting off of dimethyl(ethyl)amine [227]

When dialkylated p-nitrosoanilines are heated with alkali hydroxide, the products are p-nitrosophenolate and dialkylamine:

$$ON\!\!-\!\!\langle\bigcirc\rangle\!\!-\!\!NRR + KOH \longrightarrow ON\!\!-\!\!\langle\bigcirc\rangle\!\!-\!\!OK + NHRR$$

Accordingly, dimethyl(ethyl)aniline yields the bases dimethyl- or diethylamine, which are volatile with steam. Both of these amines condense with 2,4-dinitrochlorobenzene to yield yellow compounds which are soluble in chloroform. This constitutes the basis of a sensitive test for these amines and indirectly for compounds which furnish them as products of suitable reactions. See the test for ephedrine (page 414) regarding the chemistry of this color reaction.

Procedure. A drop of the test solution is placed in the bulb of the apparatus shown in Fig. 23 (page 49) and one drop of 20% sodium hydroxide is added. A drop of a saturated solution of 2,4-dinitrochlorobenzene in alcohol is suspended on the knob of the stopper. The closed apparatus is placed in boiling water for several minutes. The hanging drop is then rinsed into a micro test tube by means of 1 : 1 acetic acid. Several drops of chloroform are added and the mixture shaken. A yellow color appears if p-nitrosodimethyl(ethyl)aniline was present.

Limit of Identification: 2.5 γ p-nitrosodimethyl(ethyl)aniline.

76. Dimethyl(ethyl)aniline

Detection through conversion into p-*nitrosodimethyl(ethyl)aniline* [227]

Nitrous acid readily nitrosates dimethyl- and diethylaniline in the *para*-position. For example:

$$\langle\bigcirc\rangle\!\!-\!\!N(CH_3)_2 + HNO_2 \longrightarrow ON\!\!-\!\!\langle\bigcirc\rangle\!\!-\!\!N(CH_3)_2 + H_2O$$

Sensitive tests for dimethyl- or diethylaniline can be based on this fact and also on the production of dimethyl- or diethylamine from the corresponding p-nitroso compounds by treating with alkali hydroxide (compare 75).

References pp. 440–444

Procedure. The gas absorption apparatus is charged with a drop of the acidified test solution. A little solid potassium nitrite is added and if need be a drop of hydrochloric acid. The nitrous vapors are driven off by vigorous warming. The remainder of the Procedure is as given in the preceding test. *Limit of Identification:* 3 γ dimethyl- or diethylaniline.

77. Benzoyl peroxide

The characteristic redox reaction of inorganic and organic derivatives of hydrogen peroxide, in which iodine is liberated from acidified alkali iodide solution, is not applicable to the very stable benzoyl peroxide because of its slight solubility in water and alcohol. However, this peroxide can react in characteristic fashion in nonaqueous solution, or as a solid, or in the molten condition, and give off oxygen to appropriate reaction partners.

(1) Detection through oxidation of tetrabase [226]

Benzoyl peroxide reacts with tetrabase (tetramethyl-p,p'-diaminodiphenyl-methane) in benzene, ether, etc. solution to yield a blue quinoidal diphenyl-methane dye,

$$(CH_3)_2N-\hspace{-1em}\bigcirc\hspace{-1em}-CH_2-\hspace{-1em}\bigcirc\hspace{-1em}-N(CH_3)_2 + (C_6H_5CO)_2O_2 \longrightarrow$$

$$(CH_3)_2N-\hspace{-1em}\bigcirc\hspace{-1em}-CH=\hspace{-1em}\bigcirc\hspace{-1em}=\overset{+}{N}(CH_3)_2 + C_6H_5COO^- + C_6H_5COOH$$

It is noteworthy that this oxidation proceeds rapidly only after evaporating the mutual solvent.

The test cannot be used in the presence of considerable amounts of nitro compounds or quinones. These compounds react with tetrabase to give orange-yellow to orange-red molecular compounds (comp. page 160) and so interfere with the detection of small quantities of benzoyl peroxide.

Procedure. A drop of a 5% solution of tetrabase in benzene is placed on filter paper and then a drop of the benzene or ether solution of the sample is added. After the solvent has evaporated, a blue stain is left, the color depending on the quantity of benzoyl peroxide present.

Limit of Identification: 0.5 γ benzoyl peroxide.

(2) Detection with diethylaniline [226]

If benzoyl peroxide is warmed with an excess of diethylaniline, acetalde-hyde results (compare page 180) because of the redox reaction:

$$C_6H_5N(C_2H_5)_2 + 2 (C_6H_5CO)_2O_2 \rightarrow 2 CH_3CHO + C_6H_5NH_2 + 2 (C_6H_5CO)_2O$$

The acetaldehyde formed can be detected by the blue color which appears

References pp. 440–444

when it comes into contact with a solution of sodium nitroprusside containing morpholine. This indirect test is specific for benzoyl peroxide.

Procedure. The test is made in a micro centrifuge tube (Emich tube). One drop of the benzene or ether test solution and one drop of diethylaniline are mixed and the open end of the tube is covered with a disk of filter paper that has been moistened with the reagent solution (page 181). The tube is placed in a water bath at 90° and after the benzene has volatilized the water is brought to boiling. A deep to light blue stain appears on the colorless or light yellow paper, the shade depending on the amount of benzoyl peroxide present.

Limit of Identification: 3 γ benzoyl peroxide.

78. Citral

Detection by alkaline cleavage [228]

The unsaturated aldehyde citral (I) occurs in many ethereal oils. When it is gently warmed with aqueous caustic alkalis it splits to yield acetaldehyde and methylheptenone (II) [229]:

$$(CH_3)_2C=CH—(CH_2)_2—\underset{\underset{CH_3}{|}}{C}=CH—CHO + H_2O \rightarrow$$

$$(I)$$

$$(CH_3)_2C=CH—(CH_2)_2—\underset{\underset{CH_3}{|}}{C}O + CH_3CHO$$

$$(II)$$

Consequently, an indirect test for citral can be obtained through the detection of the resulting acetaldehyde by means of the color reaction with a sodium nitroprusside-morpholine mixture (comp. pag. 334). However, the sensitivity is low because the alkaline hydrolytic cleavage of citral also causes polymerization of the unsaturated aldehyde as shown by a browning of the reaction mixture. Opposed to this disadvantage, is the advantage of specificity since no other instance is known in which acetaldehyde is produced by the alkaline hydrolysis of an organic compound.

Procedure. The test is conducted in a micro test tube. A drop of the oil to be tested or a drop of its solution in ether, etc. is treated with a drop or two of 0.5 N sodium hydroxide. The mouth of the tube is covered with a disk of filter paper that has been moistened with the acetaldehyde reagent (page 181). The test tube is placed in boiling water. If citral is present, the paper turns blue, the depth of the color depending on the amount.

Limit of Identification: 130 γ citral.

REFERENCES

1. Concerning this and the following designations see H. Staudinger, *Anleitung zur organischen qualitativen Analyse*, 2nd edition, Berlin 1929.
2. L. Kofler and A. Kofler, *Thermo-Mikro-Methoden zur Kennzeichnung organischer Stoffe und Stoffgemische*, Innsbruck, 1954.
3. See F. Feigl, *Chemistry of Specific, Selective and Sensitive Reactions*, New York 1949, Chapter VI.
4. L. Ilosvay von Nagy Ilosva, *Ber.*, 32 (1899) 2697; see also E. Pietsch and A. Kotowski, *Z. angew. Chem.*, 44 (1931) 309.
5. J. Scheiber and H. Reckleben, *Ber.*, 41 (1908) 3816; 44 (1911) 220.
6. Compare J. A. Nieuwland and R. R. Vogt, *Chemistry of Acetylene*, New York 1925.
7. *Handbook of Chemistry and Physics*, Cleveland, 1951.
8. F. Feigl and D. Goldstein, unpublished studies.
9. E. Edwards and L. Hodgkinson, *Chem. News*, 90 (1904) 140.
10. F. Feigl, Ref. 3, p. 663.
11. F. Feigl, Ref. 3, p. 442.
12. F. Feigl and Cl. Costa Neto, *Anal. Chem.*, 28 (1956) 397.
13. E. Schmidt, *Ann.*, 9 (1832) 241.
14. Cl. Costa Neto, unpublished studies.
15. F. Feigl and D. Goldstein, unpublished studies.
16. C. Zenghelis, *Z. anal. Chem.*, 49 (1910) 429.
17. For literature see J. Schmidt, *Das Kohlenoxyd*, Leipzig 1935, p. 186.
18. A. Bistrzycki and B. v. Siemiradski, *Ber.*, 39 (1906) 51; 41 (1908) 1665.
19. F. Feigl, Cl. Costa Neto and J. E. R. Marins, unpublished studies.
20. F. Feigl and L. Hainberger, *Analyst*, 80 (1955) 807; comp. also F. Feigl and Cl. Costa Neto, *Mikrochim. Acta*, (1955) 969.
21. A. S. Komarowsky and N. S. Poluektow, *Z. anal. Chem.*, 96 (1934) 23.
22. Comp. Beilstein, *Handb. Org. Chem.*, Vol. II, Berlin 1920, p. 550.
23. E. Eegriwe, *Z. anal. Chem.*, 110 (1937) 22.
24. Regarding the condensation of aromatic hydroxy compounds with formaldehyde see W. Wolff, *Ber.*, 26 (1893) 83; J. Breslauer and A. Pictet, *Ber.*, 40 (1907) 3786; A. Castiglioni, *Z. anal. Chem.*, 113 (1938) 428.
25. Regarding the hydrolytic cleavage with liberation of formaldehyde compare C. L. Hoff pauir *et al.*, *Ind. Eng. Chem.*, *Anal. Ed.*, 15 (1943) 605.
26. F. Feigl and L. Hainberger, *Mikrochim. Acta*, (1955) 110.
27. F. Feigl and H. J. Kapulitzas, *Z. anal. Chem.*, 82 (1930) 417.
28. Ph. W. West, and B. Sen, *Anal. Chem.*, 27 (1955) 1460.
29. Cl. Costa Neto, (Rio de Janeiro), unpublished studies.
30. L. Lewin, *Ber.*, 32 (1899) 3388.
31. J. Doeuvre, *Bull. Soc. Chim.*, [4] 39 (1926) 1102.
32. J. Schmidt and W. Hinderer, *Ber.*, 65 (1932) 87.
33. O. Frehden and K. Fuerst, *Mikrochim. Acta*, 3 (1938) 133.
33a. F. Feigl and E. Silva, unpublished studies.
34. F. Feigl and J. E. R. Marins, unpublished studies.
35. T. Sandmeyer, *Helv. Chim. Acta*, 2 (1919) 237; *Organic Syntheses*, Collective Volume I, New York 1932, p. 321.
36. T. Jona, *Z. anal. Chem.*, 52 (1913) 230.
37. F. Feigl and C. Stark, *Mikrochim. Acta*, (1955) 996.
38. E. Eegriwe, *Mikrochim. Acta*, 2 (1937) 329.
39. E. Silva (Recife), unpublished studies.
40. E. Eegriwe, *Z. anal. Chem.*, 110 (1937) 22.
41. F. Feigl and D. Goldstein, unpublished studies.
42. J. W. Hopton, *Anal. Chim. Acta*, 8 (1953) 429.
43. D. Krueger and E. Tschirch, *Ber.*, 62 (1929) 2776; 63 (1930) 826.
44. A. Damour, *Compt. rend.*, 43 (1857) 976.

45. D. Krueger and E. Tschirch, *Mikrochemie*, 8 (1930) 218.
46. F. Feigl, J. V. Sanchez and R. Zappert, *Mikrochemie*, 17 (1935) 165.
47. L. Rosenthaler, *Pharm. Acta Helv.*, 25 (1950) 366.
48. J. V. Sanchez, *Chem. Abstr.*, 30 (1936) 4432.
49. F. Feigl and R. Seboth, unpublished studies.
50. F. Feigl and R. Moscovici, *Analyst*, 80 (1955) 803.
51. A. Bistrzycki and B. v. Siemiradski, *Ber.*, 39 (1906) 52.
52. V. H. Freed, *Science*, 107 (1948) 98.
53. F. Feigl and C. Stark, unpublished studies.
54. E. Eegriwe, *Z. anal. Chem.*, 89 (1932) 123.
55. G. Denigès, *Bull. Trav. Soc. Pharm. Bordeaux*, 49 (1909) 193.
56. Compare W. Wolff, *Ber.*, 26 (1893) 83.
57. Compare C. Weizman, E. Bergmann and Y. Hirschberg, *J. Am. Chem. Soc.*, 58 (1936) 1675.
58. R. S. Pereira, *Mikrochemie ver. Mikrochim. Acta*, 35/36 (1951) 398.
59. F. Feigl and C. Stark, unpublished studies.
60. E. Eegriwe, *Z. anal. Chem.*, 95 (1933) 323 ff.
61. S. Rapaport, *Biochem. Z.*, 289 (1907) 406.
62. Compare C. Neuberg and H. Lustig, *Exp. Med. Surg.*, 1 (1943) 14.
63. E. Eegriwe, *Z. anal. Chem.*, 95 (1934) 325.
64. E. Eegriwe, *Z. anal. Chem.*, 100 (1935) 34.
65. V. P. Calkins, *Ind. Eng. Chem., Anal. Ed.*, 15 (1943) 762.
66. H. Krause, *Ber.*, 52 (1919) 426.
67. M. Paget and R. Berger, *Chem. Abstr.*, 32 (1938) 4908.
68. F. Feigl and D. Goldstein, unpublished studies.
69. E. Eegriwe, *Z. anal. Chem.*, 89 (1932) 125.
70. W. Böttger, *Qualitative Analyse organischer Verbindungen*, in Berl-Lunge, *Chemisch-technische Untersuchungsmethoden*, Vol. I, Berlin, 1932, pp. 485, 488.
71. M. Paget and R. Berger, *Chem. Abstr.*, 32 (1938) 4908.
72. F. Feigl and D. Goldstein, unpublished studies.
73. F. Feigl and O. Frehden, *Mikrochemie*, 18 (1935) 272.
74. Compare P. Karrer, *Organic Chemistry*, 4th Engl. ed., New York 1950, p. 614.
75. E. Eegriwe, *Z. anal. Chem.*, 89 (1932) 121.
76. E. Eegriwe, *Z. anal. Chem.*, 95 (1933) 326.
77. F. Feigl and V. Anger, *Mikrochemie*, 17 (1935) 35.
78. Compare E. E. Leiniger, *Anal. Chem.*, 24 (1952) 1967.
79. A. Steigmann, *J. Soc. Chem. Ind.*, 62 (1943) 176.
80. A. Behrmann and A. W. Hofmann, *Ber.*, 17 (1884) 2688; see also T. H. Easterfield and W. J. Sell, *J. Chem. Soc.*, 65 (1894) 29.
81. F. Feigl and V. Gentil, unpublished studies.
82. F. Feigl, unpublished studies.
83. A. Darbey, *Anal. Chem.*, 24 (1952) 373.
84. See *The Versenes*, Bersworth Chemical Company, Framingham, Mass., 1951; Technical Bulletin, May and October 1951, The Alrose Chemical Company, Providence, Rhode Island.
85. G. Schwarzenbach *et al.*, *Helv. Chim. Acta*, 28 (1945) 828, 1133; 29 (1946) 364, 811, 1338; 30 (1947) 1798; 31 (1948) 331, 456, 495, 678; *Chimia*, 2 (1948) 56; compare also R. Přibil *Coll. trav. chim. Tchécoslov.*, 14 (1949) 320.
86. F. Feigl and D. Goldstein, unpublished studies.
87. F. Feigl and H. Blohm, unpublished studies.
88. F. Feigl and L. Hainberger, unpublished studies.
89. A. Schmitt, *Ann.*, 120 (1859) 136.
90. F. Feigl and V. Gentil, unpublished studies.
91. F. Feigl and V. Gentil, unpublished studies.
92. F. Feigl and Cl. Costa Neto, unpublished studies.
93. F. Feigl and J. E. R. Marins, unpublished studies.

94. S. Kahl, *Ber.*, 31 (1898) 148.
95. F. Feigl and Cl. Costa Neto, unpublished studies. Compare Vol. I, Chap. 4.
96. L. Mendius, *Ann.*, 103 (1853) 45, 50.
97. F. Feigl and Cl. Costa Neto, unpublished studies.
98. F. Feigl and H. T. Cardoso, *Rev. brasil. biol.*, 2 (1942) 117.
99. Comp. F. Feigl, Ref. 3, p. 115.
100. N. Bagssonoff, *Compt. rend.*, 173 (1921) 466; *Nature*, 139 (1937) 468.
101. F. Feigl and M. Steinhauser, *Mikrochemie ver. Mikrochim. Acta*, 35 (1950) 553.
102. F. Feigl and J. E. R. Marins, unpublished studies.
103. H. Tauber, *Mikrochemie*, 17 (1935) 111.
104. F. Feigl and M. Steinhauser, *Mikrochemie ver. Mikrochim. Acta*, 35 (1950) 553.
105. A. Bondi, unpublished studies.
105a. V. E. Levine, *Proc. Soc. Exp. Biol. Med.*, 35 (1936) 231.
106. F. Feigl and W. A. Mannheimer, unpublished studies.
107. F. Feigl and C. Stark, *Mikrochim. Acta*, (1955) 996.
108. F. Feigl and W. A. Mannheimer, unpublished studies.
109. F. Feigl, *Mikrochemie ver. Mikrochim. Acta*, 39 (1952) 404.
110. R. Berg, *Die analytische Verwendung des o-Oxychinolins (Oxin) und seiner Derivate*, Stuttgart 1938; F. J. Welcher, *Organic Analytical Reagents*, New York 1947, Vol. I, p. 264.
111. Compare F. Feigl, H. Zocher and C. Török, *Monatsh.*, 81 (1950) 214.
112. Compare F. Feigl, Ref. 3, p. 676.
113. E. Eegriwe, *Z. anal. Chem.*, 125 (1943) 241.
114. E. Eegriwe, *Z. anal. Chem.*, 125 (1943) 241.
115. E. Eegriwe, *Z. anal. Chem.*, 125 (1943) 242.
116. E. Eegriwe, *Z. anal. Chem.*, 125 (1943) 243.
117. E. Eegriwe, *Z. anal. Chem.*, 125 (1943) 241.
118. E. Eegriwe, *Z. anal. Chem.*, 126 (1943) 134.
119. J. Koetschet, *Helv. Chim. Acta*, 13 (1930) 482.
120. F. Feigl and O. Frehden, *Mikrochim. Acta*, 1 (1937) 137.
121. C. A. Kohn, cf. W. Fresenius, *Z. anal. Chem.*, 30 (1891) 619.
122. L. Simon, *Compt. rend.*, 125 (1897) 1105; L. Lewin, *Ber.*, 32 (1899) 3388; E. Rimini, *Gazz. Chim. Ital.*, 30 (1900) I, 279.
123. F. Feigl and W. A. Mannheimer, unpublished studies.
124. Z. H. Skraup, *Monatsh.*, 3 (1882) 536.
125. E. C. Wagner and J. K. Simons, *J. Chem. Education*, 13 (1936) 265.
126. See P. Karrer, *Organic Chemistry*, 4th Engl. ed., New York, 1950, p. 881.
127. Compare F. J. Welcher, *op. cit.*, Ref. 110, p. 264.
128. O. Frehden and C. H. Huang, *Mikrochim. Acta*, 2 (1937) 20.
129. R. Kuhn and D. Jerchel, *Ber.*, 74 (1941) 949.
130. See F. E. Smith, *Science*, 113 (1951) 751.
131. A. N. Mattson and C. O. Tensen, *Anal. Chem.*, 22 (1950) 183; *Science*, 106 (1947) 294.
132. A. Bondi (Rehovoth), unpublished studies.
133. F. Feigl and G. Frank, unpublished studies.
134. F. Feigl, *Chemistry & Industry*, 57 (1938) 1161; see also tests for aldehydes p. 218.
135. J. H. Foulger, *J. Biol. Chem.*, 99 (1932) 207; *Compt. rend.*, 196 (1933) 2984.
136. F. Feigl and R. Zappert, unpublished studies.
137. O. Frehden and L. Goldschmidt, *Mikrochim. Acta*, 2 (1937) 184.
138. Th. Zincke and G. Muehlhausen, *Ber.*, 38 (1905) 3822; W. Dieckmann and L. Beck, *ibid.*, 38 (1905) 4122.
139. F. Feigl, J. E. R. Marins and Cl. Costa Neto, unpublished studies.
140. O. Gelormini and N. E. Artz, *J. Am. Chem. Soc.*, 52 (1930) 2483; comp. P. Fleury and P. Balatre, *Les Inositols*, Paris 1947, Chap. IV.
141. Comp. P. Denigès, L. Chelle and A. Labat, *Précis de Chimie Analytique*, Vol. I, 7e ed., Paris 1930, p. 208.
142. F. Feigl and V. Gentil, *Mikrochim. Acta*, (1955) 1004.
143. F. Feigl and Cl. Costa Neto, *Anal. Chem.*, 28 (1956) 397.

144. F. Feigl and Cl. Costa Neto, *Mikrochim. Acta*, (1955) 969.
145. Th. Wallis, *Ann.*, 345 (1906) 362; E. Ott, *Ber.*, 52 (1919) 663.
146. Comp. F. Feigl and L. Hainberger, *Analyst*, 80 (1955) 807.
147. F. Feigl and C. Stark, unpublished studies.
148. F. Feigl and H. E. Feigl, unpublished studies.
149. F. Feigl, V. Gentil and D. Goldstein, unpublished studies.
150. Compare F. J. Welcher, *Organic Analytical Reagents*, New York, 1947, Vol. III, p. 463
151. E. Fischer and E. Besthorn, *Ann.*, 212 (1881) 316; see also J. H. Billman and E. S. Cleland, *J. Am. Chem. Soc.*, 65 (1943) 1300.
152. F. Feigl, Cl. Costa Neto and E. Silva, *Anal. Chem.*, 27 (1955) 1319.
153. O. Gerngross, K. Voss and H. Herfeld, *Ber.*, 66 (1933) 435.
154. A. Maciag and R. Schoental, *Mikrochemie*, 24 (1938) 250.
155. K. Nosaka, *Mikrochim. Acta*, 1 (1937) 79.
156. F. Feigl and V. Anger, *Mikrochim. Acta*, 2 (1937) 107.
157. R. Nietzki and E. Burckhardt, *Ber.*, 30 (1897) 175.
158. Compare F. Feigl, Ref. 3, p. 484.
159. O. Frehden and L. Goldschmidt, *Mikrochim. Acta*, 1 (1937) 351.
160. F. Feigl and E. Silva (Pernambuco), unpublished studies.
161. F. Feigl and D. Goldstein, unpublished studies.
162. F. Feigl and V. Gentil, *Anal. Chem.* (1956).
163. W. Koenigs, *Ber.*, 14 (1881) 98.
164. O. Heim, *Ind. Eng. Chem., Anal. Ed.*, 7 (1935) 146.
165. K. W. Merz and A. Kammerer, *Arch. Pharm.*, 86 (1953) 198.
166. V. Anger and S. Wang, *Mikrochim. Acta*, 3 (1938) 24.
167. G. Heller, *Ann.*, 263 (1891) 277.
168. Compare F. Feigl and F. L. Lederer, *Monatsh.*, 45 (1925) 115.
169. P. Cazeneuve, *J. pharm. chim.*, [6], 12 (1900) 150; *Analyst*, 25 (1900) 331.
170. F. Feigl and H. Blohm, unpublished studies.
171. F. Feigl, *Mikrochemie*, 13 (1933) 134.
172. F. Feigl, V. Gentil and D. Goldstein, unpublished studies.
173. S. Skinner and S. Ruhemann, *J. Chem. Soc.*, 53 (1888) 550; see also K. H. Slotta and K. R. Jacoby, *Z. anal. Chem.*, 77 (1929) 344.
174. Compare F. J. Welcher, *Organic Analytical Reagents*, New York, 1947, Vol. III, p. 430.
175. H. E. Feigl, unpublished studies.
176. J. B. Gibbs and P. L. Kirk, *Mikrochemie*, 16 (1934) 25.
177. F. Feigl and D. Goldstein, unpublished studies. See also G. L. Baker and L. H. Johnson, *Anal. Chem.*, 24 (1952) 1625.
178. M. L. Nichols and C. Willits, *J. Am. Chem. Soc.*, 56 (1934) 69.
179. F. Feigl and E. Chargaff, *Z. anal. Chem.*, 74 (1928) 376.
180. Compare F. Sommer, *Ber.*, 48 (1915) 1833.
181. F. Feigl and K. Weisselberg, *Z. anal. Chem.*, 83 (1931) 101.
182. L. Rosenthaler, *Pharm. Zentralhalle*, 74 (1933) 288.
183. F. Feigl and Cl. Costa Neto, unpublished studies.
184. F. Feigl and H. E. Feigl, *Helv. Chim. Acta*, 38 (1955) 459.
185. P. Karrer, *Organic Chemistry*, 4th Engl. ed., New York 1950, p. 839.
186. F. J. Smith and E. Jones, *A Scheme of Qualitative Organic Analysis*, London 1953, p. 110.
187. Staff of Hopkin and Williams Research Laboratory, *Organic Reagents for Organic Analysis*, Brooklyn 1947, p. 50.
188. F. Feigl and H. E. Feigl, *Helv. Chim. Acta*, 38 (1955) 459.
189. M. Pesez and P. Poirier, *Méthodes et Réactions de l'Analyse Organique*, Paris 1954, as well as F. Feigl and H. E. Feigl, *loc. cit.*
190. F. Feigl and L. Hainberger, unpublished studies.
191. M. Pailer and K. Porschinsky, *Monatsh.*, 80 (1949) 94.
192. F. Feigl, H. E. Feigl and D. Goldstein, *J. Am. Chem. Soc.*, 77 (1955) 4162.
193. F. Feigl, unpublished studies.
194. Compare F. J. Welcher, *Organic Analytical Reagents*, New York 1948, Vol. IV, p. 370.

195. H. L. Zermatten, *Proc. Acad. Sci. Amsterdam*, 36 (1933) 899.
196. G. Charlot, *Anal. Chim. Acta*, 1 (1947) 233.
197. F. Feigl and V. Gentil, unpublished studies.
198. Compare F. J. Welcher, *Organic Analytical Reagents*, New York, 1947, Vol. III, p. 355.
199. O. Baudisch and coworkers, *Ber.*, 45 (1912) 1164; 48 (1915) 1665; 49 (1916) 172, 180, 191, 203. See also F. Feigl, Ref. 3, p. 262.
200. F. Feigl, unpublished studies.
201. V. Meyer, *Ber.*, 15 (1882) 3813; 16 (1883) 1465.
202. W. Schlenk and O. Blum, *Ann.*, 433 (1923) 85.
203. A. Töhl, *Ber.*, 27 (1894) 665; R. Auwers and T. V. Bredt, *Ber.*, 27 (1894) 1746.
204. F. Feigl and D. Goldstein, unpublished studies.
205. V. Meyer, *Ber.*, 16 (1883) 2973.
206. H. Schiff, *Ber.*, 20 (1887) 540.
207. G. de Chalmot, *Ann.*, 271 (1892) 12.
208. Compare Th. Zincke and G. Muehlhausen, *Ber.*, 38 (1905) 3824; W. Dieckmann and L. Beck, *Ber.*, 38 (1905) 4122.
209. P. N. van Eck, *Pharm. Weekblad*, 60 (1923) 1204.
210. F. Feigl and J. E. R. Marins, unpublished studies.
211. N. B. Sastri and M. Sreenivasaya, *Mikrochemie*, 14 (1933/34) 159.
212. Compare J. B. Sumner and G. F. Somers, *Chemistry and Methods of Enzymes*, 3rd. ed., New York 1953.
213. F. Feigl and O. Frehden, unpublished studies.
214. J. Y. Yee and R. O. Davis, *Ind. Eng. Chem., Anal. Ed.*, 7 (1935) 259.
215. The potassium salt has been prepared by H. Schiff, *Ber.*, 29 (1896) 298. See also H. Ley, *ibid.*, 46 (1913) 4042.
216. F. Feigl and V. Gentil, *Biol. Jaarboek Dodonaea (Ghent)*, 20 (1953) 47.
217. F. Feigl, *Chemistry and Industry*, 57 (1938) 1164.
218. K. Nosaka, *Mikrochim. Acta*, 1 (1937) 78.
219. Comp. P. L. Kirk, *Crime Investigations*, New York 1953, p. 186 and 203.
220. F. Feigl, V. Gentil and J. E. R. Marins, *Anal. Chim. Acta*, 13 (1955) 210.
221. R. Moehlau and M. Heinze, *Ber.*, 35 (1902) 358; compare J. B. Cohen, *Practical Organic Chemistry*, London 1949, p. 268.
222. H. Biltz and W. Giese, *Ber.*, 37 (1904) 4018.
223. A. Baretto, *Rev. Quim. Ind. (Brasil)*, 10 (1941) No. 115, 12.
224. W. Deichmann and L. J. Schafer, *Ind. Eng. Chem., Anal. Ed.*, 14 (1942) 310.
225. F. Feigl and J. E. R. Marins, unpublished studies.
225a. Compare R. J. Carney, *J. Am. Chem. Soc.*, 34 (1912) 325.
226. F. Feigl and Cl. Costa Neto, unpublished studies.
227. F. Feigl and L. Hainberger, unpublished studies.
228. F. Feigl and E. Silva, unpublished studies.
229. Comp. P. Karrer, *Organic Chemistry*, 4th Engl. Ed., New York, 1950, p. 171.

Chapter 6

Application of Spot Tests for Technical Purposes

General Remarks

The inspection of materials, control tests during the course of chemical-technological processes, tests of purity of foods and pharmaceutical products, criminalistic investigations, and researches in the biological sciences often demand a rapid decision as to the presence or absence of a particular material. As shown in Chapter 7 of Volume I, it has been found that many spot reactions described for soluble or insoluble inorganic compounds can be usefully applied, either unaltered or with slight modification, for the above purposes and with the consumption of only small amounts of the sample. The same problems arise of course with respect to the detection of organic and organometallic compounds. In addition, it is often of great importance in preparative chemistry, and when studying organic natural products, to be able to determine quickly and with the expenditure of not more than a small quantity of the material, whether certain organic compounds or members of particular types of compounds have been formed or are present. Furthermore, it is of value to test pharmaceuticals and drugs by means of well established methods of spot test analysis. The use of spot reactions for such special assignments in qualitative organic analysis has not been given much consideration, or at least the literature as yet contains relatively few records along this line. The reason is that spot tests are still far less popular in organic qualitative analysis than in the corresponding inorganic field. However, the future will undoubtedly see a more intensive and extensive employment and development of spot reactions, and it may be safely assumed that the acquired experiences and findings will lead to a further growth of organic spot testing and consequently to its more wide-spread application in the solution of special technical and scientific problems.

Pertinent examples of the efficacy of organic spot test analysis in the solution of these special problems will be given in the following pages, but no claims are made regarding complete coverage of the field. A short bibliography citing other applications of organic spot tests is given; it is hoped that it will be useful and suggestive of further applications. The procedures given here have been tested repeatedly; they succeed with even small amounts of the sample. Translation from the micro- and semimicro- into the macro-scale is often possible.

This chapter does not include a discussion of the exceedingly important, sometimes even indispensable applications of organic spot tests in column and paper chromatography. Excellent monographs dealing with this topic are available.[1] It is certain that these types of chromatography, which are now so important in very many fields, will make ever-increasing use of sensitive organic spot tests based on the formation of colored reaction products, and especially those tests which can be conducted in aqueous or alcoholic solutions with an appropriate reagent.*

Two other remarks are in order here regarding the use of organic spot test analysis in testing materials. The first concerns the fact that sometimes it is possible to make semi-quantitative determinations by means of color reactions carried out in the form of spot tests. Experiences in the inorganic field have demonstrated that fairly exact determinations are possible when spot tests carried out with the test solutions are compared with the results obtained by the same procedure with standard solutions. This "spot colori-metry", which represents a simple micro or semimicro method, will assuredly also find application in the determination of certain organic compounds. The second remark relates to the use of spot tests for characterizing phar-maceutical preparations and medicinals, as well as the control examinations of food products. Previous experience leads to the assumption that spot tests, which hitherto have been recommended only in qualitative organic analysis, are adequate to meet certain requirements of the various pharma-copeias and accordingly can be considered by the authorities in charge of these important publications.** In addition, certain qualitative procedures, which are prescribed by the pharmacopeias, may be translated to the technique of spot test analysis. The same is true in the examination of food-stuffs. In both cases, the resulting economies in time, labor, and material will assuredly prove of advantage.

The examination of pharmaceutical products, medicinals and foods, as well as industrial materials of all kind by analytical procedures, is included in the chemical testing of materials and accordingly the latter branch is often considered a province of chemical analysis. Actually, the chemical examination of materials is the most important field of applying chemical analysis and it may be justifiably maintained that ultimately chemical

* To cite only one example, the iodine-azide reaction (page 228) was used to identify the sulfur-bearing amino acids separated by paper chromatography.[2]
** A start in this direction was made in Vienna in 1936 by R. Wasicky[3] following the publi-cation of the second edition of *Spot Tests.* New attempts, based on the present state of spot test analysis, were made recently by Feigl and Silva[4].

analysis is always testing of material. The improvement of established tests and the development of new analytical procedures, along with the utilization of hitherto unused or unknown analytical possibilities are not only of analytical interest but redound to the benefit of all chemistry. However, it must be remembered that the adaptation of analytical procedures to meet the requirements of actual practice is an important matter and that the decisions as to the changes in manipulations and the like must always be left to the judgment of a competent person. On the other hand, it sometimes happens that problems arising out of the testing of materials give incentives for interesting and valuable macro- and microanalytical researches.

The examples included in this chapter illustrate some of the applications of organic spot test analysis to actual examinations of commercial products and the like. The tests and procedures used are based, for the most part, on the preliminary exploratory tests and procedures for detecting functional groups and individual compounds, namely on methods which were discussed in detail in the earlier chapters. With regard to metallo-organic compounds and mixed inorganic-organic systems, the underlying discussions will be found in Volume I.

A point that was stressed in the opening chapter needs repeating here where the attention of the reader is centered on the testing of commercial materials. The point to be remembered is: No matter what the objective, chemical analysis must never be regarded as a mere means to an end or as routine labor. In view of its scientific foundations, it must always be looked on as experimental chemistry having analytical objectives. Only from this standpoint can the special character of spot test analysis be fully understood and appreciated with regard to its rightful position in pure and applied chemistry.

1. Detection of Acid and Basic Compounds in Organic Materials [5]

The presence of free carboxylic and sulfonic acids, phenols, and also salts of organic nitrogen bases with inorganic and organic acids can be tested by the behavior of the sample toward a water solution of alkali nickel biuret. The yellow alkaline solution of these salts with the inner complex anion (I) presents the equilibrium:

$$\left[\begin{array}{c} O{=}C{-}NH_2 \quad H_2N{-}C{=}O \\ | \qquad\qquad\qquad | \\ HN \quad\;\; Ni \quad\;\; NH \\ | \qquad\qquad\qquad | \\ O{-}C{=}N \quad\;\; N{=}C{-}O \end{array} \right]^{-2} + 4\,H_2O \rightleftharpoons 2 \begin{array}{c} O{=}C{-}NH_2 \\ | \\ NH \\ | \\ O{=}C{-}NH_2 \end{array} + Ni^{+2} + 4\,OH^-$$

$$(I) \qquad\qquad\qquad\qquad\qquad\qquad\qquad\qquad (II)$$

In this equilibrium (see test for urease on page 431), the concentration of nickel ions is so low that there is no precipitation of nickel hydroxide, nor of red nickel dimethylglyoxime, on the addition of dimethylgloxime. The nickel in these complex cations is masked against OH^- ions and also against dimethylglyoxime. When materials which deliver H^+ ions or consume OH^- ions are added to the equilibrium solution, the disturbance of the equilibrium causes the complex anion (I), which contains the *aci*-form of biuret, to yield the corresponding *baso*-form (II). Nickel ions are released at the same time, and their concentration rises to such a degree that the dimethyl-glyoxime reaction can occur to a visible extent. The following procedure I for the detection of acidic organic materials, even in small amounts, is based on this demasking effect.

Procedure I. A little of the solid or of its solution or suspension in alcohol or water, is placed in a depression of a spot plate. A drop of alkali nickel biuret solution is added and followed by a drop of alcoholic 1% dimethylglyoxime solution. Precipitation of crystalline red nickel dimethylglyoxime indicates the presence of carboxylic acids, sulfonic acids, phenols, or water-soluble salts of organic nitrogen bases.

The demasking of nickel from the equilibrium solution can also serve as the basis of a test for organic nitrogen bases. This test (*Procedure II*) requires that the sample be taken to dryness along with dilute hydrochloric acid. The excess acid is removed by brief heating at 110°. Because of hydrolysis, the residue containing the hydrochlorides of organic bases behaves like free hydrochloric acid, i.e. it demasks the nickel from a solution of alkali biuret. When Procedure II is used, it should be noted that hydrochlorides of certain organic bases decompose with release of hydrochloric acid when heated to 110°. Diphenylamine hydrochloride, for instance, behaves in this way. Obviously, this test should not be used in such cases. Likewise, ammonium and metal salts, whose solutions have an acid reaction because of hydrolysis, must be absent.

Procedure II. A little of the solid, liquid, or dissolved sample is placed in a microcrucible and a drop of dilute hydrochloric acid is added. The mixture is taken to dryness on the water bath and the crucible plus its contents are kept for 3–5 minutes in an oven at 110°. The cold residue is then treated with a drop of the alkali nickel biuret solution and followed by a drop of dimethylglyoxime solution. A red precipitate of nickel dimethylglyoxime appears if organic bases are present.

Reagent: Sodium nickel biuret solution: 1 g of $NiSO_4.6H_2O$ is dissolved in 50 ml water and 1 g of biuret is added. The solution is warmed and 15 ml of 1 N sodium hydroxide is added. The precipitate of nickel hydroxide is filtered off. The solution becomes turbid on long standing and should be filtered before use, if necessary.

References pp. 510–512

2. Detection of Mineral Constituents in Papers [6]
(Differentiation of Filter Papers)

Inner complex salts are precipitated by the reaction of 8-hydroxyquinoline (oxine) with many metal ions.[7] Many of these products display a yellow-green fluorescence in ultraviolet light. Oxinates are also formed when metal oxides and carbonates come in contact with solutions of oxine in organic liquids, in fact they are even formed by the action of the vapor above solid oxine (see page 378). Various sorts of papers contain calcium, magnesium, and aluminum, which are oxinate-formers. These metals are present in paper as the oxide or carbonate, and probably also as water-insoluble true or adsorption compounds of cellulose, etc. They are in a high state of dispersion and consequently provide excellent conditions for the action of oxine. If a paper which contains mineral constituents of this kind is spotted with a chloroform solution of oxine, a fluorescent fleck remains after the solvent evaporates. The ash of paper can of course be tested for calcium, magnesium, and aluminum in this same way.

Solutions of oxine derivatives can likewise be employed to provide a fluorescent system. Chloroform or alcohol solutions of tribromooxine or water solutions of 5-sulfo-7-iodooxine are suitable. These latter cases do not involve the production of a fluorescent metal complex as an independent phase. They represent, instead, chemical adsorption on the surface of a finely divided metal oxide.[8] The results obtained with various papers and ashes are summarized in Table 38.

The fluorescence test will reveal the presence of only the oxinate-forming calcium, barium, magnesium, and aluminum. Titanium, which as its dioxide, sometimes is used as a filler, and iron, which may be present as an impurity, cannot be detected in this way because their oxinates do not fluoresce. Barium sulfate does not react with oxine, whereas, because of its considerable solubility, calcium sulfate gives a distinct reaction.

The inorganic matter in paper can be converted into oxinates by exposure to oxine vapor. This can be accomplished at room temperature by placing the sample over a crucible containing solid oxine. After a few minutes, a weak fluorescence is discernible under ultraviolet light, and the intensity increases with longer exposure. It seems remarkable that even the low vapor pressure of oxine at ordinary temperatures is sufficient to produce oxinates. The action of oxine vapor can hardly be explained by assuming a transformation of the inorganic matter into stoichiometric oxinates. It is more probable that the vapor reacts with the metal on the surface of the paper without forming a new phase; in other words it is chemically adsorbed. As

TABLE 38. FLUORESCENCE TESTS OF PAPERS

Paper	Ash (from 15 cm² paper)	Original paper
Filter:		
Qual. 605*	+	—
Qual. 613*	+	+
Qual. 615*	+	+
Quant. 589 Blue**	no ash	—
Quant. 589 Red**	no ash	—
Quant. 589 White**.	no ash	—
Quant. 589 Black**.	no ash	—
Quant. 589***	no ash	—
Cr$ 200 Note.	not ignited	—
News Print	+	+
Bond	+	+
Onion Skin	+	+
Drawing	+	+
Tracing	+	+
Toilet.	+	+
Photographic	+	+

* Eaton Dikeman Co., Mt. Holly Springs, Pa.
** Schleicher and Schüll, New York.
*** Schleicher and Schüll, Germany.

a result of analogous metal-oxine bindings, the same fluorescence occurs as with the inner complex oxinates.

The procedure of forming fluorescent flecks on paper makes it possible to examine papers without damage to the specimen: there is no wear or tear which is visible in daylight. It is also possible to gain a clue as to whether the paper contains only calcium or magnesium (possibly along with alumina). In this case, the fluorescent fleck is exposed to acetic acid vapors (hot strong acetic acid is sufficient). This treatment destroys calcium and magnesium oxinates, and only the fluorescence due to aluminum oxinate persists. Consequently, if the fluorescence is quenched completely, or is distinctly weakened, it may be taken as a strong proof of the presence of calcium and/or magnesium.

It is remarkable that, in contrast to filter papers "low in ash", that are designed for use in qualitative analysis, the so-called "ashless" papers,* prepared for quantitative work, always contain slight amounts of ammonium salts. This can be established by spotting the specimen with Nessler solution

* The ash content of $5^{1}/_{2}$ cm papers is below $20\,\gamma$ in the case of quantitative filter papers and below $100\,\gamma$ for qualitative papers (C. Schleicher & Schüll Co., *Catalog 70*, N.Y.1949).

and the particular varieties of filter paper can be differentiated easily by this simple means. Samples of filter paper of about 1 cm² are adequate for this test. When spotted with Nessler solution, a brown or yellow stain means a positive response.

Ordinary (qualitative) and ashless (quantitative) filter papers can be quickly and surely distinguished by the following procedure: The reagent is an approximately saturated ether solution of the acid dye known as "Bleu ciel au chrome, solide B" (CIBA, Basel). A drop of the reagent solution is placed on the paper and the ether allowed to evaporate. The pink spot that is left is then held over ammonia water. Qualitative paper, which contains mineral matter, immediately shows a change to blue, whereas with ashless paper, the change is to yellow. The blue stain fades rather soon, but the color can be restored by again exposing the fleck to ammonia. The test can also be made with an ammoniacal water solution of the dye. If a micro drop is used, as little as 0.2 cm² of the paper suffices.

The basis of this color reaction probably is that the calcium and magnesium compounds in the ordinary paper form adsorption complexes or salts with the acid dye, and these in turn produce a blue loose addition compound with ammonia. This supposition is supported by the finding that a stable blue stain is obtained when qualitative filter paper is spotted with a solution of the dye in ethylenediamine, morpholine, or other non-volatile amines.

An excellent differentiation between all kinds of qualitative and quantitative filter paper may be based on the fact that only the former contains traces of trivalent iron, which can be detected[8a] by spotting with a 2 % solution of $\alpha\alpha'$-dipyridyl in concentrated thioglycollic acid. A red stain of ferrous $\alpha\alpha'$-dipyridyl thioglycollate appears within one minute. No more than fragments of filter paper are necessary when the spot reaction is carried out with a micro drop of the reagent. In this procedure thioglycollic acid reduces ferric iron to ferrous iron, which then gives the color reaction with dipyridyl.

3. Detection of Organic Material in Dusts, Soils, etc.[9]

Ashes, dust, soils, evaporation residues of waters, etc. can be tested for organic admixtures or contaminants by means of the procedure described on page 75, in which the sample is heated along with potassium iodate to 300—400°. Potassium iodate remains unaltered at this temperature, but in mixtures with organic materials of all kinds, whose oxidation yields carbon dioxide, water, etc., it is reduced to potassium iodide through a topochemical reaction on the surface of potassium iodate:

$$\text{>CH}_2 + \text{KIO}_3 \rightarrow \text{CO}_2 + \text{H}_2\text{O} + \text{KI}$$

The realization of this redox reaction is readily detected. On addition of acid the iodide reacts with the unused iodate:

$$5\ I^- + IO_3^- + 6\ H^+ \rightarrow 3\ H_2O + 3\ I_2$$

and the resulting free iodine can then easily be detected by extraction with chloroform or by means of starch.

When using this test it should be remembered that if oxidizable inorganic materials such as metal dust, iron[II] oxide, sulfides, and free sulfur are heated with potassium iodate, they likewise produce iodide. The presence of reducing materials can be established by spotting a little of the sample with a solution of phosphomolybdic acid. A blue color appears if such materials are present. Iron[II] oxide and sulfides can be oxidized by repeated evaporations with hydrogen peroxide. The same is true of sulfur, provided a little alkali is also introduced. Metal dust and sulfides can be brought into solution by warming with hydrogen peroxide plus dilute sulfuric acid. It is advisable to conduct the evaporation with hydrogen peroxide in a small porcelain crucible; the residue should be made basic and the evaporation to dryness repeated. The evaporation residue is then intimately mixed with excess potassium iodate and the crucible and its contents heated to 300—400°. After cooling, the sintered mass is taken up in several drops of water and a drop of dilute sulfuric acid is added. Liberation of iodine indicates the presence of organic material.

Potassium iodate is reduced to iodide not only by non-volatile but also by volatile organic materials. A pertinent example is the reduction by acetone vapor. The reduction may occur when potassium iodate comes in contact, at elevated temperatures, with solid, liquid, or gaseous organic substances.

4. Identification of Rongalite [10]

Rongalite (Formopon, Discolite, Hydralite) is the stable addition product – or more correctly condensation product – of sodium sulfoxylate and formaldehyde. It has the formula $NaHSO_2.CH_2O.2\,H_2O$. This colorless crystalline compound is a powerful reductant which, in the dry state, like the equally stable sodium hydrosulfite or hyposulfite $(Na_2S_2O_4)$ is used in the textile industry as a printing reducing agent. The reducing power of Rongalite is due to the ready oxidation of its divalent sulfur to sulfate:

$$H_2C{<}^{OH}_{O-S-ONa} + 2O \rightarrow CH_2O + NaHSO_4$$

Rongalite may be identified by sensitive tests for its formaldehyde and sulfoxylate components. The former can be detected by means of the color reaction with chromotropic acid and sulfuric acid (page 331), use being made of the fact that Rongalite loses formaldehyde above 125°.[11] The formaldehyde in the vapor phase is brought into contact with the reagent and a violet color appears (Procedure I). The sulfoxylate can be detected through its redox reaction with an alcoholic-ammoniacal solution of 1,4-dinitrobenzene (Procedure II). The reaction product is probably the violet ammonium salt of a *para*-quinoidal nitrogen acid (see page 131).

The test for Rongalite with 1,4-dinitrobenzene is not impaired by the sulfite and thiosulfite which are always present in the commercial preparations. However, any sulfide will interfere since it yields an orange color with the reagent. This interference can be averted by shaking the Rongalite with a little lead carbonate (formation of PbS), and conducting the test with a drop of the filtrate.

Procedure I (formaldehyde detection). The apparatus shown in Figure 23, page 49 is used. A little of the solid is placed in the bulb or a drop of the test solution is evaporated there. A drop of a solution of chromotropic acid in concentrated sulfuric acid is suspended on the knob of the stopper. The evaporation residue or the sample is cautiously warmed. If Rongalite was present, the hanging drop turns red-violet.

Limit of Identification: 0.02 γ Rongalite.

If solid Rongalite or the evaporation residue is treated directly with the reagent solution, as little as 0.5 γ Rongalite will give a violet color.

Procedure II (hydrosulfite detection). A micro test tube is used. A little of the solid or a drop of a solution is treated in succession with one drop of a saturated solution of 1,4-dinitrobenzene in alcohol and one drop of concentrated ammonium hydroxide. The mixture is warmed above an open flame for 30 to 60 seconds. If Procedure I gave a positive result, for formaldehyde, a violet color in the present test indicates the presence of Rongalite.

Limit of Identification: 3 γ Rongalite.

5. Detection of Traces of Sulfur in Carbon Disulfide, Ether, Organic Solvents, Motor Fuels [12]

Very small amounts of sulfur dissolved in carbon disulfide may be identified, after conversion into thiosulfate (**a**) or sulfide (**b**), by the sensitive iodine-azide reaction as described in Volume I, Chapter 4. The sulfur may be converted into thiosulfate by heating the residue left on evaporation of the carbon disulfide with an alkaline sodium sulfite solution: $Na_2SO_3 + S \rightarrow Na_2S_2O_3$. The conversion into sulfide may be effected by shaking the carbon disulfide with metallic mercury; mercury sulfide is formed immediately.

Procedures (**a**) and (**b**) may also be applied to detect traces of sulfur in ether or other organic liquids. A further important application is the detection of corrosive sulfur in motor fuels.[13]

References pp. 510–512

Procedure (a). A drop of the sample of carbon disulfide is allowed to evaporate completely on a watch glass. This may conveniently be heated on the steam outlet of the apparatus described on page 48. After evaporation *, 2 drops of a 5% alkaline solution of sodium sulfite are placed on the watch glass. The reaction mixture is then heated 2 or 3 minutes on the steamer and, after cooling, a few drops of iodine–azide solution are added. If even a trace of sulfur was originally present, the thiosulfate formed causes a more or less vigorous evolution of nitrogen.

Limit of Identification: 0.5 γ sulfur.

Reagent: Iodine-azide solution (see page 230).

Even smaller amounts of sulfur can be identified by (b), if a larger sample of carbon disulfide is taken for examination.

Procedure (b). About 6 to 8 ml carbon disulfide is shaken vigorously with a drop of mercury in a hard glass test tube or a measuring cylinder. When even very small amounts of free sulfur are present, the surface of the mercury is stained with a black or iridescent film of mercury sulfide [14] which can be identified by the iodine–azide reaction.** The carbon disulfide is poured off and the mercury is transferred to a watch glass and heated in a current of steam (see page 48) to remove the last traces of carbon disulfide. The mercury is then covered with iodine–azide solution, and a foam of nitrogen bubbles forms around the mercury. The use of the mercury dropper (page 41) is recommended.

A rapid though less sensitive test for free sulfur is based on the finding that melted benzoin (m.p. 133°) reacts quickly with sulfur to yield hydrogen sulfide:

$$C_6H_5COCHOHC_6H_5 + S° \rightarrow C_6H_5COCOC_6H_5 + H_2S$$

Benzoin functions as hydrogen donor and reductant and is converted to benzil.[15] The resulting hydrogen sulfide can be detected with lead acetate paper.

Procedure (c). Several drops of the liquid or solution are taken to dryness in a micro test tube. A few milligrams of benzoin is added to the residue.

The mouth of the test tube is covered with moist lead acetate paper and 2/3 of the tube is immersed in a glycerol bath heated to 130°. The temperature is gradually brought to 150°. If free sulfur was present, the paper acquires a black to brown stain, the color depending on the amount of sulfur present.

Limit of Identification: 0.5 γ sulfur.

6. Detection of Sulfide Sulfur in Animal Charcoal and Dyes [17]

The test for sulfide sulfur, in animal charcoal for instance, using the iodine–azide reaction as described on page 228, may be carried out on a few milligrams of sample.

* It is important that the carbon disulfide be completely removed, since it can catalyze the reaction, $2 NaN_3 + I_2 = 2 NaI + 3 N_2$, by the intermediate formation of azidodithiocarbonate. Compare page 411.

** The application of this sulfide formation for the detection of small amounts of sulfur in CS_2, has been recommended [14]. The iodine–azide reaction is positive, even for amounts of HgS too small to be detected visually.

References pp. 510–512

The so-called sulfur dyes, which are prepared by melting aromatic amines or hydroxy compounds with sulfur or alkali polysulfides, contain organically bound sulfur. Nearly all the dyes of this class, which are blue to blue-black or yellow to brown, catalyze the iodine-azide reaction, i.e. when they are placed in contact with this reagent the iodine is consumed and gaseous nitrogen appears. This result is due to the presence of mercapto groups. The constitution of most of these dyes is not known, however. The majority of them are amorphous, insoluble products; they probably are mixtures of various components.[18]

A little of the solid sample, which may be dry or moistened with water, or else a thread or piece of dyed cotton, is treated with a drop of iodine–azide solution and observed for bubbles of nitrogen. Woollen material, which is not normally dyed with sulfur dyes, cannot be tested in this way, since wool itself gives a positive azide reaction. The following results were obtained:

Primuline yellow * . . . .   no reaction
Catigen brown 2 R extra . . . .   vigorous evolution of nitrogen
Catigen brilliant green G . . . .   evolution of nitrogen
Catigen yellow GG extra . . . .   very vigorous evolution of nitrogen
Catigen black SW extra . . . .   very vigorous evolution of nitrogen
Catigen indigo CL extra . . . .   very vigorous evolution of nitrogen
Catigen violet 3 R . . . .   very vigorous evolution of nitrogen

7. Detection of Free Sulfur in Solid Organic Products [19]

When thallous sulfide, which is readily soluble in dilute mineral acids, comes into contact with elementary sulfur (dissolved in organic liquids or alkali sulfide) it is converted into thallous polysulfide. The latter is rather resistant to dilute mineral acids and dilute hydrogen peroxide. When a drop of a solution of free sulfur is placed on paper impregnated with thallous sulfide, polysulfide is formed at the site of the fleck, and on treatment of the paper with acid, a dark, brown circle or ring is left, while the rest of the black reagent paper is bleached almost instantaneously. When small amounts of sulfur are involved, a layer of thallium polysulfide is produced on the surface of the thallous sulfide, and protects the underlying Tl_2S against being dissolved by the acid. [Compare [20] regarding this protective layer effect and see also the detection of acetylene by means of this effect (page 324).]

The rapid production of the polysulfide on thallous sulfide can be used to reveal the presence of uncombined sulfur in insecticides, pharmaceutical

* Primuline yellow (base) is one of the few sulfur dyes whose constitution has been elucidated. As a mixture of di- and trithiazo compounds, all of its sulfur is in etherlike combination. Its negative response to the iodine–azide test conforms to this structure.

materials and the like. A preliminary extraction of the dry sample (finely powdered if possible) with carbon disulfide or pyridine is necessary. Often it is desirable to subject the sample to a preliminary treatment with hydrochloric acid to remove acid-soluble constituents. The residue is then dried at 105° C. for several hours. Any amorphous sulfur is thus converted into the crystalline form, which is soluble in carbon disulfide. The extraction can be made in a micro apparatus. One drop of the clear extract is placed on black, freshly prepared thallous sulfide paper. The solvent is allowed to evaporate in the air, and the paper is then placed in dilute nitric acid. If sulfur is present, a brown-red or light brown fleck, depending on the quantity, is left at the site of the spotting. The rest of the paper turns perfectly white.

Vulcanized rubber can be tested for uncombined sulfur. A particle of the sample is kept in contact with carbon disulfide for 2 or 3 minutes. A drop of the liquid is transferred to thallous sulfide paper. A distinct fleck of polysulfide remains after treatment with acid if free sulfur was present.

The following procedure will reveal free sulfur in organic materials, gas purifying masses, etc. Several milligrams of the dry, finely pulverized sample are placed on thallium sulfide paper and moistened with several drops of carbon disulfide, applied in succession at short intervals. After the solvent has evaporated, the dry powder is brushed off the paper, which is then placed in dilute acid. A dark fleck develops if free or extractable sulfur was present.

Sulfur dissolved in organic liquids can be detected by placing a drop of the solution on thallium sulfide paper, which is then treated with acid. This test can be used to determine the completion of a sulfur extraction with organic liquids.

Thallous sulfide paper is prepared by bathing filter paper (S & S 589 or Whatman 42) in 5% thallous carbonate or acetate solution for several minutes. The excess liquid is drained off and the paper then dried in a blast of heated air. Thallous sulfide is deposited by placing the paper across a beaker containing ammonium sulfide solution warmed to 80°. The conversion to Tl_2S requires not more than several minutes; the side of the paper exposed to the fumes turns perfectly black. It is ready for immediate use and is best cut into strips. Freshly prepared paper should be used when testing for sulfur. On standing, the paper deteriorates because the sulfide is oxidized.

It should be noted that only the crystalline modifications of sulfur are soluble in carbon disulfide. At room temperature, pyridine dissolves up to 4 % of amorphous sulfur also.[21]

For the detection of elementary sulphur in solid organic test material the fusion reaction with benzoin described in test 5 may also be used. Hereby hydrogen sulfide is formed due to a sensitive redox reaction between the components. The presence of inorganic and organic sulfur compounds does not interfere.

8. Detection of Carbon Disulfide in Benzene and Carbon Tetrachloride

Crude benzene and carbon tetrachloride usually contain a small amount of carbon disulfide; crude benzene about 0.1 to 0.2 %, and carbon tetrachloride 0.1 to 3.5 %. The carbon disulfide enters benzene from its preparation by the distillation of hard coals containing sulfur. The presence of carbon disulfide in carbon tetrachloride arises from its preparation from carbon disulfide by chlorination:

$$CS_2 + 2 S_2Cl_2 \rightarrow CCl_4 + 6 S$$

Contamination with carbon disulfide may be detected by the reaction based on the acceleration of the formation of sulfide from carbon disulfide and alkali in the presence of formaldehyde (page 412). The sulfide can be detected by the precipitation of lead sulfide from a plumbite solution.

Procedure.[22] Two or three drops of the benzene or carbon tetrachloride are mixed on a spot plate with 1 or 2 drops of a strongly alkaline plumbite solution and 2 drops of 40 % formaldehyde solution (formalin). If carbon disulfide is present, a dark ring of lead sulfide is formed at the boundary between the organic solvent and the water layer. Any hydrogen sulfide must be removed before carrying out the test. This removal is described on page 412.

A reliable test for minimal quantities of carbon disulfide in benzene, carbon tetrachloride etc. may be based on the formation of yellow-brown copper dimethyl dithiocarbamate directly from the components, according to

$$CS_2 + 2NH(CH_3)_2 + 1/2\ Cu^{+2} \longrightarrow SC\underset{\diagdown N(CH_3)_2}{\overset{\diagup S-Cu/2}{}} + (CH_3)_2\ \overset{+}{N}H_2$$

The details of the procedure are described on page 262.

9. Detection of Ethanol in Motor Fuels, Benzene, Chloroform, etc.[23]

A rapid test for ethanol is of value in the examination of motor fuels, organic liquids, etc. The test described on page 339 can be used to advantage. It is based on the ready oxidation of ethanol by acidified permanganate. The resulting acetaldehyde is specifically detectable in the vapor phase by the blue color produced on contact with a solution of sodium nitroprusside containing morpholine. It is noteworthy that the oxidation proceeds at a satisfactory speed at room temperature and at the comparatively small organic liquid-water interface.

Procedure. A micro test tube is used. A drop or two of the sample and a drop of the acidified solution of permanganate are mixed and the mouth of the tube is covered with filter paper moistened with the reagent solution. If ethanol is present, a blue fleck appears on the paper within 1/2–3 minutes, the time depending on the amount present.

Reagents: *1)* 1 *N* potassium permanganate in sulfuric acid (1 : 1)
         2) Freshly prepared mixture of equal volumes of 5% sodium nitroprusside and 20% morpholine solution.

Technical ether yields a distinct response and even pure ether in large amounts. This result is due in part to the alcohol actually present but it is also possible that the permanganate brings about the reaction:

$$C_2H_5OC_2H_5 + O \rightarrow C_2H_5OH + CH_3CHO$$

which is followed by oxidation of the ethanol to acetaldehyde.

The following sensitive test will reveal ethanol in motor fuels.

Procedure. One drop of the sample is placed in a micro test tube. A piece of copper wire is strongly heated and dropped at once into the liquid. The mouth of the tube is immediately covered with filter paper moistened with the reagent solution just described. A blue stain appears at once if the sample contains ethanol. This test revealed 3 γ ethanol in one drop of benzene.

Perhaps the high sensitivity is due to the oxidation of the ethanol:

$$C_2H_5OH + CuO \rightarrow CH_3CHO + Cu^{\circ} + H_2O$$

There is no further oxidation of the acetaldehyde to acetic acid, which is unavoidable when permanganate is employed as the oxidant.

10. Detection of Thiophen and Thiophen Derivatives in Benzene and Toluene

Benzene and toluene which have been produced by the distillation of coal always contain thiophen and thiophen derivatives, whose quantity varies up to 0.5 per cent. These contaminants cannot be removed by fractional distillation because the respective boiling points lie too close together. The removal of thiophen and its derivatives requires treatment with concentrated sulfuric acid, which converts them into sulfonic acids, which then remain dissolved in the sulfuric acid.

Benzene or toluene can be tested for thiophen (or thiophen derivatives with an unoccupied position *ortho* to the cyclic bound sulfur atom) by means of the color reaction with 1,2-diketones which is based on the formation of quinoidal indophenin dyes (see pages 204 and 425). One or two drops of the suspected benzene or toluene is sufficient for the test. The most sensitive reagent for thiophen is ninhydrin. It is advisable to run a comparison test with benzene or toluene known to be free of thiophen and thiophen derivatives. Such pure standards can be prepared by shaking the hydrocarbon with a freshly prepared 1 % solution of ninhydrin in concentrated sulfuric acid. The acid layer is poured away, the other layer washed with water, and the hydrocarbon then distilled.

11. Detection of Hydrogen Cyanide in Illuminating Gas [24]

Illuminating gas often contains slight amounts of hydrogen cyanide and possibly also dicyanogen, even though it is usual to pass the gas through water to retain ammonia, pyridine bases, hydrogen cyanide, dicyanogen, etc. The sensitive test for alkali cyanide (Volume I, Chap. 4) can be used to detect traces of hydrogen cyanide and dicyanogen in illuminating gas. It is based on the demasking of dimethylglyoxime from alkaline solutions of palladium dimethylglyoxime in which the complexly bound dimethylglyoxime is not responsive to nickel ions. The dimethylglyoxime liberated by the CN-ions, because of the precipitation of $Pd(CN)_2$, is then revealed by the production of red nickel dimethylglyoxime.

In contact with water, dicyanogen vapors produce CN^- ions through the hydrolysis: $(CN)_2 + H_2O \rightarrow HCN + HCNO$. Consequently, the following procedure will likewise reveal dicyanogen.

Procedure. Filter paper is impregnated with an alkaline solution of palladium dimethylglyoxime, or a drop of this solution is placed on filter paper. The moist reagent paper or the fleck is held for several seconds or minutes (according to the suspected cyanide content) about a millimeter from the end of a rubber tube (diameter 0.5 mm) connected with the gas supply. The part of the paper which has been exposed to the stream of gas is then spotted with a solution of nickel chloride. A pink to red stain of nickel dimethylglyoxime appears at once, the depth of the color varying with the cyanide content of the gas.

Reagents: 1) Alkali palladium dimethylglyoxime solution: Purest palladium dimethylglyoxime (prepared by precipitation of an acid solution of $PdCl_2$ with dimethylglyoxime and thorough washing) is shaken with 3 N potassium hydroxide, and the undissolved material filtered off.

2) Nickel ammonium chloride solution: 0.5 N $NiCl_2$ saturated with ammonium chloride.

12. Detection of Calcium Cyanamide and Urea in Fertilizers and Soils [25]

Calcium cyanamide (Nitrolime) and urea (Floramide) are often incorporated in fertilizers as sources of nitrogen[26]. They may be detected by the release of ammonia when the sample is taken to dryness along with dilute hydrochloric acid and the evaporation residue then heated to 250°.

When calcium cyanamide is boiled down with hydrochloric acid it is converted to the hydrochloride of dicyanamide:

$$2N\equiv C-NCa + 5HCl \longrightarrow 2CaCl_2 + HN=C\begin{subarray}{l} \diagup NH_2.HCl \\ \diagdown NHCN \end{subarray}$$

This product, like many other guanidine derivatives, yields ammonia on heating (see page 291). When urea is heated to 250°, it too yields ammonia because of the formation of biuret (see page 407). Since no fertilizers or soils contain materials which yield ammonia under these conditions, the following procedure can be used to reveal cyanamide salts and urea.

Procedure. Several milligrams of the solid (0.5 mg suffices for pure compounds) and 1–3 drops of dilute hydrochloric acid are boiled to dryness in a micro test tube. The tube is then immersed in a glycerol bath previously brought to 150–200°, and the mouth of the tube is covered with filter paper moistened with Nessler solution. The temperature of the bath is then raised to 230–240°. A brown or yellow stain appears on the paper.

13. Detection of Higher Fatty Acids in Paraffin Wax and Vaseline

Paraffin waxes and vaseline are natural or prepared mixtures of saturated hydrocarbons. Paraffin consists wholly of solid hydrocarbons, whereas the oily consistency of vaseline is due to its content of hydrocarbons which are liquid at ordinary temperatures. Pure paraffin wax and vaseline ought not to contain any admixed higher fatty acids with low melting points. A content of fatty acids may also come from saponified oils and fats.

Such fatty acids can be detected by the test for water-insoluble carboxylic acids described on page 116. In this procedure, the acids are converted to the corresponding ammonium salts by solution in aqueous ammonia, and a drop of the solution is taken to dryness. The evaporation residue is heated to 120° for about three minutes. At this temperature, the ammonium salts lose considerable ammonia, and the residual carboxylic acids will release iodine when warmed with iodide-iodate solution.

Procedure. [27] About 0.5 g of the wax or vaseline is dissolved in 2 ml of toluene and the solution is shaken in a small separatory funnel with one ml of concentrated ammonia. One drop of the water layer, which perhaps may be turbid because of emulsified toluene solution, is transferred to a micro test tube and evaporated to dryness. The residue is treated in succession with single drops of alcohol, 2 % potassium iodide solution, and 0.4 % potassium iodate solution. The test tube is then closed and placed in boiling water for a minute or two. After cooling, one drop of 0.1 % starch solution is added. If a blue color appears, the sample contains higher fatty acids.

This procedure definitely revealed 0.2 % of stearic acid in vaseline. Smaller proportions of fatty acid can be detected by conducting the test on the evaporation residue from several drops of the ammoniacal solution.

References pp. 510–512

A more rapid test for higher fatty acids in paraffins and the like is based on a reversal of a very sensitive test for uranium. (Comp. Vol. I, Chap. 3.) If a neutral uranyl solution is shaken with a colorless saturated solution of rhodamine B in benzene, the benzene layer fluoresces with an intense orange color in ultraviolet light if carboxylic acids, soluble in benzene, are present. The benzene layer is colorless in the absence of such acids. This effect may be explained as follows: The practically colorless benzene solution of rhodamine B contains the lacto-form (I) of the dyestuff in equilibrium (*1*) with minimal quantities of the quinone-form (II). When the uranyl salt solution is added and the mixture shaken, this equilibrium is not disturbed. If, however, the benzene solution of the dyestuff contains carboxylic acids, the latter react (*2*) with UO_2^{-2}-ions to form slight quantities of the undissociated salts of the carboxylic acids, which in turn react with (II) to yield benzene-soluble red addition compounds (*3*):

$$\ldots (1)$$

$$UO_2^{+2} + 3RCOOH \rightleftharpoons H[UO_2(RCOO)_3] + 2H^+ \qquad \ldots (2)$$

$$H[UO_2(RCOO)_3] + (II) \rightarrow \qquad \ldots (3)$$

Hence this procedure involves the slight amounts of the compounds furnished by the equilibria (*1*) and (*2*), and which, after they have been consumed, are continuously again delivered. The amounts thus made available are adequate for the color reaction (*3*) to proceed to a visible extent.

Procedure.[27a] A micro test tube is used. A drop of a benzene solution of the sample and a drop of saturated solution of rhodamine B in benzene are mixed and then treated with one or two drops of 1% solution of uranyl nitrate or acetate. The mixture is shaken. If fatty acids are present, the benzene layer turns red to pink, depending on the quantity of acid. When examined in ultra-violet light, the system exhibits an orange fluorescence. If an emulsion forms, the benzene and water layers can be separated by centrifuging.

This procedure revealed 5 γ palmitic or stearic acid in one drop of the corresponding benzene solution.

14. Detection of Acetic Acid (Acetate) in Formic Acid (Formate) [28]

Commercial formic acid and alkali formates often contain notable quantities of acetic acid or acetate even though they are designated as "pure". To test for these admixtures or impurities, use can be made of the fact that formic acid containing acetic acid yields a mixture of the calcium salts when taken to dryness with an excess of calcium carbonate. If the residue is then strongly heated, acetaldehyde results:

$$(HCOO)_2Ca + (CH_3COO)_2Ca \rightarrow 2\ CaCO_3 + 2\ CH_3CHO \qquad (1)$$

When alkali formates contain acetate, acetaldehyde is produced on ignition of the salts:

$$HCOONa + CH_3COONa \rightarrow Na_2CO_3 + CH_3CHO \qquad (2)$$

The acetaldehyde resulting from either of these reactions can be detected in the vapor phase by the color reaction with a solution of sodium nitroprusside containing morpholine (see page 334). Analogous reactions are given by lactic, butyric, and propionic acid, but the test is far less sensitive in the two latter cases than for acetic acid. [28a]

Procedure. A micro test tube is used. One drop of the suspected formic acid is stirred with a very slight excess of powdered calcium carbonate and the suspension brought to dryness in an oven or by cautious direct heating.

The mouth of the tube is covered with filter paper moistened with the reagent solution and the bottom of the tube is then heated over a micro burner. If acetic acid was present, a more or less intense blue appears on the paper, the depth of color depending on the amount present.

To test for acetate in formates, several milligrams of the solid or the evaporation residue of a solution is heated as just prescribed, but without addition of calcium carbonate.

This procedure was applied to samples of concentrated formic acid from various sources, and whose acetic acid content was given as below 0.4 %. In practically all cases, the reaction for acetic acid was very marked, and there was a positive response in some instances after the sample had been diluted with 10–20 volumes of water.

References pp. 510–512

Similarly, many samples of sodium and calcium formate gave an acetaldehyde reaction, which sometimes was strikingly strong even though milligram
quantities were taken for testing.

15. Distinction between Acid and Basic Dyes [29]

Dyes which are predominantly basic are soluble in melted stearic acid,
while predominantly acid dyes are soluble in melted urea. These properties
are connected with the electropolar nature of the substances (salt or solvate
formation). This behavior may be applied as a quick and simple means of
differentiating members of these two classes of dyes.

Probably, basic dyes form salts with stearic acid which are readily
soluble in molten stearic acid. When urea is melted, it forms biuret (see
page 407) and ammonia is given off. Consequently, there is a possibility
that ammonium salts are formed in the case of acid dyes, and the salts then
dissolve in molten urea or the biuret-urea mixture (see test for citric acid
page 360).*

Procedure. Urea and stearic acid are melted in a test tube, a grain of the
dye is added, and the mixture well shaken. When the two layers separate, one
will be colored. If the under layer (urea) is colored, an acid dye is present; if
the upper layer (stearic acid) is colored, a basic dye is present.

An excess of dye should be avoided; otherwise both layers are sometimes
colored.

16. Detection of p-Phenylenediamine and its Oxidation Products in Hair Dyes [30]

Hair, feathers and furs are often dyed with p-phenylenediamine. The
colorless compound adsorbed by the animal fibers is oxidized to black water-
insoluble products through contact with the air or by treatment with
hydrogen peroxide. Since this dye and its oxidation products are toxic,
their use in cosmetics, etc. is legally forbidden.

A rapid test for the free base involves its conversion into the blue indamine
dye (phenylene blue) by the action of aniline alkali persulfate in acetic acid
solution. The procedure for this sensitive test is outlined on page 405. The
test fails when applied to the oxidation products obtained in "ursol" dyeing.

Bandrowski's base is the most important oxidation product of p-phenylene-
diamine. It is formed, along with p-quinone imide, by the redox reaction: [31]

---

* Ammonium salts of inorganic and organic salts, and likewise free organic carboxylic and
sulfonic acids are easily soluble in molten urea. Furthermore, many primary, secondary, and
tertiary aromatic amines as well as their salts (and also benzidine sulfate) are soluble in fused
urea.[30a]

$$3 \bigg[\text{NH}_2 \text{—} \bigcirc \text{—} \text{NH}_2 \bigg] \underset{6\text{H}}{\overset{3\text{O}}{\rightleftharpoons}} \text{NH}_2 \text{—}\bigcirc\text{—N}\text{=}\bigcirc\text{=N—}\bigcirc\text{—NH}_2 + 3\,\text{H}_2\text{O}$$

As just indicated, Bandrowski's base can be reconverted to p-phenylene-diamine by reduction with nascent hydrogen. The same is true of p-quinone imide. This reduction can be accomplished by heating the sample with a mixture of sodium formate and sodium hydroxide. At 210–230°, the mixture decomposes quantitatively[32]:

$$\text{HCOONa} + \text{NaOH} \rightarrow \text{Na}_2\text{CO}_3 + 2\,\text{H}°$$

The hydrogen not only converts the Bandrowski's base to phenylene-diamine but it also facilitates the sublimation of this diamine in the vicinity of its melting point (147°). The sublimed p-phenylenediamine reacts in the vapor phase with aniline and persulfate to yield phenylene blue.

Procedure. A micro test tube is used. A slight amount of the solid is mixed with several centigrams of the formate-hydroxide mixture, stirred with a drop of water, and then taken to dryness. The tube is then suspended in a glycerol bath previously heated to 205° and the mouth of the tube is covered with filter paper moistened with a drop of the reagent solution. The temperature is then raised to 210–230°: Depending on the amount of p-phenylenediamine given off, a light to deep blue stain appears on the paper immediately or within a few minutes.

Reagents: 1) Sodium formate-hydroxide mixture. A solution of 20% sodium formate and 12% sodium hydroxide is evaporated to dryness.
   2) Solution of 2 drops of aniline in 50 ml 10% acetic acid.
   3) 2% solution of potassium persulfate.

A freshly prepared mixture of equal volumes of *2)* and *3)* is used as reagent solution.

The test revealed as little as 10 γ Bandrowski's base.

17. Detection of Dyestuffs with p-Phenylenediamine and p-Nitraniline Structure [30]

Dyes, whose production involved p-phenylenediamine or p-nitraniline, are reductively cleaved by the nascent hydrogen when they are mixed with sodium formate-hydroxide and heated to 210–230°. The action of the nascent hydrogen doubtless proceeds via intermediate stages, but p-phenylene-diamine is always one of the end products. The net reactions with aniline yellow and p-nitraniline red are:

$$\bigcirc\!\!-N=N\!-\!\bigcirc\!\!-NH_2 + 4H° \longrightarrow \bigcirc\!\!-NH_2 + H_2N\!-\!\bigcirc\!\!-NH_2$$

$$O_2N\!-\!\bigcirc\!\!-N=N\!-\!\bigcirc^{HO} + 10H° \longrightarrow H_2N\!-\!\bigcirc\!\!-NH_2 + H_2N\!-\!\bigcirc^{HO} + 2H_2O$$

The p-phenylenediamine yielded by the reductive cleavage sublimes during the heating and can be detected in the vapor phase by means of the phenylene blue reaction (page 405). The procedure is the same as that described in **16**. It revealed 5 γ aniline yellow and 6 γ p-nitraniline yellow.

The procedure was checked with minute quantities of the dyes shown in Table 39. It should be noted that textiles colored with these dyes can likewise be tested. As little as 3–5 mg of the fabrics are sufficient.

18. Detection and Differentiation of Rhodamine Dyes[33]

By means of clear-cut condensation reactions, rhodamine dyes can be prepared from either fluorescein chloride or from o-dicarboxylic acid anhydrides. In the former case, the condensation is with primary or secondary aliphatic or aromatic amines (compare page 263); in the latter case, the condensation is with m-aminophenol or its alkylated derivatives.[34] In accord with these methods of preparation, the following quinoidal structural scheme is characteristic for rhodamine dyestuffs:

$$X = COOH; COOR; SO_3H$$
$$Y = H; CH_3; C_2H_5; \text{etc.}$$

Because of their $=\overset{+}{N}\!\!<^Y_Y$ group (as well as the $-N\!<^Y_Y$ group) all rhodamines exhibit a decided basic character. If the molecule contains free SO_3H^- or COOH groups, their acidic character becomes evident and the presence of zwitter ions can be expected in the aqueous dyestuff solutions. The neutral, weakly acid, or weakly basic aqueous solutions of rhodamines are various

TABLE 39

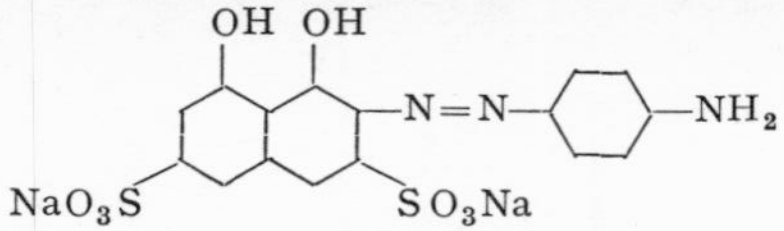

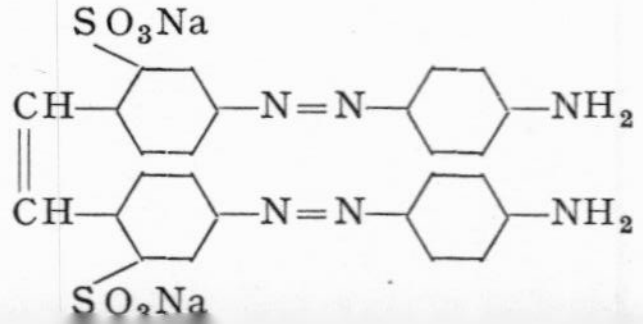

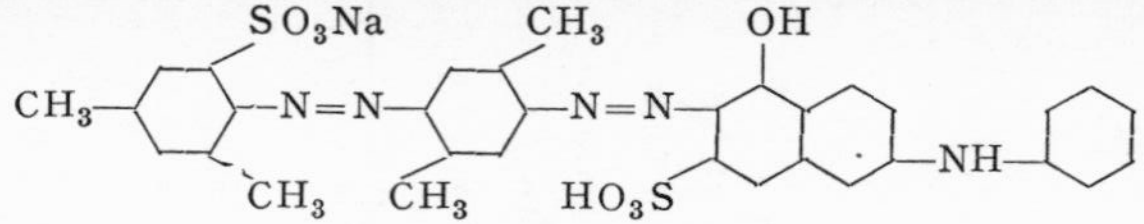

Diphenyl-brilliant-violet 2R

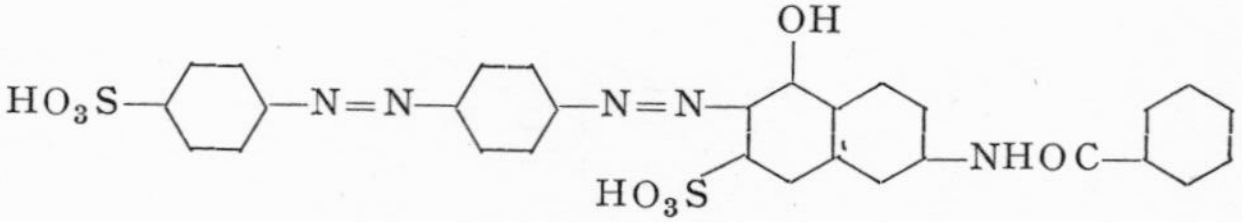

Diphenyl-fast-red 5BLN

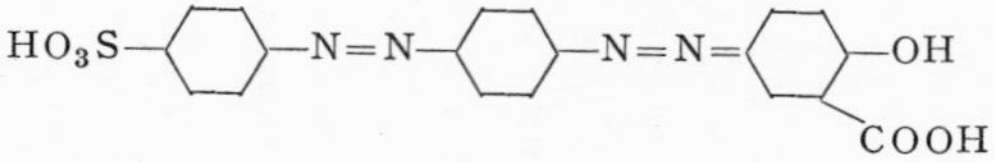

Eriochrome-orange R

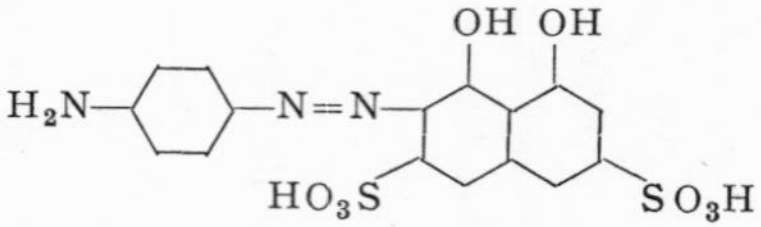

Erio-violet B

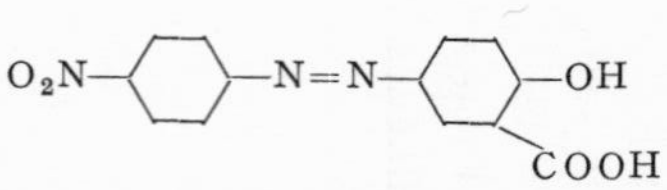

Victoria violet

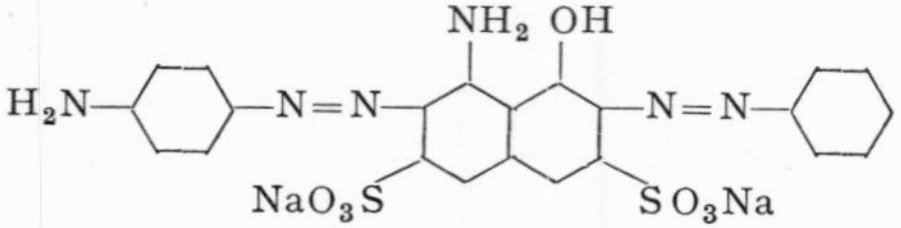

Kiton-black G

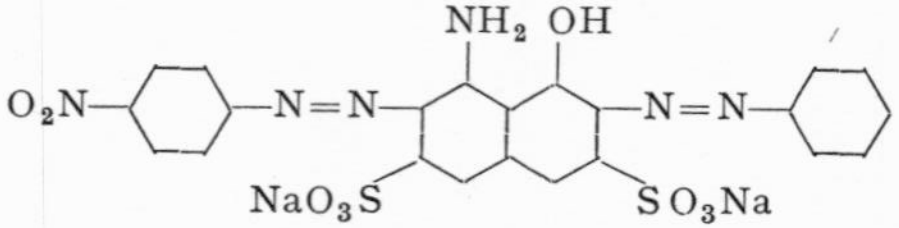

Kiton-black HA

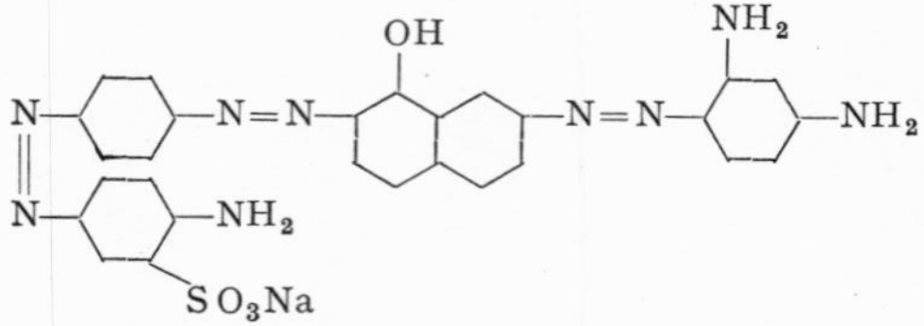

Carbide-black S

shades of red in daylight and in ultraviolet light they exhibit an intense red or orange fluorescence.

Chapter 3 of Volume I describes sensitive tests for antimony[V], gold, and thallium[III] and also for antimony[III] by means of rhodamine B (I). These tests are based on the fact that this basic dye gives violet crystalline precipitates in halogen acid solutions of the complex halogen acids $H[SbCl_6]$, $H[AuBr_4]$, $H[TlBr_4]$ and $H[SbI_4]$. The precipitates are the rhodamine B salts of the respective complex acids. The thallium[III] compound, as well as other salts, dissolves in benzene and the resulting red solution fluoresces intensely orange red in ultraviolet light. In accord with the rule that the analytical effect of organic compounds invariably is related to the presence of certain groups,[35] all rhodamine dyes react analogously to rhodamine B because of the $= \overset{+}{N}\underset{Y}{\overset{Y}{<}}$ group they contain. Differences are encountered only with respect to the extractability of the thallium[III] compounds with benzene, so that the presence of acidic and strongly hydrophilic groups in the dyestuff molecules impairs the solubility in benzene of the thallium compounds of the respective dyestuffs. Accordingly, the formation of fluorescing thallium compounds that are benzene-soluble can be used to detect strongly basic rhodamine dyestuffs. This test has been applied to the following rhodamine dyes of known constitution:[36]

(I) Rhodamine B   (II) Rhodamine G   (III) Rhodamine 3 B

(IV) Rhodamine 6 G   (V) Rhodamine S   (VI) Sulforhodamine B

The following rhodamine dyestuffs, whose structure is not given in the Schultz tables *(loc. cit.)* were likewise tested: rhodamine 3R, rhodamine 6 GH, and acid rhodamine R. The findings are included in the compilation given below.

Procedure. One drop of the aqueous test solution is placed in a micro test tube and mixed with a drop of 1:1 hydrochloric acid and a drop of a solution of thallic bromide. The mixture is shaken with 5–8 drops of benzene. The presence of rhodamine dyes is indicated by the production of a red benzene layer, which fluoresces orange in ultraviolet light.

Reagent: Thallic bromide solution: 2% solution of thallous sulfate is treated with bromine water until a distinct yellow is obtained. The excess bromine is removed by adding drops of a 10% solution of sulfosalicylic acid. The colorless mixture keeps for several days.

The behavior of rhodamine dyestuffs and the attainable identification limits can be seen in the following compilation; they all yield violet precipitates:

Rhodamine B (I)	0.5 γ	soluble in benzene	orange fluorescence
Rhodamine G (II)	0.25 ,,	,, ,, ,,	,, ,,
Rhodamine 3B (III)	0.25 ,,	,, ,, ,,	,, ,,
Rhodamine 6G (IV)	0.25 ,,	,, ,, ,,	,, ,,
Rhodamine S (V)	—	insoluble in benzene	—
Sulforhodamine B (VI)	—	,, ,, ,,	—
Rhodamine 6GH	0.5 ,,	soluble in benzene	orange fluorescence
Acid rhodamine R	5 ,,	,, ,, ,,	,, ,,
Rhodamine 3R	0.25 ,,	,, ,, ,,	,, ,,

It should be emphasized in addition that the production of red benzene solutions still is visible at dilutions at which the formation of violet thallic precipitates can no longer be seen.

The formation of fluorescent thallic-rhodamine compounds can also be used to detect rhodamine dyes directly in dyed fabrics. In this case, several threads of the sample are digested in a micro test tube with a drop or two of hydrochloric acid and several drops of the thallic bromide solution. Extraction with benzene then follows. A red benzene solution, which fluoresces orange in ultraviolet light, is proof that basic rhodamine dyes were used to color the fabric provided that a blank test shows no fluorescence.

19. Differentiation of Dyes with N-Methyl and N-Ethyl Groups [37]

Some members of certain classes of dyes differ solely in containing —$N(C_2H_5)_2$ in place of —$N(CH_3)_2$ groups or *vice versa*. In general, the colors of the solid and dissolved compounds are the same, and likewise their dyeing powers and behavior toward reagents are alike. Examples of such pairs include: methyl orange (I) and ethyl orange (Ia); malachite green (II) and brilliant green (IIa); gallamine blue (III) and coelestin blue (IIIa):

O_3S—⟨⟩—$N=N$—⟨⟩—$N(CH_3)_2$ NaO_3S—⟨⟩—$N=N$—⟨⟩—$N(C_2H_5)_2$

I   Ia

$H_3)_2N$—⟨⟩—$C=$⟨⟩$=\overset{+}{N}(CH_3)_2$ Cl^- $(C_2H_5)_2N$—⟨⟩—$C=$⟨⟩$=\overset{+}{N}(C_2H_5)_2$ Cl^-

II   IIa

$(CH_3)_2\overset{+}{N}$ Cl^- — CONH₂ structure — OH, OH

III   IIIa

The presence of I, II or III on one hand, and of Ia, IIa or IIIa on the other, can be revealed by melting the dye with benzoyl peroxide. This treatment (comp. pages 179–181) causes oxidative splitting with formation of alde- hydes. The latter can be detected in the gas phase by sensitive color reactions. I, II and III yield formaldehyde only, while Ia, IIa, and IIIa produce acetaldehyde solely. The tests can be made with slight quantities of the sample and require not more than a few minutes. The results are reliable. Textiles dyed with these materials can likewise be tested for these pairs.

20. Test for Hydroxytriphenylmethane Dyes [37a]

Most of the acid mordant dyes of this category are prepared by condensing benzaldehyde (or its derivatives) with salicylic acid (or its derivatives).[37b] When mineral acids are added to the blue alkaline solutions of these dyes, the corresponding red or red-brown dye acid is set free. The latter yields a yellow or brown solution in ether. Well known examples of these dyes include: Eriochromecyanine (I), Eriochrome Azurol (II), Bleu ciel au chrome (III) and also Chrome Azurol S, Chromate blue, and aurintricarboxylic acid.

References pp. 510–512

COONa   COONa   COONa   COONa CH_3

HO—／＼   ／＼＝O   HO—／＼   ／＼＝O   HO—／＼   ／＼＝C
H_3C—＼／—C＝＼／—CH_3 H_3C—＼／—C＝＼／—CH_3 NaOOC—＼／—C＝＼／—C

—／＼—SO_3Na Cl—／＼   Cl—／＼—Cl
＼／   ＼／   ＼／

(I)   (II)   (III)

All of these dyes contain the group (IV). It is characteristic of this group that it forms aluminum chelate rings as shown in (V).

COOH   OC—O
>C＝／＼＝O   >C＝／＼＝O ＞Al/₃

(IV)   (V)

Since the dyes contain acidic groups at other positions in the molecule, the chelate ring and hence the aluminum is a component of the anions. The aluminum chelate compounds of hydroxy-triphenylmethane dyes are dark red violet, sometimes blue. Once formed, they are stable against strong mineral acids. This fact is the basis of a sensitive and specific test for aluminum with Bleu ciel au chrome (see Volume I).

Procedure. A drop of the aqueous dye solution (sodium salts) is treated in a micro test tube with a drop of a 2% solution of aluminum sulfate and a drop of dilute ammonia water. After shaking, the mixture is made acidic with a drop of 1 : 1 hydrochloric acid. According to the quantity of dyestuff present, a pink to red color results, which persists when the solution is shaken with ether. (The latter extracts the excess dye.) When testing ammoniacal dyestuff solutions, it is not necessary to add alkali beforehand. The test reveals 0.5 γ Eriochromecyanine, Eriochrome Azurol, Chromate blue, Chrome Azurol S, aurintricarboxylic acid.

When dealing with mixtures of dyes, or when conducting identification tests, it is advisable to suspend the test portion in hydrochloric acid and then to extract with ether. One drop of the ether extract is added to a drop of the aluminum sulfate solution, the ether evaporated off, and the procedure just described is then applied.

21. Identification of Nickel Dimethylglyoxime [38]

Scarlet crystalline nickel dimethylgloyxime is well known from its formation in inorganic analysis. This nickel salt is employed as a sun-fast pigment in paints, lacquers, cellulose compounds, and cosmetics. It can be detected by utilizing its solubility in dilute mineral acids and in alkali cyanide solutions (production of light green Ni^{+2}-ions and yellow $[Ni(CN)_4]^{-2}$-ions, respectively). When ignited, it leaves nickel oxide.

If a little of the sample is treated on a watch glass with several drops of dilute hydrochloric acid (alcoholic, if need be), the color is dicharged. The red color is restored by adding concentrated ammonium hydroxide.

Digestion with dilute potassium cyanide solution discharges the color. This is restored on adding mercuric chloride solution, the nickel dimethylglyoxime being regenerated:

$$Ni(DH)_2 + 4\ KCN \longrightarrow K_2\ Ni[(CN)_4]^{-2} + 2\ DHK$$

$$[Ni(CN)_4]^{-2} + 2\ DHK + 2\ Hg^{+2} \longrightarrow 2\ Hg(CN)_2 + Ni(DH)_2 + 2K^+$$

(DH = univalent radical of dimethylglyoxime)

If the sample is ignited, the residue taken to dryness with dilute hydrochloric acid, and then treated with an ammoniacal alcoholic solution of dimethylglyoxime, the red nickel dimethylglyoxime is formed. It is readily distinguished from other red pigments or admixed organic red materials by the characteristics just cited.

22. Detection of Antimony and Tin Mordants in Fabrics

In addition to the salts of aluminum, iron, chromium, and tin, which hydrolyse extensively in aqueous solution, the mordants used to fix acid dyes (principally such as contain OH and COOH groups) include also the following antimony salts: antimony (III) fluoride, potassium antimony (III) oxalate, and potassium antimonyl tartrate. The acid dyes are fixed on the hydrolysis products of these metal salts, which, in a highly dispersed state, adhere to the fibers and form insoluble adsorption compounds with the dyestuffs. An important role is played here by the chelate binding of the dyes with metal atoms (the so-called color lakes)[39]. Tervalent antimony compounds, particularly tartar emetic, also serve in combination with tannin as mordants for basic dyes. When the fibres are treated with potassium antimonyl tartrate (or other antimony salts) and tannin, adsorption compounds of the latter with antimony salts or antimony hydroxide are formed. As a polymeric glycoside derivative of gallic acid, tannin contains a number of acidic groups. Some of these are bound with antimony in the fixation process, whereas others are free to bind basic dyes, e.g. those of the triphenylmethane series. This means that the acidic antimony-tannin ad-

sorption compound functions as adsorbent for basic dyes. Sometimes antimony compounds are used for special types of leather tanning.

A reliable test for antimony in textiles or leather is based on the fact that
soluble as well as insoluble compounds of tervalent and quinquevalent antimony are easily transformed into the water–soluble complex acid $H[SbI_4]$
or its ions. When the amphoteric dyestuff rhodamine B, which is soluble at
all pH ranges, is introduced into solutions of this acid, a red-violet precipitate
of the rhodamine salt of the complex acid is formed. Structures (I) and (II)
can be applied to this salt.

Although the solution of the dye is red, the formation of the red-violet
antimony compound, which comes out as a fine crystalline precipitate, is
readily seen, even though only slight amounts of antimony are present. The
identification limit of the test is 0.6 γ antimony.

Procedure.[40] Several mm² of the fabric being tested is ashed in a micro
crucible. After cooling the residue, which should be as free as possible from
unburned carbon, is treated in succession, with single drops of 5% potassium
iodide solution, diluted hydrochloric acid, sulfurous acid (to remove the iodine
formed by redox reaction with pentavalent antimony) and dyestuff solution.
A violet precipitate indicates the presence of antimony.

Reagent: 0.5% aqueous solution of Rhodamine B.

When fabrics are to be tested for tin mordants, several mm² of the cloth
is ashed; SnO_2 is left. The residue is warmed with concentrated sulfuric acid,
to produce $Sn(SO_4)_2$. Then an equal volume of water is added, and after
introducing several crystals of potassium iodide, the mixture is extracted
with a benzene solution of iodine. The violet benzene solution, which contains SnI_4, is spotted on filter paper and is held over ammonia to produce
$Sn(OH)_4$. The brown fleck is spotted with a drop of 5% sodium sulfite
solution to remove the free iodine. Then the fleck is spotted with a drop of
0.05% solution of morin in alcohol or acetone. The paper is bathed briefly
in dilute hydrochloric acid (1 : 10) and viewed in ultraviolet light. If tin

is present, the fleck exhibits an intense blue-green fluorescence.[41] The latter is due to an acid-resistant fluorescing adsorption compound of $Sn(OH)_4$ with morin. Chapters 3 and 7 of Volume I should be consulted regarding the chemistry of this test, whose *identification limit* is 0.05 γ tin.

Stannic chloride is used to weight silk. The procedure just given can be applied for the detection of small amounts of tin in silk.

23. Detection of Lead Tetraethyl or Lead Tetraphenyl in Motor Fuels [42]

Certain organometallic compounds (alkyl, aryl, carbonyl and acetylide metallic compounds) are sometimes added to mineral oils, since even small amounts have a decided effect on certain undesirable reactions. They usually decrease the velocity of such reactions. These substances are used chiefly as antiknock agents in motor fuels and as antioxidants in hydrocarbons. Since lead tetraethyl (phenyl), which is most frequently used, is very volatile and is also extremely toxic, a reliable test for this compound has important practical significance. The following procedure is easily applied to gasoline and other motor fuels.

Procedure. One or two drops of the gasoline is placed on filter paper and held in ultraviolet light for about 30 seconds until evaporation is complete.* A drop of a freshly prepared green 0.1 % solution of dithizone in chloroform is then placed on the paper. If $Pb(C_2H_5)_4$ or $Pb(C_6H_5)_4$ is present, a deep red stain (of lead dithizone) results; in the absence of lead salts, the paper remains green. When the gasoline is highly colored, it should be decolorized beforehand by shaking with activated charcoal.

Oils usually have a deep self color. To test for lead salts, 100 to 150 ml of the oil is mixed with 3 % benzene and steam-distilled. The lead test is made on the distillate. Alternatively, a drop of a gasoline possibly containing $Pb(C_2H_5)_4$ is shaken with a 1 % aqueous solution of potassium cyanide and exposed to ultraviolet light for a few seconds. A drop of dithizone solution is then placed on the liquid surface.[44]

Traces of nickel carbonyl in benzene solutions, sometimes used as antiknock agent, may be detected by an analogous method using ammonia water and dimethylglyoxime or rubeanic acid as reagents for nickel. Compare Volume I, Chapter 3.

24. Detection of Peroxides in Ether and Dioxan [45]

If ether or dioxan is exposed to the air for a considerable time, small amounts of organic peroxides of various kinds are likely to be formed.[46]

* It has been stated [43] that this treatment results in the decomposition of organo-lead compounds, with deposition of acid-soluble flocks.

Ether contaminated in this fashion is not suitable for extraction purposes in many instances. It can be tested by placing a drop on potassium iodide-starch paper. After volatilization, peroxide-containing ether will leave a brown stain, which turns blue when spotted with water. The blue fleck is produced immediately in the case of impure dioxan.

If filter paper impregnated with p-phenylenediamine is spotted with ether containing peroxides, a light blue spot is left (compare: Detection of benzoyl peroxide, page 438).

A somewhat more sensitive test is based on the fact that colorless ferro-thiocyanate is converted to red ferrithiocyanate. This test can be made by mixing a drop of the reagent with a drop of ether or dioxan. A spot plate or filter paper may be employed.

Preparation of the reagent solution: 9 grams of $FeSO_4.7H_2O$ is dissolved in 50 ml hydrochloric acid (1 : 1) and a little granulated zinc added. After the solution has become colorless, 5 grams of NaCNS is added. This produces a transient red color. After the color fades, 12 grams of NaCNS is added and the liquid decanted from the unused zinc. A solution prepared in this way keeps for about a day. If it has become pink because of access of air, the color should be removed by adding some granulated zinc.

25. Detection of Pyridine Bases in Amyl Alcohol [47]

Amyl alcohol, prepared by fermentation, always contains distinct amounts of pyridine bases. These can be discovered even in commercial amyl alcohol that is represented as 'pure'. The test described on page 280 can be used as a rapid method for detecting pyridine in pure amyl alcohol and in its mixtures with ethyl alcohol. A positive response, namely the production of a violet polymethine dye, is best established, by adding the necessary reagents to the diluted amyl alcohol, since the latter dissolves the resulting violet dye to give a brown solution.

26. Detection of Pyridine Bases in Ammonia [47]

Ammonia recovered from the gas liquor of illuminating gas manufactured from coal invariably contains small amounts of pyridine bases, such as pyridine, α- and β-picoline, etc. These bases, with the exception of α-picoline, can be detected by suitable modification of the test given on page 280. It is based on the production of a violet polymethine dye with benzidine.

Procedure. One drop of the ammonia to be tested is treated on a spot plate with drops of strong bromine water until a permanent yellow is produced. An additional drop of the bromine water is then added. The ammonia is thus completely destroyed. Three drops of 4% potassium cyanide solution are stirred in, and finally three drops of a suspension of benzidine acetate. Depending on the amount of pyridine bases present, a violet color appears at once or after a few minutes, or the white suspension is tinted blue. A blank test is advisable.

Reagents: 1) Saturated solution of bromine in 5% potassium bromide.

2) Benzidine acetate suspension: 100 ml of a saturated solution (room temperature) of benzidine hydrochloride plus 1 gram of sodium acetate. The resulting suspension is stable if stored in a closed container.

The procedure described will reveal 5 γ pyridine in one drop of saturated ammonia water.

27. Differentiation of Animal and Vegetable Fibers

Vegetable fibers are free from sulfur, but fibers derived from animal sources contain sulfur compounds in the cysteine components of the protein. These compounds possess an SH group, which can accelerate the iodine–azide reaction. Hence, wool and cotton may be differentiated by applying the iodine–azide test, as described on page 288.

Cotton is nearly pure cellulose. It can be detected by the furfural test described on page 428, because derivatives of this aldehyde are formed when cotton is pyrolysed or hydrolysed (comp. page 486).

Procedure.[48] The fiber, or small piece of woven material, is moistened with a drop of water or acetone on a watch glass, and treated with 1 or 2 drops of the iodine–azide solution (for preparation, see page 288). After a short while, the wool is covered with little bubbles, while the cotton shows none. Cotton fibers turn dark violet owing to the adsorption of iodine, but the color of the bubbling wool remains unchanged. Bleached or unbleached cotton may be used in the test; both are colored violet, with no bubble formation. Half-wool mixtures give a positive response.

Another method of examining textiles for wool is based on the fact that when animal fibers are thermally decomposed, the proteins they contain yield pyrrole and pyrrole derivatives. The latter can be sensitively detected in the gas phase since, on contact with a hydrochloric acid solution of *p*-dimethylaminobenzaldehyde, they give a violet quinoidal condensation product (see page 276).

Procedure. [49] Several milligrams of the test material is pressed to the bottom of a hard glass micro test tube by means of a glass rod. The mouth of the test tube is covered with a disk of filter paper that has been moistened with a 5 % solution of *p*-dimethylaminobenzaldehyde in concentrated hydrochloric acid. The lower end of the test tube is heated with a micro burner and the gaseous combustion products react with the reagent. If animal fibers are present, a red-violet fleck will appear on the paper.

Fabrics, which contain nylon, i.e. a plastic made up of a superpolymeric amide of protein-like structure,[50] behave like animal fibers when subjected to this test, since the pyrolysis of nylon obviously produces pyrrole or pyrrole derivatives which likewise react with p-dimethylaminobenzaldehyde. On the other hand, nylon does not accelerate the iodine–azide reaction. Consequently, the latter can serve to differentiate between nylon and animal fibers.

Vegetable fibers respond positively to the test for cellulose and cellulose derivatives (see page 391).

28. Test for Esters in Mixtures of Hydrocarbons [51]

Fats and fatty oils, which are esters of glycerol with higher and middle fatty acids, may be detected by the glycerol reaction given on page 387, which is based on the dehydration of glycerol to acrolein. The latter may be identified through the color reaction with sodium nitroprusside solution containing piperidine. The various kinds of waxes consist predominantly of esters of higher monobasic carboxylic acids with higher monohydric alcohols. They give no glycerol reaction but they may be detected by the ester test described on page 237. The latter involves conversion to hydroxamic acids followed by the formation of their violet inner complex ferric salts. The presence of waxes and resins in mineral oils may be demonstrated by means of this reaction.

The hydroxamic acid reaction gives the following colors with the waxes and resins:

Beeswax	violet-brown	Balsam Tolu. . . .	brown-green
		Colophony	brown-green
Carnauba wax . . .	dark brown-violet	Congo copal. . . .	brown
Candelilla wax . . .	lilac	"Soromin" (syn-	
Montan wax	green-yellow	thetic ester) . . .	violet

29. Detection of the Contamination of Fabrics by Mammalian Urine [52]

Urea may be rapidly and sensitively detected by the evolution of ammonia in the presence of urease (page 430). The ammonia can be detected by the sensitive test with manganese nitrate – silver nitrate solution described on page 91. The reaction yields manganese dioxide and elementary silver.

Procedure. The fabric suspected of being contaminated with urine is viewed (if necessary under ultraviolet light) and the stain is outlined with a pencil. Apply 2–4 drops of urease solution to the stained area and allow the enzyme solution to soak in for 5–10 seconds. The cloth is then placed on a heated steam bath and covered at once with a piece of the reagent paper so that the paper is wetted by the damp area of the cloth. A firm contact should be maintained by pressing across the stained area. If the stain was due to urine, a black spot appears on the filter paper in about 30 seconds.

Reagents: 1) Urease solution: A 10 % slurry of jack bean meal in water is allowed to settle for a few minutes; the supernatant liquid is used as urease solution. (The slurry may be stored as long as a week in a refrigerator without apparent loss of activity.)

2) Manganese-silver reagent paper: Coarse filter paper is soaked in the neutralized $Mn(NO_3)_2$–$AgNO_3$ solution (page 91) and quickly dried on a steam bath heated to about 100°. (Freshly impregnated paper is preferable.)

30. Detection of Oxalic Acid in Leather [53]

Oxalic acid is often used for bleaching vegetable-tanned leathers. It is therefore sometimes important to be able to detect oxalic acid in finished leather products. The test by the formation of aniline blue, as described on page 355, is suitable. It can be carried out directly on a small piece of leather, or on the sole of a finished shoe, for instance. The intensity of the color reaction indicates whether traces or appreciable amounts of oxalic acid are present.

Procedure. A little diphenylamine (about 0.02 g) is placed on the leather and pressed down with a thick glass rod. The reagent is melted by heating from above with a *very small flame* and carefully kept in fusion for about a minute. Then, 2 or 3 drops alcohol are gently dropped on, and the piece exposed to as much light as possible. The appearance of a blue color indicates oxalic acid. When oxalic acid and diphenylamine are melted together in a crucible, the blue color appears immediately on the addition of alcohol, but on the leather the color develops only after some time. When considerable oxalic acid is present, the blue forms after about 1 to 2 hours, but for very small amounts, 10 hours standing is necessary. The development of the blue is accelerated by light; samples kept in the dark remain unchanged for days.

31. Detection of Formaldehyde in Leather [54]

Certain tanning operations employ formaldehyde directly or in the form of formaldehyde resins. The formaldehyde, which is chemically bound in this manner by the hide substance, can be detected by the color reaction with chromotropic acid and concentrated sulfuric acid (red-violet color). The procedure is that employed to detect formaldehyde-based resins (see page 485). The test can be made with as little as 0.1–1 milligram of leather.

References pp. 510–512

32. Detection of Vegetable-Tanned [55] Leather

Leather, which has been made with vegetable tanning agents contains polyphenols. In alkaline solution, the latter reduce 1,2-dinitrobenzene to the violet salt of the *aci*-form of *o*-nitronitrosobenzene. (See page 131 regarding the detection of organic compounds which function as hydrogen donors in alkaline solution.) The test can be made on a few tiny fibers shredded from the sample and weighing not more than a fraction of a milligram.

The sample is treated with a drop of 25% sodium carbonate solution and one drop of 5% benzenic solution of 1,2-dinitrobenzene. The micro test tube is then warmed in a water bath. A deep violet color appears within a minute or two. The reaction is not given by leather prepared with synthetic tanning agents.

33. Tests for Added Materials and Undesirable Admixtures in Foods

It is often important to be able to detect certain impurities which may have been added to organic products and also to detect undesirable by-products that have not been removed. This branch of testing is especially necessary in the examination of foods, drugs and cosmetics, when a harmful impurity or unscrupulous adulteration must be detected quickly. If the impurity or adulteration is inorganic, the tests described in Volume I are available. These tests should usually be carried out on the ash or acid extract of the sample. In testing for organic substances, many of the tests described in Chapter 5 may be applied. A few pertinent examples are discussed here.

(a) Detection of formic acid

Formic acid should not be present in wood vinegar since it is injurious to health. This acid (which has a definite antiseptic action) is also an inadmissible fermentation product in fruit juices, jams, marmalade, honey, etc. If permitted at all, the quantity should be slight. Formic acid may be detected as described on page 340 (conversion to formaldehyde and detection of the latter by the color reaction with chromotropic acid). If the products are colored or have had color added to them, they should be decolorized (if necessary after solution) before carrying out the test. Animal charcoal can be used to remove the color.

(b) Detection of glycerol

The nitroprusside test for glycerol described on page 387 has many applications. It depends on a color reaction between sodium nitroprusside plus piperidine or morpholine and acrolein, the latter being readily formed by the removal of a molecule of water from glycerol. Since the latter, in the form of a glycerol ester of various organic acids, is a constituent of all plant and animal fats, it is possible to test beeswax or lanolin (*adeps lanae anhydr.*) for instance, for any admixture of plant or animal fats, which should not remain in a first-rate product. The glycerol reaction may be used successfully to detect fats in cloudy or dark products. The rapid detection of glycerol is useful in testing cosmetics, and in testing wines and liquors, which often contain glycerol as an illegal sweetening agent.

(c) Detection of citric and malic acids

The detection of citric and malic acids is important in testing fruit vinegar, as this commodity should always contain these acids. Since both citric and malic acids are hydroxy-carboxylic acids, with the carboxyl groups in the 1,2-positions, the reaction for this group, as described on page 243, may be applied as a simple and rapid means of testing "fruit vinegar".

The fusion reaction with urea (page 360) which involves the formation of the fluorescent ammonium salt of citrazinic acid, can also be used to detect citric acid and citrates in vinegars.

(d) Detection of pyridine

A test for pyridine is useful as a rapid means of characterizing commercial alcohol where it is often present as the denaturing agent. The test for tertiary ring bases (see page 305) and also the test for pyridine (page 280) may be applied for the rapid detection of slight amounts of pyridine in a small sample.

(e) Detection of saccharin (gluside)

Saccharin, the imide of *o*-sulfobenzoic acid, is sometimes substituted for sugar since it is 500 times as sweet. It may be used illegally in wine, spirits, fruit juices, jams and honey, and so its detection is very important in food analysis.

A good test for saccharin is based on its saponification when evaporated with hydrochloric acid. The products are ammonium chloride and *o*-sulfobenzoic acid:

$$C_6H_4 \underset{CO}{\overset{SO_2}{\diagdown \diagup}} NH + HCl + 2 H_2O \rightarrow C_6H_4 \underset{COOH}{\overset{SO_3H}{\diagdown \diagup}} + NH_4Cl$$

If the evaporation residue is heated to 120° to remove the excess hydrochloric acid, and then again taken to dryness with a few drops of ammonia, and the residue heated to 200°, the ammonium salt of the sulfobenzoic acid will be left along with the ammonium chloride. The production of these two ammonium salts and hence the presence of saccharin can be easily established by the Nessler test (*Identification Limit* 5 γ saccharin).[56] The test assumes the absence of ammonium salts; therefore a preliminary trial with Nessler reagent is necessary.

If colored solutions are being examined, or if caramelization occurs, it is advisable to run a comparison test. In such cases, the release of ammonia by warming with causic alkali can be detected in the vapor phase by means of qualitative filter paper (comp. page 450) moistened with Nessler solution.

The sodium salt of saccharin, namely $C_7H_4O_3NSNa.2\ H_2O$, is known as soluble gluside or crystallose. In distinction to saccharin, it is readily soluble in water. It behaves like the parent compound with respect to the procedure prescribed here.

34. Detection of Mineral Acids and Organic Hydroxy Acids in Vinegar [57]

Fruit vinegar, which is prepared by oxidation of dilute alcoholic liquors with the aid of schizomycetes, contains 3–15 % of acetic acid along with small amounts of tartaric, citric, formic, and oxalic acid. It contains no mineral acids. On the other hand, synthetic dilute acetic acid is frequently contaminated with mineral acids, such as hydrochloric, sulfuric, phosphoric acid. Consequently, the test for the presence or absence of mineral acids can be based on the fact that after the sample has been treated with excess ammonia and evaporated to dryness, the residue will consist of ammonium acetate (tartrate, etc.) plus the ammonium salts of the mineral acids. Only the latter salts can withstand heating to 250°. Ammonium acetate is completely decomposed into acetic acid and ammonia even at 120°, and the ammonium salts of the other organic acids contained in fruit vinegar are decomposed by heating to 250° for ten minutes. The residual ammonium salts of mineral acids are easily detected by the Nessler test. The detection of mineral acids in this way is reliable and requires only a few drops of the vinegar. If desired, several milliliters of the suspected vinegar can be taken to dryness and the evaporation residue then subjected to the Nessler test. If phosphoric acid is suspected, a part of the residue can be tested by the sensitive reaction with ammonium molybdate and benzidine (see page 96).

Vinegar which has been prepared by merely diluting pure acetic acid can be identified as such by evaporating a few drops of the sample with ammonia in a micro crucible and heating the residue to 120° for 5–10 minutes. If the residue gives a negative response to the Nessler test, no other organic acid is present.

As mentioned above, vinegar which is produced by fermentation of alcoholic liquids, always contains small amounts of organic hydroxy acids (citric acid, tartaric acid, glycolic acid, etc.). A general test for these acids [58] can be based on the facts that they are able to form soluble complex salts with zirconium in ammoniacal solution, and that the masked zirconium, even in small amounts, can be detected, after acidification, by a fluorescence reaction with morin (see page 421). The following steps are necessary: One drop of 1 % $ZrCl_4$ solution and a slight excess of ammonia are added to 1 or 2 drops of the vinegar to be tested. The mixture is slightly heated and filtered. One drop of 0.05 % solution of morin in acetone and one drop of concentrated hydrochloric acid are added to the filtrate. When hydroxy acids are present, a greenish yellow fluorescence appears under ultraviolet light. Vinegar produced by dilution of pure synthetic acetic acid does not show the fluorescence reaction.

It should be noted that fresh fruit juices which contain sugars, and likewise those that are fermenting, also respond positively to the zirconium-morin reaction described here.

35. Detection of Salicylic acid in Foods, Beverages, Condiments, etc. [59]

Foods, condiments, beverages, and the like, sometimes contain small amounts of salicylic acid or alkali salicylate which have been added as preservative. Salicylic acid can be detected by the test described on page 363, which is based on the volatility of this acid and the fluorescence of its magnesium salt. The acidified solution of the sample or its suspension in dilute acid must be extracted with ether, which is a good solvent for salicylic acid, and the test is then carried out with the residue, left after evaporation of the ether.

Procedure. About 10 ml of the liquid sample is treated with 10 ml of concentrated sulfuric acid. After cooling, the mixture is shaken with 4 ml of ether. After several minutes, one or two drops of the ether solution is evaporated in the bulb of the apparatus shown in Fig. 23, page 49. The evaporation residue is treated with a drop of concentrated sulfuric acid and the apparatus is then closed with the stopper, whose knob has been charged with a dab of magnesium hydroxide suspension. The closed apparatus is kept for 10–15 minutes in an oven at 130°. The knob is then viewed in ultraviolet light. A blue fluorescence indicates the presence of salicylic acid. A comparison test is advised.

Reagent: Magnesium hydroxide suspension: 30 ml of 10% magnesium sulfate solution is treated with 2 ml of 5 N sodium hydroxide. The suspension must be shaken before use.

This test will reveal 0.017% salicylic acid in wine or water if one drop of the ether extract is used. Several drops of the extract should be taken if smaller amounts of salicylic acid are suspected.

36. Test for Soybean Meal [59]

Soybean meal contains urease, an enzyme which catalytically hastens the hydrolytic decomposition of urea and biuret to ammonia and carbon dioxide (ammonium carbonate). A sensitive test for urease and consequently for soybean meal is provided by the procedure (page 430) which is based on the demasking by urease of the nickel bound in a solution of the complex nickel biuret anion. The test can be made on a spot plate; a few milligrams of the meal suffices. It is best to treat one drop of the neutral or slightly alkaline suspension of the sample with one drop of the alkaline alkali nickel biuret solution. After the mixture has stood for 10–15 minutes, it is treated with a drop of dimethylglyoxime solution. A red precipitate appears if urease (soybean) is present.

37. Tests for Rancidity of Fats and Oils [60]

When fats and oils are stored in contact with air, they deteriorate because of the production of small amounts of hydroxy fatty acids, ketones, aldehydes, and organic peroxides. The resulting alteration in taste and odor, i.e. rancidity, is due primarily to the formation of organic peroxides, hydroxy fatty acids, and aldehydes. Spot reactions can be employed to reveal the presence of these three types of compounds.

(a) *Detection of organic peroxides*

2,7-Diaminofluorene (I), in acetic acid solution, is converted into the blue quinoneimide compound (II) by the action of many oxidizing agents.[61]

$$H_2N-\text{〈〉〈〉}-NH_2 \xrightarrow[-H_2O]{+O} HN=\text{〈〉=〈〉}=NH$$

(I)   (II)

However, organic peroxides and hydrogen peroxide do not have sufficient oxidizing power to convert (I) into (II), but certain ferments, the peroxidases, such as the hemin of blood, raise the oxidation power sufficiently so that the imide formation results. This activation serves not only to reveal the presence of peroxidases (see page 433) but also can be utilized to detect organic peroxides.

Procedure. One drop of the acetic acid solution of 2,7-diaminofluorene plus hemin is placed on filter paper and spotted with one drop of a saturated solution of the fat or oil in peroxide-free ether. Depending on the peroxide content, of the sample, a blue fleck appears at once or within a short time. The intensity also varies with the peroxide content. Usually the center of the fleck is green to green-blue; presumably this is due to a mixed color containing the blue imide (II) and the yellow to red-brown condensation product of the reagent with aldehydes contained in the rancid sample.

Reagent: 100 mg 2,7-Diaminofluorene plus 5 mg hemin dissolved in 5 ml glacial acetic acid. The solution should be freshly prepared.

(b) Detection of hydroxy fatty acids

Hydroxy fatty acids can be detected by the red color which they give on contact with sym.-diphenylcarbazide.[62] The chemistry of this reaction is not known.

Procedure. One drop of the diphenylcarbazide solution is placed on filter paper and, after evaporation of the solvent, is spotted with a drop of a saturated solution of the fat or oil in ether or petroleum ether. The presence of hydroxy fatty acids is indicated by a red fleck.

Reagent: 0.5 gram of diphenylcarbazide is dissolved in 100 ml of tetrachloroethane, warmed, and filtered after cooling.

Free fatty acids in rancid fats and oils can be detected by the color (fluorescence) reaction with uranyl nitrate and rhodamine B. The procedure given on page 461 is suitable.

(c) Detection of epihydrin aldehyde

Epihydrin aldehyde is characteristic of the aldehydes which are present in rancid oils and fats. However, there is no proportionality between the degree of rancidity and the content of this rather unstable aldehyde, which is distinctly volatile at room temperature. It may readily be detected by means of its color reaction with phloroglucinol in the presence of hydrochloric acid.[63] The condensation reaction can be represented: [64]

Procedure. In a microcrucible the fat or oil is thoroughly mixed with an equal volume of concentrated hydrochloric acid. The crucible is then covered with a piece of filter paper which has been spotted with a 0.1% alcoholic solution of phloroglucinol and several drops of dilute hydrochloric acid. If epihydrin aldehyde is present, a red color appears at once or after gentle warming (40°).

38. Application of Spot Tests in the Examination of Gunpowder and Explosives [65]

Black gunpowder, which contains large amounts of nitrates, may be tested for nitrate with a drop of the water extract. The color reaction with diphenylamine or diphenylbenzidine, which yields blue quinoid ammonium salts, may be applied. Similarly, other explosives may be tested for chlorate by the reaction with manganous sulfate and phosphoric acid (formation of red complex Mn^{III} phosphate). The residue from burned black powder always contains thiosulfate, thiocyanate, and sulfide besides some elementary sulfur. Even traces of these sulfur compounds may be detected by the acceleration of the iodine-azide reaction. The test with Nessler reagent or other reagents for free ammonia may be applied for detecting ammonium salts (nitrate, etc.).

Free sulfur can be detected in explosives and gunpowder either directly by fusion with benzoin (see page 454) or indirectly by means of the protective layer effect on thallous sulfide (see page 455).

All of these tests for inorganic ingredients are discussed in detail in Volume I.

Aromatic polynitro compounds (picric acid, trinitrotoluene) may be detected by the procedure for m-dinitro compounds given on page 162.

Acidic organic nitro compounds are revealed by the rhodamine test described on page 166.

Explosives which contain esters of nitric acid (nitrocellulose, nitroglycerol, tetranitropentaerythritol, etc.) can be reduced to nitrites and identified by the Griess test.

Procedure. A few milligrams of the sample is mixed on a spot plate with a drop of sulfanilic acid and a drop of α-naphthylamine solution. A little zinc dust or Devarda alloy is added. If nitro compounds were present, the solution (or solid) is colored bright red by the resulting azo dye. The development of the color may require a few minutes.

Reagents: 1) Zinc dust or Devarda alloy
2) 1% solution of sulfanilic acid in 30% acetic acid
3) 0.1% solution of naphthylamin in 30% acetic acid.
Equal parts of 2 and 3 mixed before use.

Esters of nitric acid may also be detected in threads of textiles. Microscopic examination will reveal admixtures or nonimpregnated cotton. When nitrates and water-insoluble nitro compounds are to be detected in the presence of each other, an aqueous extract should be prepared. After centrifuging or filtration, the clear solution is tested for nitrate (see page 168). The residue, after reduction, is tested for nitrite.

39. Detection of Urea Resins [66]

The test for urea, based on the formation of the violet nickel salt of diphenylcarbazide (see page 408), can be applied for the detection of urea resins, which are polymerized condensation products of urea with formaldehyde etc. The lower polymers respond directly; the higher polymers require hydrolysis with concentrated hydrochloric acid to liberate the urea.

Procedure. A few mg of the solid material and a drop of concentrated hydrochloric acid are taken to dryness at 110° in a micro test tube. After cooling, the residue is treated with one drop of phenylhydrazine and the mixture is heated to 195° for 5 minutes in an oil bath. The cooled reaction mixture is stirred with 3 drops of 1 : 1 ammonium hydroxide and 5 drops of 10% nickel sulfate solution and then shaken with 10–12 drops of chloroform. The presence of urea and hence of a synthetic urea resin or plastic is indicated by a violet to red color in the chloroform.

40. Detection of Formol Plastics [67]

Plastics or resins prepared by the condensation of formaldehyde with urea, melamine, or phenols can be detected through the release of formaldehyde when the sample is heated with concentrated sulfuric acid. The formaldehyde can be identified in the vapor phase by the chromotropic acid color reaction (see page 331). The splitting of formaldehyde from the plastics is brought about by the water contained in the concentrated sulfuric acid; it reacts in the form of superheated steam.

Procedure. A little of the sample is placed in the bottom of the outer tube of the gas absorbing vessel (Fig. 23, page 49). A drop of the reagent solution is suspended on the knob of the inner vessel. The apparatus is assembled and the outer tube is then heated by placing the apparatus in an oil bath previously heated to 170–180°. Care must be taken not to immerse the gas absorption tube more than 0.5–1 centimeter. If formaldehyde is released, the drop turns violet. Phenolic resins require 1–2 minutes heating, but urea resins need to be heated longer (at most 10 minutes). Even faint colors can be seen if the drop is wiped onto a white surface (spot plate). In the latter case, it is well to run a comparison blank.

Reagent: A pinch (tip of knife blade) of purest chromotropic acid is intimately stirred with 2–3 ml of concentrated sulfuric acid in a centrifuge tube. The supernatant liquid, usually turbid, obtained by centrifuging the suspension is used. It is best to prepare fresh reagent solution at not too long intervals.

This procedure was applied to samples of formaldehyde-phenol and formaldehyde-urea plastics. As little as 0.1 mg suffices for the test. Even such minute amounts of powders, splinters, etc. gave distinct positive results.

41. Detection of Cellulose and Cellulose Derivatives [68]

When cellulose is heated it disintegrates and the resulting superheated steam reacts with unchanged cellulose to produce hexoses, which in turn hydrolyze to give ω-hydroxymethyl furfural. The latter is volatile with steam and can be detected in the gas phase in the same manner as furfural, i.e. by means of the sensitive color test with aniline acetate. The chemistry of this reaction is discussed on page 428.

The furfural reaction can be employed for the detection of cellulose (Procedure I) and, if certain conditions are observed, to reveal the presence of cellulose derivatives such as cellulose acetate (Procedure II). All sugars, starches, and vegetable gums likewise yield furfural when they are thermally decomposed or hydrolyzed by strong acids.

Procedure I. A little of the solid sample, say a thread of the fabric to be tested for cotton, is placed in a microcrucible. The latter is then covered with filter paper moistened with aniline acetate solution and held in place by a watch glass. The bottom of the crucible is heated for 30 seconds with a microburner and the sample is slowly brought to charring. A red fleck appears on the paper if cotton is present.

Methyl cellulose, ethyl cellulose and acetyl cellulose do not respond to Procedure I, because they do not undergo the loss of water which is essential to the production of furfural. If, however, such cellulose derivatives are heated with concentrated phosphoric acid, they are saponified with production of cellulose which, since it is a carbohydrate, does produce furfural when heated. The latter then responds to the test with aniline acetate.

Procedure II. A little of the solid test material is placed in a microcrucible along with a drop of syrupy phosphoric acid. The mouth of the crucible is covered with filter paper moistened with aniline acetate solution and weighted down with a watch glass. After cautious heating with a micro burner for 30–60 seconds, a red fleck will appear on the filter paper if a cellulose derivative is present.

Reagent: 10% solution of aniline in 10% acetic acid.

Procedure II, which is more sensitive, may also be applied, in place of Procedure I, for the detection of cellulose.

An excellent test for cellulose, methyl-, ethyl-, and acetyl cellulose (and carbohydrates) is based on the formation of acetaldehyde when these substances are heated.[69] The aldehyde in the vapor phase can be detected by means of the color reaction with sodium nitroprusside containing morpholine (page 334).

Procedure III. A few mg of the dry sample is heated in a micro test tube. The mouth of the tube is covered with filter paper moistened with a drop of the reagent solution. The heating over a micro burner is continued until charring is seen. A blue stain appears on the colorless or light yellow reagent paper. See page 335 regarding the preparation of the reagent solution.

42. Differentiation of Methyl- and Ethyl Cellulose [69]

The tests for methoxy and ethoxy groups described on pages 179 and 181 can be used to distinguish methyl and ethyl cellulose. The procedure is based on the production of formaldehyde and acetaldehyde, respectively, when the cellulose ethers are oxidatively cleaved by warming with benzoyl peroxide. The aldehydes are detected in the vapor phase. Milligram quantities are adequate.

43. Detection of Naphthol- and Naphthylamine-sulfonic Acids [70]

A test for naphthol- and naphthylamine-sulfonic acids is of interest because many of these compounds are important starting materials in the manufacture of dyes.[71] Likewise, the control of the sulfonation of naphthol and naphthylamine has industrial importance. The two procedures given here can be conducted with small samples. The basis of Procedure I is that aqueous solutions of naphthol- and naphthylamine-sulfonic acids, which have a free position *ortho* to OH or NH_2 groups, yield brown water-soluble cobalt (III) salts of *o*-nitrosonaphtholsulfonic acids when warmed with sodium cobaltinitrite. In these salts, cobalt is a constituent of the inner complex anion. (See test for phenols, page 186.) Procedure II is based on the fact that many, but not all of the sulfonic acids of these classes are oxidatively split when warmed with potassium chlorate and concentrated hydrochloric acid and yield chloranil (tetrachloroquinone) or similar quinoidal compounds. The latter oxidizes tetrabase to a blue quinoidal product (see test for chloranil page 433).

Procedure I. A micro test tube is used. A drop of the test solution or a pinch of the solid is heated with 1–3 drops of a freshly prepared 5% water solution of sodium cobaltinitrite and 2 drops of 1 : 1 acetic acid. If very small amounts of sulfonic acid are involved, a blank is advisable. The blank will show a color change (orange to light pink) because of the decomposition of the nitrite and release of cobalt ions, whereas the solution containing a naphthol- or naphthylamine-sulfonic acid will become brown or light yellow, depending on the amount of sulfonic acid present.

TABLE 40

Sulfonic acid	Structure	Procedure I, Phenol test	Procedure II, Chloranil test
1,4-Naphtholsulfonic acid (Nevile-Winther acid)		+ + (5 γ)	+ + (5 γ)
1,5-Naphtholsulfonic acid		+ + (5 γ)	—
2,6-Naphtholsulfonic acid (Schaeffer's β-acid)		+ + (2.5 γ)	+ (50 γ)
2,7-Naphtholsulfonic acid		+ +	W (250 γ)
2,3,6-Dihydroxynaphthalene-sulfonic acid		+ + (5 γ)	
1,3-Naphthylaminesulfonic acid		+ (25 γ)	—
2,6-Naphthylaminesulfonic acid (Brönner's acid)		+ + (2.5 γ)	W (250 γ)
1,4-Naphthylaminesulfonic acid (Naphthionic acid)		+ + (2.5 γ)	+ (50 γ)
2,6,8-Naphtholdisulfonic acid (G acid)		W (500 γ)	—
1,8,3,6-Dihydroxynaphthalenedisulfonic acid (Chromotropic acid)		+ + (5 γ)	—
2,3,6-Naphthylaminedisulfonic acid (Amino R acid)		+ + (5 γ)	—
8-Aminonaphthol-(1)-disulfonic acid-(3,6) (H acid)		+ +	—

Procedure II. A drop of the test solution or a pinch of the solid is warmed in a micro test tube with a drop of a saturated aqueous solution of potassium chlorate and one drop of concentrated hydrochloric acid. Several drops of water are added and the cold solution shaken with 5–10 drops of ether. After the layers have separated, several drops of the ether solution are placed on filter paper and the fleck is spotted with one drop of 1% ether solution of tetrabase. If the sample contains sulfonic acids, a blue stain remains.

The results of tests for naphthol- and naphthylamine-sulfonic acids by Procedures I and II are given in Table 40. The figures in parentheses show the limits of identification. ++ signifies strongly positive; + positive; — negative; W weak.

From the compilation it is evident that, with the exception of 2,6,8-naphtholdisulfonic acid, even small amounts of all naphthol- and naphthyl-amine-sulfonic acids respond to the phenol test. In contrast, the oxidative splitting to produce chloranil is obviously dependent on steric factors. In particular, the chloranil test fails with di- and tri-sulfonic acids.

44. Differentiation of Naphthol- and Naphthylamine-sulfonic Acids [72]

Naphthol- and naphthylamine-sulfonic acids display characteristic differences toward a mixture of formaldehyde and concentrated sulfuric acid.

Almost all naphtholsulfonic acids give a characteristic violet- red or yellow color at once, whereas naphthylaminesulfonic acids remain without color change even though warmed with the reagent. The color reaction is probably due to a condensation of the formaldehyde with the particular naphtholsulfonic acid (under the influence of the concentrated sulfuric acid) to yield diarylmethane compounds with OH- and SO_3H-groups in the aryl ring. Since such compounds cannot be expected to be colored, this initial step is doubtless followed by an oxidation to quinoidal colored products, the sulfuric acid functioning as the oxidant. This postulate is in harmony with the fact that the color reactions of naphtholsulfonic acids are closely related to the results of the Le Rosen test for aromatic compounds (page 133) and the chromotropic acid test for formaldehyde (page 331).

The most favorable conditions for the realization of the color reaction are provided by employing the most concentrated sulfuric acid, and since the addition of aqueous formaldehyde necessarily results in dilution, it is best to use hexamethylenetetramine as the source of formaldehyde, and to make the test with solid naphtholsulfonic acids or their alkali salts. It should be noted that the products of the reaction between certain naphtholsulfonic acids and formaldehyde plus concentrated sulfuric acid exhibit a characteristic fluorescence in ultraviolet light.

References pp. 510–512

Procedure. A granule of the sample or the evaporation residue of a drop of its aqueous solution is treated, in a micro test tube, with several milligrams of hexamethylenetetramine and a drop or two of concentrated sulfuric acid. Depending on the amount of naphtholsulfonic acid, a more or less intense violet-red or brown color appears. Gentle warming is needed only in the case of chromotropic acid. A quartz lamp should be used to determine a possible fluorescence of the product, but it must be remembered that certain varieties of glass fluoresce.

Table 41 gives the results and limits of identification obtained by this procedure. The statements of color and fluorescence refer to 0.25 mg amounts.

TABLE 41.

Sulfonic acids	Behavior toward $(CH_2)_6N_4$ + conc. H_2SO_4	
	Color (Fluorescence)	Identification limit
1,4-Naphtholsulfonic acid	dark brown (lemon)	$1\,\gamma$ $(0.1\,\gamma)$
1,5-Naphtholsulfonic acid	orange (lemon)	$1\,\gamma$ $(0.1\,\gamma)$
2,6-Naphtholsulfonic acid	red-brown (yellow-green)	$2\,\gamma$ $(1\,\gamma)$
2,7-Naphtholsulfonic acid	orange (no fluorescence)	$2\,\gamma$
2,3,6-Dihydroxynaphthalenesulfonic acid	red (no fluorescence)	$3\,\gamma$
2,6,8-Naphtholdisulfonic acid	no reaction	
1,8,3,6-Dihydroxynaphthalenedisulfonic acid	violet (no fluorescence)	$0.5\,\gamma$
1,3-Naphthylaminesulfonic acid	no reaction	
2,6-Naphthylaminesulfonic acid	no reaction	
1,4-Naphthylaminesulfonic acid	no reaction	
2,3,6-Naphthylaminedisulfonic acid	no reaction	
8-Aminonaphthol-(1)-disulfonic acid-(3,6)	red-brown (no fluorescence)	$1\,\gamma$

The difficulty of obtaining pure specimens made it impossible to include still other naphthol- and naphthylamine-sulfonic acids. However, the available observations indicate strongly that a mixture of hexamethylenetetramine and concentrated sulfuric acid can be successfully used to detect

References pp. 510–512

most naphtholsulfonic acids, since only one of those tried gave a negative response.

Naphthylaminesulfonic acids can be detected through their condensation with p-dimethylaminobenzaldehyde to yield orange Schiff bases provided that primary aromatic amines are absent.

Procedure. One drop of the test solution and one drop of a saturated solution of p-dimethylaminobenzaldehyde in glacial acetic acid are mixed on a spot plate. Depending on the amount of naphthylaminesulfonic acid present, an orange to light yellow color develops.

This procedure revealed:

0.5 γ 1,3- naphthylaminesulfonic acid   0.25 γ 2,3,6-naphthylaminedisulfonic

0.1 γ 2,6-   ,,   acid

0.5 γ 1,4-   ,,   0.5 γ 8-aminonaphthol-(1)-disulfonic

acid-(3,6)

45. Test for Pharmaceutical Preparations Which Split off Formaldehyde [73]

Certain important pharmaceutical preparations release formaldehyde when warmed with concentrated sulfuric acid. This hydrolytic splitting is accomplished by the small but definite water content of the concentrated sulfuric acid. The formaldehyde can be detected by means of the delicate color (violet) reaction with chromotropic acid dissolved in concentrated sulfuric acid (see page 331). Consequently, preparations which yield formaldehyde give a violet color when they are warmed with chromotropic acid and concentrated sulfuric acid.

Procedure. A little of the solid is placed in a micro test tube or a drop of the test solution is evaporated there. Four drops of concentrated sulfuric acid and 1 or 2 mg of chromotropic acid (as pure as possible) are added. Depending on the amount of formaldehyde released, a more or less intense violet develops at once or within a few minutes.

The hydroysis by means of concentrated sulfuric acid may also be conducted in the gas absorbing apparatus (Fig. 23, page 49). The formaldehyde is detected in the vapor phase by coming in contact with the suspended drop of chromotropic acid reagent solution.

The procedure will serve to characterize the preparations listed here under (a)–(e). The spot reactions used as supplementary identification test are discussed in detail at other places in this volume.

(a) Methenamine Compounds

Methenamine (hexamethylenetetramine) and its salts are cleaved by concentrated sulfuric acid:

$$(CH_2)_6N_4 + 6\,H_2O \rightarrow 6\,CH_2O + 4\,NH_3$$

References pp. 510–512

The procedure was tried with success on very slight amounts of the following solids: methenamine, anhydromethylene citrate (Halmitol), methenamine camphorate (Amphotropin), methenamine mandelate, methenamine salicylate (Saliformin).

(*b*) *Choligen* (*Billamid*)

Choligen (Billamid) is the trade name applied to N-hydroxymethylnicotinamide (I). It is chemically related to the widely used nicotinamide (II) and nikethamide (III):

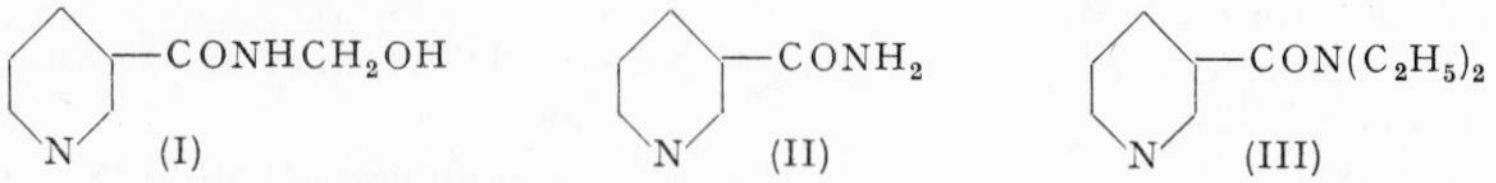
—CONHCH$_2$OH
N
—CONH$_2$
N
—CON(C$_2$H$_5$)$_2$
N

(I) (II) (III)

Only (I) yields formaldehyde when warmed with concentrated sulfuric acid. The hydrolysis can be represented:

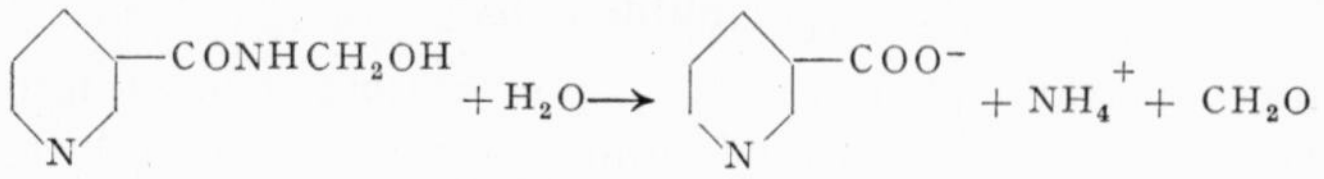
—CONHCH$_2$OH
N
+ H$_2$O→
—COO$^-$
N
+ NH$_4^+$ + CH$_2$O

Exposure of the pyridine component can serve as a supplementary identifying test and to differentiate choligen from the other formaldehyde-yielding compounds named here. This test is based on the conversion of pyridine and its derivatives (except its α-substituted derivatives) into glutaconic aldehyde (or its derivatives) by means of bromcyanogen. Glutaconic aldehyde and its derivatives form red-violet Schiff bases with benzidine (compare the test for pyridine page 280).

(*c*) *Sulfoxone Sodium* (*Diazone Sodium*)

In 1954 this compound was recommended as a remedy for leprosy.[74] It is split by concentrated sulfuric acid:

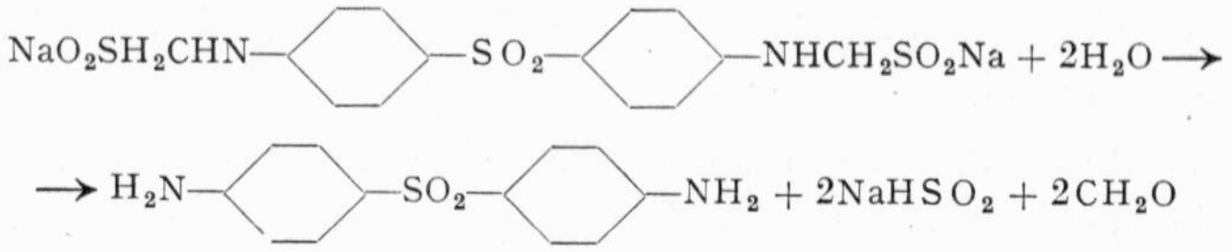
NaO$_2$SH$_2$CHN—
—SO$_2$—
—NHCH$_2$SO$_2$Na + 2H$_2$O →
→ H$_2$N—
—SO$_2$—
—NH$_2$ + 2NaHSO$_2$ + 2CH$_2$O

An additional identification test is based on its high reducing strength, which is due to its being a derivative of Rongalite (formaldehyde-sodium sulfoxylate) whose detection is outlined on page 452. Consequently, a water extract of preparations containing sulfoxone sodium yield the color reaction (orange) on treatment with an ammoniacal alcohol solution of 1,4-dinitrobenzene.

In addition, the release of hydrogen sulfide when the dry compound is heated at 250° according to:

$$2 \text{ NaHSO}_2 \rightarrow \text{Na}_2\text{SO}_4 + \text{H}_2\text{S}$$

can be utilized to recognize the sulfoxylate component[75] (see *d*).

(*d*) *Neosalvarsan and Myosalvarsan*

Neosalvarsan (I) and Myosalvarsan (II) are derivatives respectively

of formaldehydesulfoxylate and formaldehyde bisulfite. Accordingly, they yield formaldehyde when warmed with concentrated sulfuric acid: salvarsan is regenerated.

These preparations may be distinguished from each other because only neosalvarsan, as a derivative of Rongalite, gives the color reaction with an ammoniacal solution of 1,4-dinitrobenzene and also the test based on the evolution of hydrogen sulfide described in (*c*).

As little as 0.1 γ neosalvarsan and 0.5 γ myosalvarsan can be detected by the formaldehyde test. The sulfoxylate test will still reveal 15 γ neosalvarsan.

Due to its sulfoxylate component, the neosalvarsan, when heated at 250°, splits off H_2S which may be detected by lead acetate paper (PbS formation). In this way, a distinction between neosalvarsan and myosalvarsan is possible.

(*e*) *Pyramidone*

In the case of pyramidone, the splitting off of formaldehyde is not the result of a hydrolysis but comes about because of an oxidation by concentrated sulfuric acid (compare page 494).

46. Detection of Antipyrine [76]

The test given on page 399 for the detection of α-naphthylamine by means of nitrosoantipyrine is based on the formation of a red-violet azo dye (pyrazolone dyestuff). It may be reversed to constitute a specific test for antipyrine (1,5-dimethyl-2-phenyl-3-pyrazolone). It thus becomes possible to distinguish between this analgesic and antipyretic agent and pyramidone, which is used for the same purposes.

The antipyrine is nitrosated in acetic acid [77] as shown in (*1*), the excess nitrous acid is destroyed by sodium azide (*2*), and then naphthylamine is introduced to accomplish the condensation to the azo dye (*3*):

$$\text{(antipyrine structure)} + HNO_2 \rightarrow \text{(nitroso structure)} + H_2O \tag{1}$$

$$HNO_2 + HN_3 \rightarrow H_2O + N_2O + N_2 \tag{2}$$

$$\text{(naphthylamine)} \cdot NH_2 + \text{(nitroso structure)} \rightarrow \text{(azo structure)} + H_2O \tag{3}$$

Under the conditions prescribed here, 0.1–0.5 mg of pyramidone gives a very pale pink color, which probably arises from a slight content of antipyrine, which is the starting material in the preparation of pyramidone.

Procedure. A micro test tube is used. A drop of the test solution is treated with a drop of glacial acetic acid and a drop of 5% sodium nitrite solution. After 5 minutes standing and occasional shaking, a pinch of sodium azide is added. After the evolution of gas has stopped, several mg of solid α-naphthylamine is added and the tube is warmed in a water bath for a minute or two. Depending on the amount of antipyrine, a deep or pale violet color appears. A blank is advisable if small amounts of antipyrine are suspected.

Limit of Identification: 2 γ antipyrine.

The structure of antipyrine shows that it contains a $>NCH_3$-group. This group may be identified through the formation of formaldehyde when fused with benzoyl peroxide (see p. 179). 100 γ Antipyrine can be detected in this way.

47. Detection of Pyramidone (4-Dimethylamino-antipyrine) [78]

Pyramidone (4-dimethylamino-1,5-dimethyl-2-phenyl-3-pyrazolone) is widely used as an analgesic and antipyretic. It differs from its parent substance, antipyrine, not only in the fact that it cannot be nitrosated but also in two characteristics which are related to its $N(CH_3)_2$ group. In contrast to antipyrine, which is neutral, pyramidone is a base and in addition it has reducing powers which are lacking in antipyrine.

The reducing action of pyramidone is related to the tendency to tautomerize, which is a general characteristic of pyrazolones.[79] The oxidation probably begins with the isomeric methoxy form[80] of the pyrazolone:

$$\text{(pyramidone form)} \rightleftharpoons \text{(methoxy form)} + O \rightarrow \text{(OH form)} + CH_2$$

References pp. 510–512

The basic character of pyramidone can be demonstrated by means of a drop of nickel dimethylglyoxime equilibrium solution (page 112). Red nickel dimethylglyoxime is precipitated if a grain of the solid is moistened with a drop of this reagent.

The reducing action is shown by treating a little of the solid or a drop of its solution in dilute acid with a drop of ferri-ferricyanide solution. A blue color or precipitate appears (comp. USA Pharmacopeia).

Another identification test involves the formaldehyde produced when pyramidone is oxidized. If the solid is gently warmed with a mixture of chromotropic acid and sulfuric acid, the oxidizing action of the latter results in the violet color which is characteristic for formaldehyde (page 331). The *limit of identification* of this test is 10 γ pyramidone.

When testing salts of pyramidone, obviously the only tests that may be applied are those based on the reducing action of the parent compound.

48. Tests for Isonicotinic Acid Hydrazide

The hydrazide of isonicotinic acid (p-pyridine carboxylic acid) has come to the fore as a remedy for tuberculosis. As such it goes under a great variety of trade names (INH, Nihydrazide, Neoteben, Dinacrin, Cotinazine, etc.). It can be identified in pharmaceutical preparations by condensation with salicylaldehyde [81] or through its redox reaction with phosphomolybdate,[82] i.e., by Procedures I and II, respectively.

If a saturated water solution of salicylaldehyde is added to a neutral solution of isonicotinic acid hydrazide (I), the resulting yellow-white crystalline precipitate is characterized by a strong yellow-green fluorescence in ultraviolet light. This product (II) is a Schiff base; it results from the condensation:

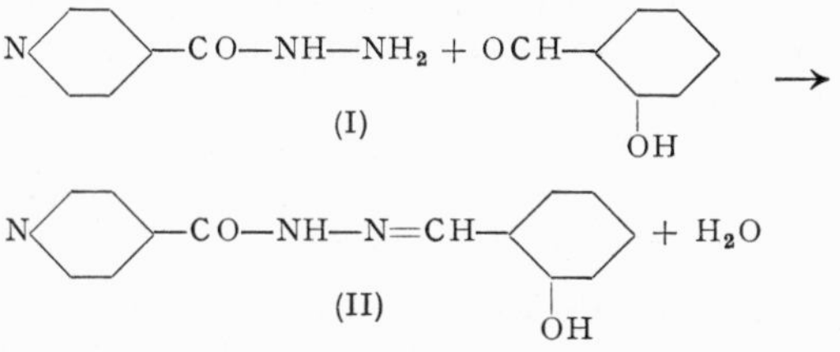

This condensation is analogous to the condensation of hydrazine with salicylaldehyde and other o-hydroxyaldehydes, which yield water-insoluble aldazines that fluoresce orange-yellow (see pages 220 and 376). However, in contrast to the acid-resistant aldazines, compound (II), by virtue of the pyridine component of its molecule, is soluble in dilute acids and gives a lemon yellow solution. Furthermore, the fluorescence then disappears. With dilute hydrochloric or sulfuric acid, the hydrochloride or sulfate of (II) is present in the yellow solutions. The latter are also formed if mineral acid solutions of isonicotinic acid hydrazide (containing colorless cations (III)), are treated with a water solution of salicylaldehyde; the yellow cation (IV) is formed:

$$(2)$$

The color reaction (2) is specific in the form of a spot test; the *identification limit* is 10 γ. If the yellow solution is placed in contact with calcium carbonate or if it is alkalized by means of ammonia, (IV) is transformed into the water-insoluble compound (II), which can be discerned even in small amounts because of its fluorescence. Since neutral solutions are rarely encountered in actual practice, it is advisable always to start with acid solutions when testing for isonicotinic acid hydrazide.

Procedure I. The acid solution to be tested is treated with an equal volume of a water solution of freshly distilled salicylaldehyde. One drop of the light yellow solution, which may appear to be colorless when only slight amounts of the hydrazide are present, is placed on filter paper. After 4 minutes, the fleck is held over a dish containing ammonia. (The exposure to air is necessary in order to volatilize and oxidize the excess salicylaldehyde.) If isonicotinic hydrazide was present, there remains a fleck which fluoresces yellow-green in ultraviolet light, the intensity depending on the quantity of hydrazide involved. The fluorescence disappears when the paper is dried in the air, but it reappears if the paper is held over ammonia. A comparison blank test is advised.
Limit of Identification: 0.1 γ isonicotinic acid hydrazide.
The test also succeeds at a like dilution with the volume of a microdrop (0.001 ml), which corresponds to an identification limit of 0.002 γ isonicotinic hydrazide.

Isonicotinic acid hydrazide is a derivative of pyridine and so, it can be precipitated from acid solution by phosphomolybdic acid. The crystalline phosphomolybdate is yellow. If the precipitate is treated with excess ammonia, it not only dissolves with production of water-soluble hydrazine, ammonium phosphate, and ammonium molybdate, but a concurrent redox reaction occurs between the hydrazine group and the complexly bound molybdenum. The intensely colored molybdenum blue results. It is not necessary to isolate the phosphomolybdate of isonicotinic acid hydrazide in order to realize the color reaction based on the production of molybdenum blue. It suffices to add phosphomolybdic acid to the acid solution and then alkalize with ammonia. Free hydrazine and oxidizable amines must not be present. The former reduces phosphomolybdic acid to molybdenum blue even in acid solution; the latter are likewise precipitated from acid solution by phosphomolybdate, and molybdenum blue results after addition of ammonia.

Procedure II. One drop of the neutral or mineral acid test solution is mixed on a spot plate with a drop of a saturated water solution of phosphomolybdic acid. After 1–2 minutes, the solution is made alkaline with ammonia. Depending on the quantity of isonicotinic acid hydrazide, a blue precipitate or color appears.

Limit of Identification: 0.5 γ isonicotinic acid hydrazide.

49. Tests for Penicillin G Salts [83]

The antibiotics known as penicillin G salts contain not less than 85 % of the sodium or potassium salt, $C_{16}H_{17}K(Na)N_2O_4S$. The potassium salt has the structure

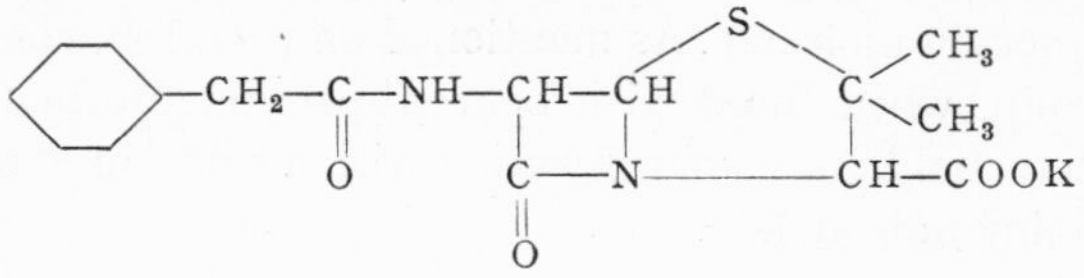

Similar preparations are "Buffered crystalline Penicillin", which is a mixture of the sodium or potassium salt with 4–5 % of sodium citrate, and "Penicillin G Procaine", which is the procaine salt of penicillin G [84]. The procaine has the structure:

If the samples are pure preparations, the behavior of the ignition residues is characteristic. With the exception of the procaine salt, which burns without leaving a residue, the other preparations yield alkali carbonate. The ignition tests can be conducted in a microcrucible with as little as 0.2–0.5 milligram of the sample. The test for alkalinity is best made with nickel dimethylglyoxime equilibrium solution as described on page 70.

Another test for penicillin preparations of all kinds consists in treating a tiny portion (fractions of a milligram are sufficient) with a drop or two of a saturated (room temperature) water solution of phosphomolybdic acid. The test tube containing the mixture is plunged into boiling water for an instant. An intense blue color appears within several seconds if penicillin G compounds are present. The color reaction involves several steps: (a) liberation of the parent acid from its salts by phosphomolybdic acid; (b) hydrolysis of the acid to give β, β-dimethylcysteine [85]

$$\underset{\underset{SH}{|}}{\overset{\overset{CH_3}{|}}{H_3C-C}}-\underset{\underset{NH_2}{|}}{CH}-COOH$$

Since the latter is a mercaptan, it is immediately oxidized to the corresponding disulfide by the phosphomolybdic acid with simultaneous formation of molybdenum blue. The limit of identification is 4 γ in the case of the sodium salt of penicillin G. No color reaction with phosphomolybdic acid is given by streptomycin and dihydrostreptomycin.

The test is not applicable in the presence of strong reducing agents, such as ascorbic acid, phenols, etc. They reduce phosphomolybdic acid even in the cold, whereas the formation of molybdenum blue by means of penicillin occurs only on warming.

Penicillin G procain can be distinguished from Penicillin G not only by the lack of residue when ignited, but also by a test for the $N(C_2H_5)$-group present in the procain molecule. As mentioned on page 180, compounds containing this group, when fused with benzoyl peroxide, form acetaldehyde, which can be detected by the color reaction with a solution of sodium nitroprusside containing morpholine.

50. Tests for Streptomycin and Dihydrostreptomycin [86]

The basic antibiotic streptomycin is usually sold as the hydrochloride, $C_{21}H_{39}N_7O_{12} \cdot 3HCl$; as the hydrochloride double salt with calcium chloride, $(C_{21}H_{39}N_7O_{12} \cdot 3HCl)_2 \cdot CaCl_2$; as the phosphate, $C_{21}H_{39}N_7O_{12} \cdot H_3PO_4$; or as the sulfate, $(C_{21}H_{39}N_7O_{12})_2 \cdot 3H_2SO_4$. The streptomycin base has the structure:

Dihydrostreptomycin is produced by hydrogenation of streptomycin. It contains the primary alcohol group —CH_2OH in place of the central aldehyde group —CHO. It is usually available as the hydrochloride $C_{21}H_{41}N_7O_{12}\cdot3HCl$ or as the sulfate $(C_{21}H_{41}N_7O_{12})_2\cdot3H_2SO_4$.

The structural formula shows that streptomycin and also dihydrostreptomycin should be regarded as derived from guanidine by virtue of the two $\overset{HN}{\underset{H_2N}{\diagup}}C$—NH-groups in the molecule. As was pointed out on page 291, when solid guanidine salts are heated to 250° ammonia is evolved. These characteristics persist in the salts of streptomycin and dihydrostreptomycin. Accordingly, the detection of the residual ammonium salts by means of Nessler reagent is a useful confirmatory test when these antibiotics are being sought. The procedure given on page 291 will reveal as little as 5 γ streptomycin hydrochloride through a distinct response to the Nessler test.

The salts of the streptomycin and the dihydrostreptomycin base behave as free acids toward alkali nickel biuret solution, i.e., they demask the complexly bound nickel of this reagent so that the dimethylgloxime reaction occurs. Since preparations of streptomycin and dihydrostreptomycin contain no admixtures of other acidic compounds, the procedure described on page 447 for the detection of acid compounds can be applied for identification purpose in the present instances.

The procedures given in Volume I, Chap. 4 may be used to determine the presence of chloride, phosphate, or sulfate.

The presence of double salts of streptomycin hydrochloride with calcium chloride can be shown by ashing 0.2–0.4 mg of the sample, and then testing the residue with dimethylglyoxime equilibrium solution as described on page 70. The ashing leaves part of the calcium as oxide, which brings about the precipitation of red nickel dimethylglyoxime. Another rapid test for calcium is provided by spotting a little of the solid sample with a drop of a 1 % ammoniacal solution of sodium rhodizonate. Violet insoluble calcium rhodizonate is formed. (See page 508.)

To identify streptomycin,[87] about 0.5 mg is placed in a microcrucible and dissolved in a drop of water. One drop of 1 N sodium hydroxide is added and the solution is warmed in the water bath for about 5 minutes. After cooling, a drop of a solution containing 100 mg of ferric ammonium sulfate in 5 ml of 1 N sulfuric acid is added: a purple-red color is produced. Dihydrostreptomycin yields a pink color at most.

51. Detection of Chloromycetin [88]

Chloromycetin (2-dichloroacetamido-1-*p*-nitrophenyl-1,3-propanediol) is the only known antibiotic which has the character of an aromatic nitro compound. The nitro group can readily be converted into the nitroso group by warming a solution of chloromycetin with calcium chloride and zinc.[89] The nascent hydrogen serves as reductant:

$$O_2N-\langle\ \rangle-\overset{\overset{\displaystyle OC-CHCl_2}{|}}{\underset{HO}{\underset{|}{C}}H}-\overset{\overset{\displaystyle NH}{|}}{\underset{}{C}H}-CH_2OH \ + 2H^0 \longrightarrow ON-\langle\ \rangle-\overset{\overset{\displaystyle OC-CHCl_2}{|}}{\underset{HO}{\underset{|}{C}}H}-\overset{\overset{\displaystyle NH}{|}}{\underset{}{C}H}-CH_2OH + H_2O$$

(1)

The nitroso compound thus produced from chloromycetin condenses, in acetic acid solution, with α-naphthylamine to yield a violet azo dye (compare test for antipyrine, page 493):

$$\text{naphthyl}-NH_2 + ON-\langle\ \rangle-\overset{OC-CHCl_2}{CH}-\overset{NH}{CH}-CH_2OH \longrightarrow$$

$$\longrightarrow \text{naphthyl}-N=N-\langle\ \rangle-\overset{OC-CHCl_2}{CH}-\overset{NH}{CH}-CH_2OH + H_2O$$

(2)

The test given here is based on the micro-realization of (1) and (2). ·

Procedure. A micro test tube is used. A little of the solid or a drop of the test solution is treated with two drops of 10% calcium chloride solution and several milligrams of metallic zinc powder. After warming the mixture in the water bath for two minutes, it is treated with two drops of 5% solution of α-naphthylamine in acetic acid and the warming continued for two minutes longer. In the presence of chloromycetin, a more or less intense violet color appears, the depth of color depending on the amount present. A blank is necessary only when very small amounts are being sought.

Limit of Identification: 10 γ chloromycetin.

Chloromycetin is water-soluble. It gives a strong alcohol reaction on treatment with a benzene solution of vanadium oxinate. Consequently, the test (reddening of the benzene layer) described on page 172 can be used to characterize chloromycetin. The *limit of identification* is 10 γ chloromycetin in one drop of solution. No alcohol reaction is given by streptomycin or dihydrostreptomycin.

52. Detection of Aminophylline and Euphylline [90]

Aminophylline and euphylline are water-soluble addition products of ethylenediamine with theophylline (1,3-dimethylxanthine), which is only slightly soluble in water. Aminophylline is the addition compound of two molecules of theophylline with one molecule of ethylenediamine, whereas euphylline contains two molecules of ethylenediamine to three molecules of theophylline. Both preparations are widely used as diuretics and as myocardial stimulants. Other water-soluble theophylline preparations with the same action include: [91] theophylline-diethanolamine, theophylline-calcium salicylate, theophylline-sodium acetate, theophylline-sodium salicylate, and theophylline-methyl glucamine. Aminophylline and euphylline can be identified with certainty through the ethylenediamine contained in them, since it reacts with sodium rhodizonate to produce a water-insoluble violet ethylenediamine compound of rhodizonic acid (see page 396). The realization of the test requires the previous transformation of the ethylenediamine contained in the theophylline preparations into its neutral hydrochloride (or acetate). This is easily accomplished.

Procedure. A little of the test material (fractions of a milligram are enough) is placed in a microcrucible along with a drop of hydrochloric acid (1 : 1) and the mixture is taken to dryness on a water bath. The residue is freed completely of any unbound hydrochloric acid by keeping it at 110° for several minutes. After cooling, the residue is treated with a drop of freshly prepared sodium rhodizonate solution. A violet precipitate indicates the presence of aminophylline and/or euphylline. If preferred, a little of the solid sample can be pulverized and placed on filter paper and exposed to the vapors of hydrochloric acid or acetic acid for 1–2 minutes, and after standing in the air for 1–2 minutes, the material is spotted with sodium rhodizonate solution. Under these conditions, enough ethylenediamine hydrochloride or acetate is formed to respond to sodium rhodizonate.

This test is valid for aminophylline or euphylline only when no theophylline-calcium salicylate is present, since the latter yields violet basic calcium rhodizonate under the conditions prescribed here. To differentiate between theophylline-calcium salicylate and aminophylline or euphylline, a little of the test material should be stirred in a microcrucible with a drop of ammonia and then treated with a drop of sodium rhodizonate solution. Under these conditions, only calcium rhodizonate is produced (compare page 508) but there is no production of the equally violet ethylenediamine rhodizonate. Consequently, if no reaction is obtained in ammoniacal solution, a positive response to the rhodizonate test after treating the sample with hydrochloric or acetic acid indicates the presence of aminophylline or euphylline. If ethylenediamine compounds of theophylline are to be detected in the presence of theophylline-calcium salicylate, a little of the sample should be digested with sodium carbonate solution to remove the calcium, and the resulting calcium carbonate is separated from the solution by filtering or centrifuging. The detection of ethylenediamine with sodium rhodizonate can then be conducted in one drop of the clear solution, after adding hydrochloric acid and evaporating.

A rapid but somewhat less sensitive test for the ethylenediamine that is loosely bound in aminophylline and euphylline makes use of its condensation with 2,4-dinitrochlorobenzene (comp. page 414):

$$
\begin{array}{c}
H_2C-NH_2 \\
| \\
H_2C-NH_2
\end{array}
+ 2Cl-\underset{NO_2}{\underset{|}{\bigcirc}}-NO_2 \rightarrow
\begin{array}{c}
H_2C-NH-\underset{NO_2}{\underset{|}{\bigcirc}}-NO_2 \\
| \\
H_2C-NH-\underset{NO_2}{\underset{|}{\bigcirc}}-NO_2
\end{array}
+ 2HCl
$$

The yellow product appears within several minutes under the prescribed conditions.

Procedure. A little of the solid is treated in a micro crucible with one drop of a saturated solution of 2,4-dinitrochlorobenzene in alcohol. The mixture is taken to dryness on a water bath. A yellow benzene-soluble residue remains.

The absence of primary aliphatic and aromatic amines is necessary when this test is employed, since they too react with 2,4-dinitrochlorobenzene.

53. Identification of Guaiacol Carbonate[92]

Guaiacol (o-methoxyphenol) is used for medicinal purposes in the form of its benzoate, cacodylate, cinnamate, salicylate, phosphate, valerate, ethylene ether, and carbonate.[93] The carbonate(I) can be distinguished from the other guaiacol preparations through the fact that when warmed with phenylhydrazine, it condenses with the latter to produce diphenylcarbazide (diphenylcarbohydrazone) (II) and guaiacol is set free:[94]

$$
OC\begin{array}{c} OC_6H_4(OCH_3) \\ \\ OC_6H_4(OCH_3) \end{array}
+ 2\ NH_2NHC_6H_5 \rightarrow
OC\begin{array}{c} NH-NHC_6H_5 \\ \\ NH-NHC_6H_5 \end{array}
+ 2\ C_6H_4(OH)(OCH_3)
$$

$$\text{(I)} \qquad\qquad\qquad\qquad\qquad \text{(II)}$$

The diphenylcarbazide produced by this condensation can be detected with high sensitivity by adding ammonia and a solution of a nickel salt. There the water-insoluble, blue-violet, inner complex nickel diphenylcarbazide, results; it can be extracted by means of chloroform. (Compare the test for urea, page 408.)

Procedure. A little of the solid, or the dry evaporation residue of a solution, is treated in a micro test tube with a drop of phenylhydrazine and heated in an oil bath for five minutes at 170°. After cooling, the contents of the test tube are treated with five drops of ammonia (1:1) and five drops of 10% nickel sulfate solution. The reaction mixture is then shaken with ten drops of chloroform. A red-violet color in the chloroform layer indicates the presence of guaiacol carbonate. *Limit of Identification:* 50 γ guaiacol carbonate.

54. Identification of 8-Hydroxyquinoline Compounds [95]

8-Hydroxyquinoline and its derivatives are much used preparations against amoebic dysentery. Pertinent compounds can be detected with great sensitivity by the formation of fluorescing adsorption compounds with magnesium oxide or hydroxide. The procedure is indicated on page 190.

55. Detection of Salicin (Populin)

Salicin is the glucoside of salicyl (= *o*-hydroxybenzyl) alcohol (saligenin) and populin is the benzoate of this glucoside. They occur in certain plants, especially in the leaves and bark of the poplar and willow.[96] Salicin, which finds greater use in veterinary practice than in human medicine,[97] can be detected by the procedure given on page 377, which is based on saponification of the glucoside, oxidation of the liberated saligenin to salicylaldehyde, and condensation of the latter with hydrazine to form salicylaldazine, which displays a yellow-green fluorescence. A much quicker and more specific method [98] of detecting salicin and populin makes use of the fact that when these compounds are heated, they split off salicylaldehyde, which, in the vapor phase, on contact with alkali hydroxide or hydrazine sulfate forms the alkali salt or the aldazine which respectively, display a characteristic blue-violet or yellow-green fluorescence. Compare page 374.

The mechanism of this hitherto unknown thermal splitting of salicin to produce salicylaldehyde probably involves the following stages. When salicin (m.p. 201°) is heated to higher temperatures, there is caramelization of some of the sugar. The resulting superheated steam saponifies the glucoside as shown in *(1)* to produce *o*-hydroxybenzyl alcohol. The latter condenses at the temperature of its formation to form saliretin* as shown in *(2)*. In its turn, the latter undergoes thermal fission and disproportionates to give salicylaldehyde and benzyl alcohol as shown in *(3)*:

* H. Schiff, *Ber.*, 14 (1881) 304 proved that saliretin is formed when the glucoside salicin is heated to 230–240°.

$$\text{(structure)} \quad \rightarrow \quad \text{(structure)} + \text{(structure)} \qquad (3)$$

Though not yet verified experimentally, this succession of reactions *(1)—(3)* appears to be plausible.

Procedure. A little (1–2 mg is enough) of the dry sample is placed in a micro test tube or microcrucible. The reaction vessel is covered with a disk of filter paper, which has been moistened with dilute caustic alkali or with a solution of hydrazine sulfate containing sodium acetate. The paper is kept in place with a small watch glass. The bottom of the vessel is heated with a micro flame. If salicin is present in not too small amounts, a yellow stain appears on the paper; it is due to the alkali salt or aldazine of salicylaldehyde. Viewed in ultraviolet light, the blue-violet or yellow-green fluorescence of these products is visible, even when the paper shows no yellow in daylight.
Reagent: See page 377.

The test may also be carried out with powder of the sample heated in a micro capillary. In case aqueous solutions or extracts are to be examined, a few drops should be taken to dryness and the test conducted with the evaporation residue.

The following procedure [99] revealed 5 γ salicin: A drop of the test solution was taken to dryness along with a little moist manganese dioxide. The residue was then heated to 240°. This treatment saponifies the glucoside and the liberated salicyl alcohol is oxidized to salicylaldehyde, which is sufficiently volatile. The method given for the detection of salicyl alcohol on page 377 should be followed.

56. Detection of Coumarin in Plant Material [100]

As stated on page 419, coumarin may be detected through the yellow-green fluorescent alkali salt of *trans-o*-hydroxycinnamic acid, which is formed by the rearrangement of the non-fluorescing *cis-o*-hydroxycinnamic acid resulting from the cleavage by alkali of coumarin. This characteristic photo-effect can be used to detect coumarin in plant materials with advantage being taken simultaneously of the volatility of coumarin. The test is made on several centigrams of the ground moist sample; smaller quantities of the dried sample suffice. The test portion is placed in a test tube (3 or 4 cm long) and the mouth of the tube covered with filter paper moistened with dilute sodium hydroxide. The test tube is kept in boiling water for several minutes and the paper is then exposed to ultraviolet light. If coumarin is present, a yellow-green fluorescence appears within a few minutes.

When fruits, Tonka beans, etc. are being studied, a freshly cut surface is pressed for several minutes against filter paper moistened with sodium hydroxide solution. The surface is then held under the quartz lamp. Impressions of leaves, powders, etc. on hydroxide paper can likewise be tested in this way. Since many plant materials have a faint self-fluorescence, greater certainty in the test for coumarin can be secured if the stain obtained by sublimation or pressing against hydroxide paper is half covered with a coin or black paper and then irradiated. If the shielded area is then uncovered under the lamp, there will be distinct differences in the intensity of the fluorescence of the irradiated and unexposed areas if coumarin is present. The difference in the intensity of the fluorescence gradually disappears if the exposure is continued.

57. Detection of Antimonial Pharmaceutical Preparations[101]

A number of organic compounds containing ter- and quinquevalent antimony are used to combat protozoal diseases. The most important of these preparations are :[102]

Tartar emetic (potassium antimonyl tartrate)

$KOOC—CH(OH)—CH(OH)—COO(SbO)$

Stibamine (sodium p-aminophenyl-antimonate)

$C_6H_4\!\!\nearrow^{NH_2}_{\searrow SbO(OH)(ONa)}$

Neostibosan (diethylamino-p-amino-phenylantimonate)

$C_6H_4(NH_2)—SbO(OH)OH·NH(C_2H_5)_2$

Stibenyl (sodium p-acetylamino-phenylantimonate)

$C_6H_4\!\!\nearrow^{NHCOCH_3}_{\searrow SbO(OH)(ONa)}$

Antimony thioglycolamide

$Sb(SCH_2CONH_2)_3$

Antimony sodium thioglycolate

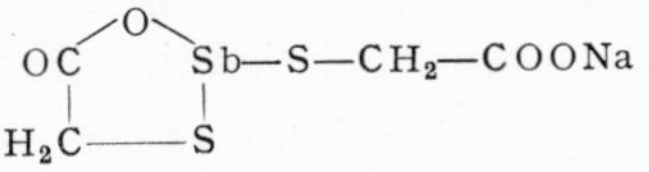

Fuadin (sodium antimony[III] bis pyrocatechol-3,5-disulfonate)

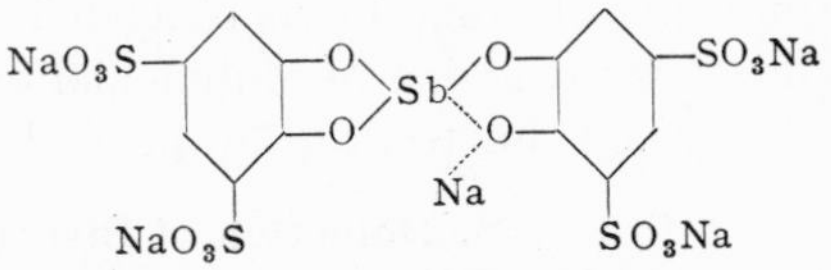

Glucantime (N-methylglucamine-antimonate)

$CH_2OH—(CHOH)_4—CH_2—NH·HSbO_3$
$\qquad\qquad\qquad\qquad\qquad\qquad\quad CH_3$

p-Chlorophenylstibonic acid

$C_6H_4Cl—SbO(OH)_2$

The antimony can readily be detected directly in all of the compounds listed here. On treatment with hydrochloric acid, potassium iodide, and sulfurous acid (the latter in the case of quinquevalent antimony) the complex acid $H[SbI_4]$ or its ions is produced at once or within a few minutes. Addition of a water solution of the amphoteric dye rhodamine B gives a violet precipitate of the rhodamine B salt. Compare page 471 regarding the detection of antimonial mordants in textiles.

Procedure. A minimal quantity of the solid preparation, or a drop of the solution, is placed in a depression of a spot plate. Drops of potassium iodide solution and dilute hydrochloric acid are added in succession. If the mixture turns brown because of the liberation of iodine, this in itself is an indication of the presence of quinquevalent antimony. In this case, the iodine is removed by adding a drop of sulfurous acid* and a drop of the dye solution is introduced. The separation of a red-violet precipitate proves the presence of antimony.

Reagents: See page 472.

The sensitivity of the test is demonstrated by the finding that this reaction with rhodamine B will reveal 1 γ of antimony.

This test is not directly applicable in the presence of organic bismuth compounds, since the latter are converted into $H[BiI_4]$ or its ions by hydrochloric acid and potassium iodide, and this complex acid reacts with rhodamine B in the same manner as $H[SbI_4]$, i.e. a violet precipitate is formed. Compare **58** regarding the detection of organic bismuth compounds.

If organic antimony compounds are to be detected in the presence of organic bismuth compounds, the sample should be digested with excess ammonium sulfide. Soluble ammonium sulfoantimonite is formed along with insoluble bismuth sulfide. After filtering (or centrifuging), a drop of the alkaline solution is warmed or taken to dryness with hydrogen peroxide to convert the $(NH_4)SbS_3$ into $Sb(OH)_5$, and the $(NH_4)_2S$ into $(NH_4)_2SO_4$. The solution may then be tested for antimony by means of rhodamine B using the procedure just outlined.

Another, though admittedly less sensitive, test for antimony in organic compounds, consists in igniting the sample and treating the residue, which contains Sb_2O_5 and Sb_2O_4, with a drop of a solution of diphenylamine or diphenylbenzidine in concentrated sulfuric acid. On stirring, a blue color develops; it is due to a quinoidal oxidation product of diphenylbenzidine. Regarding this test for antimony, see Volume I, Chapter 3.

58. Detection of Bismuth-bearing Medicinals [104]

Numerous medicinals contain organic compounds in which bismuth is a constituent of normal or complex salts. The most important preparations

---

* Complete discharge of the color is not attained, because solutions of alkali iodides on treatment with sulfurous acid assume a honey yellow color due to the formation of addition compounds such as $KI \cdot 4SO_2$; $NaI \cdot 2SO_2$, etc. [103]

of this kind are: [105] bismuth subsalicylate, sublactate, subgallate, iodosub-gallate, bismuth sodium triglycolamate, basic bismuth pyrogallate, bismuth ethyl camphorate, bismuth glycolyl arsanilate, bismuth tribromophenate.

A preliminary decomposition of the organic substance is not required for the detection of the bismuth. The slight concentration of Bi^{+3}-ions provided by contact of even difficultly soluble compounds with aqueous stannite solution is sufficient to achieve the redox reaction: [106]

$$2\,Bi^{+3} + 3\,SnO_2^{-2} + 6\,OH^- \longrightarrow 2\,Bi^\circ + 3\,SnO_3^{-2} + 3\,H_2O$$

The elementary bismuth separates in a high state of division and its black color provides a sensitive detection of the metal (compare Volume I, Chapter 3).

The test may not be applied directly in the presence of organic compounds of silver and mercury, since they too are reduced to the respective metals by stannite. In contrast to organic bismuth compounds, which leave Bi_2O_3 on ignition, the ignition residues of organic mercury compounds are free of mercury. Accordingly, when the presence of mercury compounds must be taken into account (for detection see page 106), the test material must be ignited before making the test for bismuth. When organic silver compounds are ignited, metallic silver is left. (Sulfur-bearing compounds yield silver sulfate.) If the presence of a silver-bearing ignition residue is suspected, the latter should be digested with warm dilute hydrochloric acid and the solution then subjected to the test with stannite. Compare Volume I, Chap. 3 regarding a sensitive test for silver which can be accomplished in one drop of a nitric acid solution of the ignition residue.

Procedure. The solid test material (ignition residue) is treated in a micro crucible with a drop of stannite solution. A black precipitate or a black-grey color indicates the presence of bismuth.

Reagent: Alkali stannite solution: Five grams of stannous chloride is dissolved in 5 ml of concentrated hydrochloric acid and diluted to 100 ml with water. Shortly before use, several milliliters of the stannous chloride solution is mixed with an equal volume of 25% sodium hydroxide solution.

59. Detection of Mercurial Pharmaceutical Preparations [107]

Most of the mercury compounds used in medicine are salts of phenols, carboxylic-, sulfonic-, and arsonic acids, or compounds containing HgOH- and HgCN-groups attached to carbon. Some are water-soluble, others are only slightly soluble, and in general they dissociate to only a small extent to yield Hg-ions. This is also true of mercuric cyanide and oxycyanide, which likewise are used medicinally.

The procedure given in Chapter 3 can be employed to reveal mercury in pharmaceutical preparations. The demasking of $[Fe(CN)_6]^{-4}$ ions to yield Fe^{+2} ions by means of mercury compounds in the presence of a,a'-dipyridyl is recommended particularly. Even slight quantities of solid or dissolved mercury preparations give a distinct red color when warmed with a drop or two of the colorless reagent. This procedure was successful with mercuric cyanide, succinimide, diiodosalicylate, Mercurin (Mercusan), mercurosal, and mercurophen.

60. Differentiation of Mercuric Cyanide and Mercuric Oxycyanide [108]

Because of their slight dissociation, solutions of $Hg(CN)_2$ and $HgO \cdot Hg(CN)_2$ do not respond to the reactions for cyanide ions. The formation of dicyanogen when mercuric cyanide is dry heated is characteristic:

$$Hg(CN)_2 \rightarrow Hg° + (CN)_2$$

The dicyanogen can be detected in the vapor phase by means of the color test, described on page 329, employing a cyanide solution of 8-hydroxyquinoline.

Mercuric cyanide and oxycyanide can be differentiated by the behavior of solutions of these salts toward potassium iodide. The cyanide yields potassium tetraiodomercuriate:

$$Hg(CN)_2 + 4 KI \rightarrow K_2HgI_4 + 2 KCN$$

whereas the oxycyanide gives in addition the reaction:

$$HgO + 4 KI + H_2O \rightarrow K_2HgI_4 + 2 KOH$$

In other words, only the oxycyanide yields a solution of Nessler reagent, from which the yellow-brown $HgI_2 \cdot HgNH_2I$ is precipitated on addition of ammonia.

Procedure.[109] A spot plate is used. One drop of the test solution or a tiny portion of the solid is treated in succession with one drop of 0.5% solution of potassium iodide and 1 : 5 ammonium hydroxide. If mercuric oxycyanide is present, a yellow-brown precipitate or yellow color appears.

The *limit of identification* is 100 γ mercuric oxycyanide.

Commercial preparations contain about 33% oxycyanide and 67% cyanide. Pure oxycyanide, it should be noted, explodes on contact with a flame and also when struck.

61. Detection of Calcium-bearing Pharmaceutical Preparations [110]

Calcium is a very important biogenic element, and there are many pharmaceutical calciferous preparations. They usually contain soluble calcium salts of organic acids, either in the pure form or as admixtures. Calcium salts of organic acids containing iodine serve as substitutes for sodium iodide, which is tolerated to only a slight extent. Moreover, certain active acid compounds are prescribed frequently in the form of their stable water-soluble calcium salts by physicians and veterinarians. A rapid direct test for calcium in preparations of this kind is based on the fact that sodium rhodizonate plus sodium hydroxide produces a violet crystalline precipitate when added to aqueous solutions or suspensions of almost all organic calcium salts. This reaction probably involves the formation of a water-insoluble basic calcium salt of rhodizonic acid. Since a water suspension of gypsum behaves similarly to a quite soluble calcium salt, it may be assumed that organic calcium salts, whose solubility lies in the region of that of calcium sulfate (0.3 g per 100 ml), can likewise be detected by the reaction with sodium rhodizonate. No reaction toward this (ammoniacal) reagent is shown by calcium phosphate, oxalate, arsenate, or fluoride, which are practically insoluble in water. Water-soluble barium and strontium salts behave similar to calcium salts (compare Volume I, Chapter 3). With the exception of barium sulfate (X-ray contrast agent) which does not react with sodium rhodizonate, no strontium and barium compounds are used in medicine to any extent.* Consequently, the following test can be used with confidence to reveal the presence of calcium in pharmaceutical products.

Procedure. A little of the solid is stirred with a drop of water on a spot plate. The solution or suspension is treated with a drop of a freshly prepared 0.2% solution of sodium rhodizonate and a drop of 0.5 N sodium hydroxide. A violet color indicates the presence of calcium-bearing preparations.

When dealing with calcium compounds which are less water-soluble than gypsum, a little of the sample is ashed in a microcrucible, and the residue strongly ignited (formation of calcium oxide). After cooling, it is sufficient to add a drop of the reagent solution to the ignition residue.

This procedure was tested successfully with the following calcium preparations:

–glycerinophosphate (Neurosin),	–salicylate,
–gluconate,	–dibromobehenate (Sabronin),
–lactate,	–iodobehenate (Catioben),
–levulinate,	–penicillin G,
–mandelate,	–pantothenate,
–naphthol monosulfonate (Asaprol),	–creosotate (after ashing).

* Barium sulfate, used as shadow agent in X-ray photography, may not contain any soluble barium salts since they are toxic. The purity can be tested by stirring 0.01 g of the sample with 2 or 3 drops of sodium rhodizonate solution and a drop of ammonia. Pure preparations remain unchanged, whereas if soluble barium salts are present, the barium sulfate is colored red-violet, the shade depending on the proportion of soluble salt present.

References pp. 510–512

The following points should be noted. The preparation, known as "Calcium Lactophosphate soluble", which is a mixture of calcium lactate, calcium acid lactate, and calcium biphosphate, is soluble in 20 parts of water. However, it does not react with alkaline sodium rhodizonate solution, whereas the ignition residue of this preparation gives a decided reaction. The reason probably is that the ignition residue contains calcium oxide along with calcium pyrophosphate, while only tertiary calcium phosphate is present when the solution is made alkaline, and the latter does not react with sodium rhodizonate (see page 509). Likewise, the basic solution of the complex calcium salt of ethylenediaminetetraacetic acid (see page 362) shows no reaction with sodium rhodizonate, but the ignition residue from a drop of the test solution of this salt readily shows the presence of calcium. Therefore, when examining pharmaceutical calcium preparations, it is advisable to test the solution or water suspension with sodium rhodizonate solution, and if the result is negative, the test should be repeated with the ignition residue of the product in question.

62. Detection of Iodine-bearing Pharmaceutical Preparations [111]

Organic iodine compounds are widely used as contrast medium in Roentgen diagnosis, as anti-protozoan agents, and in cases of thyroid deficiency. The test for iodine can be executed with minimal quantities of the test material, according to the procedure indicated in Chapter 3, page 83, which is based on the oxidation of organically bound iodine into iodic acid, directly by bromine.

REFERENCES

1. R. J. Block, R. LeStrange and G. Zweig, *Paper Chromatography, A. Laboratory Manual*, New York 1952; J. N. Balston and B. E. Talbot, *A Guide to Filter Paper and Cellulose Powder Chromatography*, London 1952; F. Cramer, *Papierchromatographie*, 2nd Ed., Berlin 1953; E. Lederer and M. Lederer, *Chromatography, A Review of Principles and Applications*, 2nd Ed., Amsterdam 1956; R. C. Brimley and F. C. Barrett, *Practical Chromatography*, New York 1953.
2. E. Chargaff *et al.*, *J. Biol. Chem.*, 175 (1948) 67.
3. R. Wasicky and O. Frehden, *Mikrochim. Acta*, 1 (1937) 55.
4. F. Feigl and E. Silva, *Drug Standards*, 23 (1955) 113.
5. F. Feigl and Cl. Costa Neto, unpublished studies.
6. F. Feigl and G. B. Heisig, *Anal. Chim. Acta*, 3 (1949) 561; F. Feigl and D. Goldstein, unpublished studies.
7. Compare F. J. Welcher, *Organic Analytical Reagents*, New York 1947, Volume I, p. 263.
8. Compare F. Feigl, *Chemistry of Specific, Selective and Sensitive Reactions*, New York 1949, p. 676.
8a. F. Feigl and A. Caldas, *Anal. Chem.*, 28 (1956) in press.
9. F. Feigl and D. Goldstein, unpublished studies.
10. F. Feigl and L. Hainberger, *Mikrochim. Acta*, (1955) 105.
11. G. Panizzon, *Melliand Textilber.*, 12 (1931) 119.
12. F. Feigl and L. Weidenfeld, *Mikrochemie (Emich Festschrift)* (1930), p. 133.
13. K. Weisselberg, *Petroleum Z.*, 31 (1935) No. 10, p. 7.

14. E. Obach, *J. prakt. Chem.*, [2], 18 (1878) 258.
15. W. E. Zmaczynski, *Z. anal. Chem.*, 106 (1936) 32.
16. F. Feigl and C. Stark, *Anal. Chem.*, 27 (1955) 1838.
17. Compare F. Feigl, *Mikrochemie*, 15 (1934) 1.
18. Comp. P. Karrer, *Organic Chemistry*, 4th Ed., New York 1950, p. 626.
19. F. Feigl and N. Braile, *Chemist-Analyst*, 32 (1943) 76.
20. Compare F. Feigl, Ref. 8, p. 663.
21. R. Edge, *Ind. Eng. Chem., Anal. Ed.*, 2 (1930) 371.
22. F. Feigl and K. Weisselberg, *Z. anal. Chem.*, 83 (1931) 101.
23. F. Feigl and C. Stark, *Chemist-Analyst*, 45 (1956) 39.
24. F. Feigl and H. E. Feigl, *Anal. Chim. Acta*, 3 (1949) 300.
25. F. Feigl and C. Stark, unpublished studies.
26. Comp. G. H. Collings, *Commercial Fertilizers*, 2nd Ed., Philadelphia 1938, pp. 81, 91; as wel as W. B. Andrews, *The Response of Crops and Soils to Fertilizers*, State College, Mississippi, 1947, pp. 72, 103.
27. F. Feigl and V. Gentil, unpublished studies.
27a. F. Feigl, D. Goldstein and V. Gentil, unpublished studies.
28. F. Feigl and C. Stark, *Chemist-Analyst*, 45 (1956) 46.
28a. J. V. Sanchez, *Chem. Abstr.*, 30 (1936) 4432.
29. D. Reichinstein, *Helv. Chim. Acta*, 20 (1937) 882.
30. F. Feigl and Cl. Costa Neto, *J. Soc. Dyers and Colourists*, 72 (1956) 239.
30a. F. Feigl, unpublished studies.
31. J. J. Ritter and G. H. Schmitz, *J. Am. Chem. Soc.*, 51 (1929) 1587.
32. F. Haber and E. Bruner, *Z. Elektrochem.*, 10 (1904) 706.
33. F. Feigl and J. E. R. Marins, unpublished studies.
34. Beilstein's *Handbuch der Organischen Chemie*, 4. Aufl., Band 19 (1934), pp. 342 ff.
35. Comp. F. Feigl, Ref. 8, Chapter 6.
36. Comp. G. Schultz, *Farbstofftabellen*, 7th Ed., Berlin 1928–31.
37. F. Feigl and E. Silva, unpublished studies.
37a. F. Feigl and D. Goldstein, unpublished studies.
37b. Comp. G. Schultz, *Farbstofftabellen*, 7th Ed., Leipzig 1931, Vol. I, p. 310.
38. F. Feigl, unpublished studies.
39. Comp. F. Feigl, Ref. 8, pp. 534, 540.
40. F. Feigl and V. Gentil, unpublished studies.
41. F. Feigl and V. Gentil, *Mikrochim. Acta*, (1954) 90.
42. B. Steiger, *Petroleum Z.*, 33 (1937) No. 27.
43. H. Kiemstedt, *Z. angew. Chem.*, 42 (1929) 1107.
44. B. Steiger, *Mikrochemie*, 22 (1937) 227.
45. Cl. Costa Neto (Rio de Janeiro), unpublished studies.
46. Comp. A. Rieche, *Die Bedeutung der organischen Peroxyde für die chemische Wissenschaft und Technik*, Stuttgart 1936.
47. F. Feigl and D. Goldstein, unpublished studies.
48. F. Feigl, *Mikrochemie*, 14 (1934) 7.
49. F. Feigl and E. Silva, unpublished studies.
50. Compare *The Merck Index*, 6th edition, Rahway, N. J., 1952, page 690.
51. F. Feigl, V. Anger and O. Frehden, *Mikrochemie*, 15 (1934) 18.
52. N. H. Ishler, K. Sloman and M. E. Walker, *J. Assoc. Off. Agr. Chemists*, 30 (1947) 670.
53. K. Klanfer and A. Luft, *Mikrochim. Acta*, 1 (1937) 142.
54. F. Feigl, unpublished studies.
55. F. Feigl and Cl. Costa Neto, unpublished studies.
56. F. Feigl and D. Goldstein, unpublished studies.
57. F. Feigl, unpublished studies.
58. F. Feigl and J. E. R. Marins, unpublished studies.
59. F. Feigl and V. Gentil, unpublished studies.
60. O. Frehden, *Mikrochim. Acta*, 2 (1937) 214.
61. J. Schmidt and W. Hinderer, *Ber.* ,65 (1932) 87.

62. J. Stamm, *Z. Unters. Lebensmittel*, 62 (1931) 413; St. Korpáczy, *ibid.*, 67 (1934) 75.
63. K. Taeufel and P. Sadler, *Z. Unters. Lebensmittel*, 67 (1934) 268.
64. J. Pritzker and R. Jungkunz, *Z. Unters. Lebensmittel*, 54 (1927) 247; J. Pritzker, *Helv. Chim. Acta*, 11 (1928) 445.
65. A. A. Azzam, *Mikrochim. Acta*, 2 (1937) 283.
66. F. Feigl and V. Gentil, unpublished studies.
67. F. Feigl and L. Hainberger, *Chemist-Analyst*, 44 (1955) 47.
68. F. Feigl, J. E. R. Marins and Cl. Costa Neto, unpublished studies.
69. F. Feigl and E. Silva, unpublished studies.
70. F. Feigl and V. Gentil, unpublished studies, see also *Anal. Chim. Acta*, 13 (1955) 210.
71. P. Karrer, *Organic Chemistry*, 4th Ed., New York 1950, p. 446.
72. F. Feigl and L. Hainberger, *Mikrochim. Acta*, (1955) 112.
73. F. Feigl and E. Silva, *Drug Standards*, 23 (1955) 113.
74. *New and Non-official Remedies*, ed. by The Council on Pharm. and Chem., Am. Med. Ass., Philadelphia 1954, p. 120.
75. F. Feigl and Cl. Costa Neto, unpublished studies.
76. F. Feigl, Cl. Costa Neto and E. Silva, *Anal. Chem.*, 27 (1955) 1319.
77. L. Knorr, *Ber.*, 17 (1884) 2038.
78. F. Feigl and E. Silva, *Drug Standards*, 23 (1955) 113.
79. P. Karrer, *Organic Chemistry*, 4th Ed., New York 1950, p. 798.
80. J. A. Sanchez, *Curso de Quimica Analytica Funcional de Medicamentos Organicos*, 2a ed., Vol. I, Buenos Aires 1947, p. 438.
81. F. Feigl and H. E. Feigl, unpublished studies.
82. F. Feigl and W. A. Mannheimer, unpublished studies.
83. F. Feigl and D. Fontes (Pernambuco), unpublished studies.
84. Compare the *United States Pharmacopeia*, 15th revision, 1950, p. 427.
85. E. P. Abraham, E. Chain, W. Baker and R. Robinson, *Nature*, 151 (1943) 107. Compare *The Chemistry of Penicillin*, Princeton 1949, p. 10 ff.
86. F. Feigl, D. Fontes and E. Silva (Pernambuco), unpublished studies.
87. *The United States Pharmacopeia*, 15th revision, 1950, pp. 189, 572.
88. F. Feigl and E. Silva, *Drug Standards*, 23 (1955) 113.
89. S. Ohkuma, *J. Japan. Chem. Soc.*, 4 (1950) 622.
90. F. Feigl and E. Silva, *Anais Farm. Quim. (São Paulo)*, 6 (1953) 5.
91. *The Merck Index*, 6th edition, Rahway, N. J., 1952, p. 948.
92. F. Feigl and E. Silva (Pernambuco), unpublished studies.
93. *The Merck Index*, 6th edition, Rahway, N. J., 1952, p. 477.
94. K. H. Slotta and K. R. Jacoby, *Z. anal. Chem.*, 77 (1929) 344.
95. F. Feigl and E. Silva, *Drug Standards*, 23 (1955) 124.
96. G. Klein, *Handbuch der Pflanzenanalyse*, Vol. 3, Part 2, Berlin 1932, p. 815.
97. *The Merck Index*, 6th edition, Rahway, N.J., 1952, p. 843.
98. F. Feigl, unpublished studies.
99. F. Feigl and C. Stark, *Mikrochim. Acta*, (1955) 1000.
100. F. Feigl, H. E. Feigl and D. Goldstein, *J. Am. Chem. Soc.*, 77 (1955) 4162.
101. F. Feigl and E. Silva, *Drug Standards*, 23 (1955) 115.
102. Comp. *The Merck Index*, 6th ed., Rahway, N. J., 1952.
103. F. Ephraim and I. Kornblum, *Ber.*, 49 (1916) 2007; comp. also A. Hantzsch, *ibid.*, 54 (1921) 2606.
104. F. Feigl and E. Silva (Pernambuco), unpublished studies.
105. Comp. *The Merck Index*, 6th ed., Rahway, N.J., 1952.
106. L. Vanino and F. Treubert, *Ber.*, 31 (1898) 1113.
107. F. Feigl and A. Caldas, *Anal. Chim. Acta*, 13 (1955) 526.
108. J. Golse, *Bull. Soc. Pharm. Bordeaux*, 66 (1928) 209.
109. F. Feigl and E. Silva (Pernambuco), unpublished studies.
110. F. Feigl and E. Silva, *Drug Standards*, 23 (1955) 114.
111. F. Feigl and E. Silva, *Drug Standards*, 23 (1955) 116.

Chapter 7

Papers dealing with the Use of Spot Reactions in Organic Qualitative Analysis

The following list contains papers dealing wholly or in part with the use of spot reactions in qualitative organic analysis. It makes no pretence at being complete. The present volume either does not refer to the contents of these publications or refers to them only cursorily. Some of the entries contain information or suggestions regarding the use and elaboration of spot reactions.

The scope of this book is to treat only spot and drop reactions which may be executed directly with the solid or dissolved test material. Therefore no papers are cited which deal with the identification of chromatographically (adsorptionally) separated components of a solution. This vast field of spot test application, based on fundamental researches of F. F. Runge (comp. H. Weil and T. Williams, *Naturwissenschaften*, 40 (1953) 1) has been the subject of many excellent monographs.

H. K. Alber and C. J. Rodden, Microchemical analysis of colored specks and crystalline occlusions in soap bars. *Ind. Eng. Chem., Anal. Ed.*, 10 (1938) 47.

J. Aloy, A. Valdigué and R. Aloy, Transformations induced by solar light in presence of uranium compounds – characteristic reactions of strychnine, morphine, codeine and formol. *Bull. soc. chim. France*, [4], 39 (1926) 792; *Chem. Abstr.*, 20 (1926) 2952.

E. P. Alvarez, Color reactions of pyruvic acid with α- and β-naphthol in sulfuric acid solution. *Chem. News*, 91 (1905) 209.

W. J. Blackie, New color reactions for *Cannabis sativa* resin. *Ind. Eng. Chem., Anal. Ed.*, 13 (1941) 96.

H. C. Brinker, Color test for oils and resins, using Hirschsohn reagent for cholesterin. *Ind. Eng. Chem., Anal. Ed.*, 17 (1945) 130.

H. P. Burchfield, Qualitative spot tests for rubber polymers. *Ind. Eng. Chem., Anal. Ed.*, 17 (1945) 807.

S. I. Burmistrov, Qualitative analysis of rubber formulations. *Zavodskaya Lab.*, 15 (1949) 1039; *Chem. Abstr.*, 45 (1951) 379.

A. Castiglioni, A color reaction of carbon disulfide. *Ann. chim. appl.*, 36 (1946) 276.

A. M. Chaletzki, Use for spot tests in examination of several medicinals. *Pharm. u. Pharmakol.* (Russian), (1937) 15; *Chem. Zentr.*, (1938) III, 353.

B. V. Christensen and J. A. Abdel-Latif, Borntraeger reaction for anthraquinone drugs. *J. Am. Pharm. Assoc., Scient. Ed.*, 38 (1949) 651.

A. v. Christiani and V. Anger, Test for ergosterol and differentiation of ergosterol and ergosterol esters. *Ber.*, 72 (1939) 1124.

N. M. Cullinane and S. J. Chard, 2,7-Diaminodiphenylene oxide as a reagent in analysis. *Analyst*, 73 (1948) 95.

D. W. Dijkstra, Detection of war gases. *Chem. Weekblad*, 34 (1937) 351.

F. R. Duke, Color test for the carboxyl group. *Ind. Eng. Chem., Anal. Ed.*, 16 (1944) 110.

P. N. van Eck, Benzidine as reagent for aldehydes. *Pharm. Weekblad*, 60 (1923) 1204.

P. N. van Eck, Macro-microreactions. *Pharm. Weekblad*, 62 (1925) 369; 63 (1926) 913; *Chem. Abstr.*, 19 (1925) 1828.

A. Edeler, Ground glass for spot testing in solvent extractions. *Ind. Eng. Chem., Anal. Ed.*, 15 (1943) 282.

E. Eegriwe, Reactions and reagents for detection of organic compounds. *Z. anal. Chem.*, 89 (1932) 121; 95 (1933) 323; 100 (1935) 31.

E. Eegriwe, Microchemical detection of certain phenols. *Mikrochemie*, 23 (1937) 173.

O. Erämetsä, Sulfosalicylic acid as reagent for detecting oxalic acid. *Suomen Kemistilehti*, 15 (1942), Abt. B. 2; *Chem. Abstr.*, 37 (1943) 6208.

R. Fearon and J. A. Drum, The fructose urea and fructose acetone reactions as selective tests for sugars, *Analyst*, 75 (1950) 56.

F. Feigl and H. E. Feigl, Sensitive and selective test for gallotannin (tannic acid) and other tannins. *Ind. Eng. Chem., Anal. Ed.*, 18 (1946) 62.

F. Feigl and O. Ribeiro, Microreaction for vitamin B_1. *Rev. soc. brasil. quim.*, 2 (1942) 1.

H. J. H. Fenton, Reagent for identification of urea and certain other nitrogen compounds. *J. Chem. Soc.*, 83 (1903) 187.

P. Fleury, Characteristic reaction of morphine. *Ann. chim. anal. chim. appl.*, 6 (1901) 417.

E. Fränkel, Use of spot analysis in laundry operations. *Deut. Wäschereiztg.*, 34 (1932) 410, 421.

O. Frehden and K. Fuerst, Detection of aldehydes with a permanent test paper. *Mikrochemie ver. Mikrochim. Acta*, 26 (1939) 39.

O. Frehden and C. H. Huang, Detection of free chlorine in air, water, bleaching agents, detergents etc. *Mikrochemie ver. Mikrochim. Acta*, 26 (1939) 41.

O. Frehden and C. H. Huang, Microdetection of morphine and heroine in urine by spot reactions. *Pharm. Monatsh.*, 18 (1937) 73.

H. Freytag, Photoanalysis in the pyridine and indole series. *Z. anal. Chem.*, 103 (1935) 344.

H. Freytag, Photoanalytical detection of the Castrix base (2-chloro-4-dimethylamino-6-methyl-pyrimidine). *Z. anal. Chem.*, 129 (1949) 366.

H. Freytag, Knowledge and application of the detection of hydrogen peroxide with lead sulfide. *Z. anal. Chem.*, 131 (1950) 7; see also *Naturforschung*, 5 (1950) number 2.

H. Freytag, Comparison of several mercapto compounds. *Z. anal. Chem.*, 138 (1953) 259.

H. Freytag, Luminescence detection of ascorbic acid and several mercapto compounds. *Z. anal. Chem.*, 139 (1953) 263.

H. Freytag, Detection of barbituric acid, 2-thiobarbituric acid and pyridine. *Z. anal. Chem.*, 142 (1954) 12.

H. Freytag, Observations on the detection of SH-groups. *Z. anal. Chem.*, 143 (1954) 401.

R. Fuchs, R. C. Waters and C. A. Van der Werf, General qualitative test for epoxides. *Anal. Chem.*, 24 (1952) 1514.

K. Fuerst, Rapid and simple detection of formaldehyde with *o*-condensed pyrroles. *Mikrochemie ver. Mikrochim. Acta*, 33 (1948) 348.

H. Garcia-Fernandez, Some colloidal reactions of sulfur. *Bull. soc. chim. France*, (1947) 594.

M. Geldmacher-Mallinckrodt, Detection and differentiation of sugars and polysaccharides by sensitive spot tests on silk. *Biochem. Z.*, 324 (1953) 186.

J. Guilhon, Test for iron pigments (hemosiderin) in liver. *Compt. rend. soc. biol.*, 115 (1934) 376.

M. Haitinger, Thalleioquinine reaction in ultraviolet light. Contribution to fluorescence analysis in microchemistry. *Mikrochim. Acta*, 1 (1937) 1.

H. Hamburg, Spot test analysis and its use in examination of brewery water. *Brau-u. Malzind.*, 25 (1932) 23.

H. D. Hartough, Color reactions of thiophen compounds with ceric nitrate alcohol reagent. *Ind. Eng. Chem., Anal. Ed.*, 20 (1948) 860.

E. Heilbronner, The tetranitromethane test. *Helv. Chim. Acta*, 36 (1953) 1121.

C. E. Hubach, Detection of cyanides and ferrocyanides in wines. *Ind. Eng. Chem., Anal. Ed.*, 20 (1948) 1115.

K. Imai and K. Furuya, A new method for the identification of crude drugs containing anthraquinones. *J. Pharm. Soc. Japan*, 73 (1953) 646; *Chem. Abstr.*, 48 (1954) 5163.

A. Inokawa, The color reactions of amines with 2,4-dinitrofluorobenzene. *J. Chem. Soc. Japan*, 75 (1954) 1203.

B. Jelinek, Characteristic test for mustard gas (yperite). *Bull. soc. chim. France*, [5], 4 (1937) 1813.

T. Kariyone and Y. Hashimoto, Detection of triterpenoids in plant cuticle. *J. Pharm. Soc. Japan*, 70 (1950) 727.

J. Kisser and Y. Kondo, Microchemical detection of di- and trihydric phenols by spot reactions, *Mikrochemie* (Molisch Festschrift), (1937) 259.

J. Kisser and K. Lettmayr, Studies of applicability of spot reactions for quantitative purposes. *Mikrochemie*, 12 (1932) 234.

L. M. Kul'berg, G. A. Blokh and E. A. Golubkova, Applications of drop analysis for the detection of compounds of rubber mixes. *Zavodskaya Lab.*, 15 (1949) 1034; *Chem. Abstr.*, 45 (1951) 379.

L. M. Kul'berg and I. S. Mustafin, Specific reaction for traces of piperidine in presence of pyridine. *Zhur. Anal. Khim.*, 7 (1952) 84; *Chem. Abstr.*, 47 (1953) 1545.

L. M. Kul'berg and I. S. Mustafin, Use of dimedon for the drop detection of aldehydes. *Zhur. Anal. Khim.*, 8 (1953) 122; *Chem. Abstr.*, 47 (1953) 10409.

J. W. Kulikow and T. N. Krestowosdwigenskaja, Detection and determination of small amounts of pyridine. *Z. anal. Chem.*, 79 (1930) 452.

F. Künkele, Testing aniline ink writings. *Z. Unters. Lebensmittel*, 77 (1939) 596.

V. I. Kuznetsov, Differentiation between dry distilled turpentine and turpentine from resins. *Lesnaya Prom.*, No. 10/11 (1943) 16; *Chem. Abstr.*, 38 (1944) 3859.

V. I. Kuznetsov and Z. M. Pimenova, Color reaction for dichloroethane. *Zhur. Anal. Khim.*, 7 (1952) 89; *Chem. Abstr.*, 47 (1953) 1533.

O. Liebreich, Method for examination of reactions of animal tissue. *Ber.*, 1 (1868) 48.

L. S. Malowan, Spot tests for phenols. *Mikrochem. ver. Mikrochim. Acta*, 38 (1951) 212.

Ch. E. Morgan and N. Apolonik, Adaption of a color test to minute amounts of caffeine, *Ind. Eng. Chem., Anal. Ed.*, 17 (1945) 526.

R. Neu, Microgram detection of 3-hydroxyflavones with aromatic diarylboric acids. *Mikrochim. Acta*, (1956) 1169.

F. Neuber, Qualitative differentiation of asphalts and tar pitches. *Öle, Fette, Wachse, Seife, Kosmetik*, 5 (1938) 5.

S. Nussenbaum, Differentiation of amylopectin, amylodextrins, and amylose fatty acid complexes. *Anal. Chem.*, 23 (1951) 1478.

S. Ohkuma, Color test for diethylamine. *J. Pharm. Soc. Japan*, 75 (1955) 232; *Chem. Abstr.*, 49 (1955) 8046.

S. Ohkuma, Color reaction of phenol compounds with pentacyano iron complex salts and hydroxylamine. *J. Pharm. Soc. Japan*, 72 (1952) 872.

J. H. Player, Identification of polyvinylidene chloride and its copolymers. *Analyst*, 80 (1955) 633.

J. B. Polya, New reaction of 2,2'-dichlorodiethyl sulfide. *Ind. Eng. Chem., Anal. Ed.*, 15 (1943) 360.

F. O. Ritter, Differentiating between primary, secondary, and tertiary alcohols. *J. Chem. Education*, 30 (1953) 395.

M. J. Rosen, Detection of surface-active phenol ethers with sulfuric acid and formaldehyde. *Anal. Chem.*, 27 (1955) 111.

L. Rosenthaler, Contributions to the detection of organic compounds. (Detection of antipyrine.) *Pharm. Acta Helv.*, 25 (1950) 365.

J. H. Ross, A color test for chloroform and chloral. *J. Biol. Chem.*, 58 (1923) 641.

S. Sabetay, Antimony trichloride, new reagent for the double bond. *Compt. rend.*, 197 (1933) 557.

E. Sawicki, Spot test for sulfonyl chlorides and unhindered aromatic amines. *Chemist-Analyst*, 42 (1953) 8.

J. Seifter and H. R. Trattner, Simplified qualitative analysis of gallstones by spot reactions. *J. Urol.*, 42 (1939) 452.

Sh. Shibata and A. Kasahara, A new detection method for flavanones. *J. Pharm. Soc. Japan*, 72 (1952) 1386.

L. Silverman and W. Bradshaw, Rapid spot test for identification of biphenyl, *o, m, p*-terphenyl and certain other phenyls, *Anal. Chem.*, 27 (1955) 96.

S. Soloway and A. Lipschitz, Colorimetric tests for amides and nitriles. *Anal. Chem.*, 24 (1952) 898.

S. Soloway and P. Rosen, Differentiation of chelating from non-chelating phenols. *Anal. Chem.*, 25 (1953) 595.

S. Soloway and S. H. Wilen, Improved ferric chloride test for phenols. *Anal. Chem.*, 24 (1952) 979.

L. Sommer, Detection and determination of carbazole. *Z. anal. Chem.*, 146 (1955) 96.

L. Sommer, Capillary separation of anthracene, phenanthrene and carbazole. *Analyst*, 78 (1953) 679.

H. A. Stiff, Jr. and J. C. Castillo, Field test for surface DDT. *Ind. Eng. Chem., Anal. Ed.*, 18 (1946) 316.

E. Storfer, Detection of phthalic acid. *Farben-Ztg.*, 42 (1937) 483.

H. Tauber, New micro method for detecting monoses in presence of reducing bioses. *Mikrochemie*, 14 (1934) 167.

H. Tauber, Color test for pentoses. *Proc. Soc. Exptl. Biol. Med.*, 37 (1937) 600.

O. Tunmann, Detection of nicotine. *Apoth. Ztg.*, 33 (1918) 485.

F. Weber, Spot reactions for approximate determination of vitamin C content of plants. *Protoplasma*, 33 (1939) 475.

C. L. Wilson, Microtests for elements in organic compounds (P, As, Sb). *Analyst*, 65 (1940) 405.

C. Whitworth and D. W. Poxon, Detection of acid or basic substances in damaged fabrics. *Nature*, 151 (1943) 198.

E. Wolthuis, S. Kolk and L. Schlaep, Detection of aromatic nitro compounds. *Anal. Chem.*, 26 (1954) 1239.

H. Yagoda, Localization of certain chemical constituents in plant and animal tissues. *Ind. Eng. Chem., Anal. Ed.*, 12 (1940) 698.

J. H. Yoe and E. C. Coghill, Organic reagents for the identification of certain vesicants. *Mikrochemie ver. Mikrochim. Acta*, 38 (1951) 492.

Chapter 8

Tabular Summary of the Limits of Identification Attained by Spot Tests

For the limits of identification are given the lowest and highest values obtained by tests for elements and functional groups, when different compounds are examined.
Unless otherwise stated, a macrodrop (about 0.05 ml) is implied.

1. ELEMENTS

Element identified	Reagents or test reactions	Limit of identification, γ	Page
Antimony	Rhodamine B	0.5	100
	Formation of benzidine blue	5	100
Arsenic	Conversion to arsenate	1.4–60	98
Bismuth	Alkali stannite	—	507
Bromine	Conversion to volatile copper bromide	0.25	80
	Conversion to silver bromide	—	81
Calcium	Sodium rhodizonate and alkali	—	509
Carbon	Ashing with molybdenum trioxide	1–8	73
	Reduction of silver arsenate	5	74
	Heating with potassium iodate	0.5–6	75
Chlorine	Conversion to volatile copper chloride	0.5	80
	Conversion to silver chloride	—	81
Fluorine	Conversion to alkali fluoride	100–200	84
	Conversion to hydrofluoric acid	12.5–50	86
Hydrogen	Heating with sodium sulfite	—	77
	Reaction with fused potassium thiocyanate	—	78
Iodine	Conversion to volatile copper iodide	0.25	80
	Conversion to silver iodide	—	81
	Conversion to iodic acid	0.05–1	83
Lead	Dithizone	—	473

Element identified	Reagents or test reactions	Limit of identification, γ	Page
Mercury	Volatilization	1.8	106
	Demasking of potassium ferrocyanide	2	106
Metals	Oxidative decomposition	—	102
Nitrogen	Conversion to ammonia	1–3	90
	Conversion to cyanide	4–12	92
Oxygen	Ferric thiocyanate	5000–10 000	101
Phosphorus	Conversion to phosphate	1–8	96
Sulfur	Conversion to potassium sulfide	0.3–1.2	87
	Reduction to sulfide in alcohol flame	0.03	88
	Conversion to silver sulfide	0.05	89
	Conversion to hydrogen sulfide	0.5–20	90
Tin	Morin	0.05	472

2. CHARACTERISTIC GROUPS

Group identified	Reagents or test reactions	Limit of identification, γ	Page
Acetates —O—COCH₃	Saponification to acetic acid	5–40	247
Acylides Ar—NH—COR	Nitrous acid and α-naphthol	0.5–1	244
Alcohols (polyhydric)	Vanadium oxinate	3–500	172
	Periodic acid, oxidation to formaldehyde	2.5–100	177
	Periodic acid, oxidation to formic acid	2.5–20	178
Alcohols (primary) —C—OH	Vanadium oxinate	5–20	172
	Conversion to xanthate	100–1000	173
	Cerium double nitrate	400	178
Alcohols (secondary) —C—C—OH C	Vanadium oxinate	5–10	172
	Conversion to xanthate	500	173
	Sulfur	2–200	174
	Cerium double nitrate	400	178

Group identified	Reagents or test reactions	Limit of identification, γ	Page
Alcohols (tertiary)	Vanadium oxinate	—	172
	Cerium double nitrate	400	178

$$\overset{\displaystyle \mathrm{C}}{\underset{\displaystyle \mathrm{C}}{-\mathrm{C}-\mathrm{C}-\mathrm{OH}}}$$

Aldehydes	Fuchsin and sulfurous acid	1–1000	208
	o-Dianisidine	0.02–200	210
	Azobenzenephenylhydrazine sulfonic acid	0.1–130	213
	p-Phenylenediamine and hydrogen peroxide	0.01–50	214
(see also Carbonyl compounds)	1,2-Dianilino-ethane (for water-soluble aldehydes)	0.2–29	215
	Benzenesulfohydroxamic acid	2–100	218
	Reduction of silver oxide	—	218
	Fuchsin and ammonia	—	219

$-\mathrm{C}\overset{\displaystyle \nearrow \mathrm{O}}{\searrow \mathrm{H}}$

Aldehydes (a, β-unsaturated and aromatic)	Hydrogen sulfide and sodium penta-cyanoammine ferroate	1–4	219

$>\!\mathrm{C}\!=\!\mathrm{C}\!-\!\mathrm{CHO}$

Allyl compounds	Phloroglucinol-hydrochloric acid	0.1–400	308

$>\!\mathrm{C}\!-\!\mathrm{CH}\!=\!\mathrm{C}\!<$

Amides —$CONH_2$; —CONHR	Acid saponification	2–40	288

Amines (cyclic)	Alkali nitrate or nitrite, and sulfuric acid (for carbazole and derivatives)	0.5–10	277
	p-Dimethylaminobenzaldehyde (for pyrrole bases)	0.04–0.1	278
	Melting with fluorescein chloride and zinc chloride (for pyrrole bases)	12–40	278
	Conversion in polymethine dyes (for pyridine and derivatives)	0.1–6	280

Group identified	Reagents or test reactions	Limit of identification, γ	Page
Amines (primary aliphatic) —NH₂	Conversion to dithiocarbamate	3–100	257
	Melting with fluorescein chloride	10–30	263
	Fused potassium thiocyanate	15–25	269
	Furfural	—	273
Amines (primary aromatic) NH₂Ar	Melting with fluorescein chloride	1–10	263
	Fused potassium thiocyanate	50	269
	Glutaconic anhydride	0.05–2	271
	Sodium pentacyanoaquoferriate	0.1–100	272
	Aromatic nitroso compounds	1–100	273
	Furfural	0.1–200	273
	Chloranil	0.2–200	273
	Carbon disulfide	1–5	273
	Ethyl nitrite and resorcinol	—	273
Amines (secondary aliphatic) ＞NH	Conversion to dithiocarbamate	0.6–140	257
	Sodium nitroprusside and acetaldehyde	0.5–100	260
	Melting with fluorescein chloride	4–20	263
	Fused potassium thiocyanate	—	269
	Furfural	—	273
Amines (secondary aromatic) —NH—Ar	Formation of copper dithiocarbamates	0.2–10	262
	Melting with fluorescein chloride	4–8	263
	Fused potassium thiocyanate	50	269
	Furfural	—	273
	Chloranil	—	273
	Oxidation to quinoneimides	0.17–0.40	275
Amines (tertiary alicyclic)	Citric acid and acetic acid anhydride	2–7	270
Amines (tertiary aliphatic) —N＜	Melting with fluorescein chloride	—	263
	Fused potassium thiocyanate	—	269
	Citric acid	—	270
	Furfural	—	273
Amines (tertiary aromatic) ＞N—Ar	Melting with fluorescein chloride	2–400	263
	Fused potassium thiocyanate	50	269
	Citric acid	4	270
α-Amino acids —CHNH₂ | COOH	Furfural	—	273
	Conversion to aldehyde	50–100	281
	Ninhydrin	0.4–10	282
	Fused potassium thiocyanate	15–50	285

Group identified	Reagents or test reactions	Limit of identifi·cation, γ	Page
Amino sulfo-acids $HO_3S—X—NH_2$	Fused potassium thiocyanate	50	285
Anhydrides of carboxylic acids —CO—O—CO—	Conversion to ferric hydroxamates	5–10	240
Anilides —CONHC$_6$H$_5$	Splitting off aniline	2–50	290
Arylurethans Ar—NH—COR	Nitrous acid and α-naphthol	5	244
Azoxy compounds —N=NO—	Conversion to hydroxydiazo compounds	—	170
Carbazole derivatives	See Amines (cyclic)		
Carbonyl compounds —CO—	Bisulfite See further Aldehydes; Ketones (methylene-)	0.05–500	197
Carboxylic acids —COOH	Conversion to ferric hydroxamates	11–100	237
1,2-Dicarboxylic acids $>$C—COOH $>$C—COOH	Resorcinol	2.5–40 (daylight) 1–25 (U.V. light)	243
1,2-Diketones (1,2-Dioxo compounds) —CO—CO—	Benzilic acid transformation	1–2.5	199
	Conversion to nickel dioxime salts (for aliphatics)	0.5	200
	Conversion to oxazine dyes (for aromatics)	0.25–2	201
	Ethylenediamine	6–55	203
	Thiophen	1.5–10	204
	Formaldehyde and o-dinitrobenzene	0.05–30	205

Group identified	Reagents or test reactions	Limit of identification, γ	Page
o-Diphenol-methylene ethers	Sulfuric acid	0.1–0.5	190
Dithiocarbamates	Conversion to cupric salts	1.2–2.5	234
Dyestuffs with p-phenylene-diamine and p-nitraniline structure	Formation of phenylene blue	5–6	464
Enols OH | —C=C—	Bromine and potassium iodide	40–100	196
Esters of carboxylic acids —COOR	Conversion to ferric hydroxamates	2.5–13	237
Esters (aliphatic) of fatty acids	Sodium and o-dinitrobenzene	5–10	241
Ethoxy compounds —OC_2H_5	Alkali bichromate	30–200	181
N-Ethyl compounds —NC_2H_5	Benzoyl peroxide	15–50	180
Fatty acids (higher)	Uranyl salts	5	461
Guanidine and derivatives $HN=C<^{NH_2}_{NH-}$	Pyrolysis	0.3–100	291
Hydrazides of carboxylic acids —$CONHNH_2$	Formation of salicylaldazine	0.15–5	297
	Condensation with salicylaldehyde	0.5–2	298
	p-Dimethylaminobenzaldehyde	0.05–0.5	300

Group identified	Reagents or test reactions	Limit of identification, γ	Page
Hydrazines (aliphatic and aromatic) $>$N—NH$_2$	Sodium pentacyanoammineferroate Aldehydic azo dyestuffs	0.12–7 1–5	292 292
Hydrazines (aryl) Ar—NHNH$_2$	Selenious acid and α-naphthylamine	0.03–10	294
Hydrazones (aryl) =NNHAr	Selenious acid and α-naphthylamine	0.09–2	295
Hydrogen (reactive) $>$CH$_2$; —NH$_2$	Sodium 1,2-naphthaquinone-4-sulfonate	C: 0.6–12 N: 0.6–6	301
Hydroxamic acids —NHOH	Oxidation of hydroxylamine to nitrous acid Benzoyl peroxide	0.2–0.9 30–40	225 226
Hydroxy acids OH $\mid$ —C—C$_x$—COOH	s-Diphenylcarbazide	—	483
o-Hydroxy-aldehydes —OH —CHO	Formation of aldazines	0.8–6.4	220
o-Hydroxyketones —OH —CO—	Formation of ketazines	0.5	220
8-Hydroxy-quinoline and Derivatives N OH	Adsorption on magnesium hydroxide	0.4–1	188
Hydroxytriphenyl-methane dyes	Formation of aluminum chelate compounds	0.5	469
Imides —CONHCOR	Acid saponification	0.5–10	288

Group identified	Reagents or test reactions	Limit of identification, γ	Page
Ketones (methylene) —CH$_2$CO—	Conversion to 1,2-diketones Sodium nitroprusside Conversion to indigo See also Carbonyl compounds	2.5–50 2–15 40–300	200 223 224
Methoxy compounds —OCH$_3$	Benzoyl peroxide	20–40	179
N-Methyl compounds —NCH$_3$	Benzoyl peroxide	10–100	179
Monoarylureas Ar—NH—COR	Nitrous acid and α-naphthol	0.1–5	244
Monocarboxylic acids (benzene-soluble)	Uranyl acetate and rhodamine B	0.1–200	120
Naphtholsulfonic acids	Potassium chlorate, HCl and tetrabase	5–250	487
	Sodium cobaltinitrite	2.5–500	487
Naphthylamine-sulfonic acids	Potassium chlorate, HCl and tetrabase	50–250	487
	Sodium cobaltinitrite	2.5–25	487
Nitrates and Nitrites —ONO$_2$; —ONO	Diphenylamine Diphenylbenzidine	0.5 0.07	168 168
Nitro compounds —NO$_2$	Tetrabase or diphenylamine Reduction to nitroso compounds Potassium cyanide (for m-dinitro compounds) Saponification to alkali nitrite (for aromatic polynitro compounds) Rhodamine B (for acidic polynitro compounds)	0.1–50 0.25–15 1–10 0.1–1 0.25–5000	160 161 162 165 166

Group identified	Reagents or test reactions	Limit of identification, γ	Page
Nitroso compounds —NO	Phenol and sulfuric acid	0.4–1	154
	Sodium pentacyanoammine ferroate	0.15–3	154
	Hydrazoic acid (denitrosation)	1–500	158
N-Nitroso compounds $>$N—NO	Hydrazoic acid (removal of nitrous acid)	0.4–20	156
p-Nitroso- aromatic amines $>$N—⟨ ⟩—NO	Palladium chloride	0.05	158
o-Nitrosophenols —OH —NO	Chelation with trivalent cobalt salts	0.25–5	159
Osazones —C=NNHAr —C=NNHAr	Selenious acid and α-naphthylamine	0.1–0.7	295
Oximes =NOH	Oxidation of hydroxylamine to nitrous acid	0.03–8	225
	Benzoyl peroxide	10–40	228
Oxomethylene compounds —CH$_2$—CO—	See Ketones, methylene-		
Peroxides —O—O—	2,7-Diaminofluorene and peroxidase	—	482
Phenols Ar—OH	Nitrous acid	1–10	182
	5-Nitroso-8-hydroxyquinoline	1–10	183
	Nitrous acid and mercuric nitrate	0.5–10	183
	Chloroform and alkali	2.5–50	185
	Sodium cobaltinitrite	0.5–5	186
	Chloranil	—	273
Polyhalogen compounds —CHal$_3$; —CHHal$_2$	Pyridine and alkali hydroxide	0.5–50	313

Group identified	Reagents or test reactions	Limit of identification, γ	Page
Polyhydroxy-anthraquinones	Zirconium salts	0.1–2.5	193
Propenyl compounds $CH_3CH=CH—$	Benzoyl peroxide	40–100	310
Pyridine derivatives	See Amines (cyclic)		
Pyridine-a-carboxylic acid and derivatives	Ferrous sulfate	5–10	287
Pyrrole bases	See Amines (cyclic)		
Quinones	Formaldehyde and o-dinitrobenzene	0.002–0.5	205
Rhodamine dyes	Thallic bromide	0.25–5	465
Ring bases	Methyl iodide and sodium 1,2-naphtha-quinone-4-sulfonate	N: 12–100 O: 25	304
	Hydrogenation tertiary → secondary	N: 2–100	305
Sulfinic acids —SO_2H	Sodium formate	—	249
	Fusion with alkali to sulfite	6–12	250
Sulfonamides —SO_2NH_2	Sodium formate	—	249
	Fusion with alkali to sulfite	—	250
Sulfones $>SO_2$	Sodium formate	—	249
	Fusion with alkali to sulfite	6–10	250
	Pyrolysis	5–20	256

Group identified	Reagents or test reactions	Limit of identification, γ	Page
Sulfonic acids —SO₃H	Sodium formate	0.25–5	249
	Fusion with alkali to sulfite	3–20	250
	Conversion to ferric acethydroxamate	10–30	252
	Methylenedisalicylic acid	10–50	254
Sulfoxylate compounds —CH₂SO₂Na	Pyrolysis	—	312
Thioketones >C=S	Catalysis of iodine-azide reaction	0.003–15	228
Thiols (Mercaptans) —SH	Catalysis of iodine-azide reaction	0.0003–0.05	228
	Precipitation of cuprous salts	0.5–5	232
Thiourea derivatives —NHCSNH—	Phenylhydrazine	—	409
	Release of hydrogen sulfide	—	409
Urea derivatives —NHCONH—	Phenylhydrazine	100–150	409
Urethans —NHCOOC₂H₅	Phenylhydrazine	100–300	409
Xanthates S=C<S— \OR	Molybdic acid	1	235

3. INDIVIDUAL COMPOUNDS

Compound identified	Reagents or test reactions	Limit of identification, γ	Page
Acetaldehyde	Piperidine and sodium nitroprusside	1	334
Acetic acid	Lanthanum nitrate and iodine	50	342
	Formation of indigo	60	342
	Sodium nitroprusside and piperidine, after conversion to acetaldehyde	10–15	343
	Ferric chloride	10	343
Acetone	Guaiacoldialdehyde	0.2	385

Compound identified	Reagents or test reactions	Limit of identification, γ	Page
Acetylene	Formation of cuprous acetylide	1	323
	Protective layer effect on silver chromate	1	324
Adrenaline	1,2-Dinitrobenzene	5	416
	Hydramine cleavage	5	416
Aminoacetic acid	See Glycine		
Aminophylline	Sodium rhodizonate	—	501
Aniline sulfonic acids	Release of sulfuric acid	0.05	365
Anthracene	Conversion to anthraquinone	2	326
	Picric acid	3	327
Anthraquinone sulfonic acids	Catalysis of glucose-alkali hydroxide reaction	0.4–30	367
	Conversion to polyhydroxyanthraquinones	2	367
Antipyrine	Naphthylamine after diazotisation	2	493
Ascorbic acid	Reduction of manganese dioxide	0.03 (in 0.004 ml)	370
	Reduction of ammonium phospho-molybdate	0.1 (in 0.01 ml)	371
	Precipitation of cuprous ferrocyanide	0.5	372
	Chloranil	0.5	373
	Ferric ferricyanide	3	373
	p-Dimethylaminobenzylidenerhodanine, copper sulfate and sodium pyro-phosphate	0.05	374
	Potassium thiocyanate, copper sulfate and sodium pyrophosphate	2	374
	Benzidine and PbO_2 or Tl_2O_3	—	374
	Ninhydrin	10	374
	Triphenyltetrazolium chloride	0.2	374
Benzoyl peroxide	Diethylaniline	3	438
	Tetrabase	0.5	438
Bromoform	Benzoyl peroxide	50	339
Calcium cyanamide	Release of ammonia	—	459
Carbohydrates	Triphenyltetrazolium chloride (for reducing sugars)	0.2	389
	Reduction of silver oxide (for reducing sugars)	0.1	390

Compound identified	Reagents or test reactions	Limit of identification, γ	Page
Carbohydrates (continued)	Various reagents (for reducing sugars)	0.1–10 (in 0.04 ml)	390 Table 36
	Stannous chloride, sulfuric acid and urea (for ketohexoses)	8–30	391
	o-Dianisidine after hydrolysis to furfural by heating (for di- and poly-saccharides)	5–100	391
	Aniline acetate after hydrolysis to furfural by syrupy phosphoric acid (for di- and poly-saccharides)	2.5–5	392
Carbolic acid	Conversion to salicylaldehyde	50	378
Carbon disulfide	Catalysis of iodine-azide reaction	0.14	411
	Formaldehyde and plumbite	3.5	412
	Formation of copper dimethyl-dithiocarbamate	3	413
Carbon monoxide	Phosphomolybdic acid and palladium chloride	5–25	327
Catalase	Hydrogen peroxide and titanium salts	—	433
	Hydrogen peroxide and lead sulfide	—	433
Cephaeline	Formation of copper dithiocarbamate	—	417
Chloral	Conversion to isatin-β-imine	2.5	336
	Conversion to acetaldehyde	10	338
Chloranil	Oxidation of tetrabase	0.25	433
Chloroform	Conversion to alkali cyanide	16	335
Chloromycetin	α-Naphthylamine after conversion into nitroso compound	10	500
	Vanadium oximate	10	500
Choline	Release of formaldehyde	0.5	395
Cinchonine	Hydramine cleavage	20	418
Citral	Alkaline cleavage	130	439
Citric acid	Conversion to ammonium citrazinate	1	358
	Fusion with urea	2	360
Coumarin	Formation of o-hydroxycinnamic acid	0.5	419
Cupferron	Gallium chloride and morin	0.125	423
Dicyanogen	Potassium cyanide and oxine	1	329

Compound identified	Reagents or test reactions	Limit of identifi- cation, γ	Page
Dihydrostrepto- mycin	Nessler reagent	—	499
Dimethyl(ethyl)- aniline	Conversion to p-nitrosodimethyl(ethyl)- aniline	3	437
Emetine	Formation of copper dithiocarbamate	2	417
Emulsin	Liberation of prussic acid from amygdalin	—	432
Enzymes	See Catalase, Emulsin, Lipases, Peroxidase, Urease, and Zymase		
Ephedrine	Hydramine cleavage	5–7	414
Epihydrin- aldehyde	Phloroglucinol	—	483
Ethyl alcohol	Oxidation to acetaldehyde	150	339
Ethylenediamine	Sodium rhodizonate	0.3	396
Ethylenediamine- tetraacetic acid	Masking the formation of nickel dimethylglyoxime	1.7	362
	Prevention of the formation of zinc 8-hydroxyquinoline	8	363
Euphylline	Sodium rhodizonate	—	501
Formaldehyde	Chromotropic acid	0.14	331
	Demasking of nickel or silver	Ni: 0.5 Ag: 3.5	332
Formic acid	Conversion to formaldehyde	1.4	340
	Mercuric chloride	5	341
Furfural	Condensation with aniline	0.05	428
Glyceric acid	Naphthoresorcinol and sulfuric acid	10	349
Glycerol	Conversion to acrolein	5	387
	Formation of 8-hydroxyquinoline	0.5	387
	Catalysis of decomposition of oxalic acid	5–40	389
Glycine	Conversion to glycolic acid	10	346
Glycolic acid	2,7-Dihydroxynaphthalene and sulfuric acid	0.2	346
	Chromotropic acid	0.2	348

Compound identified	Reagents or test reactions	Limit of identification, γ	Page
Glyoxalic acid	Pyrogallolcarboxylic acid and sulfuric acid	1	350
	Conversion to glycolic acid	0.5	352
	Phenylhydrazine and oxidizing agents	1	352
Guaiacol carbonate	Phenylhydrazine, ammonia and nickel sulfate	50	502
Hydrogen cyanide	Demasking of dimethylglyoxime	—	459
Hydroquinone	o-Phthalaldehyde	7	382
	Phloroglucinol	0.5	383
Hydroxyflavonols	See Morin		
Hydroxy-hydroquinone	p-Phthalaldehyde	5	384
8-Hydroxy-quinoline	Adsorption on alumina or magnesia	0.25	378
Inositol	Oxidation to alicyclic ketones	5	393
Isonicotinic acid hydrazide	Salicylaldehyde	0.1	495
	Phosphomolybdic acid	0.5	496
Lactic acid	p-Hydroxydiphenyl and sulfuric acid	1.5	348
	o-Hydroxydiphenyl and sulfuric acid	1	349
Lipases	Conversion of carboxylic acid to ferric hydroxamate	—	432
Malic acid	β-Naphthol and sulfuric acid	10	356
Methyl alcohol	Conversion to formaldehyde	3.5	339
Monochloracetic acid	Chromotropic acid	5	344
Morin	Formation of metal compounds	0.005–0.01	421
α-Naphthylamine	Condensation with nitrosoantipyrine	0.5	399
Neocupferron	Gallium chloride and morin	0.05	423
Nickel dimethyl-glyoxime	Hydrochloric acid or potassium cyanide	—	470
Nitrosodimethyl(ethyl)aniline	Release of dimethyl(ethyl)aniline	2.5	437

Compound identified	Reagents or test reactions	Limit of identification, γ	Page
Nitrosodiphenyl-amine	Concentrated sulfuric acid	0.5	436
Oxalic acid	Conversion to glycolic acid	1	353
	Conversion to glyoxalic acid	1	354
	Formation of aniline blue	5	355
Oxamide	Dehydration to cyanogen	0.35	394
Penicillin G salts	Phosphomolybdic acid	Na: 4	498
Pentachlorophenol	Conversion to chloranil	2.5	435
Peroxidase	Catalysis of the oxidation of benzidine by hydrogen peroxide	—	433
Phenanthrene	Conversion to phenanthraquinone	3	326
Phenoxyacetic acids	Chromotropic acid	0.05	345
p-Phenylene-diamine	Conversion to phenylene blue	0.5	405
Phenylhydrazine	Conversion to dithizone	5	398
Phloroglucinol	2-Hydroxy-5-methoxybenzaldehyde	1	384
Phosgene	Conversion to diphenylcarbohydrazide	0.5	406
$\beta(\gamma)$-Picoline	Formation of polymethine dyes	—	403
Piperine	Release of piperidine	4	416
isoPropyl alcohol	Conversion to acetone	3	386
Propylenediamine	Sodium rhodizonate	—	396
Proteins	Tetrabromophenolphthalein ethyl ester	0.35–5	401
	Fission to amino and imino compounds	1–100	402
Pyramidone	Chromotropic acid and sulfuric acid	10	494
Pyridine	Conversion to polymethine dyes	0.2	280
	Same, from vapor phase	2.5	403
Pyrocatechol	Metaldehyde	4	380
	Phloroglucinol	0.5	381
Pyrogallol	Phloroglucinol	1	385
Pyruvic acid	o-Hydroxydiphenyl and sulfuric acid after reduction to lactic acid	3	350

Compound identified	Reagents or test reactions	Limit of identification, γ	Page
Quinine	Hydramine cleavage	50	418
Quinoline	Oxidation or bromination, after hydrogenation	2.5–20	403
Resorcinol	Pyrocatechol and alkali hydroxide	1	382
Rhodizonic acid	Formation of barium rhodizonate	0.1	366
Rongalite	Chromotropic acid	0.02	453
	1,4-Dinitrobenzene	3	453
Saccharin	Nessler test, after saponification	5	480
Salicyl alcohol and Salicin	Conversion to salicylaldehyde	2	377
Salicylaldehyde	Conversion to alkali phenolate	0.5	374
	Conversion to salicylaldazine	1	376
Salicylic acid and esters	Conversion to alkali salicylates	5	363
Streptomycin	Ferric ammonium sulfate	—	499
	Nessler reagent	5	499
Sulfosalicylic acid	Methylenedisalicylic acid	10	368
	Conversion to salicylic acid	1.5	369
Tartaric acid	Gallic acid and sulfuric acid	2–100	357
	β, β-Dinaphthol and sulfuric acid	10	358
Thiophen	Condensation with isatin	1.5	425
	Condensation with benzil	5	426
	Condensation with ninhydrin	0.2	427
Thiourea	Release of hydrogen sulfide	1	409
Tyrosine	α-Nitroso-β-naphthol	0.05	400
Urea	Deamination	10	407
	Phenylhydrazine	10	408
	Enzymatic hydrolysis to ammonia	1	409
Urease	Liberation of ammonia	—	430
	Splitting of biuret and urea	—	431
Urethan	Phenylhydrazine	—	409
Zymase	Fermentation of sugar to alcohol and carbon dioxide	—	432

AUTHOR INDEX

SUBJECT INDEX

A

Acetaldehyde, as cleavage product, 16
  color reaction with sodium nitroprusside
    and piperidine, 17
  detection of, 17, 198, 209, 211, 214,
    216, 218, 225, 335
    by morpholine-sodium nitroprusside
      paper, 67
  formation of, 62
    as test for acetates, 462
      for benzoyl peroxide, 438
      for bromal, 338
      for cellulose and derivatives, 486,
        487
      for chloral, 338
      for citral, 439
      for ethoxy compounds, 181
      for ethyl alcohol, 339, 457
      for ethyl groups in dyes, 469
      for procaine, 498
      for propenyl compounds, 310
    by alkaline hydrolysis, 439
  interference in demasking test for
    formaldehyde, 334
    in oxidation test for propenyl com-
      pounds, 311
    in test for chloral, 338
  reaction with 2,7-dihydroxynaphtha-
    lene, 347
    with p-hydroxydiphenyl, 348
    with sodium nitroprusside and sec-
      ondary aliphatic amines, 260
    with sulfohydroxamic acids, 252
  role in pyrolysis tests, 67
  summary of tests, 527
  test for, with sodium nitroprusside and
    piperidine or morpholine, 334, 439,
    457, 462, 487, 498
Acetaldehyde alcoholate acetal, indigo
  test for, 225
Acetaldehyde ammonia, detection of, 217
Acetaldehyde bisulfite, interference in test
  for chloral, 338
Acetaldehyde sodium bisulfite, indigo

  test for, 225
Acetals, indigo test for, 225
Acetamide, odor by contamination, 64
m-Acetamidobenzotrifluoride, detection of
  fluorine in, 87
3-Acetamino-4-methoxybenzenesulfinic
  acid, detection of sulfur in, 90
Acetaminophenol, detection of, 291
Acetanilide, detection of, 139, 247, 268, 291
  of hydrogen in, 78
  saponification of, 248
Acetates, detection in formates, 462
  saponification test for, 247
  summary of tests, 518
Acethydroxamic acid, formation of, 252
  reaction with ferric chloride, 252
Acetic acid, anhydrous, formation of, 247
  detection of, 247, 248, 342, 343
    in formic acid, 462
    in presence of formic acid, 342
      of mineral acids, 342
    in test for volatile acids, 119
      of halogenoacetic acid in presence of,
        121
  interference in saponification test for
    acetates, 248
  lanthanum nitrate and iodine test for,
    342
  nitroprusside and piperidine test for,
    343
  reaction with potassium iodide-iodate,
    247
  summary of tests, 527
  test for, by formation of ferric acetate,
    343
    by formation of indigo, 342
Acetic anhydride, detection of, 240
Acetic esters, hydrolysis of, 247
Acetindoxyl, detection of, 278
Acetoacetic ester, detection of, 197, 224,
  225
Aceto-(2-chloromercuryethyl)mesidide,
  detection of mercury in, 108
Acetofluoroglucose, detection of fluorine
  in, 85

Amines, secondary, basic, differentiation from non-basic secondary aliphatic amines, 262

Amines, tertiary, color reactions with aromatic citric, and malonic acids, 270

  test for, with citric acid, 270
    with fluorescein chloride, 263
    with potassium thiocyanate, 269

Amines, tertiary alicyclic, summary of tests, 520

Amines, tertiary aliphatic, summary of tests, 520

Amines, tertiary aromatic, summary of tests, 520

Aminoacetic acid (*see also* Glycine), summary of tests, 528

Amino acids, detection of, in presence of free amines, 286

  differentiation from ascorbic acid, 283

  reaction with alkali thiocyanate, 79
    with *p*-dimethylaminobenzaldehyde, 273
    with hypochlorites or hypobromites, 281

  sulfur-bearing, identification by iodine-azide reaction, 446

α-Amino acids, ninhydrin test for, 282

  reaction with ninhydrin, 282
    with 1,2-naphthaquinone-4-sulfonates, 302

  summary of tests, 520

  test for, by conversion to aldehyde, 281

  thiocyanate test for, 285

β-Amino acids, reaction with ninhydrin, 283

β-Aminoanthraquinone, detection of, 267

o-Aminobenzaldehyde, detection of, 267

p-Aminobenzaldehyde, diazotized, reaction with crocein acid, 292

p-Aminobenzenesulfonamide (Prontosil album), detection of, 287

p-Aminobenzenesulfonic acid, *see* Sulfanilic acid

o-Aminobenzoic acid, *see* Anthranilic acid

p-Aminobenzoic acid, detection of, 121

Aminobutyric acid, formation from piperidine, 140

2-Amino-4,6-dihydroxypyrimidine, detection of, 271

2-Amino-5-dimethylaminophenol, reaction with aromatic 1,2-diketones, 201

  with phenanthraquinone, 201

p-Aminodiphenyl, detection of, 274

α-Amino*iso*caproic acid, *see* Leucine

Aminoethanesulfonic acid, detection of, 123

β-Aminomethylpyridine, detection of, 281

2-Amino-4-methylthiobutanoic acid, *see* Methionine

α-Amino-*β*-methylvaleric acid, *see* Isoleucine

1-Amino-2-naphthol-4-sulfonic acid, detection of, 287

1-Amino-8-naphthol-3,6-disulfonic acid (*see also* H-acid), detection of nitrogen in, 92

  of nitrogen and sulfur in, 96

  of sulfur in, 88

1-Amino-8-naphthol-4,6-disulfonic acid, *see* K-acid

m-Aminophenol, melting with *o*-dicarboxylic anhydrides, 465

o-Aminophenol, reaction with acrolein, 388

Aminophenols, interference in palladium chloride test for *p*-nitroso-aromatic amines, 159

p-Aminophenol sulfate, detection of, 129

3-Amino-4-phenyl-5-thiotriazole, detection of, 231

α-Amino-*β*-phenylpropionic acid, *see* Phenylalanine

Aminophylline, behavior on pyrolysis, 66

  detection of, 500

  differentiation from theophylline-calcium salicylate, 501

  summary of tests, 528

2-Aminopyridine, detection of, 271, 274

4-Aminopyridine, formation of, 271

Amino R-acid (2,3,6-Naphthylaminedisulfonic acid), detection of, 488, 491

p-Aminosalicylic acid, detection of, 287

Aminosuccinic acid, *see* Aspartic acid

Amino sulfo-acids, summary of tests, 521

Aminotetrazole, detection of, 274

2-Aminothiazole hydrochloride, detection of, 271

Ammonia, color test for metal phosphates, 71

  detection in lime test for nitrogen, 91

  of pyridine bases in, 474

  enzymatic hydrolysis to, as test for urea, 409

  fixing of, detection of organic acids through, 119, 460

  formation from hydroxylamine and hydrazine derivatives, 125

  from urea, 407, 463

  in pyrolysis reactions, 16

summary of tests, 528
test for, by release of sulfuric acid, 365
Aniline yellow, detection of, 465
reaction with sodium formate and hydroxide, 16
reductive cleavage of, 16, 465
Animal fibers, differentiation from nylon, 476
from vegetable fibers, 475
Animal tissue, examination of reactions, 515
localization of chemical constituents in, 516
Anisaldehyde, character of odor, 63
detection of, 198, 209, 211, 214, 217, 220
reaction with 2,7-dihydroxynaphthalene, 347
Anisaldehyde bisulfite, detection of, 217
o-Anisidine, reaction with alicyclic compounds, 210
Anisole, color reaction in formalin test, 135
detection of, 180
Anol, detection of, 311
Anthracene, capillary separation from phenanthrene and carbazole, 516
color reaction, in formalin test, 135
with picric acid, 327
detection of, 135, 326, 327
in presence of naphthalene, 326
differentiation from phenanthrene, 327
heating with sodium sulfite, 77
reaction with nitric acid, 326
summary of tests, 528
test for, by conversion to anthraquinone, 326
Anthragallol, detection of, 195
Anthranilic acid (o-Aminobenzoic acid), detection of, 121, 238, 287
reaction with potassium thiocyanate, 285
Anthraquinone, catalysis of formaldehyde-o-dinitrobenzene reaction by, 326
detection of, 208
formation of, as test for anthracene, 326
Anthraquinonedisulfonic acid, conversion to polyhydroxyanthraquinone, 367
detection of, 368
Anthraquinone drugs, Borntraeger reaction for, 513
identification of, 515
Anthraquinonesulfonic acid(s), detection by preparation of alizarin, 10
oxidation to alizarin, 10
summary of tests, 528
test for, by catalysis of glucose-alkali

hydroxide reaction, 367
by conversion to polyhydroxyanthraquinones, 367
Anthraquinone-2-sulfonic acid, detection of, 367, 368
reaction with alkali hydroxide, 367
Anthraquinone-6-sulfonic acid, detection of, 256
Anthraquinonetrisulfonic acids, conversion to polyhydroxyanthraquinones, 367
Antiknock agents in motor fuels, detection of, 473
Antimonic acid, organic salts of, behavior in ignition test, 69
Antimony, detection of, 100
in leather and textiles, 472
in organic compounds, 516
diphenylamine test for, 100
in organic compounds, summary of tests, 517
in pharmaceutical preparations, detection of, 505
rhodamine test for, 100
test by ignition, 506
Antimony^V chloride-rhodamine B, oxidative decomposition of, 104
Antimony compounds, detection in presence of bismuth compounds, 506
interference in lime test for arsenic, 98
reaction with lime, 98
tanning of leather by, 472
Antimony ions, reaction with rhodamine dyes, 467
Antimony mordants in fabrics, detection of, 471
Antimony oxide, color test with diphenylbenzidine, 71
diphenylamine test for, 506
diphenylbenzidine test for, 506
Antimony pentoxide, reaction with diphenylamine or diphenylbenzidine, 100
with potassium iodide, 100
Antimony^{III} pyrogallate, oxidative decomposition of, 104
Antimony sodium thioglycolate, detection of antimony in, 505
Antimony sulfide paper, 53
Antimony tetroxide, reaction with potassium iodide, 100
Antimony thioglycolamide, detection of antimony in, 505
Antimony trichloride, reagent for double bond, 515
Antimony triiodide, formation of, 100

with primary and secondary alcohols, 173
with primary and secondary aliphatic amines, 257
with primary and secondary amines, 234, 413
summary of tests, 529
test for, by formation of copper dimethyl dithiocarbamate, 413, 457
in presence of hydrogen sulfide, 412
test for primary amines, 273
Carbon monoxide, interference in volatilization test for mercury, 107
phosphomolybdic acid and palladium chloride test for, 327
reaction with palladium ions, 327
with phosphomolybdic acid, 327
summary of tests, 529
Carbon tetrachloride, color reaction with pyridine and alkali, 313
detection of, 314
of carbon disulfide in, 457
of phosgene in, 407
Carbonyl compounds, bisulfite test for, 197
summary of tests, 519, 521, 523
Carboxyl group, color test for, 514
Carboxylic acids, see also Fatty acids
color reaction of uranyl ions with rhodamine B in presence of, 461, 483
detection of, 448
of formic acid or formates in presence of, 341
interference in dithiocarbamate test for ethylenediamine, 260
in potassium thiocyanate test for amino acids, 286
in rhodamine B test for acidic polynitro compounds, 168
in saponification test for amides and imides, 289
reaction with uranyl ions, 461, 483
summary of tests, 521
test for alkali salts of, 122
test for, by conversion to ferric hydroxamates, 237
Carboxylic acids, tertiary, decomposition of, 328
Carius disintegration of organic compounds, 72
of organometallic compounds, 103
Carnauba wax, behavior in hydroxamic acid test for esters, 476
insaponifiable residue of, color reaction with vanadium oxinate, 173

Carriers in spot test analysis, 56
Carvacrol, character of odor, 63
Carvone, detection by odor, 64
Casein, detection of, 402
Castor oil, detection of lipase by, 432
Castrix base (2-Chloro-4-dimethylamino-6-methylpyrimidine), photoanalytical detection of, 514
Catalase, summary of tests, 529
test for, by decomposition of hydrogen peroxide, 432
Catalysis reactions, 23, 25
Catalysts, detection of, 24
Catalytic action, test by, for enzymes, 429
Catechol, color reaction in formalin test, 135
Catigen dyes, catalysis of iodine-azide reaction by, 455
Catioben, see Iodobehenate, calcium
Caustic alkali, in tests for basic or acidic behavior, 111
Cellulose, behavior on dry heating, 16
detection of, 392
formation of ω-hydroxymethylfurfural from, 486
in test for monochloracetic acid, 344
test for, by formation of acetaldehyde, 486
Cellulose and derivatives, aniline acetate test for, 486
detection of, 486
disintegration by heating, 486
Cellulose acetate, detection by furfural reaction, 486
Cellulose formals, detection of, 332
Centrifuge tubes, cleaning of, 46
Centrifuging, 44
Cephaeline, summary of tests, 529
test for, by formation of copper dithiocarbamate, 417
Ceric nitrate and alcohol, color reactions with thiophen compounds, 514
Cerium double nitrate test for alcohols, 178
Cetyl alcohol, detection of, 173
Cetyl palmitate, detection of, 239
Characteristic groups, detection of, 151ff
survey of reaction types in tests for identification of, 25
Characterization of material in micro quantities, 320
Charcoal, animal, detection of sulfide sulfur in, 454
Chelate compounds of organic acids, 72
Chelidonic acid, detection of, 306
Chelidonine, detection of, 192

P

Palladium, colorimetric determination by p-nitroso-aromatic amines, 158
free, formation of, as test for mercury, 106
ions, reaction with carbon monoxide, 327
organic compounds of, interference in test for mercury, 106
Palladium chloride, paper, 327
reaction with p-nitroso-aromatic amines, 159
with nitrosonaphthols, 159
test for p-nitroso-aromatic amines, 158
Palladium chloride and phosphomolybdic acid test for carbon monoxide, 327
Palladium-dimethylglyoximate, oxidative decomposition of, 104
Palladium-furildioximate, oxidative decomposition of, 104
Palladium-α-nitroso-β-naphthol, oxidative decomposition of, 104
Palladium oxinate, oxidative decomposition of, 104
Palmitic acid, detection of, 121, 238
of acidic behavior of, 117, 118
in paraffin wax and vaselin, 462
reaction with sulfur, 175
Pancreatin, detection of, 402
Pantothenate, calcium, detection of calcium in, 509
Papaverine, behavior on dry heating, 191
detection of, 180
Papaverine hydrochloride, detection of, 139, 307
Paper, as active participant in spot reactions, 299
detection of mineral constituents in, 449
recommended for spot test use, 56
Paraffin, heating with sodium sulfite, 77
reaction with potassium thiocyanate, 79
Paraformaldehyde, detection of hydrogen in, 78
Paraldehyde, color reaction with p-hydroxydiphenyl, 348
detection of, 211, 214
fluorescence test with o-hydroxydiphenyl, 349
Para-oxon, see Diethyl p-nitrophenyl phoshate
Parathion, see O,O-Diethyl-O-p-nitrophenyl thiophosphate

Pattern trials, 323
Penicillamine (β,β-Dimethylcysteine), formation of, 498
Penicillin G, structure of, 497
calcium salt of, detection of calcium in, 509
distinction from penicillin G procaine, 498
salts, summary of tests, 531
Penicillin G procaine, behaviour on ignition, 497
detection of, 181
distinction from penicillin G, 498
Penicillin salts, test for alkalinity, 497
by ignition, 497
with phosphomolybdic acid, 497
Pentachlorophenol, detection of, 121, 139, 436
summary of tests, 531
test for, by conversion to chloranil, 435
Pentacyano complexes, see Sodium pentacyano...
Pentacyanoiron complexes and hydroxylamine, color reaction for phenol compounds, 515
Pentoses, color test for, 516
conversion to furfural, 391
Pepsin, detection of, 402
Peptone, dried, detection of, 402
Perchloric acid, concentrated, halochromism and halofluorism in, 62
oxidative action, 105
Percompounds, organic, interference in oxidation test for iodine, 84
oxidation of lead sulfide as test for, 124
test for, by release of iodine, 124
Perfluorodicyclohexylethane, detection of fluorine in, 87
Periodic acid, reaction with cane sugar, 177
with 1,2-glycols, 126
with monosaccharides, 177
with polyhydric alcohols, 176
reduction of, 126
test for polyhydric alcohols, 176
Peroxidase, benzidine blue test for, 433
catalysis of oxidation of 2,7-diaminofluorene by, 482
2,7-diaminofluorene test for, 482
summary of tests, 532
test for, by catalysis of benzidine blue formation, 433
Peroxides, detection in dioxan and ether, 473
in fats and oils, 482

pounds, 170
release of, as test for anilinesulfonic acids, 365
Sulphuric acid and chromotropic acid, test for glycolic acid, 348
for monochloracetic acid, 344
for phenoxyacetic acids, 345
Sulfurous acid, addition compounds with alkali iodides, 506
Synthaline, detection of, 292
Syntheses, as indirect tests, 25

T

Tannic acid, color reaction with p-phthalaldehyde, 384
detection of, 132
sensitive and selective test for, 514
Tannin, detection of hydrogen in, 78
oxidative decomposition of, 104
reaction with potassium thiocyanate, 79
Tannins, sensitive and selective test for, 514
Tannin and tartar emetic, as mordant for basic dyes, 471
Tanning of leather by antimony compounds, 472
Tanning agents, synthetic, detection of, 477
vegetable, detection of, 478
Tar pitches, qualitative differentiation of, 515
Tarry products, interference in volatilization test for mercury, 107
Tartar emetic, see Potassium antimonyl tartrate
Tartaric acid, color reaction with 2,7-dihydroxynaphthalene, 347
with naphthoresorcinol, 350
detection of, 120, 123, 128, 177, 245, 358
of hydrogen in, 78
in presence of cinnamic, citric, malic, oxalic, or succinic acid, 358
in vinegar, 480
distinction from citric acid, 177
β,β'-dinaphthol test for, 358
gallic acid test for, 357
oxidation to glyoxalic acid, 177
pyrolysis with nitrosamines, 67
reaction with sulfuric acid, 357
summary of tests, 533
Tartrazine, detection of, 253
Tartronic acid, color reaction with β,β'-dinaphthol, 358
with naphthoresorcinol, 350
interference in gallic acid test for tar-

taric acid, 357
Taurine, detection of, 250
of sulfur in, 90
Techniques, special, 52
of spot tests, 29
Temperature, influence of, 19
Terephthalaldehyde, see p-Phthalaldehyde
Terpenes, detection of, 173
Terphenyl, identification of, 516
Terpineol, character of odor, 63
detection of, 173
Terpinol hydrate, color reaction with o-phthalaldehyde, 383
Terracotta 2RN, detection by reductive cleavage, 466
Tervalent metals, salts, behavior of ignition residue, 68
Test tube, micro, as reaction medium, 2
Textiles, antimony in, test for, 472
detection of cotton in, 484
of nitric esters in, 484
Tetra-alkyl rhodamines, formation of, 265
Tetrabase (Tetramethyl-p,p'-diaminodiphenylmethane), in chloranil test for ascorbic acid, 373
detection of, 128, 139
of basic behavior of, 113
of chloranil by, 138
formation of, as test for pentachlorophenol, 435
in fusion test for nitro compounds, 160
oxidation of, 434
as test for chloranil, 433
for benzoyl peroxide, 438
reaction with benzoyl peroxide, 438
with chloranil (or bromanil, iodanil), 434, 487
with nitro compounds, 21
with quinones, 21
Tetrabromophenolphthalein ethyl ester test for proteins, 401
Tetrachlorohydroquinone, reduction of chloranil to, 433
Tetrachloro-p-quinone, see Chloranil
Tetraethyl dithiopyrophosphate (Sulfotepp), detection of, 182
of phosphorus in, 98
Tetrahydro-β-nitroso-α-naphthol, detection of, 155
1,2,5,8-Tetrahydroxyanthraquinone, detection of, 195
1,3,6,8-Tetrahydroxyanthraquinone, detection of, 196
Tetrahydroxydinaphthylmethane, formation and oxidation of, 347

W

X

Y

Z

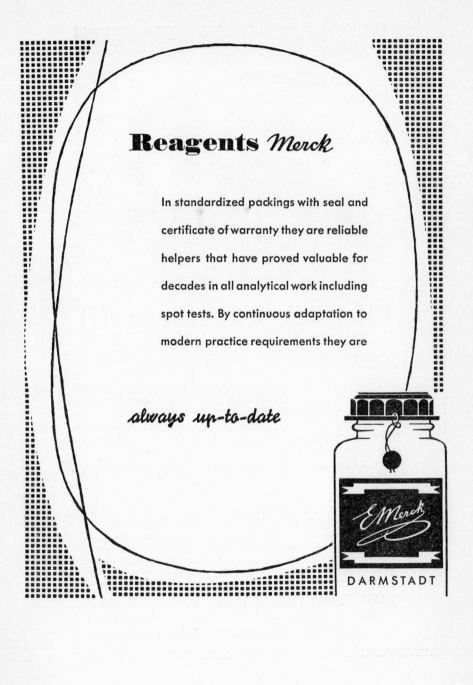

Reagents *Merck*

In standardized packings with seal and certificate of warranty they are reliable helpers that have proved valuable for decades in all analytical work including spot tests. By continuous adaptation to modern practice requirements they are

always up-to-date

E Merck

DARMSTADT

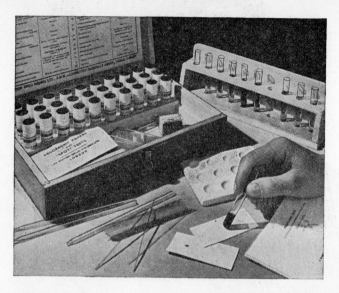

THE B.D.H. SPOT-TEST OUTFIT

This convenient outfit provides a collection of thirty organic reagents of general application, with accessories for their use, in a polished wooden cabinet measuring $10\frac{1}{2} \times 7\frac{1}{2} \times 3$ inches. The 66-page handbook supplied with the Outfit describes comprehensively recommended methods of applying them, with very full references to the literature. The selection of reagents, which among them illustrate the precipitation of insoluble compounds, the development of colours in solution and micro-crystal formation, as well as 'spot' colourings, is useful in all laboratories and particularly valuable in schools and colleges.

Outfit, with handbook, in wooden cabinet   **£6. 3s. 9d.**
Postage and packing extra

B.D.H. have been closely associated with this special field of analysis for many years, and supply a wide range of organic reagents for the detection and determination of metals and radicles.

THE BRITISH DRUG HOUSES LTD.
B.D.H. LABORATORY CHEMICALS GROUP
POOLE   DORSET   ENGLAND

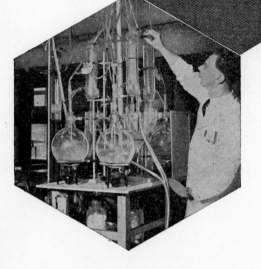

H&W Chemicals for Science

Organic Reagents for Metals

Organic Reagents for Organic Analysis

'P.V.S.' Reagents, Purified for Volumetric Standardisation.

'Spectrosol' Solvents for Absorption Spectroscopy.

'AnalaR' Laboratory Chemicals.

'G.P.R.' Reagents.

Hopkin & Williams have been famous for over 100 years in the manufacture of pure chemicals for research and analysis. At the present time over 5,000 items are listed in the H.&W. Chemical Catalogue and these are manufactured to the high standard which has always been the Company's aim since its foundation. In recent years Research, Development and Analytical Laboratories have been installed so that the Company is in a position to keep abreast of the rapid changes that are taking place in the needs of scientists engaged in every branch of science.

Hopkin & Williams Limited specialise in the preparation of Organic Reagents for Metals and Organic Reagents for Organic Analysis, and a complete list of these reagents will be sent on request.

HOPKIN & WILLIAMS Limited

Manufacturers of fine chemicals for Research and Analysis

Member of

CHADWELL HEATH, ESSEX, ENGLAND